Impact maths

For each chapter of textbook 1G, this Pupil Performance Pack provides:

Chapter overview

The overview gives a detailed list of all the homework, assessment, remediation and extension exercises for the chapter. Any remediation advice is also given here, as are links to ICT activities and software that you may use.

Also, the overview lists any equipment that you will need and activity sheets that will be useful.

Programme of study references are given for each section in the pupils' book – ks3 references are in roman type, ks2 references are in italic.

Homework

At least 4 exercises for each chapter.
This should provide two homework exercises for every week of study.

Assessment

An end of chapter assessment test consolidates the work that the pupils have done in the chapter and gives an indication of possible remediation areas.

Remediation

The remediation sheets are directly linked in to the assessment sheets to give you focused, effective remediation to help your less able pupils.

... and Lesson Starters

Each chapter has a bank of material for use in introductory sessions.

There is more information on how these are integrated with the pupils' book on p.vii.

How to use this pack

For each chapter in the pupil's book, this pack has:

- A chapter overview of content, resources provided and equipment required
- A bank of lesson starters with references to the pupil book
- Homework exercises – at least four for each chapter
- An end of chapter assessment test
- Assessment test answers and remediation guidance
- Remediation exercises
- Extension questions (red book only)
- Answers to pupil book, homework, remediation and extension exercises
- A Questionbank CD-ROM with all homework exercises on

Assessment sheets

Each chapter has an associated assessment test which will assess:

- the pupils' level of achievement and understanding of the concepts involved
- specific remediation needs for each pupil

The answer sheets target pupil's problem areas and link directly to the relevant remediation sheets.

Remediation sheets

The remediation worksheets provide an alternative approach to topics some pupils find challenging. The worksheets can be used to address any problems picked up by the assessment tests or even just as an additional resource when a new topic is introduced. The chapter overview lists all the sheets applicable to that chapter, sometimes giving guidance on ways to present or introduce topics.

How to use the Questionbank CD-ROM

The CD contains all of the homework and extension material from the pack. All the data is fully customizable so that you can create tailor-made tests to cater for all your pupils' needs. On pages xvii and xviii there is a quick guide that tells you all you need to know about how to get the most out of the CD. Your 10 user licence is at the back of this pack.

Impact maths and the National Curriculum

Impact maths offers complete coverage of the KS3 Programme of Study. It is suitable for pupils in years 7, 8 and 9 and contains material from NC level 2 up to NC level 8.

This guide shows you which NC levels are covered in which book. NC level tests on page 264 will help you choose the most appropriate tier for your pupils.

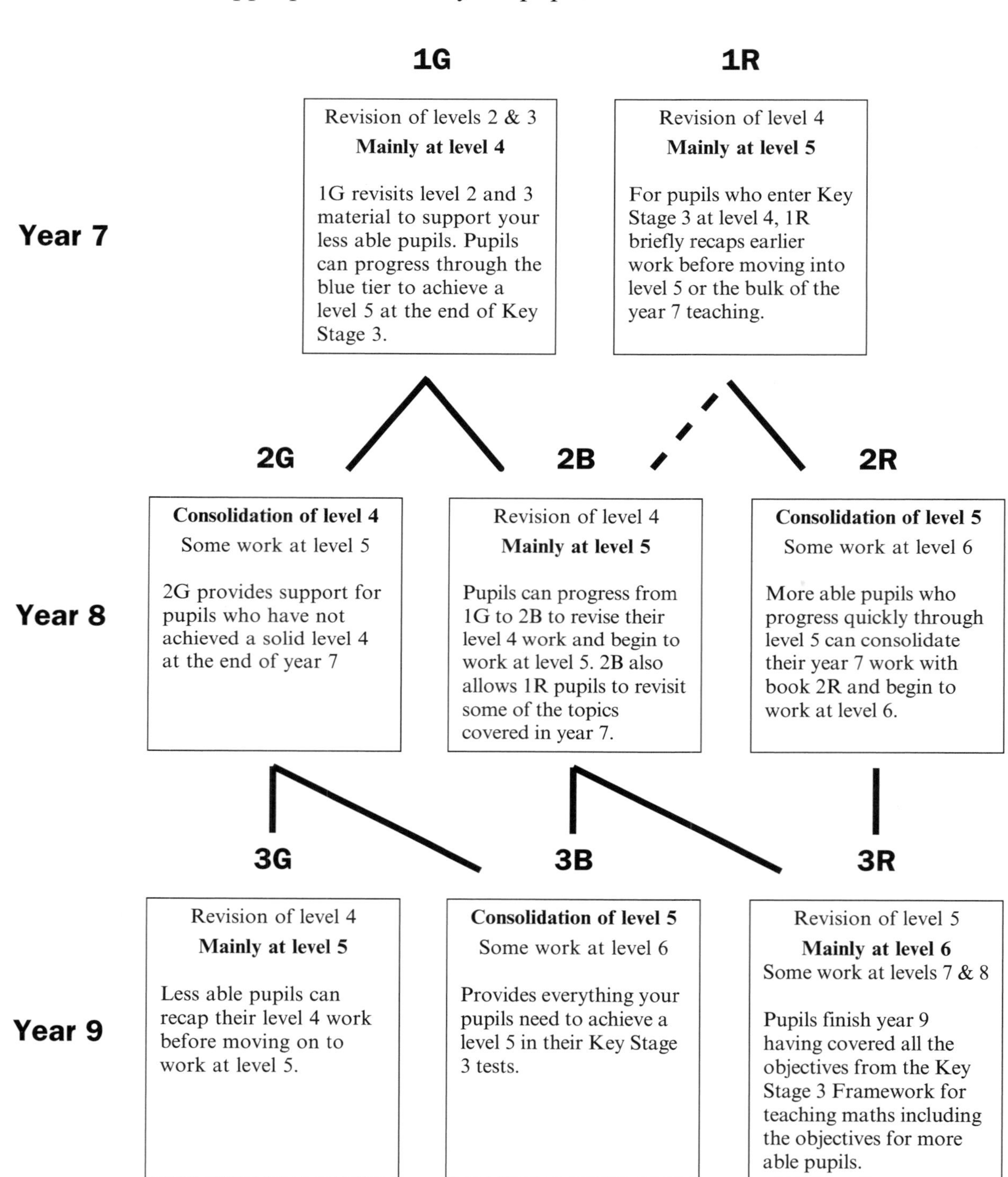

1G
1R
Year 7
Revision of levels 2 & 3
Mainly at level 4
1G revisits level 2 and 3 material to support your less able pupils. Pupils can progress through the blue tier to achieve a level 5 at the end of Key Stage 3.
Revision of level 4
Mainly at level 5
For pupils who enter Key Stage 3 at level 4, 1R briefly recaps earlier work before moving into level 5 or the bulk of the year 7 teaching.
2G
2B
2R
Year 8
Consolidation of level 4
Some work at level 5
2G provides support for pupils who have not achieved a solid level 4 at the end of year 7
Revision of level 4
Mainly at level 5
Pupils can progress from 1G to 2B to revise their level 4 work and begin to work at level 5. 2B also allows 1R pupils to revisit some of the topics covered in year 7.
Consolidation of level 5
Some work at level 6
More able pupils who progress quickly through level 5 can consolidate their year 7 work with book 2R and begin to work at level 6.
3G
3B
3R
Year 9
Revision of level 4
Mainly at level 5
Less able pupils can recap their level 4 work before moving on to work at level 5.
Consolidation of level 5
Some work at level 6
Provides everything your pupils need to achieve a level 5 in their Key Stage 3 tests.
Revision of level 5
Mainly at level 6
Some work at levels 7 & 8
Pupils finish year 9 having covered all the objectives from the Key Stage 3 Framework for teaching maths including the objectives for more able pupils.

Impact maths and the National Numeracy Strategy

In April 2001 the DFEE published the National Numeracy Strategy Key Stage 3 Framework for teaching mathematics. Together with a programme of inset and support, the framework aims to set appropriately high expectations for pupils in Key Stage 3 maths. It helps to place topics within an appropriate mathematical context and provides planning advice and support to show how lessons and schemes of work can be structured to improve performance across Key Stage 3.

Structuring lessons

Effective lessons are structured so that learning objectives are clear and pupils can recognise what they have achieved. A typical lesson features three parts – an introduction, the main teaching activity and a final plenary.

There is more about teaching strategies on pages 26–31 of the Framework.

The introduction:
This is usually 5 to 10 minutes, and may include a starter activity, designed to sharpen and develop pupils' mental and communication skills. The starter activities might include factual recall and number skills, but it is also worth spending time on interpreting data, making estimates, developing vocabulary etc. The starters will be more effective if they are planned into your scheme of work, so that pupils are able to practise previously acquired skills, or to focus on the understanding and skills needed for the main part of the lesson.

The main lesson:
This is likely to be 25 to 40 minutes, and should

- provide pupils with information about the main learning objective
- include combinations of whole-class teaching and pupil activities.

The plenary
This is usually 5 to 15 minutes and should

- provide answers for any work the pupils were expected to complete
- summarize the key facts, ideas and vocabulary
- clarify any questions that have arisen during the course of the lesson
- allow time to set homework or prepare for future lessons.

Impact maths lesson starters

This pack provides a bank of lesson starters with links to the relevant teaching objective from the Framework. Impact maths lesson starters provide:

- the material you need to introduce a topic by building on pupils' intuitive and/or acquired understanding of the work
- links to the relevant section of the pupils' book so that you can match the starter activity to the relevant material for the main section of your lesson.

Planning and the National Numeracy Strategy

As well as delivering objective-based lessons, you should structure your medium- and long-term planning around the objectives from the Framework. There are three stages to building effective medium- and long-term plans for Key Stage 3 maths:

There is more about planning on pages 44–55 of the Framework

- Compare the objectives in the yearly teaching programmes in the Framework document to your current scheme of work. Decide which topics you cover effectively and which topics you need to review.
- Look at the supplement of examples and compare your current expectations with those in the Framework. Decide whether your pupils are working at an appropriate level.
- Group objectives together to form units of work. These will draw on objectives from higher and lower years to provide a fully differentiated set of objectives from which to plan lessons for all your pupils.

The National Numeracy Strategy provides sample units of work for years 7, 8 and 9. These show how the objectives can be grouped together to form appropriate units of work. Together with your own lesson plans, the National Numeracy Strategy Sample medium-term plans effectively form a scheme of work for Key Stage 3.

How Impact helps you deliver

Impact maths can help you meet the needs of the Framework in two different ways:

Produce your own medium-term plans

No single grouping of objectives into units of work will be appropriate for every school and every pupil.

If you plan to group objectives into units of work to produce medium-term plans that are suited to your school or scheme of work, the objective matching chart on page ix will show you exactly where the material for each objective is covered in the pupils' book.

The objective matching chart also contains references to the other tiers of Impact maths to help you prepare a programme of support and extension.

Use the sample medium-term plans provided by the NNS

A matching guide (showing where the relevant teaching material for each unit of work can be found in your Impact maths resources) will be available from Heinemann in Autumn 2001.

There are accompanying notes for each unit of work. Written by a Numeracy Consultant with experience of the National Numeracy Strategy in both Primary and Secondary schools, these notes help you deliver the sample medium term plans using Impact maths.

Framework teaching objective:	1R reference (Book page or starter number)	1G reference (Book page or starter number)
Numbers and the number system		
Place value, ordering and rounding		
• Understand and use decimal notation and place value.	Starter 6.1 Starter 6.2 Starter 6.4 Chapter 6 P 116–118 P 122–127	Starter 6.1 Starter 6.3/6.4 Chapter 6 P 90–93
• Compare and order decimals in different contexts.	Starter 6.3 Chapter 6 P 121–122, P 142–143, P 132–133	
• Round positive whole numbers to the nearest 10, 100 or 1000 and decimals to the nearest whole number or one decimal place.	Chapter 2 P 53–58, Chapter 6 P 134–135	
Integers, powers and roots		
• Understand negative numbers as positions on a number line; order, add and subtract positive and negative numbers in context.	Starter 12.1 Starter 12.2 Starter 12.6 Chapter 2 P 41–43 Chapter 12 P 237–243	Starter 11.1 Starter 11.2 Starter 11.3 Starter 11.5 Chapter 2 P 36–38 Chapter 11 P 164–71
• Recognise and use multiples, factors and primes (less than 100); use tests of divisibility.	Chapter 5 P 92–94, P 96–99, P 100	Chapter 5 P 69–72, P 84–86 (not primes)
• Recognise the first few triangular numbers, squares of numbers to at least 12 × 12 and the corresponding roots.	Chapter 3 P 73–74 Chapter 5 P 94–96	Chapter 3 P 55, P 57 Chapter 5 P 73–74
Fractions, decimals, percentages, ratio and proportion		
• Use fraction notation to describe parts of shapes and to express a smaller whole number as a fraction of a larger one; **simplify fractions by cancelling all common factors and identify equivalent fractions;** convert terminating decimals to fractions; use a diagram to compare two or more simple fractions.	Starter 8.3 Starter 8.5 Chapter 8 P 154–163	Starter 8.1 Chapter 8 P 121–126

Framework teaching objective:	1R reference (Book page or starter number)	1G reference (Book page or starter number)
Numbers and the number system *(continued)*		
Fractions, decimals, percentages, ratio and proportion *(continued)*		
• Begin to add and subtract simple fractions and those with common denominators; calculate simple fractions of quantities and measurements (whole-number answers); multiply a fraction by an integer.	Chapter 8 P 163–168	Starter 8.3 Starter 8.4 Chapter 8 P 126–130
• Understand percentage as the 'number of parts per 100'; **recognise the equivalence of percentages, fractions and decimals**; calculate simple percentages and use percentages to compare simple proportions.	Starter 8.8 Starter 16.2 Starter 16.3 Chapter 8 P 166–167 Chapter 16 P 316–325	Starter 15.1 Starter 15.2 Chapter 15 P 216–220
• Understand the relationship between ratio and proportion; use direct proportion in simple contexts; use ratio notation, reduce a ratio to its simplest form and divide a quantity into two parts in a given ratio; solve simple problems about ratio and proportion using informal strategies.	Chapter 8 P 170–177	
Calculations		
Number operations and the relationships between them		
• Understand addition, subtraction, multiplication and division as they apply to whole numbers and decimals; know how to use the laws of arithmetic and inverse operations.	Starter 5.1 Chapter 2 P 48–55, Chapter 5 P91–94, 100–108, 110–112	Starter 5.1 Starter 5.6 Starter 5.7 Chapter 2 P 38–44 Chapter 5 P 68–69, 74–84
• **Know and use the order of operations.**	Starter 11.4 Chapter 11 P 226–227 Chapter 20 P 359	
Mental methods and rapid recall of number facts		
• Consolidate the rapid recall of number facts, including multiplication facts to 10×10, and quickly derive associated division facts.	Chapter 5 P91–92	Chapter 5 P 68–69

Framework teaching objective:	1R reference (Book page or starter number)	1G reference (Book page or starter number)
Calculations *(continued)*		
• Consolidate and **extend mental methods of calculation to include decimals, fractions and percentages** (accompanied where appropriate by suitable jottings).	Chapter 6 P 122–127	Chapter 8 P 126–127
Written methods • Use standard column procedures to add and subtract whole numbers and decimals with up to two places.	Chapter 2 P 48–53	Chapter 2 P 38–44 Chapter 6 P 96–99
• **Multiply and divide three-digit by two-digit whole numbers; extend to multiplying and dividing decimals with one or two places by single-digit whole numbers.**	Chapter 5 P 109–112 Chapter 6 P 127–131	
Calculator methods • Carry out calculations with more than one step using brackets and the memory; use the square root and sign change keys.	Chapter 20 P 357–358 P 367–369 (not [√])	Chapter 17 P 231–232
• Interpret the display in different contexts (fractions, decimals, money, metric measures, time).	Chapter 20 P 357–367	
Checking results • **Check a result by considering whether it is of the right order of magnitude and by working the problem backwards.**	Chapter 2 P 58–60 Chapter 6 P 134–137	
Algebra		
Equations, formulaes and identities • **Use letters or symbols to represent unknown numbers or variables.**	Starter 9.1 Starter 11.1 Starter 11.3 Chapter 9 P 179 Chapter 11 P 221	Starter 10.3 Chapter 10
• **Know that algebraic operations follow the same conventions and order as arithmetic operations.**	Starter 11.4 Chapter 9 P 179 Chapter 11 P 221	Chapter 10

Framework teaching objective:	1R reference (Book page or starter number)	1G reference (Book page or starter number)
Algebra *(continued)*		
Equations, formulae and identities *(continued)*		
• Simplify linear algebraic expressions by collecting like terms; begin to multiply a single term over a bracket.	Starter 9.3/9.4/9.5 Chapter 5 P 181–186, P 188–189	
• Construct and solve simple linear equations, selecting an appropriate method.	Starter 11.1 Chapter 11 P 230–236	Chapter 10 P 158–160
• Use formulae from mathematics and other subjects, substitute numbers in simple formulae and, in simple cases, derive a formula	Starter 11.3 Chapter 11 P 221–230	Starter 10.1 Chapter 10
Sequences, functions and graphs		
• Generate and describe simple integer sequences.	Chapter 3 P 61–67	Starter 3.1 Chapter 3 P 46–48, P 50–52
• **Generate terms of a sequence, given a rule** (e.g. finding one term from the previous term, finding a term given its position in the sequence).	Chapter 3 P 65–70	Starter 3.4 Chapter 3 P 48–50, P 52–54
• Generate sequences from practical contexts and describe the general term in simple cases.	Chapter 3 P 61–67 P 70–72	Chapter 3 P 46–48
• Express simple functions in words, then using symbols; represent them in mappings.	In 2R	
• Generate co-ordinate pairs that satisfy a simple linear rule; **plot the graphs of simple linear functions**, where y is given explicitly in terms of x, on paper and using ICT; recognise straight line graphs parallel to the x-axis or y-axis.	Starter 13.1 Chapter 13 P 252–265	Starter 12.1 Starter 12.3 Chapter 12 P 175–183
• Begin to plot and interpret the graphs of simple linear functions arising from real-life situations.	Starter 13.8 Chapter 13 P 266–273	Chapter 12 P 179–183

Framework teaching objective:	1R reference (Book page or starter number)	1G reference (Book page or starter number)
Shape, space and measures		
Geometrical reasoning: Lines, angles and shapes		
• Use accurately the vocabulary and notation associated with lines, angles and shapes.	Starter 14.3 Chapter 14 P 281–282, Chapter 1 P 12–14	Chapter 13 P 193–194
• Identify parallel and perpendicular lines; **know the sum of angles at a point, on a straight line and in a triangle**, and recognise vertically opposite angles.	Chapter 1 P 10–12 Chapter 14 P 284–289	Chapter 1 P 10
• Begin to identify and use angle, side and symmetry properties of triangles and quadrilaterals; solve geometrical problems involving these properties, using step-by-step deduction and explaining reasoning with diagrams and text.	Chapter 18 P 337–344	Starter 1.5
• Use 2-D representations to visualise 3-D shapes and deduce some of their properties.	Starter 1.9 Chapter 1 P 14–21	Chapter 1 P 12–17
Transformations		
• Understand and use the language and notation associated with reflections, translations and rotations.	Chapters 1, 14 and 18	Starter 13.1 Chapter 1 P 4–18 Chapter 13 P 187–191
• Recognise and visualise the transformation and symmetry of a 2-D shape: – reflection in given mirror lines, and line symmetry; – rotation about a given point, and rotation symmetry; – translation; explore these transformation and symmetries using ICT.	Starter 18.2 Chapter 1 P 4–10 Chapter 18 P 388–342	Starter 13.3 Chapter 1 P 4–18 Chapter 13 P 187–191
Co-ordinates		
• Use conventions and notation for 2-D co-ordinates in all four quadrants.	Starter 13.1/13.2 Chapter 13 P 252–255	Chapter 12 P 175–178

Framework teaching objective:	1R reference (Book page or starter number)	1G reference (Book page or starter number)
Shape, space and measures *(continued)*		
Co-ordinates *(continued)*		
• Find co-ordinates of points determined by geometric information.	Starter 1.4 Chapter 13 P 257–258	Starter 12.1 Chapter 12 P 178–179
Construction		
• Use a ruler and protractor to measure and draw lines to the nearest millimetre and angles, including reflex angles, to the nearest degree.	Chapter 8 P 139–140 Chapter 14 P 278–280	Chapter 7 P 102–103 (nearest cm) Chapter 13 P 191–193 (not reflex)
• Use a ruler and protractor to construct a triangle given two sides and the included angle (SAS) or two angles and the included sides (ASA); explore these constructions using ICT.	Chapter 14 P 290–291	
• Use ruler and protractor to construct simple nets of 3-D shapes e.g. cuboid, regular tetrahedron, square-based pyramid, triangular prism.	In 2R	
Measures and mensuration		
• Use names and abbreviations of units of measurement to measure, estimate, calculate and solve problems in everyday contexts involving length, area, mass, capacity, time and angle.	Starter 7.1 Starter 7.9 Chapter 7 and Chapter 14 P 278–280	Starter 7.1 Starter 7.2 Chapter 7 and Chapter 13 P 191–193
• **Convert from one metric unit to another** (e.g. grams to kilograms).	Starter 7.3 Chapter 7 P 140–141, P 144–146	Starter 7.3 Chapter 7 P 104–107, P 108–110
• **Read and interpret scales on a range of measuring instruments.**	Chapter 7 P 146–147	Starter 7.7 Chapter 7 P 110–111
• Use angle measure; distinguish between and estimate the size of acute, obtuse and reflex angles.	Starter 14.4 Chapter 14 P 282–283	Starter 13.7/13.9 Chapter 13 P 196–197
• Know and use the formula for the area of a rectangle; calculate the perimeter and area of shapes made from rectangles.	Starters 10.1–10.6 Chapter 10 P 198–199, P 204–205, P 211–213 and 2R P 252	Starter 9.1/9.6/ 9.8 Chapter 9 P 139–140 P 146–148

Framework teaching objective:	1R reference (Book page or starter number)	1G reference (Book page or starter number)
Shape, space and measures *(continued)*		
Measurement and mensuration *(continued)* • Calculate the surface area of cubes and cuboids.	Chapter 10 P 218–219	
Handling data		
Specifying a problem, planning and collecting data • Given a problem that can be addressed by statistical methods, suggest possible answers.	Starter 15.1	
• Decide which data would be relevant to an enquiry and possible sources.	Starter 15.2	Chapter 14 P 200
• Plan how to collect and organise small sets of data; design a data collection sheet or questionnaire to use in a simple survey; construct frequency tables for discrete data, grouped where appropriate in equal class intervals..	Chapter 15 P 294–297	Starter 14.3 Chapter 14 P 200–209
• Collect small sets of data from surveys and experiments, as planned.	Chapter 15 P 294–297	Starter 14.3 P 200–209
Processing and representing data using ICT as appropriate • Calculate statistics for small sets of discrete data: – find the mode, median and range, and the modal class for grouped data; – calculate the mean, including from a simple frequency table, using a calculator for a larger number of items.	Starter 17.1 Chapter 17 P 326–336 Chaper 20 P 372–375	
• Construct, on paper and using ICT, graphs and diagrams to represent data, including: – bar line graphs; – frequency diagrams for grouped discrete data; Use ICT to generate pie charts.	Chapter 15 P 292–315 Chapter 20 P 371–372 (Pie charts in 3G and 3B Chapter 18)	Starter 14.6 Starter 14.7 Chapter 14 P 199–214 Chapter 17 P 242–243
• Interpret diagrams and graphs (including pie charts), and draw simple conclusions based on the shape of graphs and simple statistics for a single distribution.	Starter 15.6 Chapter 15 P 297–309, P 312–314	Chapter 14 P 211–214

Framework teaching objective:	1R reference (Book page or starter number)	1G reference (Book page or starter number)
Handling data *(continued)*		
Processing and representing data *(continued)* • **Compare two simple distributions using the range and one of the mode, median or mean.**	Starter 17.6 Chapter 17 P335–336	
• Write a short report of a statistical enquiry and illustrate with appropriate diagrams, graphs and charts, using ICT as appropriate; justify choice of what is presented.		
Probability • Use vocabulary and ideas of probability, drawing on experience	Starter 4.1 Chapter 4 P 76–79, P 85	Starter 4.1 Starter 4.2 Starter 4.4 Chapter 4 P 58–64
• **Understand and use the probability scale from 0 to 1; find and justify probabilities based on equally likely outcomes in simple contexts.**	Starter 4.6 Chapter 4 P 80–84	Starter 4.6 Chapter 4 P 64–66
• Identify all possible outcomes of an experiment.	Chapter 4 P 85	
• Collect data from a simple experiment and record in a frequency table; estimate probabilities based on the data.	Chapter 4 P 89	
• Compare experimental and theoretical probabilities in simple contexts.	Starter 4.10 Chapter 4 Ex 4J, P 89	

Using your Questionbank CD-ROM

To install the software, put the CD in your CD drive, find the file setup.exe and double click it. To run the program, double click on the program icon in the Heinemann program group.

You select the chapter and section that you want to choose questions from on this screen:

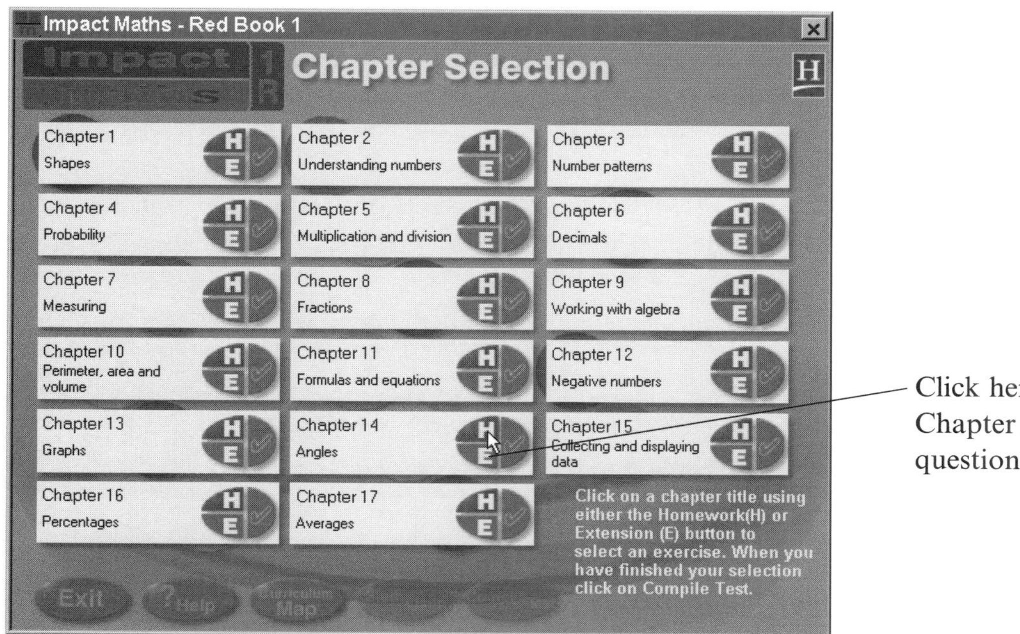

Click here to select the Chapter 14 homework questions.

Next you choose which questions you want to have in the test. As you select a question a preview will appear in the right-hand pane and a tick confirms your selection. Clicking on the confirm button will add these questions to your selection.

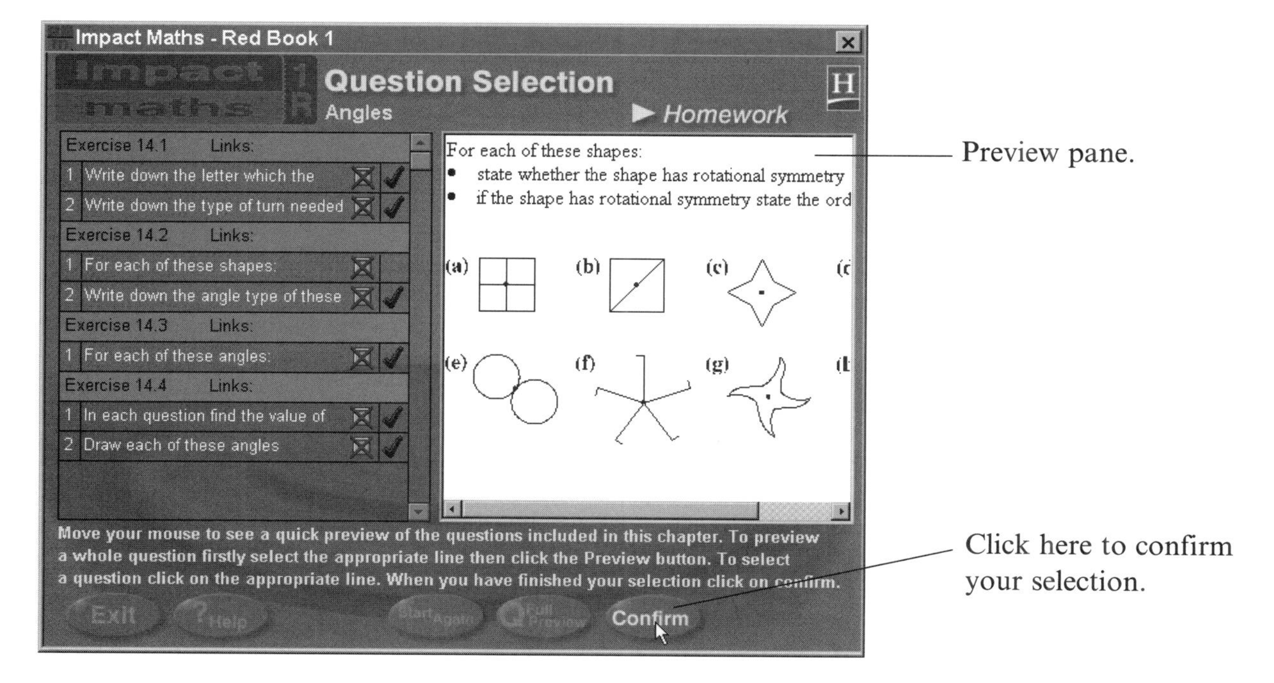

Selecting compile test from the chapter selection screen will give you the option to order the questions. To change the order, just click and drag the question to its new position. Clicking on preview test shows you how the finished test will look

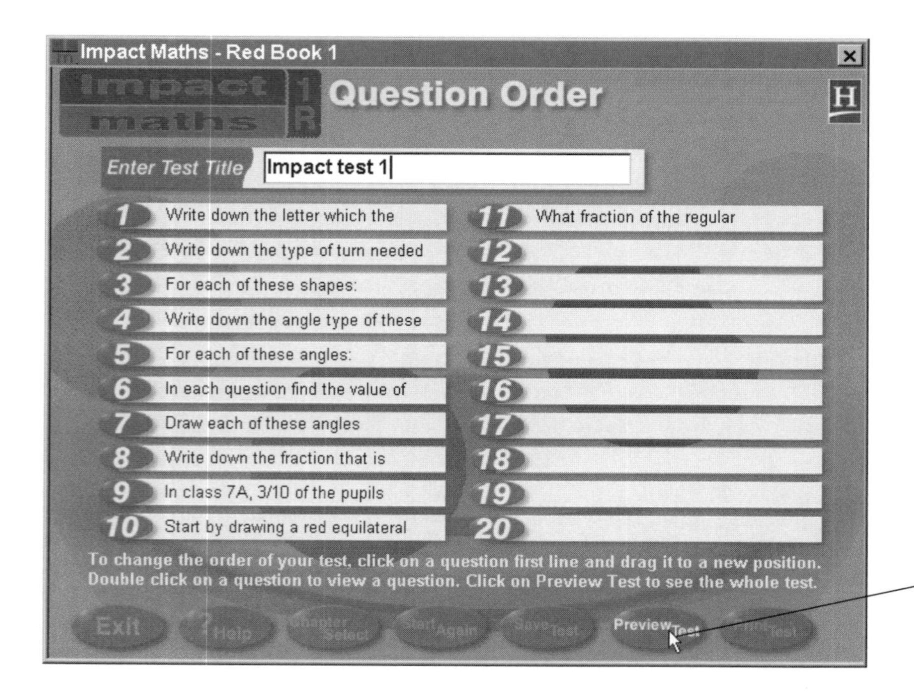

Click here to preview the test.

The questions are numbered and now you can print test or save it to disk (both choices giving you the option to select just questions or questions and answers). You can customise your test by opening the file in your word processor. For best results set the font to times new roman at 12 point size.

Tests are saved to: C:\Program files \Heinemann\Imrbl \User data files

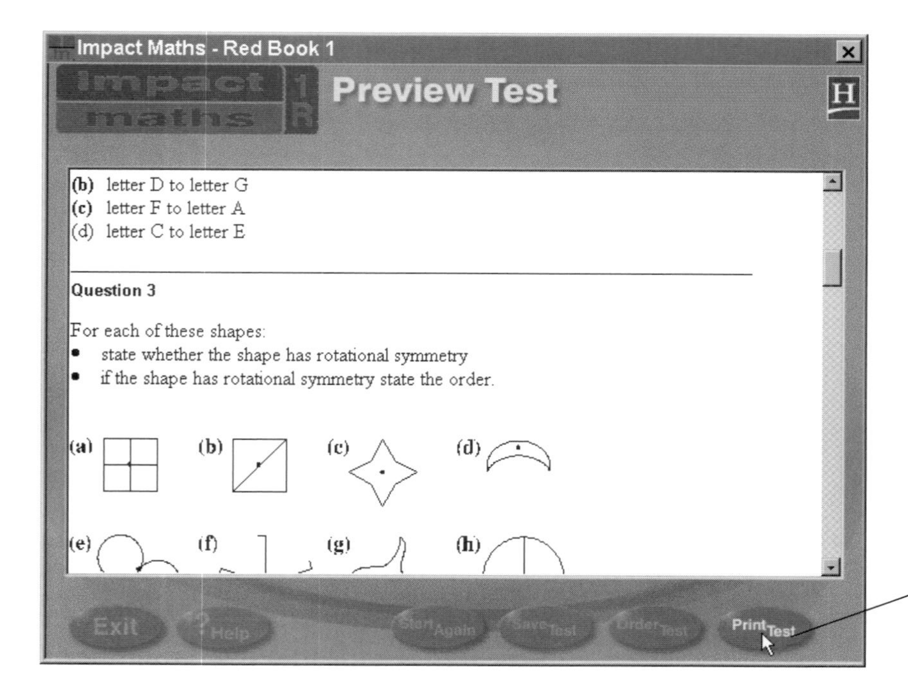

Click here to print the test.

Note: If your screen image appears cropped in Windows 95, you may need to set your taskbar to autohide.

Questionbank technical support:

The minimum specification needed to run the Questionbank CD-ROM is an IBM compatible PC with Windows 95 installed.

If you experience any problems with the CD-ROM, please phone our technical support line on 01865 888108.

Further information is contained in the file readme.txt on the CD.

Website addresses and contact details for ICT Links

ICT Links 7.8 and 7.9 [Higher] 7.11 [Foundation] – timetables

http://www.railtrack.co.uk/home.html
UK Rail Schedules

http://www.british-airways.com/flights/flights.cgi
British Airways Flight Schedules

http://reservations.amtrak.com/novus/process-form?home&arrival
USA Rail Schedules

ICT Links Unit 15 and Unit 17 [Higher] Unit 14 [Foundation] – data

http://espn.go.com/editors/atlanta96/almanac/index.html
100 years of Olympic Results

http://www.rhegeds.freeserve.co.uk/extremes.htm
Extreme weather UK

http://www.ncdc.noaa.gov/extremes.html
Extreme weather USA

http://www.ishlt.org/
Organ transplants

Software Information

Smile Mathematics
Isaac Newton Centre
108A Lancaster Road
London W11 1QS
http://www.rmplc.co.uk/orgs/smile/index.html

Virtual Image
184 Reddish Road
South Reddish
Stockport SK5 7HS
http://www.virtualimage.co.uk/

Key Curriculum Press
http://www.keypress.com/index.html
for **Geometer's Sketchpad** can be ordered in England from
QED Books
Room 1 Stonehills House
Welwyn, AL8 6NH
England
England Tel: 0345-402275
England Fax: 01707-334233
Outside England Tel: +44-345-402275
Outside England Fax: +44-1707-334233
Email: qed@enterprise.net
http://www.keypress.com/ordering-international.html

Logotron supply
Winlogo.
http://www.logo.com/catalogue/titles/winlogo/index.html
and
Versatile
http://www.logo.com/

Omnigraph and Geomat for Windows
SPA, Tewksbury
Tel: 01684 833700 Fax: 01684 833 718

Key Plus 2000 Database
http://www.anglia.co.uk/utility_KeyPlus2000.htm

Thames and Hudson's ESCHER
http://www.thameshudson.co.uk/

BT Numbers You Need

Cambridge Training and Development Ltd
Block D2, The Westbrook Centre, Milton Road, Cambridge
CB4 1YG
Tel: +44(0) 1223 582582 Fax: +44(0) 1223 582551
http://www.ctad.co.uk/noframes/products/nyn.htm

Software Reviews and Other Resources

http://www.becta.org.uk/

Mathematics Resources and Links

University of Exeter Centre for Innovation in Mathematics Teaching
http://www.ex.ac.uk/cimt/

Mathematics Resources and Links and Software Information Oundle School

http://www.argonet.co.uk/oundlesch/

Please forward any good Mathematics Web Sites and Software, giving brief details, to
David Benjamin at
Davidben@clara.net

Unit 1 Shapes

Content summary

This unit uses symmetry as the underlying theme to the study of '2D' and '3D' shapes.
In '2D' it covers triangles, quadrilaterals and the simple polygons.
In '3D', cubes, cuboids, prisms and pyramids are covered.

NC level

Level 2: Names of '2D' and '3D' shapes.

Level 3: Reflective symmetry.

Level 4: Reflecting simple shapes in a vertical mirror line.

S2b *S2c* *S2d* *S2f* *S3b*

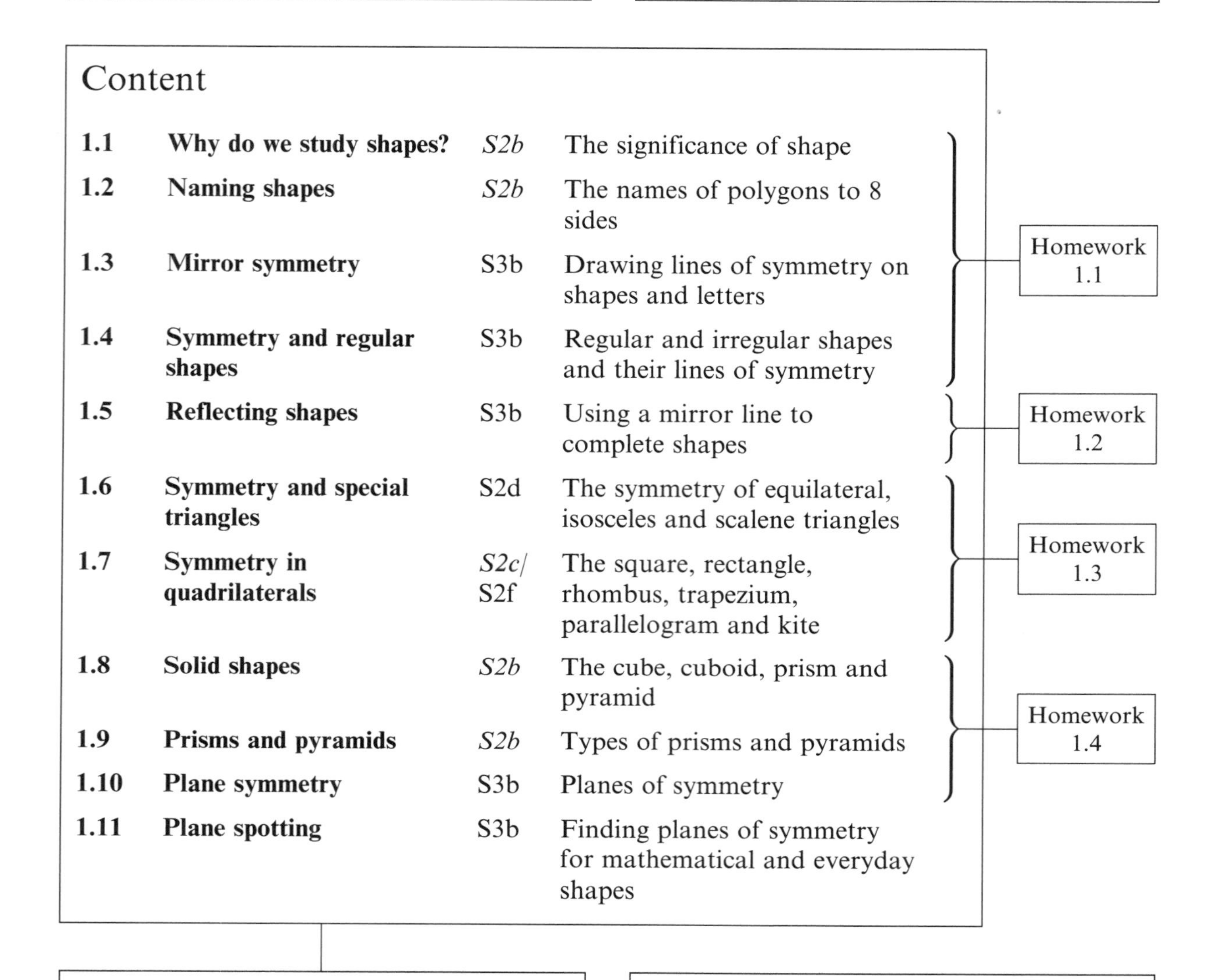

Content

1.1	**Why do we study shapes?**	*S2b*	The significance of shape	Homework 1.1
1.2	**Naming shapes**	*S2b*	The names of polygons to 8 sides	
1.3	**Mirror symmetry**	S3b	Drawing lines of symmetry on shapes and letters	
1.4	**Symmetry and regular shapes**	S3b	Regular and irregular shapes and their lines of symmetry	
1.5	**Reflecting shapes**	S3b	Using a mirror line to complete shapes	Homework 1.2
1.6	**Symmetry and special triangles**	S2d	The symmetry of equilateral, isosceles and scalene triangles	Homework 1.3
1.7	**Symmetry in quadrilaterals**	*S2c*/ S2f	The square, rectangle, rhombus, trapezium, parallelogram and kite	
1.8	**Solid shapes**	*S2b*	The cube, cuboid, prism and pyramid	Homework 1.4
1.9	**Prisms and pyramids**	*S2b*	Types of prisms and pyramids	
1.10	**Plane symmetry**	S3b	Planes of symmetry	
1.11	**Plane spotting**	S3b	Finding planes of symmetry for mathematical and everyday shapes	

Assessment

Assessment 1 covers the key concepts in Unit 1.

Remediation

Remediation sheets 1.1 and 1.2.

Assessment

The assessment is marked out of 30.
Achievement of 20 or more marks indicates a good understanding of the key concepts.
Marking guidance, answers and links to remediation are provided on page 265.

Equipment

	Pupils' Book page
Activity sheet 1	3
Mirrors	4, 8
Activity sheet 2	5
Scissors, card	12

ICT links

1.1
View some wonderful shapes from nature on the *Virtual Image* range of CDs and battle with impossible drawings on the *Escher Interactive* CD.

1.2 and 1.4
Use *Versatile* to create regular polygons and draw in lines of symmetry.

1.5
Use *Geomat* to reflect shapes in mirror lines.

1.8–1.10
Use a drawing package to create some 3-D shapes.

Remediation

Lines of symmetry:
The teacher should first give a demonstration of the first practical activity. Excellent displays can be made of the resulting work, especially if coloured paper is used instead of plain white. The text gives ideas for possible cutouts but the pupils should be encouraged to make up their own. The paint and ink work can become very messy so it could make a good homework activity!

The practical work should make the dotted paper work more straightforward. The diagonal lines may need some more practical back up, which can be done with tracing paper or by using a mirror and 'drawing in the reflection'.

Planes of symmetry:
It may be useful to start with a practical demonstration of slicing a tomato or something similar to get across the idea of a plane.

Questionbank CD

All homeworks and extension questions also appear on the CD.

Pages xvii and xviii of this pack show you how to use the CD to select questions from the Questionbank and further customize them if you wish to.

1 Shape

framework teaching objective	§	lesson starter	f/w ref
Use correctly the vocabulary, notation and labelling conventions for lines, angles and shapes.	1.1/ 1.2	Looking at different ways of sorting shapes. This activity requires drawings on board or using pictures of shapes: What groups can we sort these shapes into? 'Ones with 3 sides.' 'Ones with 4 sides.' Students should sort the shapes. 3 sides: A, C, G 4 sides: B, D, E, H, I Which shape is left out? F What can we call our groups? '3-sided shapes – triangles.' Why are they called 'triangles'? 'three angles' French word for 3 is 'trois.' Spanish word is 'tres.' What about the 4-sided shapes? What can we call them? Students encouraged to invent a word given that the French word for 4 is 'quatre.' Encourage them also to think of 4 **angles** or 4 **sides** when inventing word.	178–9
Use correctly the vocabulary, notation and labelling conventions for lines, angles and shapes.	1.1/ 1.2	Ask pupils to think of other ways of sorting shapes: – equal and unequal sides – regular + irregular. – symmetrical and asymmetrical. Ask pupils to think of ways of subdividing the quadrilaterals the triangles?	178–9

framework teaching objective	§	lesson starter	f/w ref
Use correctly the vocabulary, notation and labelling conventions for lines, angles and shapes.	1.4	'Draw a square.' 'Draw on its diagonals' – i.e. connect opposite corners. 'Rub out the top horizontal side of the square.' 'Describe the shape you now have.' 'What maths words can help you?' Get students to read out their descriptions and follow them on the board. Does the shape on the board faithfully reproduce the shape in their book? How can the instruction be altered so that it does?	178–9
Begin to identify and use angle, side and symmetry properties of triangles and quadrilaterals.	1.5	Ask pupils to consider how they would keep the shape's symmetry in this activity: 'Draw this shape.' 'Draw on the line of symmetry.' 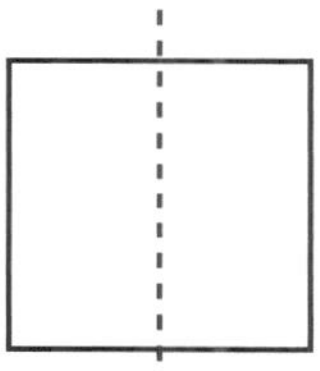 'Add a line here.' Add another line to keep the shape symmetrical. 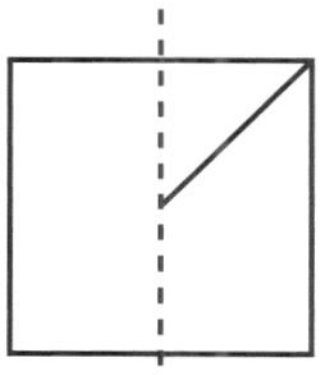 Continue to add or remove features from either side so that students have to reproduce changes to retain symmetry. 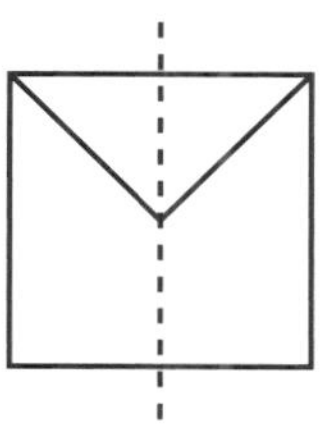 then 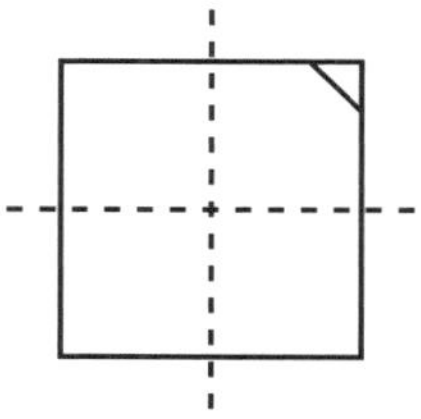 Make changes to the square that involve retaining symmetry in 2-lines.	184–9

framework teaching objective	§	lesson starter	f/w ref
Recognise and visualise the transformation and symmetry of a 2-D shape	1.6/ 1.7	Ask pupils to: **1** 'Draw a shape which has 4 sides.' Has everyone drawn the same shape? **2** 'Draw a shape which has 4 sides and 4 equal angles.' Now has everyone drawn the same shape? **3** 'Draw a shape which has 4 equal sides.' Has everyone drawn the same shape? Why did instruction **3** generate the same shape and not instructions **1** and **2**? **1** 'Draw a shape which has three sides.' Has everyone drawn the same shape? **2** 'Draw a shape which has 3 sides and one right angle.' Can I adapt instruction **2** so that everyone draws exactly the same right-angled triangle? – Students consider the 'slope' of the hypotenuse in terms of the two non-right angles in the triangle.	202–212

1 Shapes

Exercise 1.1 Links: 1A, 1B, 1C

Activity You need to make two squares which are the same size from paper or cardboard.

Then put them down so that they overlap and make a symmetrical shape. Make a drawing of your shape.

Make as many different shapes as you can.

(a) Under each shape write down how many lines of symmetry it has.

(b) Draw and name the shape of the part where there are two thicknesses of card.

e.g.

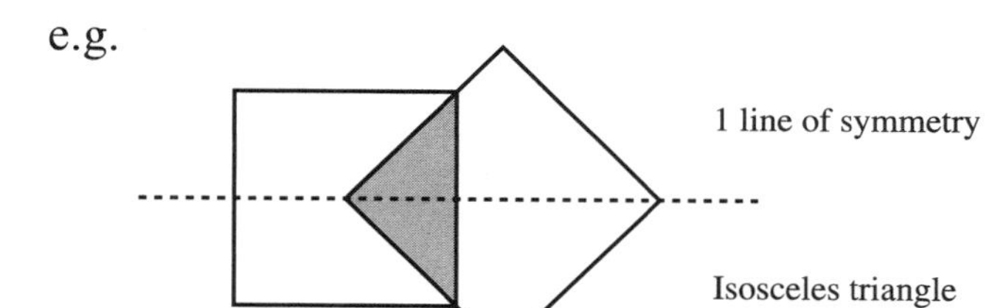

(Hint: there are at least 7 different shapes to make).

Exercise 1.2 Links: 1D

1 Complete these shapes using each dotted line as a line of symmetry.

(a)

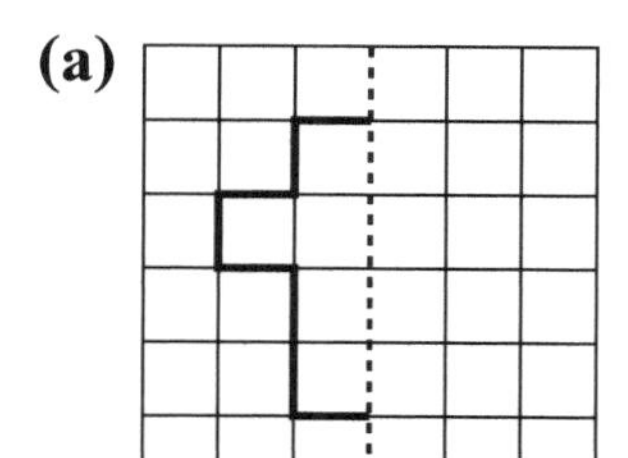

(b)

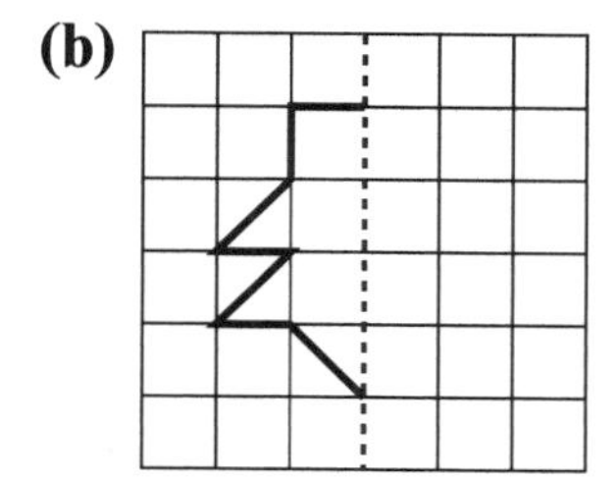

(c)

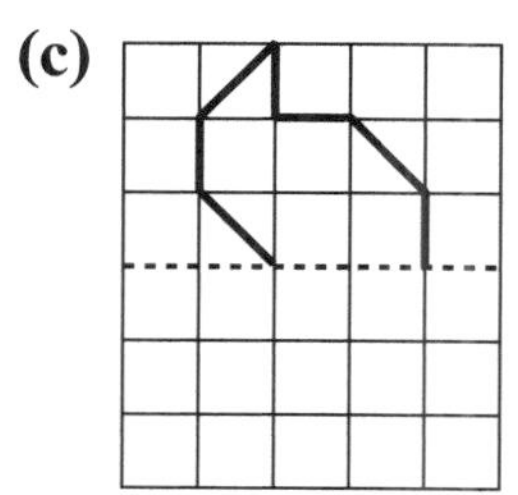

(d)

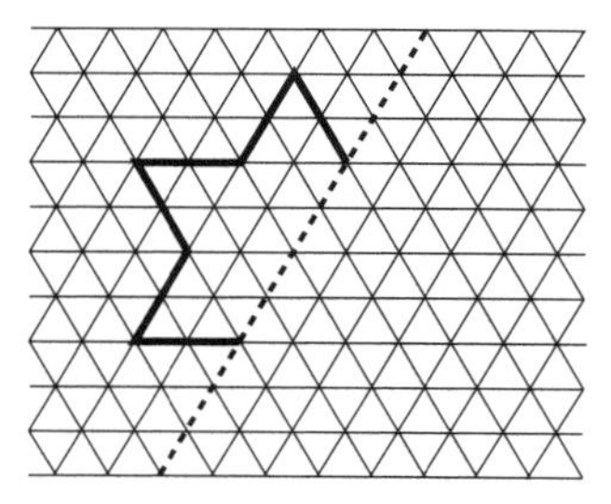

(e)

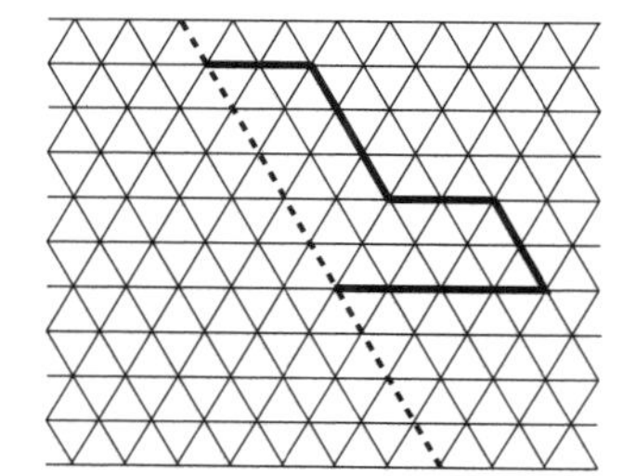

(f)

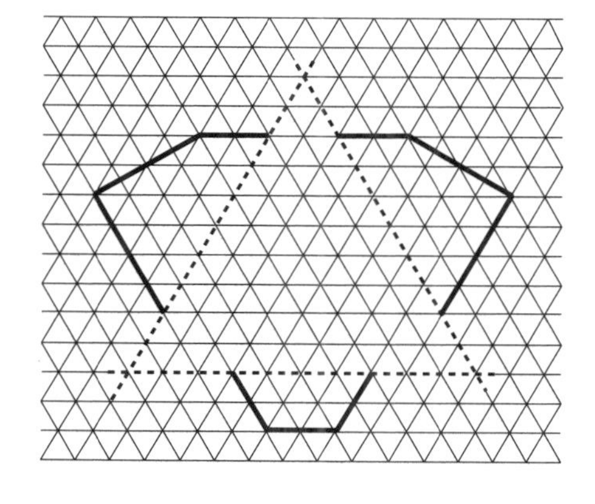

Exercise 1.3 Links: 1E, 1F

Make four tracings of this pentagon.

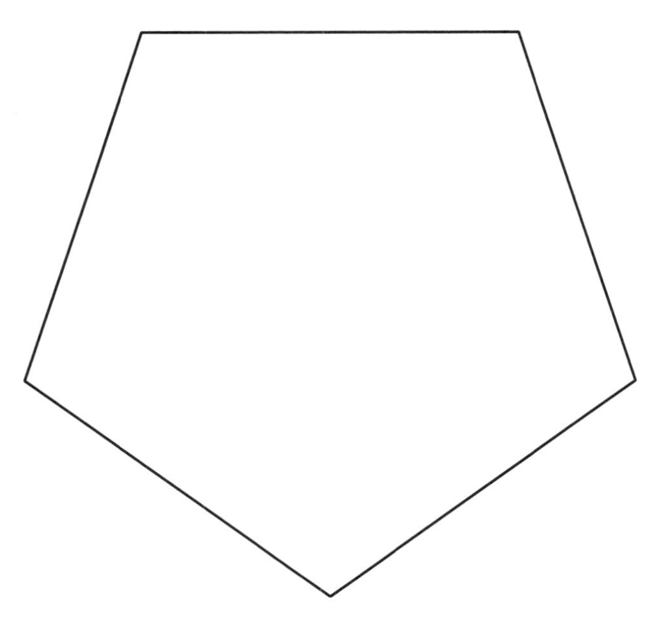

Join all the corners to each other.

Use your tracings to show isosceles triangles, kites, rhombuses and trapeziums.

Say how many of each there are.

....

Exercise 1.4 Links: 1G, 1H

Activity Copy these shapes on to card or paper.

Cut them out.

Fold along the dotted lines and Sellotape them to see what shapes they make.

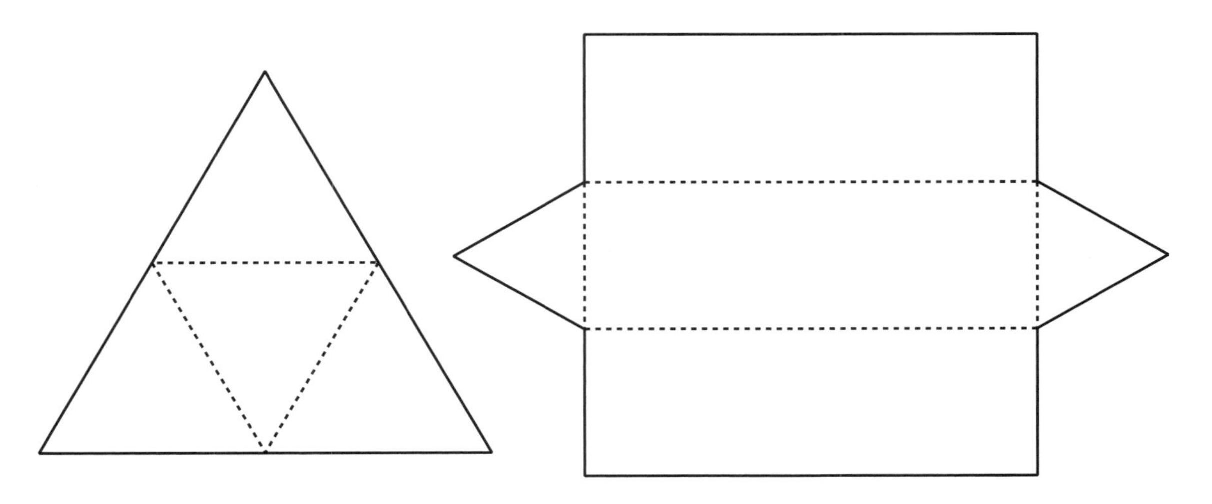

Name ....

1 Shapes

1 For each of these shapes count the number of sides and name the shape.

(a) 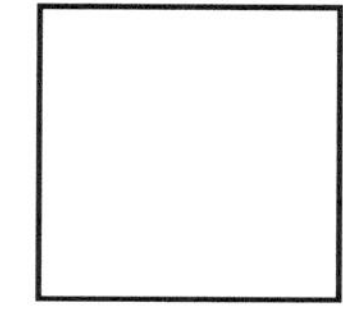

Number of sides ...... Name ....

(b) 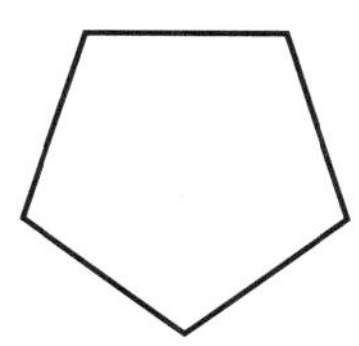

Number of sides ...... Name ....

(c) 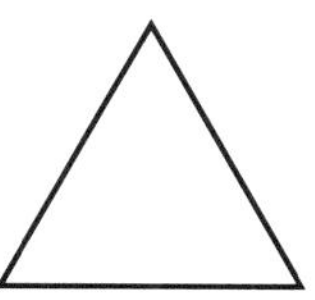

Number of sides ...... Name ....

(d) 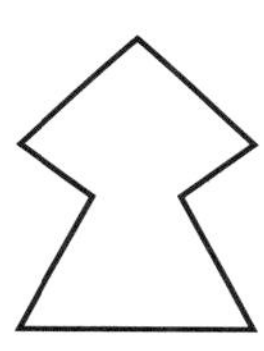

Number of sides ...... Name .... **(4 marks)**

---

2 **(a)** Sketch a hexagon.

(b) Sketch an octagon.

(2 marks)

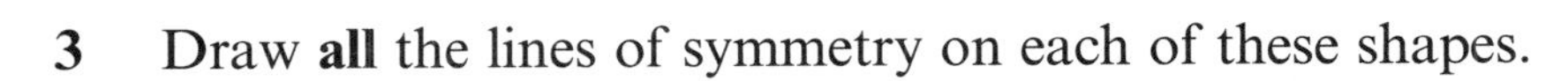

3 Draw **all** the lines of symmetry on each of these shapes.

(a)

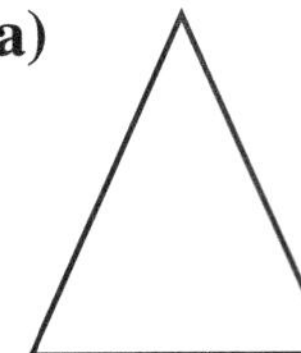

(b)

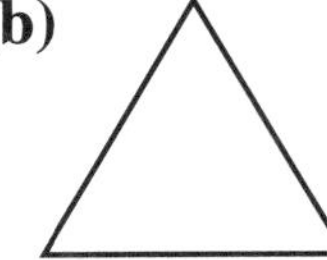

(c)

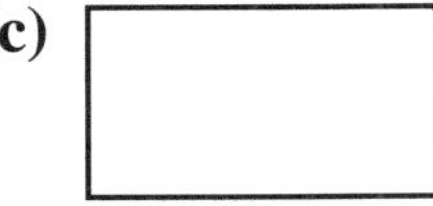

(d) **You can use a mirror in this question.**

On the grid below reflect each shape in the dotted mirror line.

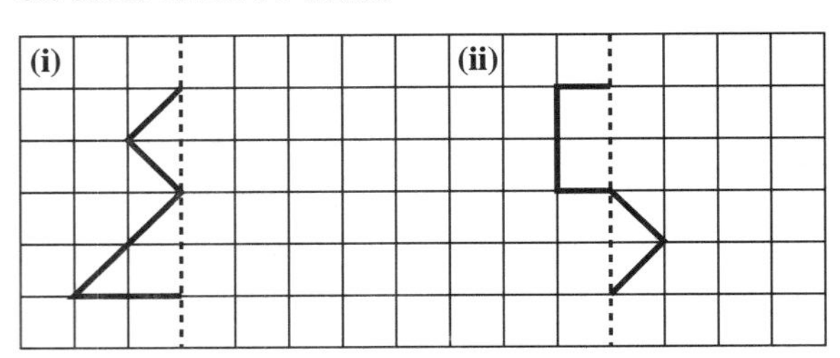

(6 marks)

---

4 Look at the three triangles drawn below.

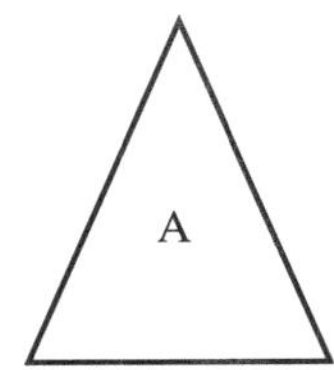

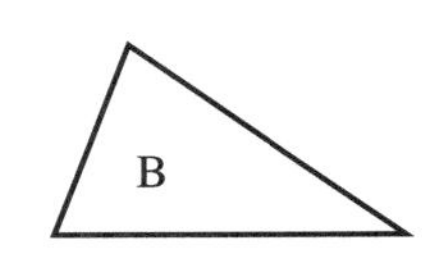

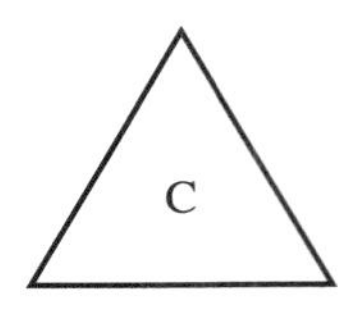

Here are the special names of three types of triangle.

Equilateral **Isosceles** **Scalene**

Match the names to the triangles.

A is .... B is .... C is ....

(2 marks)

---

5 **(a)** Look at the pictures of quadrilaterals.

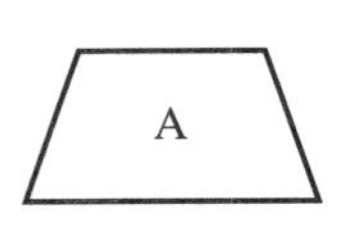

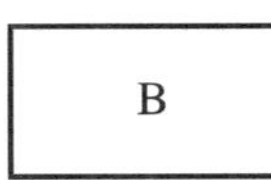

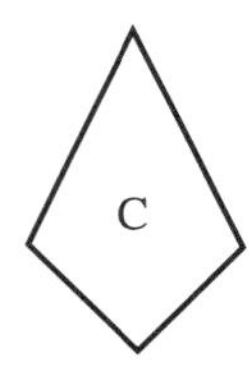

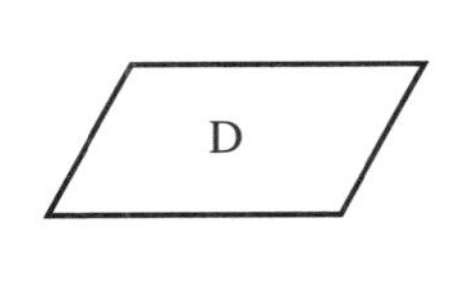

Here are the special names of four types of quadrilateral.

Kite **Parallelogram** **Rectangle** **Trapezium**

Match the names to the quadrilaterals.

A is a .... B is a ....

C is a .... D is a ....

(3 marks)

(b) On the grid below draw and give the **special name** for a **regular** quadrilateral.

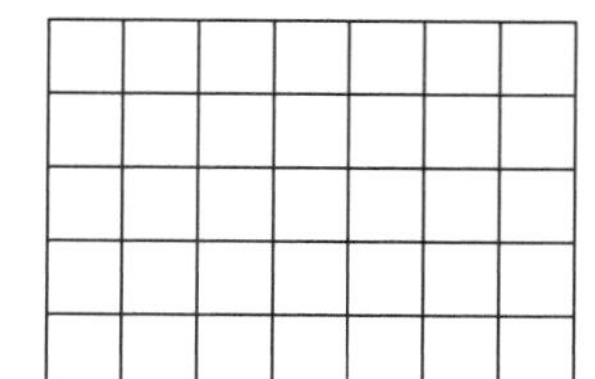

Special name is a ....

(1 mark)

---

6 Look at the drawings of some solid shapes.

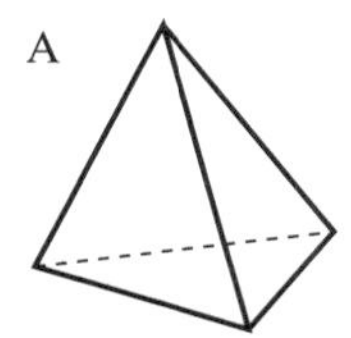

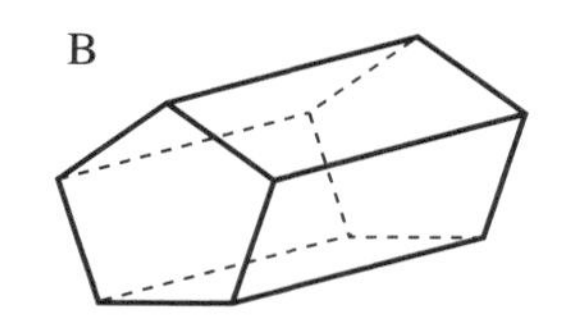

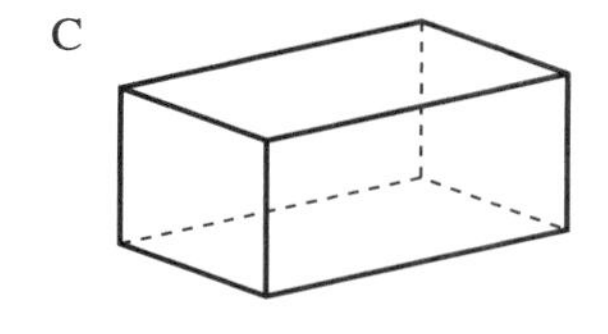

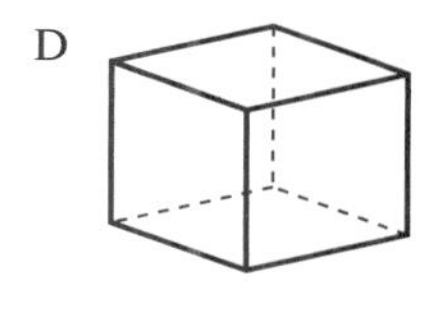

Here are the names of four types of solid.

Cube **Cuboid** **Prism** **Pyramid**

Match the names to the boxes.

A is a .... B is a ....

C is a .... D is a ....

(4 marks)

---

7 Look at this picture of Sally's bedroom.

Mark with the letter **R** each object which is a PRISM.
Mark with the letter **Y** each object which is a PYRAMID.

(3 marks)

---

8 The end face of a prism is an **equilateral** triangle.

(a) Draw a sketch of this prism.

(1 mark)

(b) Find the number of **planes of symmetry** of this prism.

…………

(2 marks)

---

9 **(a)** Draw a **plane of symmetry** on the cuboid.

(b) Find the number of planes of symmetry for the cuboid.

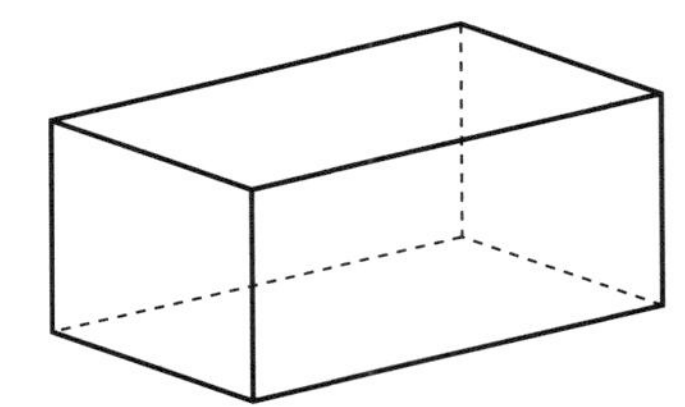

(2 marks)

Unit 1 Shapes

Question		Answer	Marking guidance and remediation sheet links	
1	(a)	4 square	A1 for both	
	(b)	5 pentagon	A1 for both	
	(c)	3 equilateral triangle	A1 for both (accept triangle)	
	(d)	7 heptagon	A1 for both	
2	(a)	Any 6 sided figure	A1	
	(b)	Any 8 sided figure	A1	
3	(a)	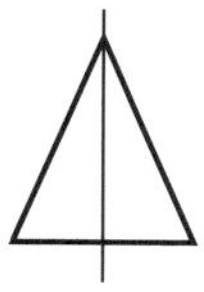	B1 for 1 line only	less than $\frac{4}{6}$, use remediation sheet 1.1
	(b)	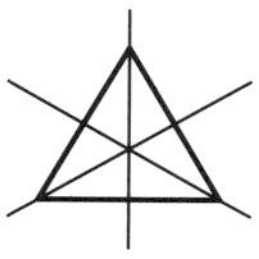	B1 for all three lines	
	(c)	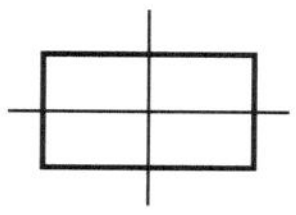	B1 for each line (max 2) If diagonals are drawn as well then just give B1	
	(d) (i)	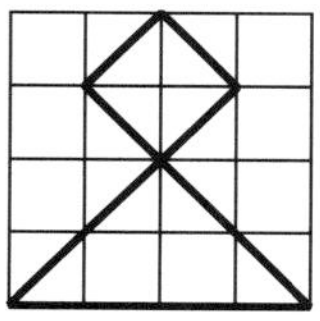	B1 for all correct	
	(ii)	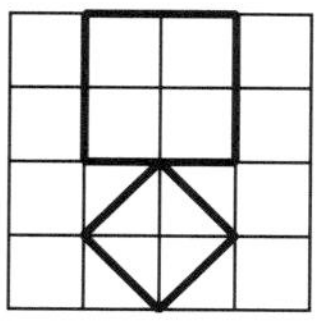	B1 for all correct	
4		A is Isosceles B is Scalene C is Equilateral	B2 for all 3 correct B1 for 1 correct	

Key to mark scheme
A marks: correct answer
M marks: correct method
B marks: independent work

Page 265 gives a general guidance on use of this assessment scheme with some examples.

Assessment and remediation links

Question		Answer	Marking guidance and remediation sheet links
5	**(a)**	A is a Trapezium B is a Rectangle C is a Kite D is a Parallelogram	B3 for all 4 correct B2 for 2 correct B1 for 1 correct
	(b)	any square on grid	B1 for a square drawn of side 1, 2, 3, 4 or 5 AND the word 'square'
6		A is a Pyramid B is a Prism C is a Cuboid D is a Cube	B1 B1 B1 B1
7		Prisms and pyramids marked on picture	B3 for all marked correctly B1 for one prism marked B1 for one pyramid marked
8	**(a)**		B1 (ignore dotted lines)
	(b)	4	B2 for 4 B1 for 3
9	**(a)**		B1 for any one plane } less than $\frac{1}{2}$ use remediation sheet 1.2
	(b)		B1 for 3

Key to mark scheme
A marks: correct answer
M marks: correct method
B marks: independent work

Page 265 gives a general guidance on use of this assessment scheme with some examples.

1.1 Lines of symmetry

You can make symmetrical shapes by folding and cutting paper:

Fold a sheet of paper in half:

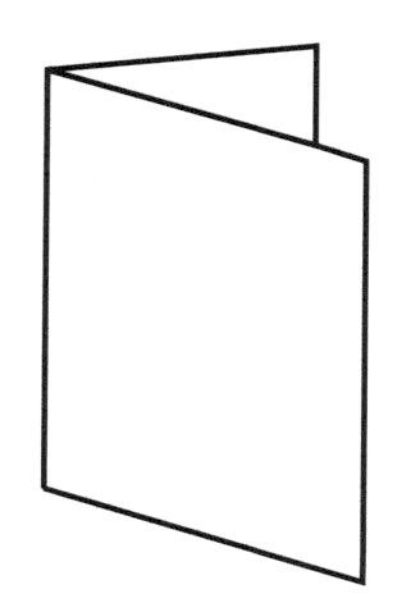

Draw a shape …

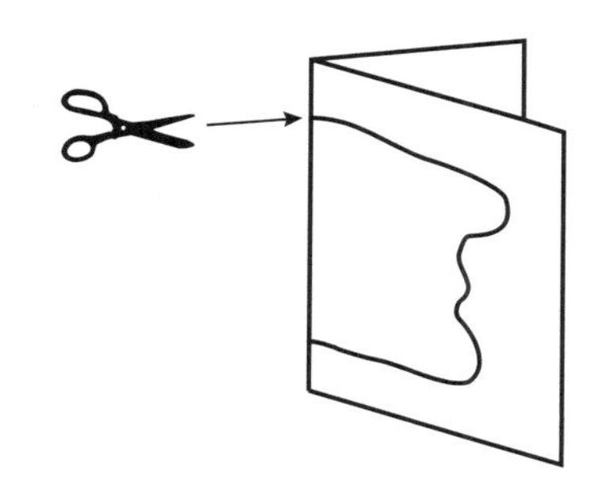

… and cut it out like this.

Open the sheet out:

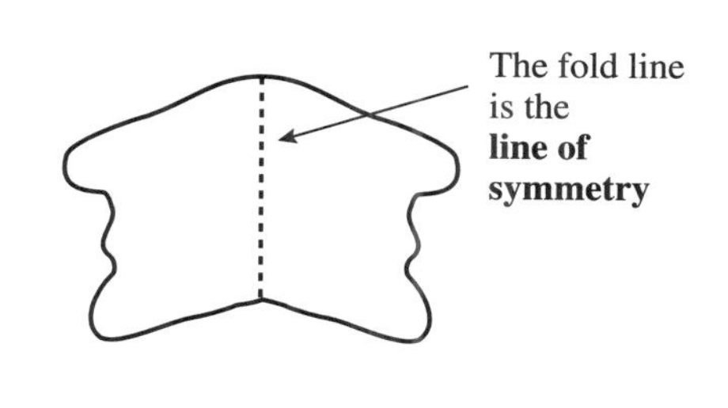

The two sides are reflections of each other.

Exercise 1

1 Try folding and cutting these shapes:

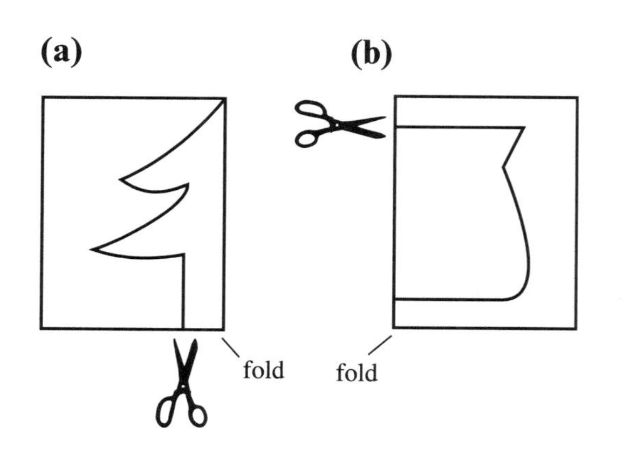

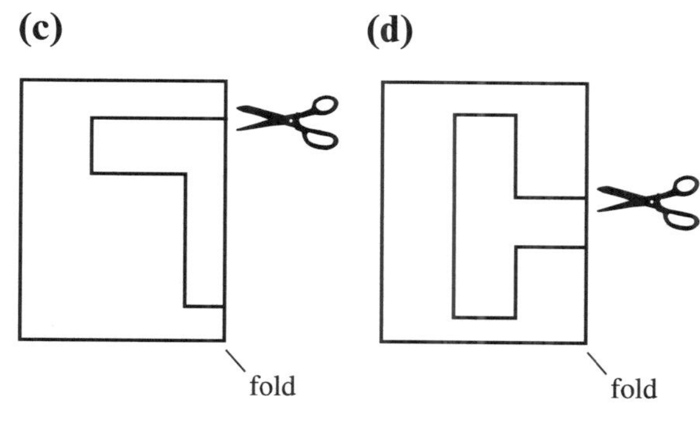

2 Try folding and cutting some shapes of your own.

You can also make symmetrical designs with paint or ink:

Fold a sheet of paper in half and open out:

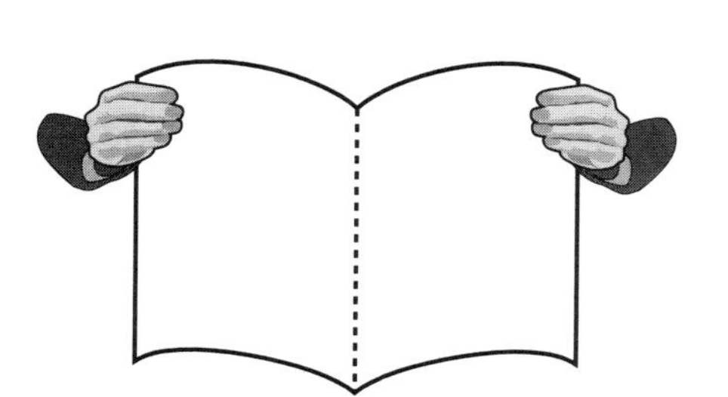

Put paint or ink on one side…

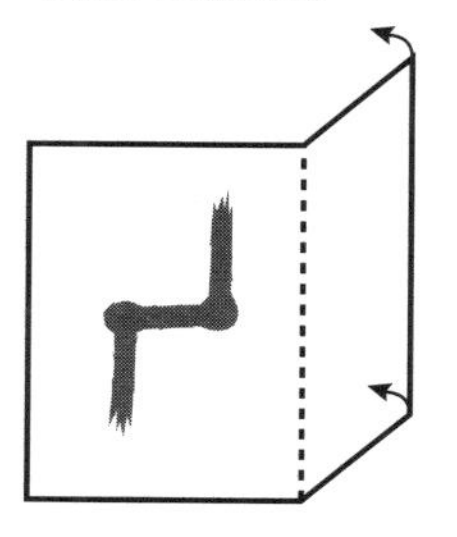

…and press the other side on top.

Open out:

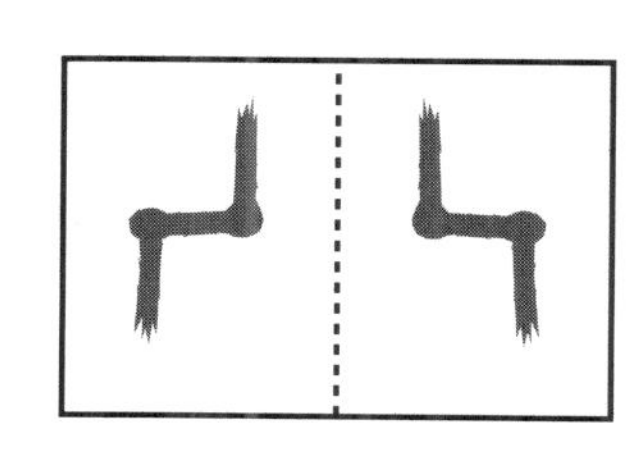

The picture is symmetrical.

Exercise 2

Try making some ink or paint designs of your own.

You can find lines of symmetry with a mirror.

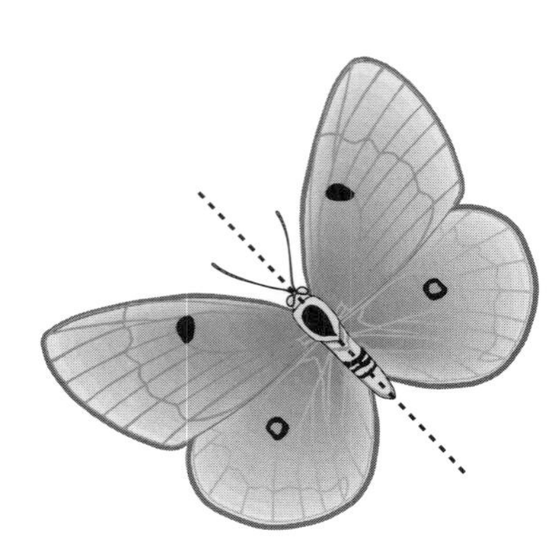

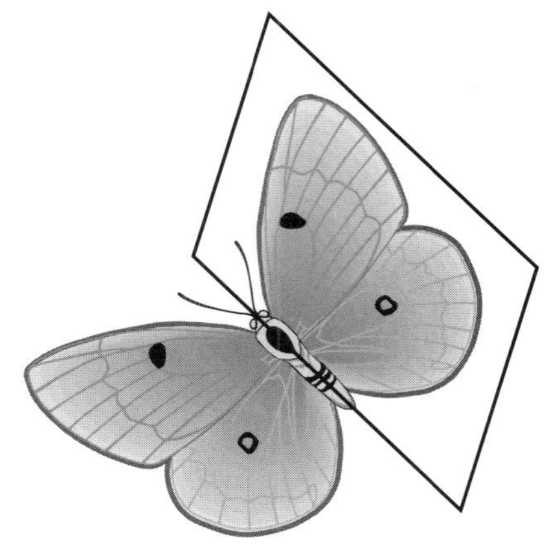

Put a mirror on this line . . .

. . . the butterfly looks the same

Example 1

Complete this symmetrical shape:

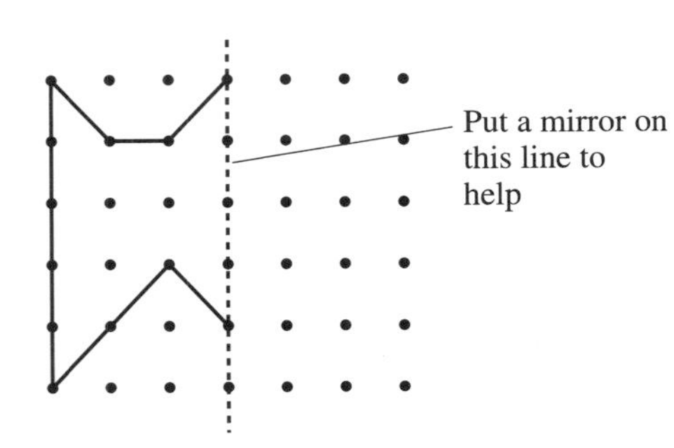
Put a mirror on
this line to
help

Answer:

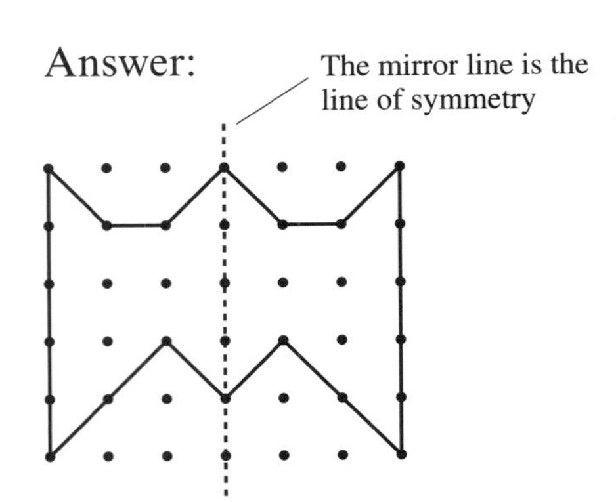
The mirror line is the
line of symmetry

Exercise 3

Complete these shapes.

Use a mirror to help.

(a)

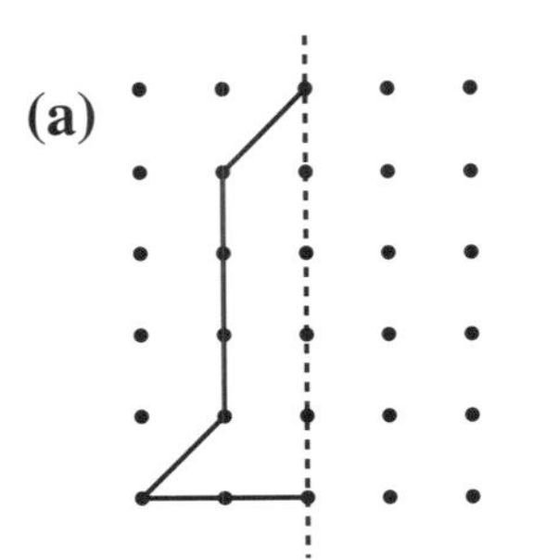

(b)

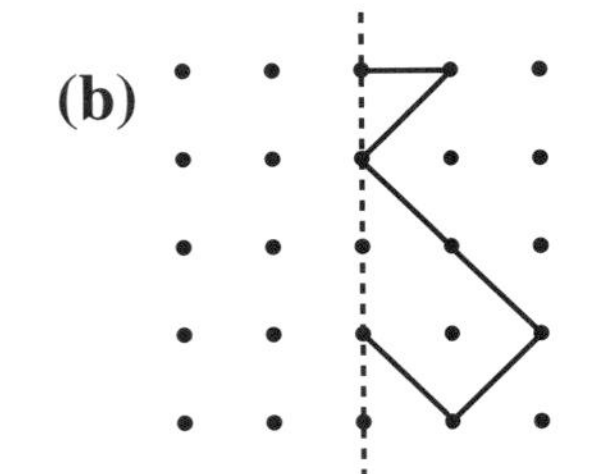

(c)

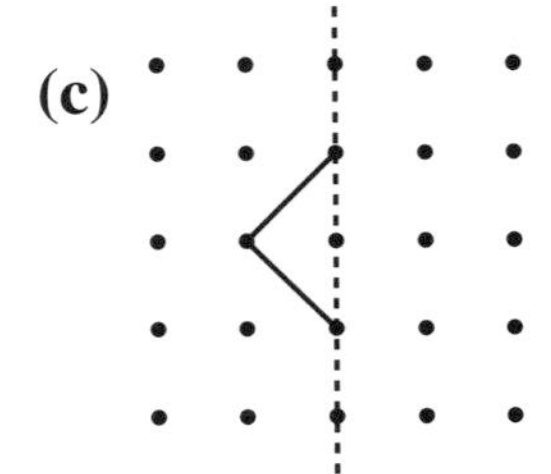

(d)

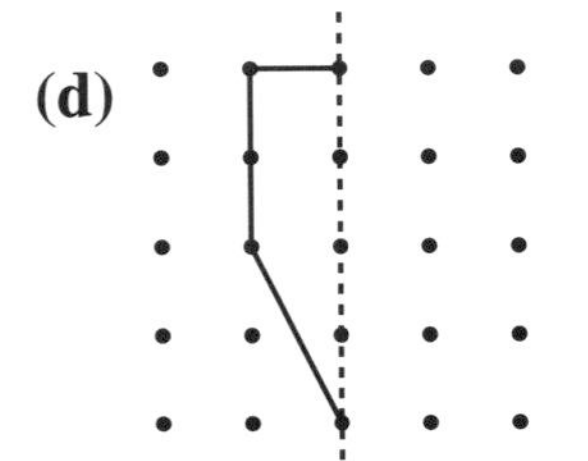

(e)

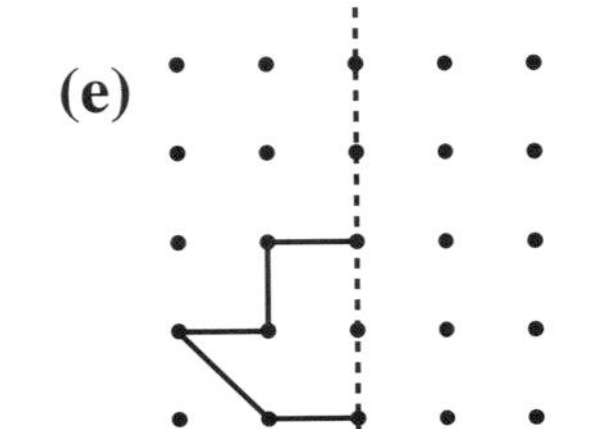

(f)

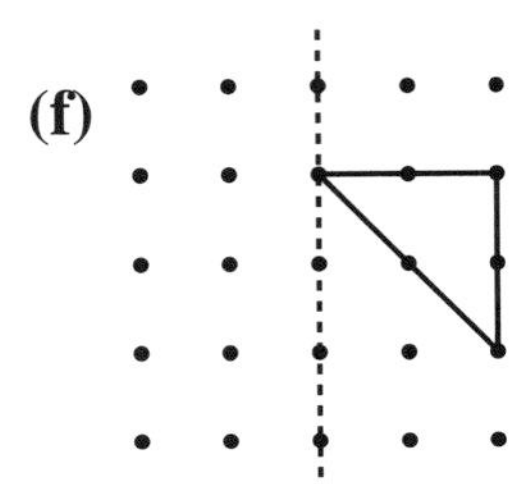

Exercise 4

1 Complete these shapes.

Use a mirror on the dotted lines to help.

(a)

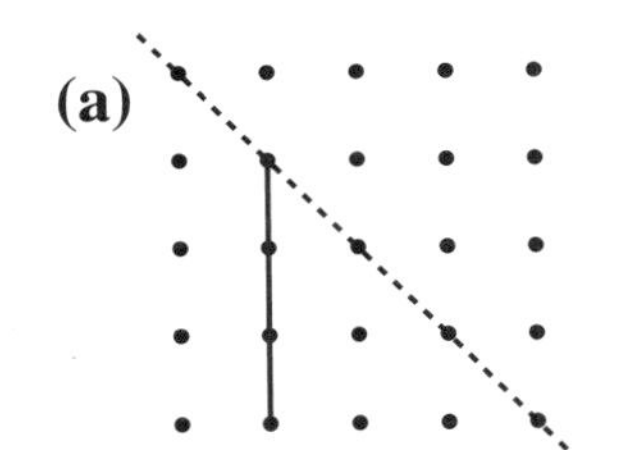

(b)

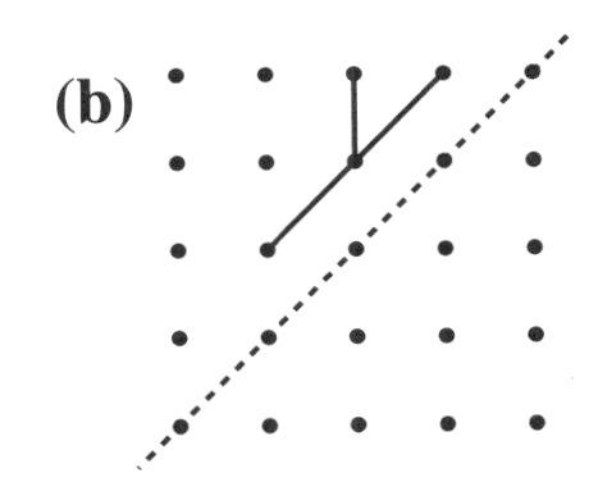

(c)

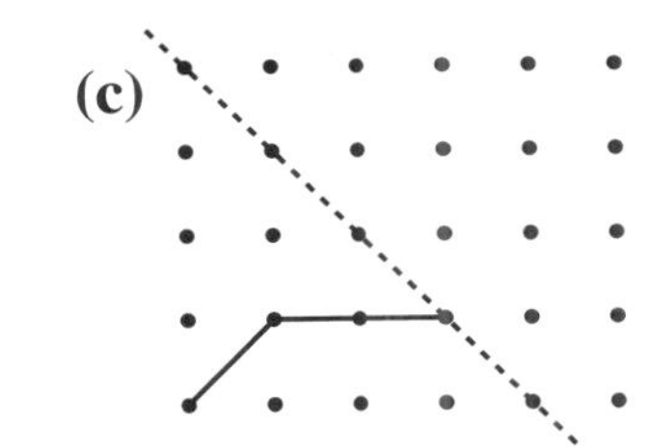

(d)

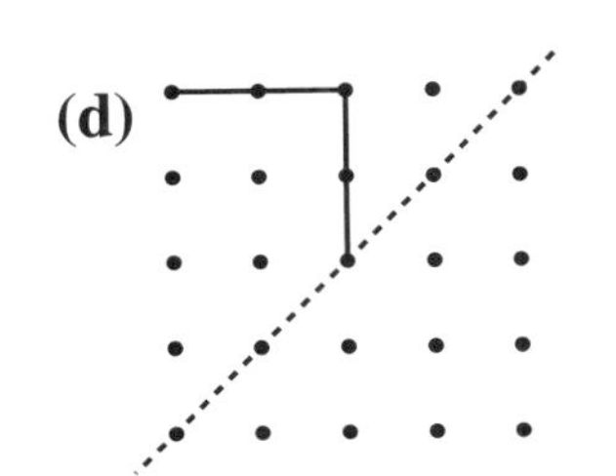

(e)

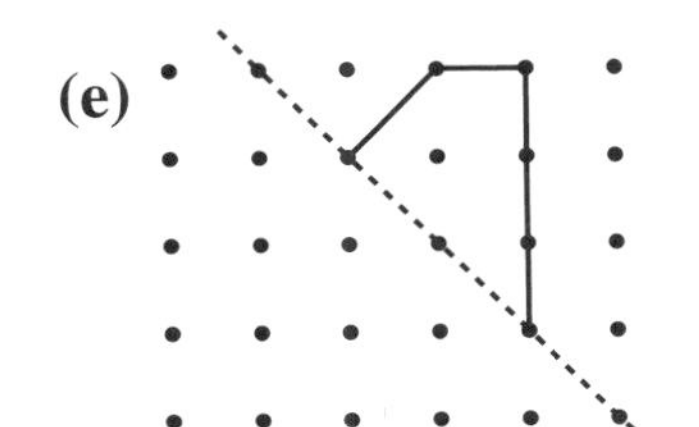

(f)

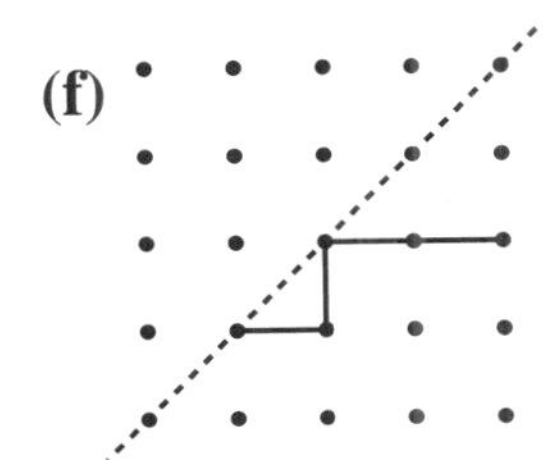

(g)

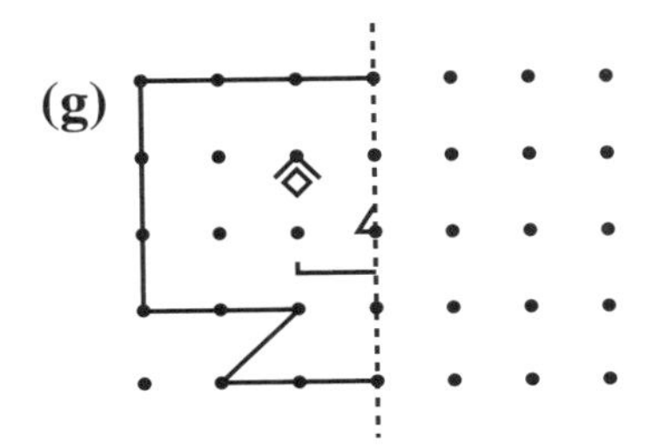

(h)

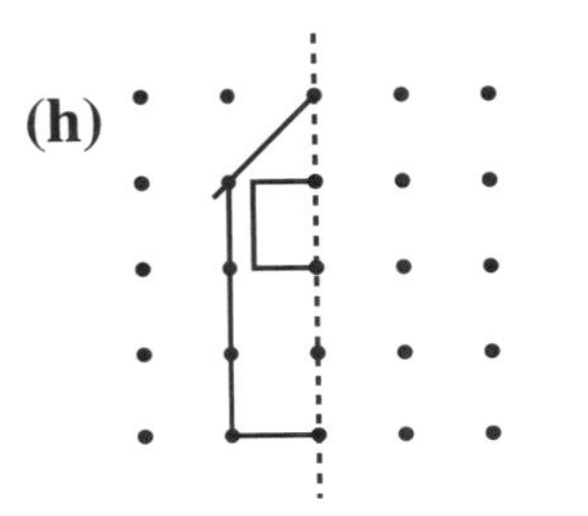

(i)

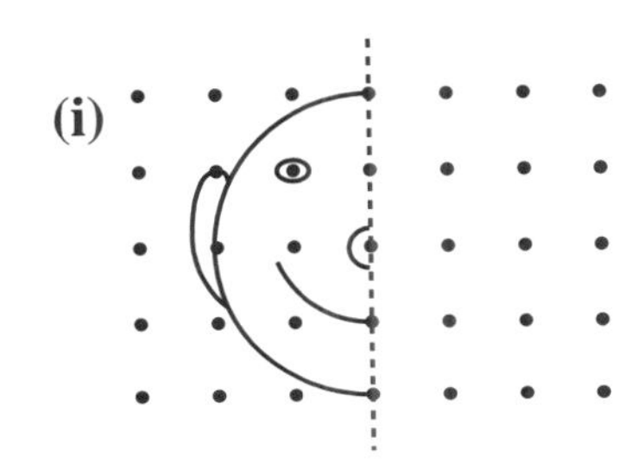

2 Draw in the lines that cut these shapes in half:

(a)

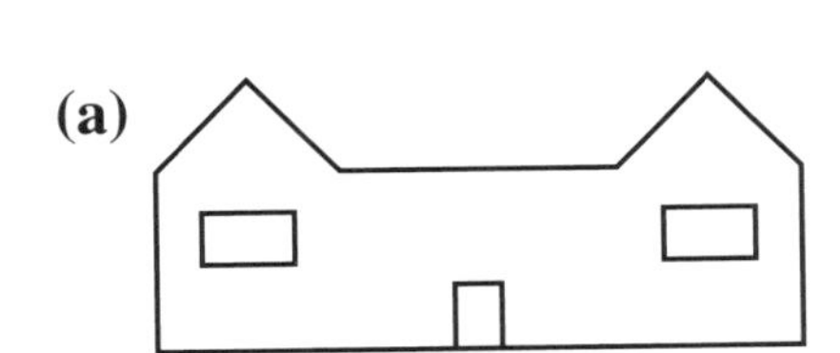

(b)

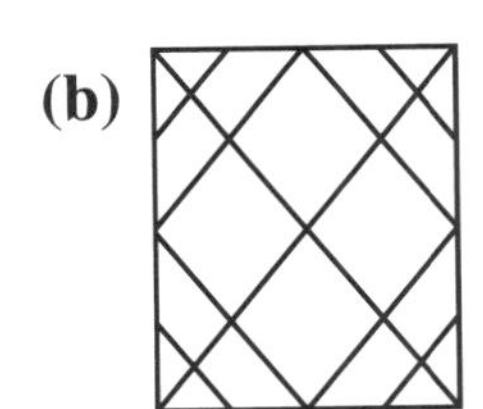

(c)

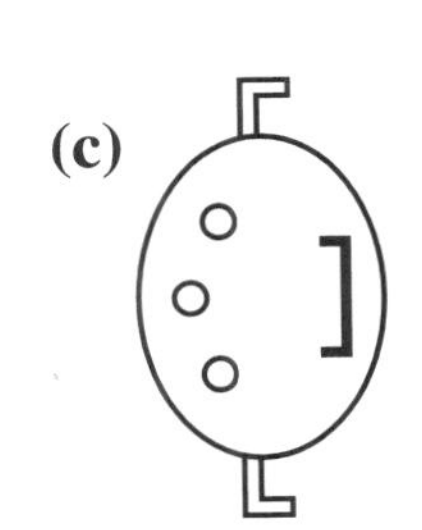

1.2 Planes of symmetry

These things have all been cut in half.

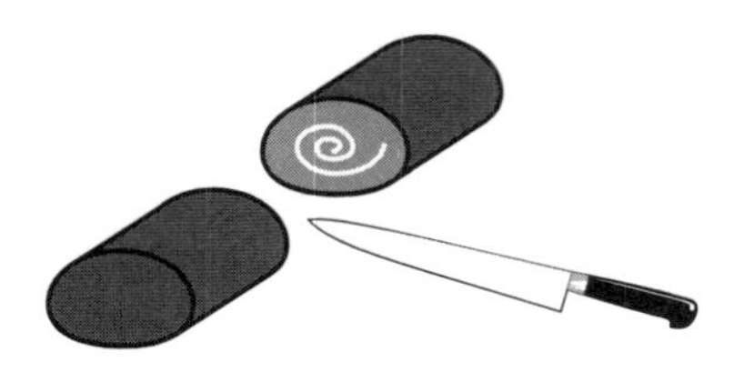

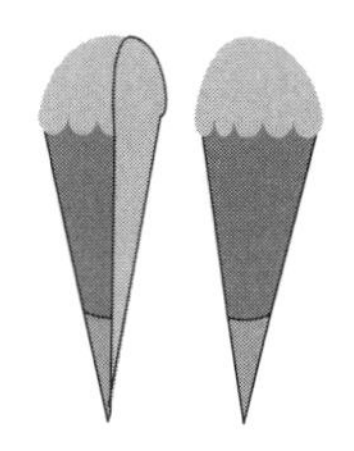

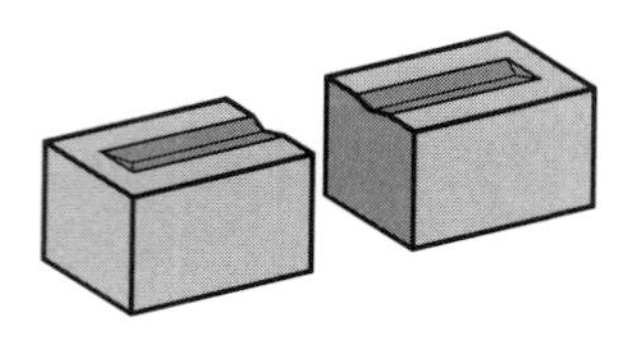

Each half is a mirror image of the other.
Each shape is made from two matching halves.

Exercise 1

1 Which of these things are made from two matching halves?

(a)

(b)

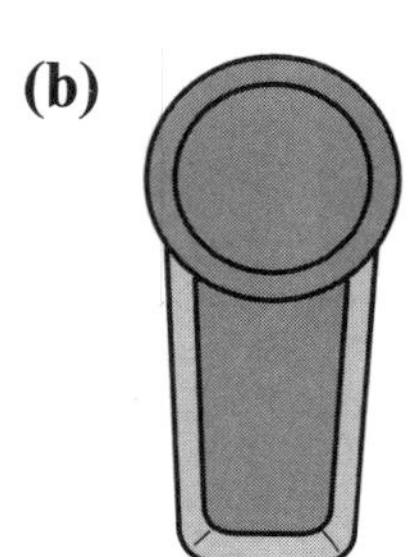

(c)

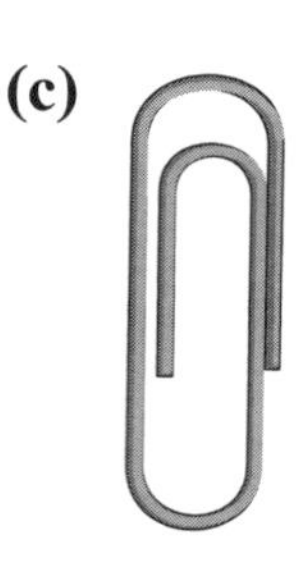

(d)

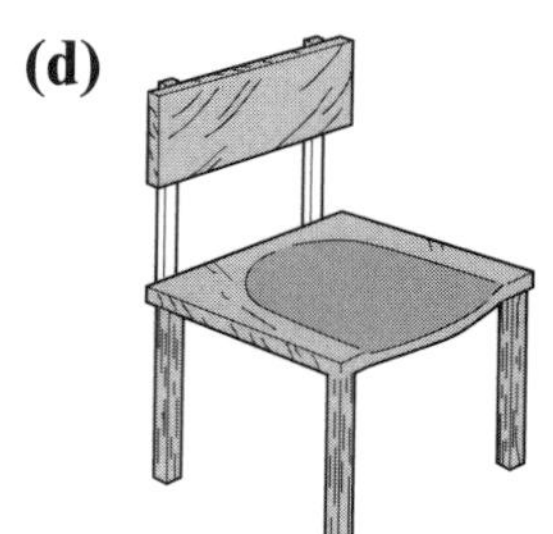

2 Make a list of things in your classroom that have matching sides.

John uses a curtain to cut his tent into two matching halves:

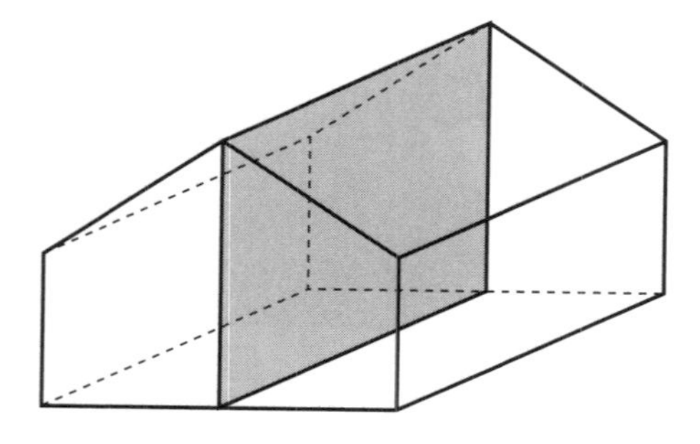

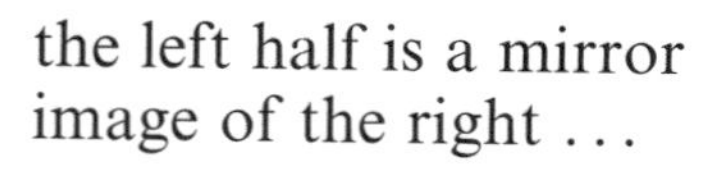

the left half is a mirror image of the right ...

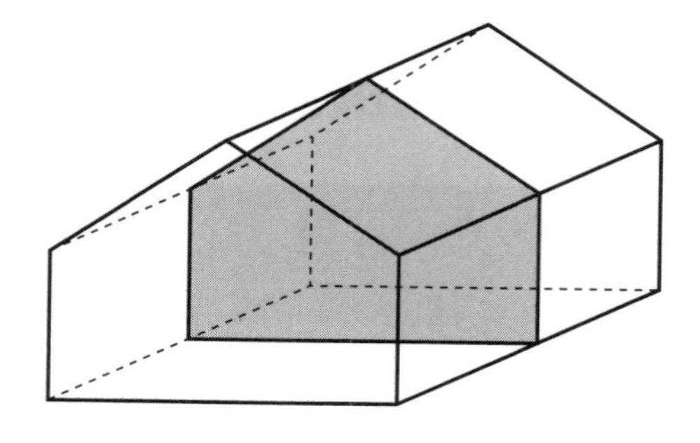

... the front half is a mirror image of the back.

The curtain forms a **plane of symmetry**.

- **A plane of symmetry cuts a shape into two matching halves.**

Exercise 2

1 How many planes of symmetry does each shape have? (Hint: Think how many ways you could make two matching halves).

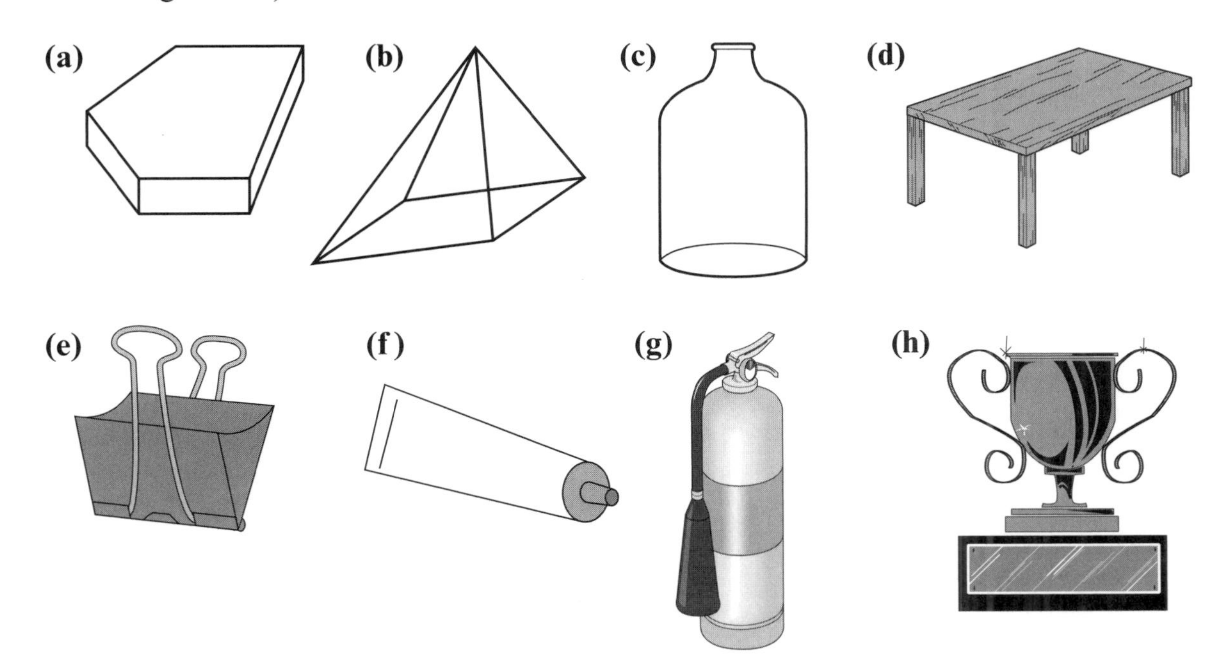

2 How many ways can you find to cut a cube in half?

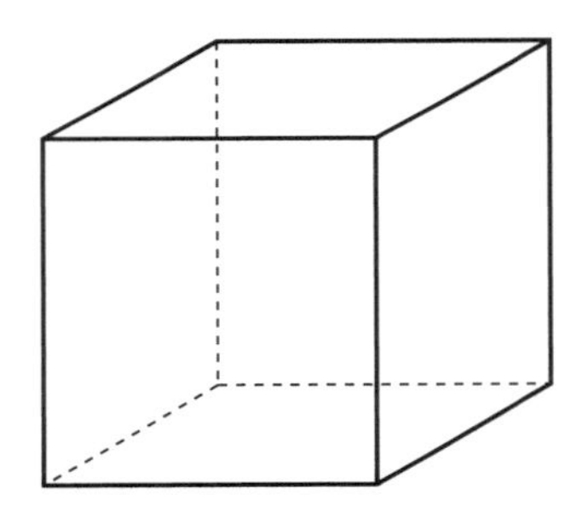

Answers to Pupils' Book

1 Shapes

Exercise 1A

1 (a) 3, triangle (b) 8, octagon
(c) 6, hexagon (d) 7, heptagon
(e) 4, quadrilateral (f) 5, pentagon
(g) 7, heptagon (h) 3, triangle
(i) 6, hexagon (j) 5, pentagon
(k) 8, octagon (l) 4, quadrilateral
2 (a) 6 (b) 9
3 (a) 16 (b) 1 (c) 2 (d) 2
4 (i) pentagon 8, quadrilateral (rectangle) 4, hexagon 3
(ii) pentagon 16, quadrilateral (rhombus) 4
(iii) pentagon 8, hexagon 4, quadrilateral 7
(iv) quadrilateral 6, pentagon 4, octagon 1

Exercise 1B

1 (a) 2 (b) 1 (c) 4 (d) 1
(e) 1 (f) 1 (g) 2 (h) 1
(i) 2 (j) 1 (k) 2 (l) 2
2 horizontal only B, D, E, C; vertical only A, W, M; both horizontal and vertical H, I, O, X
3 1, 0, 1, 2, 0
4 DECODED

Exercise 1C

1 regular 4 2 regular 5
3 not regular 1 4 regular 8
5 not regular 1 6 regular 7
7 not regular 0 8 regular 3
9 not regular 2 10 not regular 1
11 not regular 1 12 not regular 2
13 (b) 6, 6 (c) 5, 5, 5 (d) 3, 3, 3
(e) 8, 8, 8 (f) 7, 7, 7

Exercise 1D

1 quadrilateral 2 square
3 regular pentagon 4 regular hexagon
5 quadrilateral 6 quadrilateral
7 regular octagon 8 rectangle
9 hexagon
10 equilateral triangle
11 heptagon
12 hexagon

Exercise 1E

1 3, equilateral, 3 2 2, isosceles, 1
3 0, scalene, 0 4 2, isosceles, 1
5 3, equilateral, 3 6 2, isosceles, 1
7 0, scalene, 0 8 2, isosceles, 1
9 2, isosceles, 1

Exercise 1F

1 parallelogram, 0 2 kite, 1
3 trapezium, 0 4 parallelogram, 0
5 square, 4 6 rectangle, 2
7 parallelogram, 0 8 trapezium, 0
9 rectangle, 2 10 kite, 1
11 rhombus, 2 12 square, 4
13 (a) 4 (b) 4 (c) 1
(d) 2 (e) 2 (f) 0
14 (a) 1 (b) Rhombus (diamond)
15 (a) Trapezium (triamond)
(b) Equilateral triangle, parallelogram, hexagon (the tetramonds)
(c) kite and parallelogram
(d) pentagon and trapezium
(e) parallelogram, isosceles triangle, hexagon, heptagon

Exercise 1G

Note cubes and cuboids are also prisms.
1 cuboid 2 pyramid
3 cube 4 prism
5 cube 6 pyramid
7 cube 8 cuboid
9 prism 10 prism
11 pyramid 12 prism
13 (a) equilateral triangle
(b) pentagon
(c) hexagon
14 (a) square
(b) triangle
(c) hexagon

Exercise 1H

1 triangular prism
2 cuboid
3 square based pyramid
4 pentagonal prism
5 triangular prism
6 octagonal prism
7 trapezoidal prism

Exercise 1I

1 (a) 3 (b) 2
(c) ∞ (d) 1
(e) 3 (f) 6
(g) 1 (h) 8
2 (a) cuboid 3
(b) equilateral triangular based pyramid (tetrahedron) 9
(c) isosceles triangular prism 2
(d) cube 9
(e) pentagonal prism 2
(f) pentagonal based pyramid 5
(g) hexagonal based pyramid 0 or 1
(h) right hexagonal based pyramid 6
(i) hexagonal prism 7
3 1 4 2 5
3 4 4 6
5 2 6 9
7 2

Answers to Homeworks

1 Shapes

Exercise 1.2 Links: 1D

1 (a) (b) (c) (d)

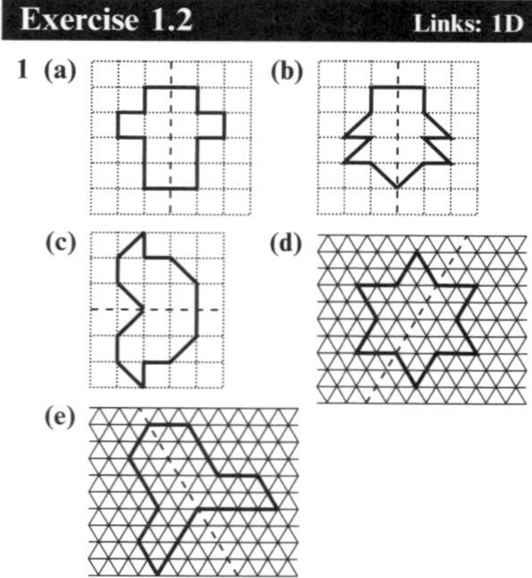

(e)

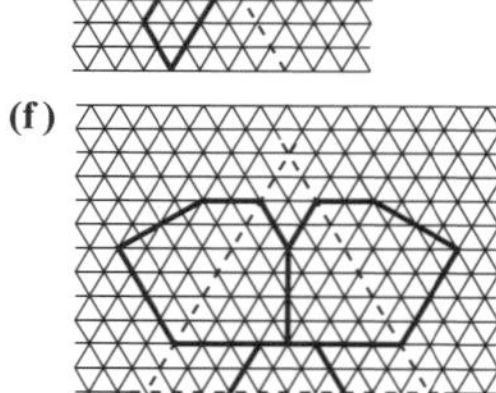

(f)

Exercise 1.3 Links: 1E, 1F

All answers come in multiples of 5 e.g. trapeziums 5, rhombuses 5, kites 5, isosceles triangles 30.

Remediation answers

1.1 Lines of symmetry

Exercise 3

(a) (b) (c) (d)

(e)

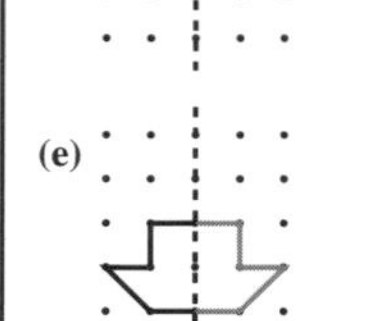

(f)

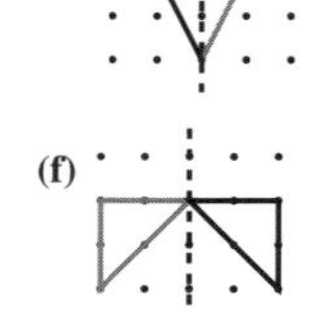

Exercise 4

(a) (b) (c) (d)

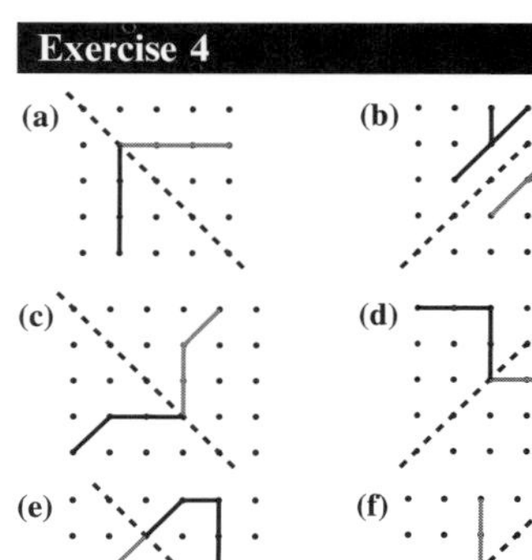

(e) (f)

(g)

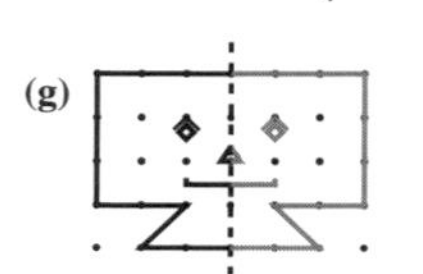

(h)

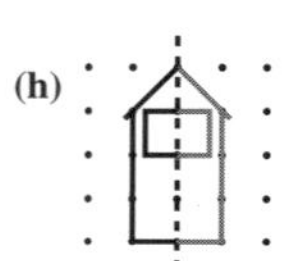

(i)

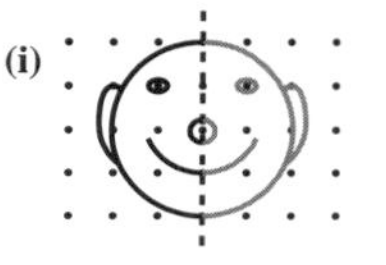

2 (a)

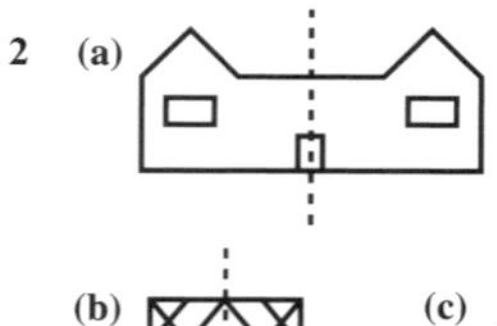

(b) (c)

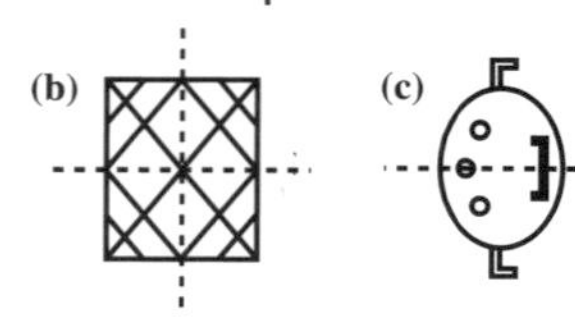

1.2 Planes of symmetry

Exercise 1

(b) Tap (d) Chair.

Exercise 2

1 (a) 2

(1 of these)

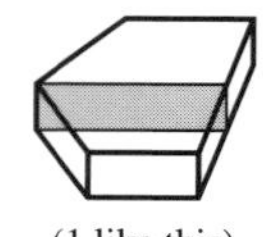

(1 like this)

Answers

(b) 4

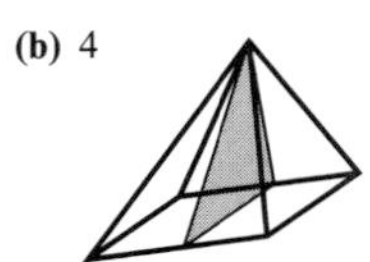

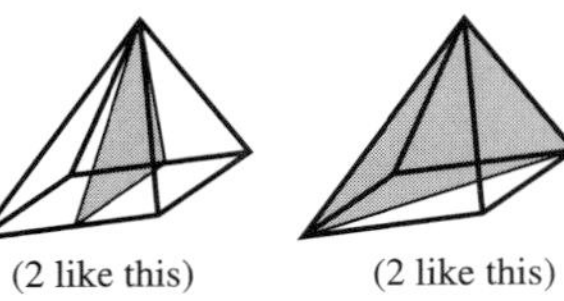

(2 like this) (2 like this)

(c) Lots – so many they cannot be counted 'infinite'.

(d) 2

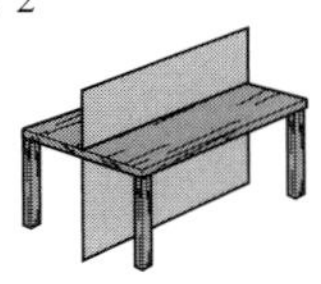

(2 like this)

(e) 2

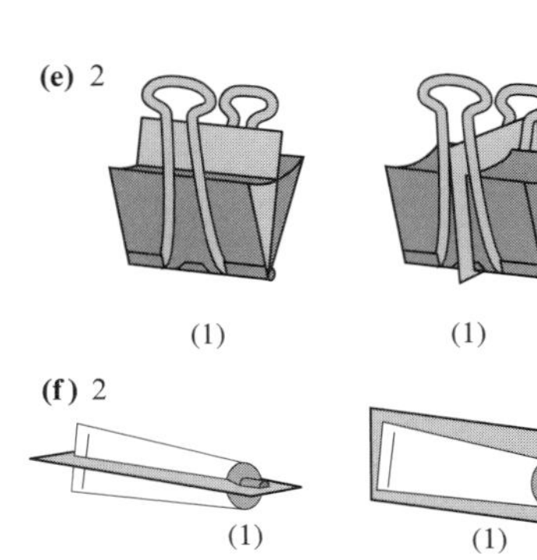

(1) (1)

(f) 2

(1) (1)

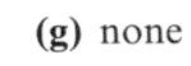

(g) none

(h) 2

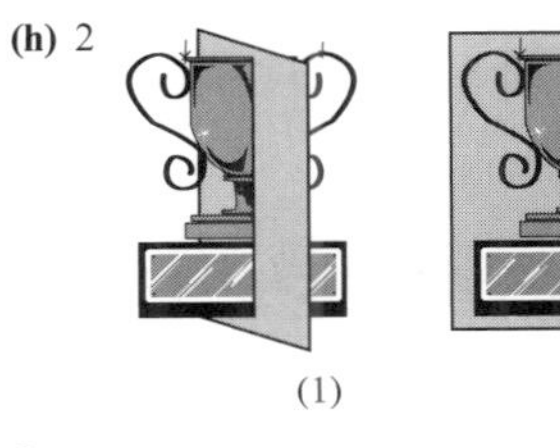

(1) (1)

2 9

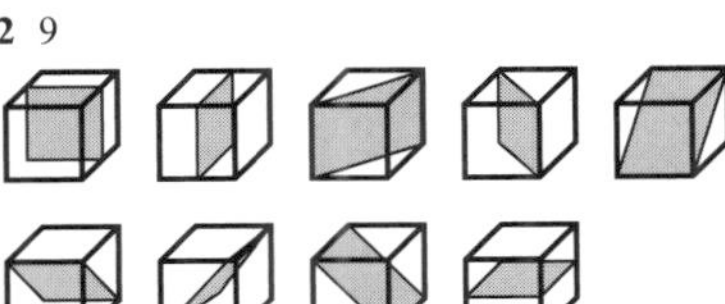

Unit 2 Understanding numbers

Content summary

This unit shows the significance of digits and place value to hundred thousands. Mental methods and pencil and paper methods for addition and subtraction are developed.

NC level

Level 2: Digits and place value to hundreds.

Level 3: Digits and place value to thousands.
Use of mental recall in addition and subtraction.

NA2a NA3a NA3i

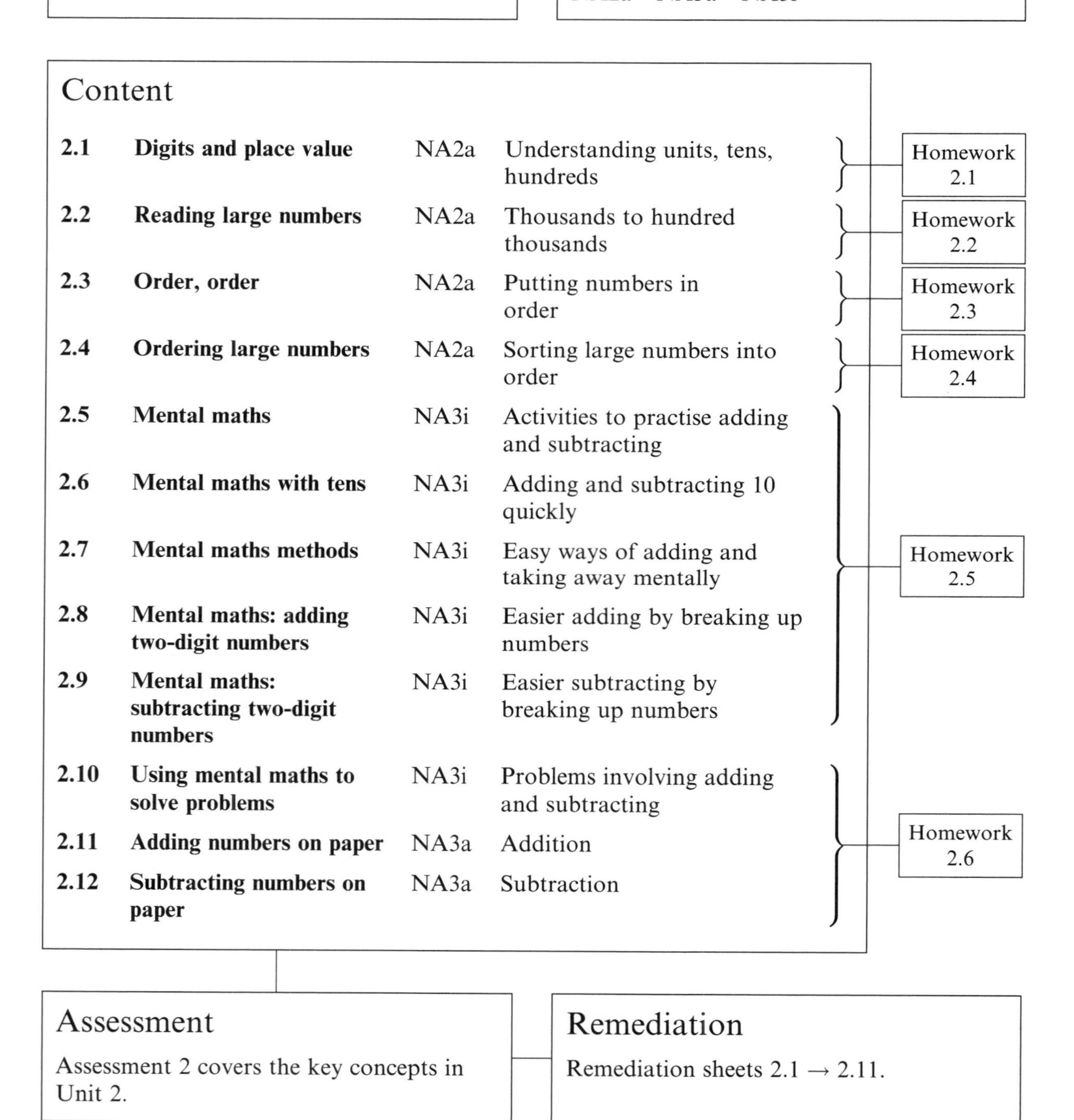

Content

2.1	**Digits and place value**	NA2a	Understanding units, tens, hundreds	Homework 2.1
2.2	**Reading large numbers**	NA2a	Thousands to hundred thousands	Homework 2.2
2.3	**Order, order**	NA2a	Putting numbers in order	Homework 2.3
2.4	**Ordering large numbers**	NA2a	Sorting large numbers into order	Homework 2.4
2.5	**Mental maths**	NA3i	Activities to practise adding and subtracting	Homework 2.5
2.6	**Mental maths with tens**	NA3i	Adding and subtracting 10 quickly	
2.7	**Mental maths methods**	NA3i	Easy ways of adding and taking away mentally	
2.8	**Mental maths: adding two-digit numbers**	NA3i	Easier adding by breaking up numbers	
2.9	**Mental maths: subtracting two-digit numbers**	NA3i	Easier subtracting by breaking up numbers	
2.10	**Using mental maths to solve problems**	NA3i	Problems involving adding and subtracting	Homework 2.6
2.11	**Adding numbers on paper**	NA3a	Addition	
2.12	**Subtracting numbers on paper**	NA3a	Subtraction	

Assessment

Assessment 2 covers the key concepts in Unit 2.

Remediation

Remediation sheets 2.1 → 2.11.

Assessment

The assessment is marked out of 30.
Achievement of 20 or more marks indicates a good understanding of the key concepts.
Marking guidance, answers and links to remediation are provided on page 265.

ICT links

2.1
Use *MicroSmile for Windows Pack 3* to gain confidence with place value.

2.3 and 2.4
Use *MicroSmile for Windows Pack 3 and 6* to practice the ordering of numbers.

2.5–2.12
Use *MicroSmile for Windows Pack 8* to supplement addition and subtraction.

Equipment

	Pupils' Book page
Numbered cards 0–9	25, 27, 34
100 square	34
Calculators	30

Remediation

Place value:
Use Cuisinaire or multilink to give pupils a practical base for this work. Start with oral work, encouraging pupils to say out loud 'one ten and four units', as shown in the first example. Move on to 'two tens and . . .', and 'three tens and . . .' before tackling the text and working in the abstract. This process can be extended to introduce hundreds, tens and units. For the practical work on thousands, cut out 10×10 squares from cm^2 paper to use as 'thousands'.

Adding:
Start practically with plenty of oral work, counting cubes, pencils, rulers and other classroom objects. Use cubes to demonstrate blocks of 10 and link in with the practical place value work. Do not go on to abstract sums in the text until the pupil is secure in completing similar examples orally. Demonstrate 'carrys' using cubes, again giving plenty of oral practice before attempting the questions in the text.

Subtracting:
Start practically, covering cubes with your hand as in the first example. As with adding, start with oral work before moving on to writing down answers. Using flash cards with '10 – 2', '10 – 3', etc. can be an oral activity to reinforce 10's number bonding – 'how many can we do in a minute today'.

Use cubes to demonstrate alternative subtraction methods and develop mental skills and understanding, especially to reinforce 'sums that go together'.

Questionbank CD

All homeworks and extension questions also appear on the CD.

Pages xvii and xviii of this pack show you how to use the CD to select questions from the Questionbank and further customize them if you wish to.

2 Understanding number

framework teaching objective	§	lesson starter	f/w ref
Consolidate the rapid recall of number facts.	2.8/ 2.9	Divide a page into two columns, A and B. Give students a series of numbers in column A. A | B 6 8 2 3 They have to write complementary numbers in B to add to 10. Now try adding to 100. Try also 50, 70, etc Aaron says '74 and 36 add together' to make 100.' What mistake has he made?	88–91
Consolidate the rapid recall of number facts.	2.11	Class 6 N: 67 students Class 6 S: 45 students Katie says: 'there are 1012 students altogether in Class 6 'N and S.' How can we quickly see that she is wrong? What mistake has she made? Class 6 E: 60 students Class 6 W: 23 students Daniel says: 'there are 43 more students in Class 6 E than in 6 W'. What maths has Daniel used? What mistake has he made? What maths can we do to check his answer?	88–91
Consolidate the rapid recall of number facts.	2.9	Fill in the numbers on the snake to reach 100. 2 →(?) 11 →(?) 25 →(?) 33 →(?) 42 →(?) 65 →(?) 79 →(?) 87 →(?) 100 What maths can we use to check our answers? Devise a snake which counts backwards from 50 to zero.	88–91

framework teaching objective	§	lesson starter	f/w ref
Consolidate the rapid recall of number facts.	2.7	Introduce pupils to the idea of tearing numbers apart. 'Numbers must be torn apart into a tens box and a units box.' 'Then they can be added and stuck back together.' 2 3 → 2 tens, 3 units; 5 6 → 5 tens, 6 units 'I've torn these 2 numbers apart.' 'How many tens are there in the box?' 7 tens 'How many units are there in the box?' 9 units What number is this if I glue it back together? Next: Students should 'tear apart' a number which gives 10 or more in the units box.	88–91

1 G

Homework

2 Understanding numbers

Exercise 2.1 Links: 2A

1 What does the 3 mean in each of these numbers?
(a) 631 (b) 23 (c) 359 (d) 403
(e) 374 (f) 3 (g) 139 (h) 34

2 Write a two-digit number which has:
(a) 4 tens and 5 units (b) 6 tens and 2 units
(c) 3 tens and 0 units (d) 7 units and 4 tens
(e) 8 units and 2 tens (f) 9 units and 4 tens
(g) 4 units and 8 tens (h) 1 ten and 3 units

Hint: 7 units and 4 tens **not** 7 tens and 4 units

3 Write down a three-digit number which has:
(a) 4 hundreds, 5 tens and 6 units
(b) 8 hundreds, 3 tens and 6 units
(c) 5 tens, 3 units and 6 hundreds
(d) 7 units, 2 hundreds and 4 tens
(e) 6 hundreds, 0 units and 3 tens
(f) 0 tens, 4 hundreds and 0 units

Hint: Read the question carefully

4 Write down all the two-digit numbers that can be made using the digits 3, 5 and 8.

5 How many three-digit numbers have 7 tens?

Exercise 2.2 Links: 2B

1 What does the 3 mean in each of these numbers?
(a) 3 241 (b) 231 906 (c) 367 855 (d) 43 004
(e) 31 022 (f) 397 045 (g) 83 567 (h) 3 412

2 How many thousands are there in each number?
(a) 26 431 (b) 2 583 (c) 236 579 (d) 40 873
(e) 193 702 (f) 391 254 (g) 103 890 (h) 35 404

3 Write the numbers in question **2** in words.

4 Write these numbers using digits.
(a) Two thousand seven hundred and three.
(b) Three hundred and eight thousand and forty nine.
(c) Twenty one thousand seven hundred and fifty.
(d) A thousand and ninety one.

5 5225 is a palindromic number as it reads the same forwards as backwards. How many four-digit palindromic numbers are there?

Exercise 2.3 Links: 2C

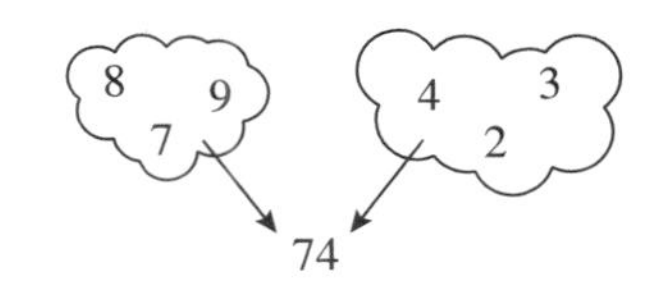

1 Choose a digit from each cloud and use them to make a two-digit number.

(a) Find all the two-digit numbers you can make by this method.

(b) Put the two-digit numbers you have made in order of size starting with the smallest.

2 The table shows the points scored by five teams in a sports quiz. Rearrange the table to show the teams in order, putting the team with the largest number of points at the top of the table.

Team	Points
Bears	48
Allstars	71
Egg-heads	38
Top-lot	29
Gold	64

3 There are six members of the Clark family. Susie is aged twenty one, Gavin is fourteen, Jennifer is forty eight, Charlie is seventy six, Florry is thirty nine and Jamie is eight.

(a) Write the names of the Clark family in the order of their ages, starting with the youngest.

(b) Who do you think is the grandfather?

Exercise 2.4 Links: 2D

1 Put each set of numbers in size order, smallest first:

(a) 738, 924, 246, 338, 405 **(b)** 406, 369, 420, 373, 691

(c) 833, 492, 401, 882, 452 **(d)** 415, 309, 78, 364, 387

2 The table shows the distance from Plymouth of six cities. Rearrange the table to put the cities in order with the nearest to Plymouth at the top.

City	Distance in miles
Hull	346
Newcastle	416
Aberdeen	631
London	241
Edinburgh	496
Norwich	354

3 Use the information below to complete the table:
The *Lake District* is the largest.
Exmoor is the smallest.
The *Peak District* is just larger than the *North York Moors*.
The *Yorkshire Dales* is the second largest.
The second smallest is *Dartmoor*.
The other National Park is *Northumberland*.

National Park	Area in square miles
	368
	268
	885
	405
	554
	683
	555

Exercise 2.5 Links: 2E, 2F, 2G, 2H, 2I

1 Find pairs of numbers with a total of:

(a) 7 **(b)** 14 **(c)** 19 **(d)** 13 **(e)** 16 **(f)** 17

2 Find pairs of numbers, each less than 20, with a difference of:

(a) 3 **(b)** 9 **(c)** 6 **(d)** 11 **(e)** 14 **(f)** 7

3 Find as many ways as you can to fill the square and triangular boxes.

(a) □ + △ = 15 **(b)** △ − □ = 2

(c) □ − 2 = △ **(d)** △ + 4 = □

(e) □ + 1 = △ + 4 **(f)** 10 − □ = △

4 Pick a number from each cloud and add them together.
How many different answers can you make by doing this?

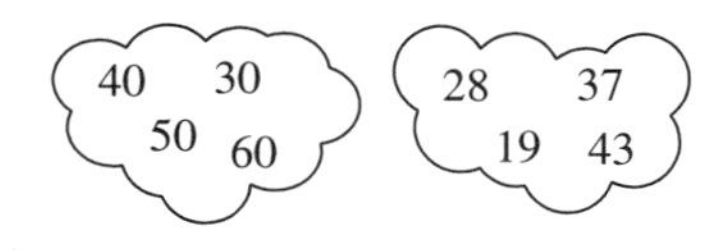

5 How many different ways can you work out each of these mentally?

(a) 16 + 21 **(b)** 64 − 25 **(c)** 46 + 45 **(d)** 38 + 29

Exercise 2.6 Links: 2J, 2K, 2L

1 Jane bought a CD for £13.
She paid with a £20 note.
How much change did she receive?

2 Eleanora bought two mugs for £4 each and a teapot.
The total cost was £20.
How much did the teapot cost?

3 Pick pairs of numbers, one from each box, and subtract them.
Which pair of numbers gives:

(a) the biggest answer

(b) the smallest answer

(c) the answer closest to 250.

573 735
648 894

320 489
397 541

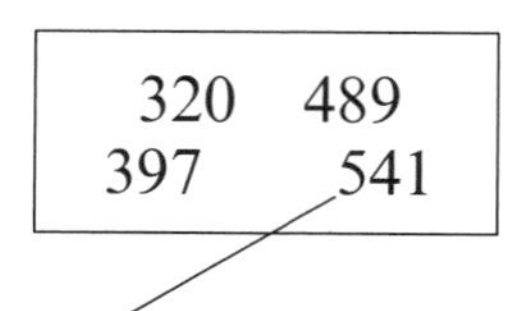

4 Find the missing digits in each of these subtractions:

(a)
```
  5 □ 2
− □ 4 □
  3 4 9
```

(b)
```
  □ 4 □
− 3 □ 4
  4 6 3
```

(c)
```
  7 □ □
− □ 8 9
  1 3 9
```

(d)
```
  □ 6 3
− 2 □ □
  2 5 6
```

Name ....

2 Understanding numbers

1 What does the **3** mean in each of these numbers?

(a) 357 .... **(1 mark)**

(b) 253 .... **(1 mark)**

(c) 138 .... **(1 mark)**

(d) 3419 .... **(1 mark)**

(e) 23 597 .... **(1 mark)**

---

2 Here is a number machine for sorting numbers.

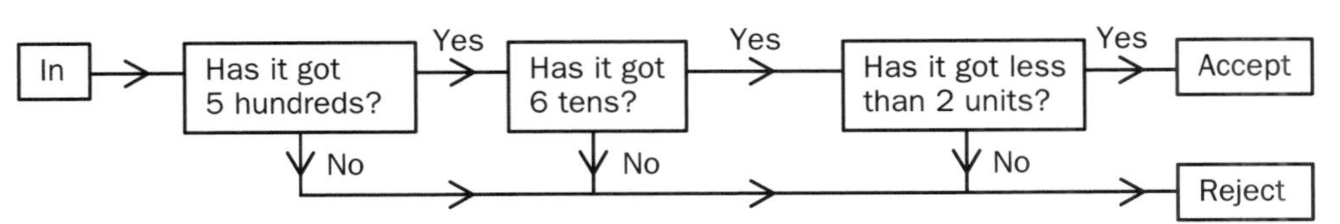

Write down all of the numbers this machine will accept.

.... **(2 marks)**

---

3 How many thousands are in each of these numbers?

(a) 4 294 .... **(1 mark)**

(b) 21 048 .... **(1 mark)**

---

4 Write these numbers in figures.

Five thousand two hundred and seven .... **(1 mark)**

Seventy four thousand two hundred and forty three .... **(1 mark)**

---

5 Put these numbers in order. Start with the smallest.

47 56 12 18 80

.... **(2 marks)**

---

6 Put these numbers in order. Start with the smallest.

721 **712** **127** **172** **217** **271**

.... **(2 marks)**

---

7 Write down the answer to

(a) $4 + 5$ ....

(b) $15 + 20$ ....

(c) $15 - 6$ ....

(d) $56 - 20$ ....

(e) $80 - 57$ .... **(5 marks)**

---

8 Write down the answer to

(a) $36 + 27$ ....

(b) $82 - 27$ .... **(2 marks)**

---

9 Work out:

(a)
$$\begin{array}{r} 2\ 8\ 6 \\ +\ 1\ 5\ 4 \\ \hline \\ \hline \end{array}$$

(b)
$$\begin{array}{r} 3\ 9\ 7 \\ 5\ 6\ 8 \\ +\ 2\ 7\ 9 \\ \hline \\ \hline \end{array}$$

(c)
$$\begin{array}{r} 3\ 7\ 4 \\ -\ 1\ 5\ 9 \\ \hline \\ \hline \end{array}$$

(d)
$$\begin{array}{r} 7\ 0\ 0 \\ -\ 1\ 5\ 6 \\ \hline \\ \hline \end{array}$$

(4 marks)

---

10 Mrs Khan is 37 years old.

(a) How old will she be in 23 years time? .... **(1 mark)**

(b) How old was she 28 years ago? .... **(1 mark)**

(c) Mrs Khan is 19 years older than her daughter. Work out the age of her daughter. .... **(2 marks)**

Unit 2 Understanding numbers

Question		Answer	Marking guidance and remediation sheet links	
1	(a)	300 or 3 hundreds or hundreds	A1	less than $\frac{7}{11}$ use remediation sheets 2.1→2.3 (Questions 1–4(a))
	(b)	3 or 3 units or units	A1	
	(c)	30 or 3 tens or tens	A1	
	(d)	3000 or 3 thousands or thousands	A1	
	(e)	3000 or 3 thousands or thousands	A1	
2		560 and 561	A1, A1	
3	(a)	4 or 4 thousands	A1	
	(b)	21 or 21 thousand	A1	
4	(a)	5207	A1	
	(b)	74 243	A1	
5		12, 18, 47, 56, 80	A2; A1 if largest first or one number out of place	less than $\frac{3}{4}$ use remediation sheets 2.1→2.3 (Questions 5–6)
6		127, 172, 217, 271, 712, 721	A2; A1 if largest first or one number out of place	

Key to mark scheme A marks: correct answer M marks: correct method B marks: independent work	Page 265 gives a general guidance on use of this assessment scheme with some examples.

Assessment and remediation links

Question		Answer	Marking guidance and remediation sheet links	
7	**(a)**	9	A1	less than $\frac{10}{15}$ use remediation sheets 2.4→2.11
	(b)	35	A1	
	(c)	9	A1	
	(d)	36	A1	
	(e)	23	A1	
8	**(a)**	63	A1	
	(b)	55	A1	
9	**(a)**	440	A1	
	(b)	1244	A1	
	(c)	215	A1	
	(d)	544	A1	
10	**(a)**	60	A1	
	(b)	9	A1	
	(c)	37–19 18	M1 for subtraction A1 for 18.	

Key to mark scheme
A marks: correct answer
M marks: correct method
B marks: independent work

Page 265 gives a general guidance on use of this assessment scheme with some examples.

2.1 Tens and units

Use multilink cubes or cuisinaire rods.

Here are some cubes:

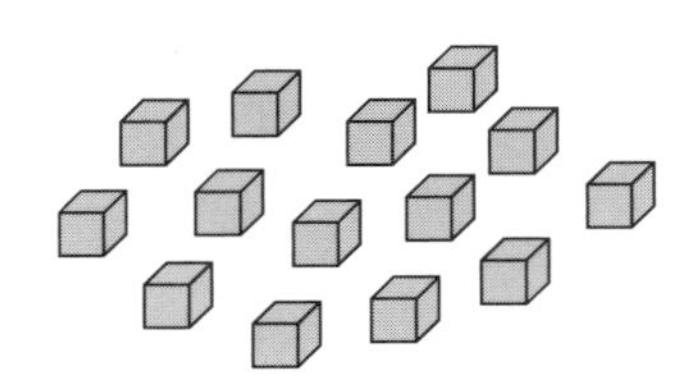

To help count them group ten together.

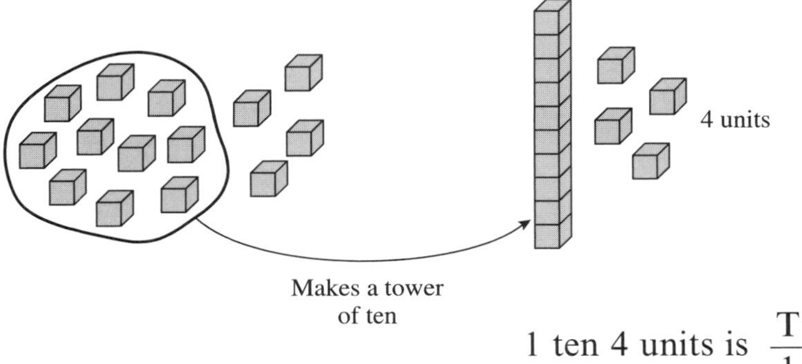

1 ten 4 units is

T	U
1	4

Example 1

1 How many tens and units?
Fill the gaps:

(a)

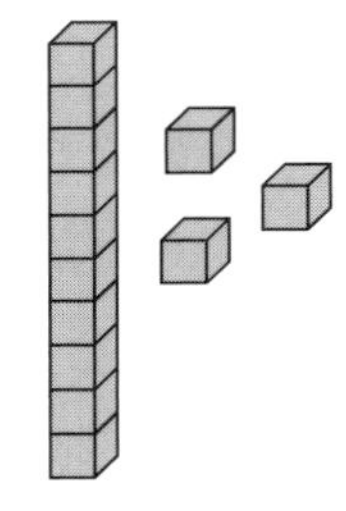

_ ten and _ units is

T	U

Count the cubes:

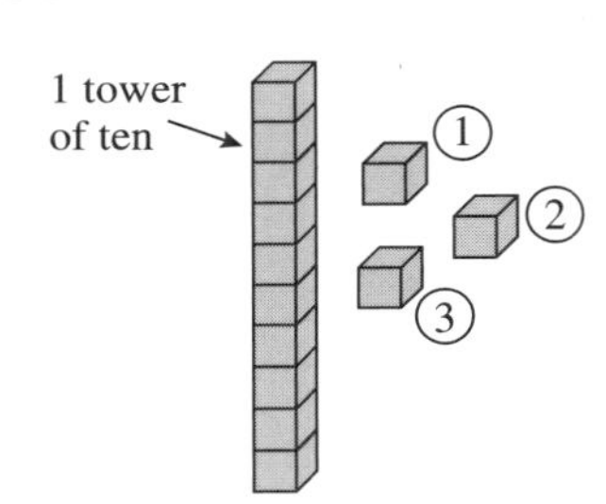

Answer: 1 ten and 3 units is

T	U
1	3

(b)

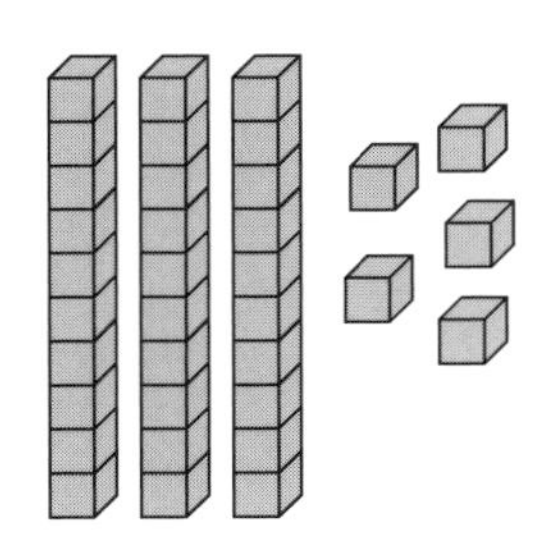

_ ten and _ units is

T	U

Count the cubes:

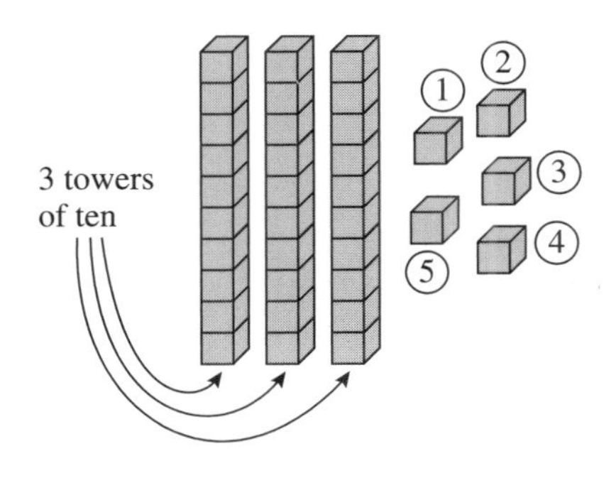

Answer: 3 tens and 5 units is

T	U
3	5

Exercise 1

1 How many tens and units?
Fill the gaps:

(a)

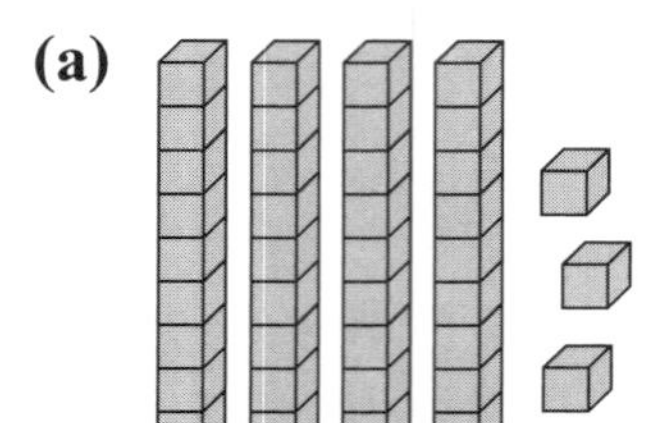

__ tens and __ units is T | U

(b)

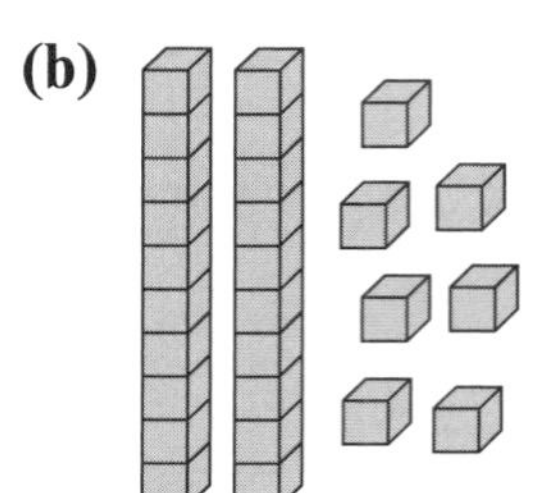

__ tens and __ units is T | U

(c)

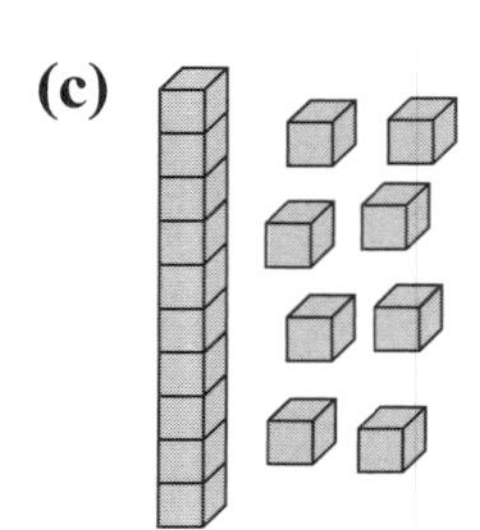

__ ten and __ units is T | U

(d)

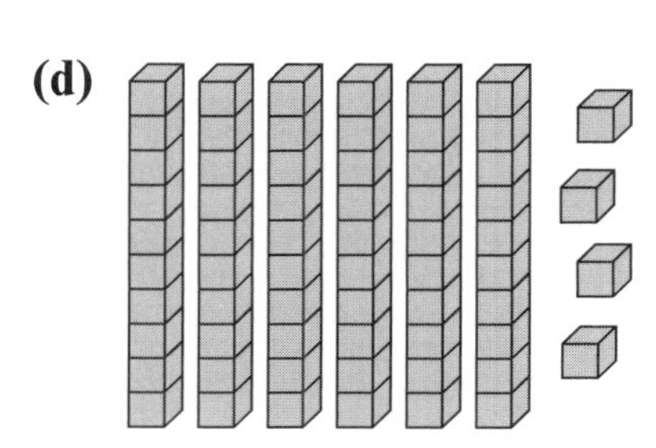

__ tens and __ units is T | U

(e)

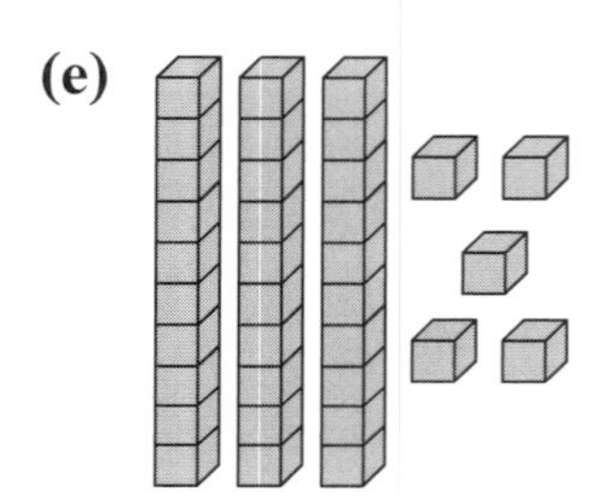

__ tens and __ units is T | U

(f)

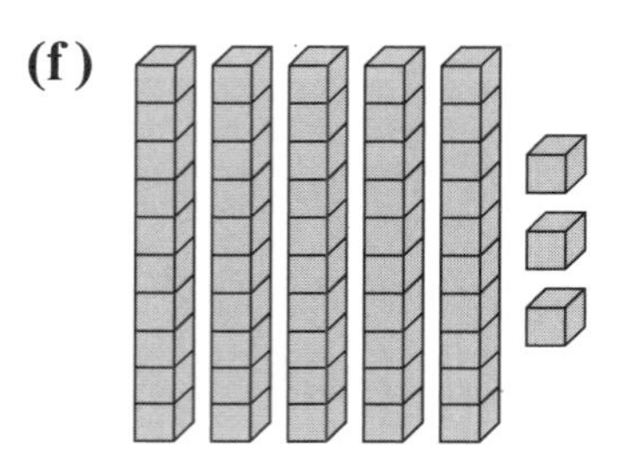

__ tens and __ units is T | U

Example 2

Draw 73.

7 tens and 3 units

Answer:

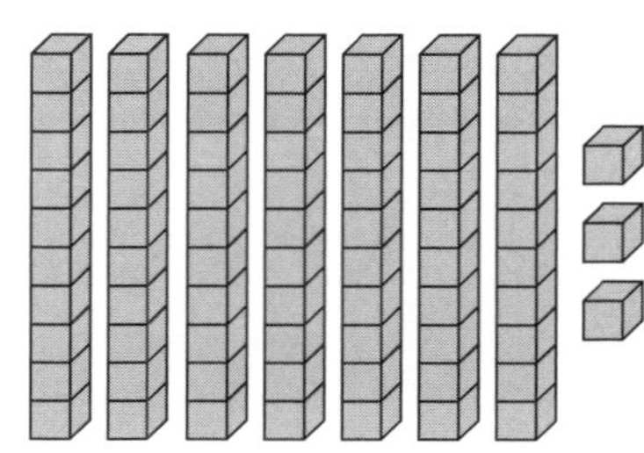

Exercise 2

1 Draw:

(a) 17 **(b)** 24 **(c)** 62 **(d)** 41 **(e)** 58

(f) 36 **(g)** 40 **(h)** 56 **(i)** 27 **(j)** 14

2.2 Hundreds, tens and units

Use multilink cubes or cuisinaire rods.

100 is [10 towers] which is

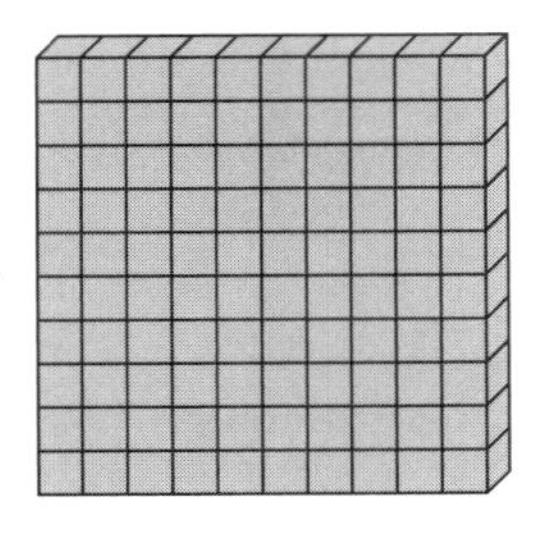

10 'towers' or 10 'tens' — 100 block

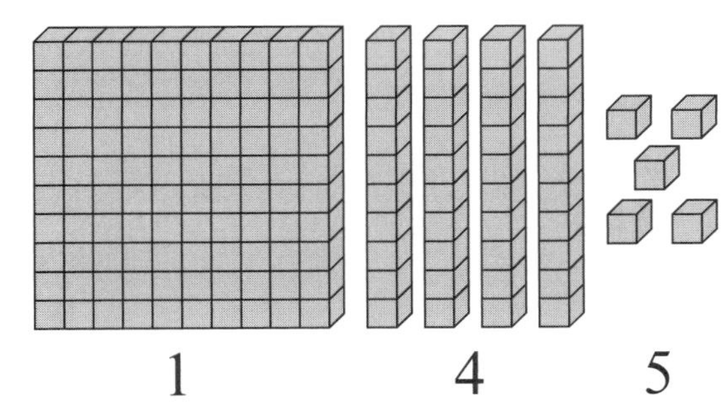

1 4 5

1 hundred block, 4 towers of ten and 5 units

H	T	U
1	4	5

Example 1

How many cubes?

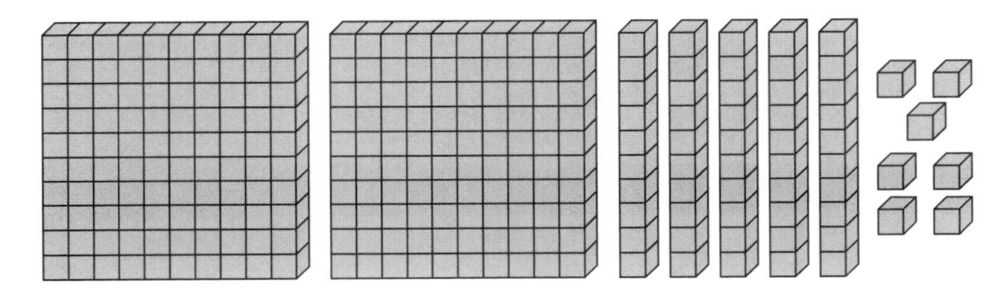

Answer:

257 because there are 2 hundred blocks, 5 towers of ten and 7 units

H	T	U
2	5	7

Exercise 1

1 How many cubes?

(a)

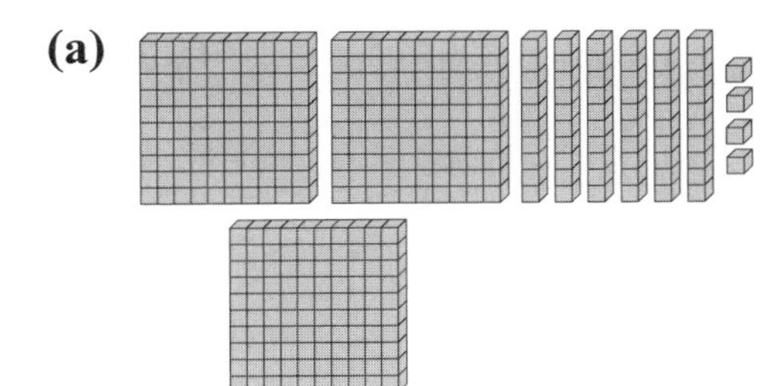

(b)

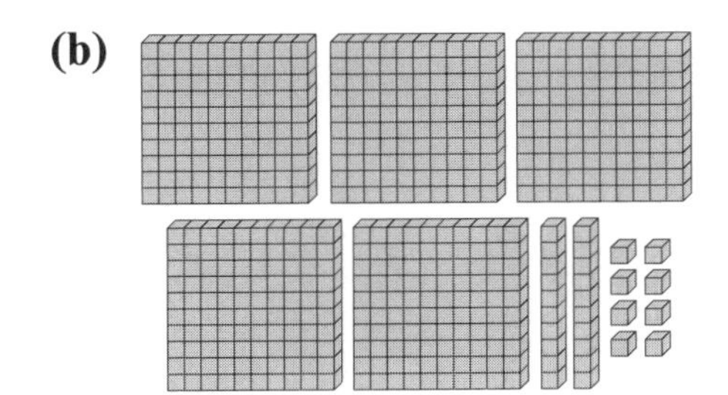

(c)

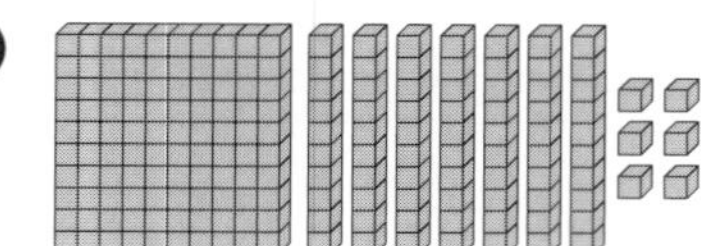

(d)

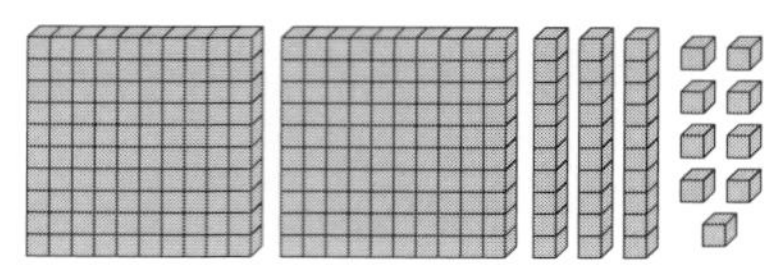

(e)

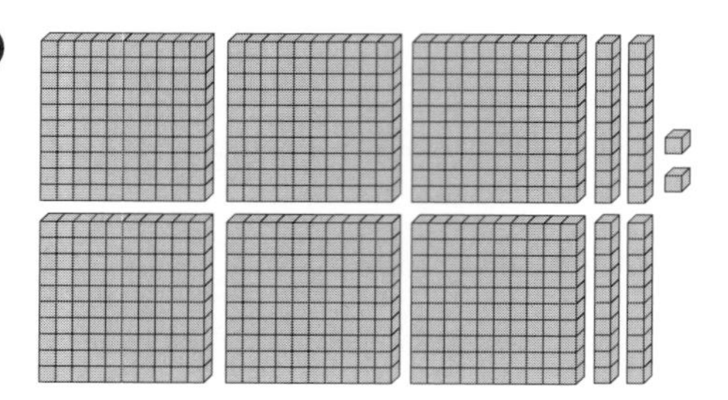

(f)

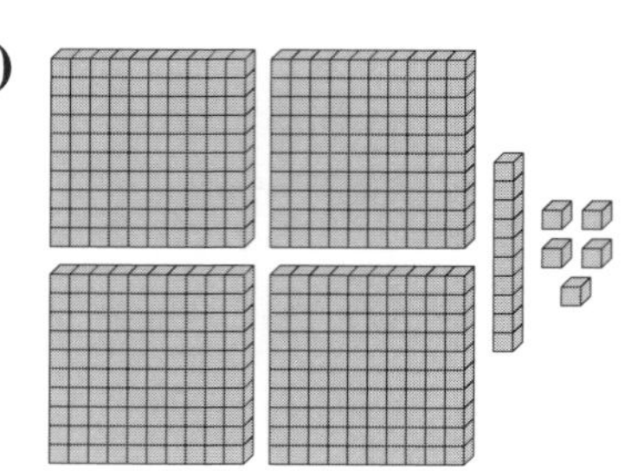

Example 2

Draw 126

Answer:

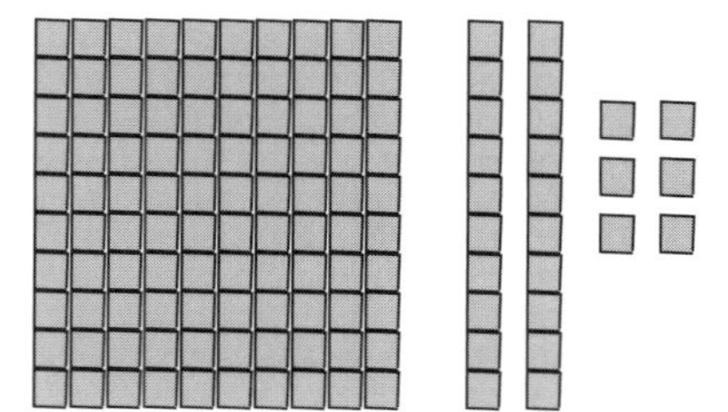

Exercise 2

1 Draw:

(a) 132	**(b)** 247	**(c)** 459	**(d)** 375
(e) 102	**(f)** 230	**(g)** 412	**(h)** 519

R2.2

2.3 Thousands

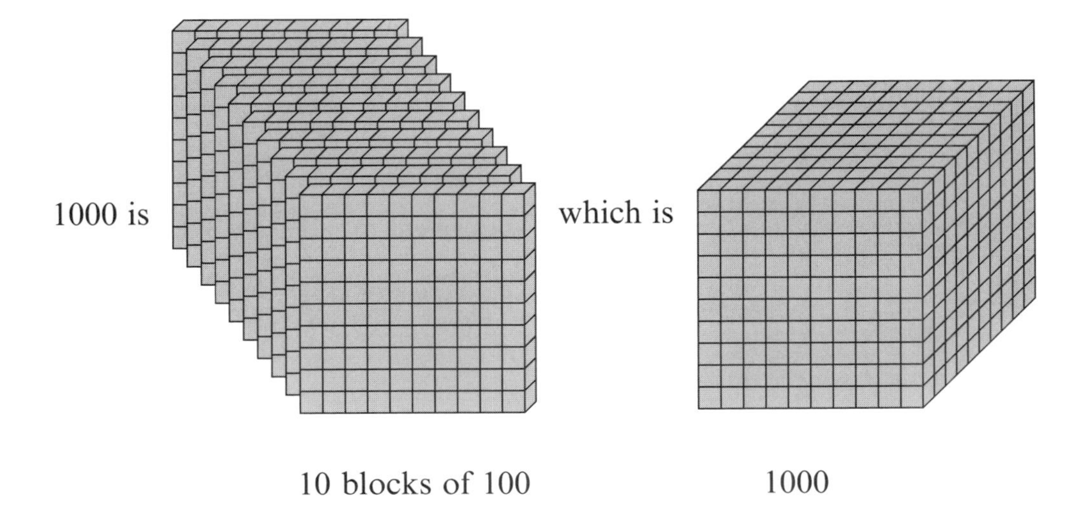

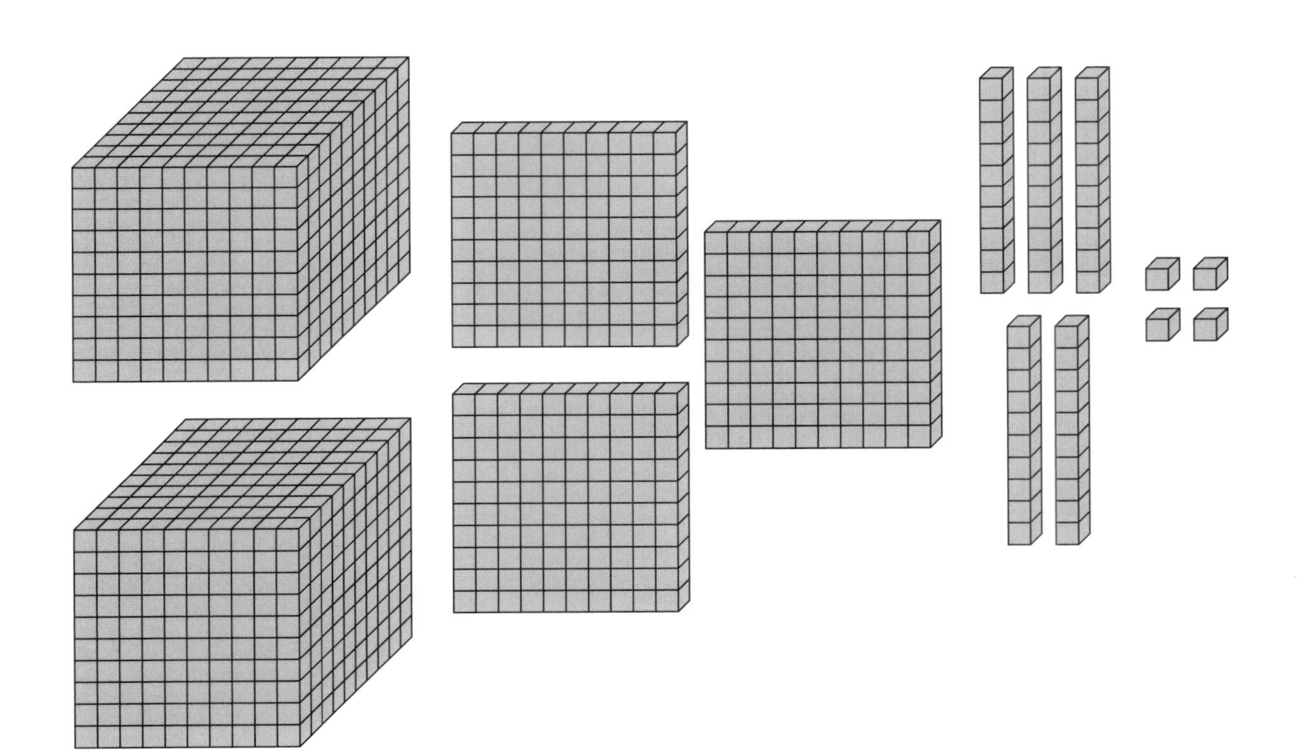

2 3 5 4

_2_ thousand _3_ hundred blocks _5_ towers of ten and _4_ units

Th	H	T	U
2	3	5	4

Example 1

How many cubes?

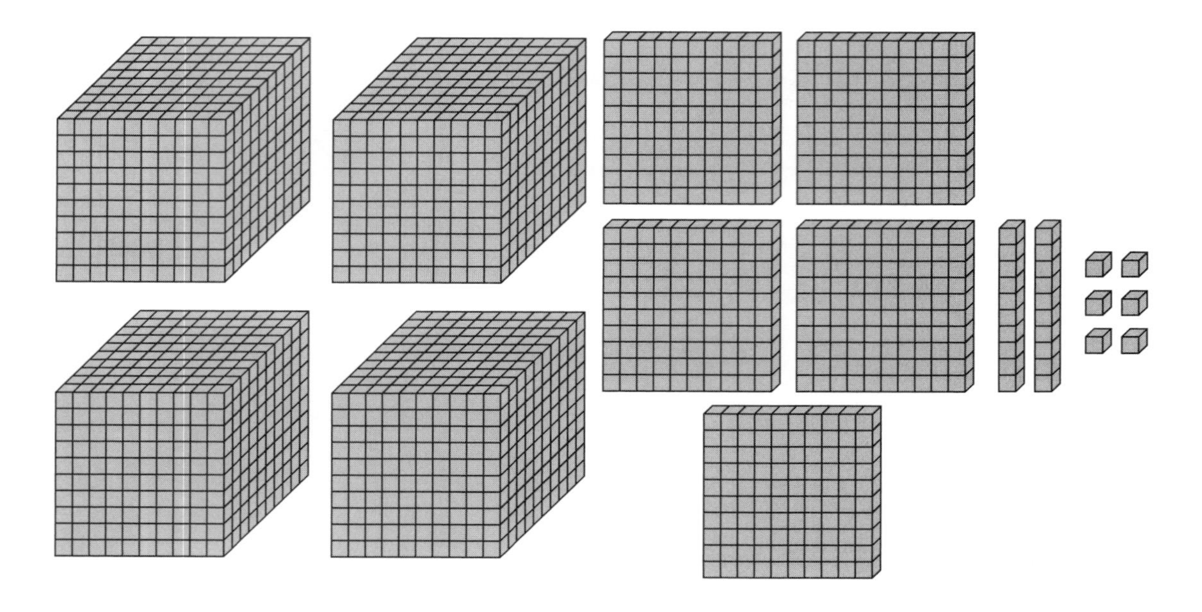

Answer:

4526 because there are 4 thousands, 5 hundreds, 2 tens and 6 units

Th	H	T	U
4	5	2	6

Exercise 1

1 How many cubes?

(a)

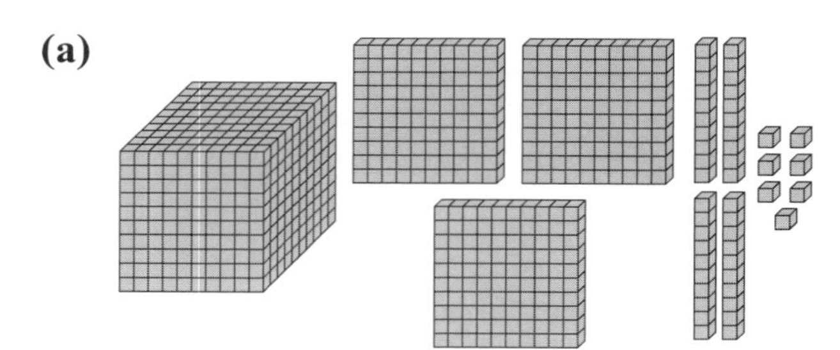

(b)

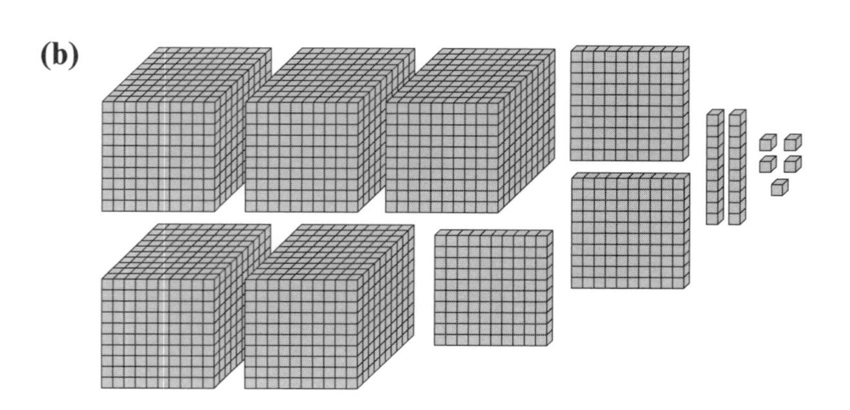

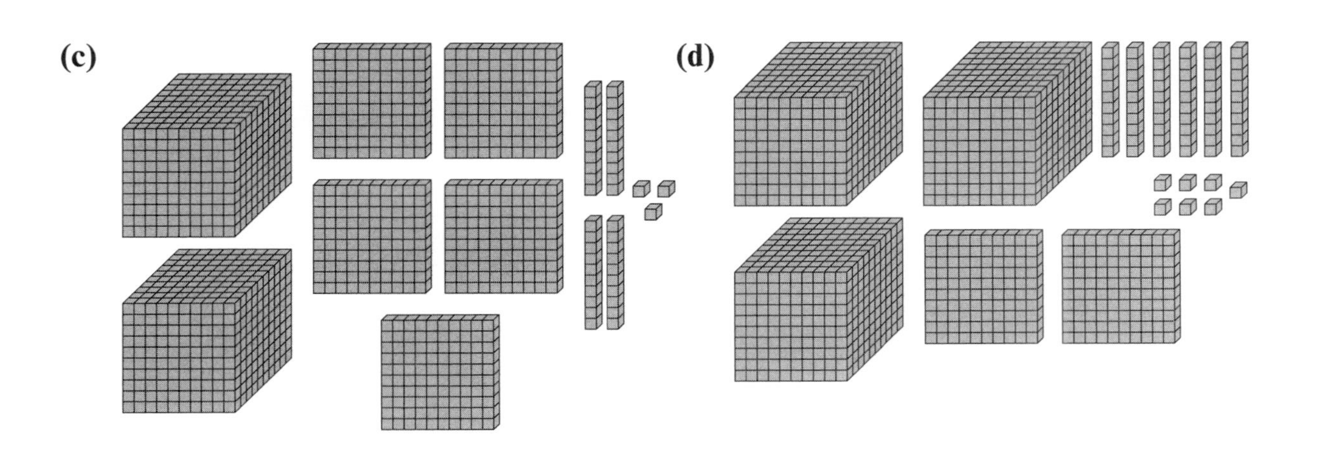

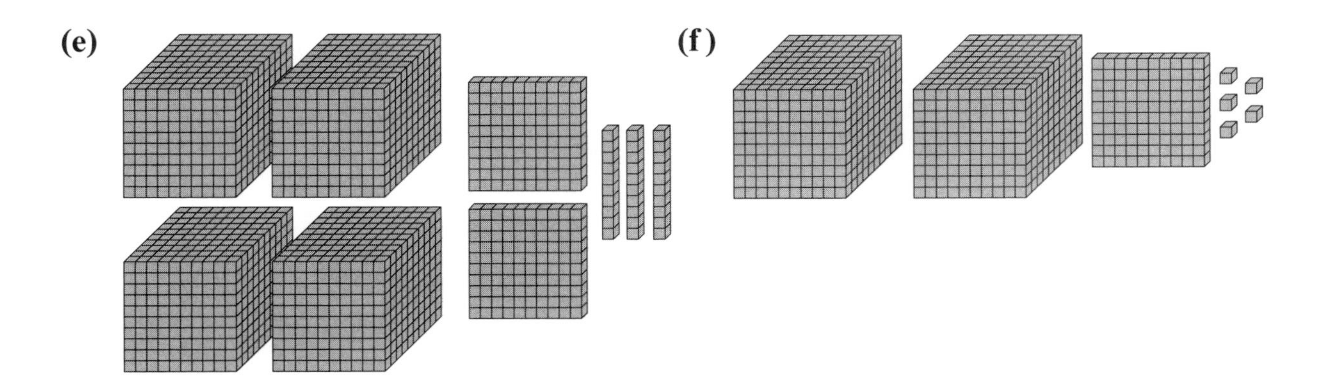

Example 2

Draw 2365

Answer:

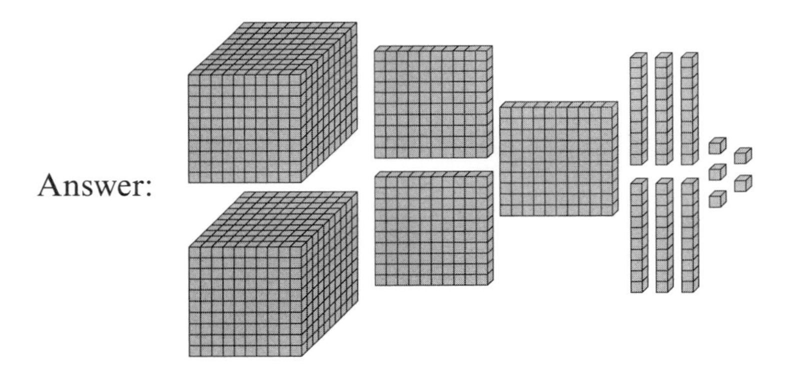

Exercise 2

1 Draw:

(a) 1237 **(b)** 3569 **(c)** 4107 **(d)** 1025 **(e)** 2240

2.4 Adding by counting on

How many cubes altogether?

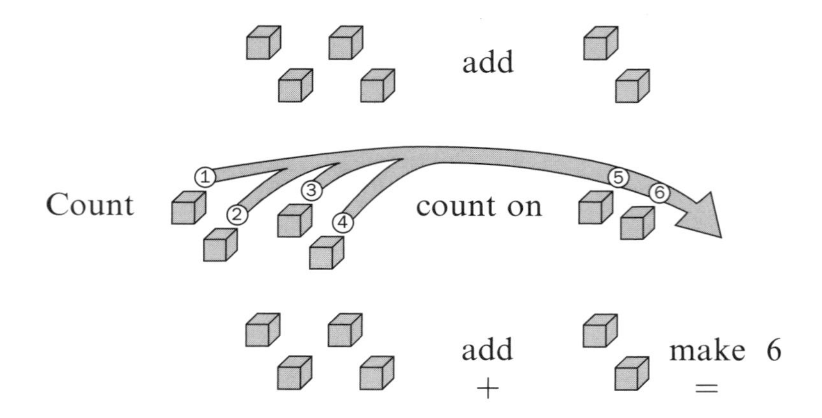

Example 1

How many videos altogether?

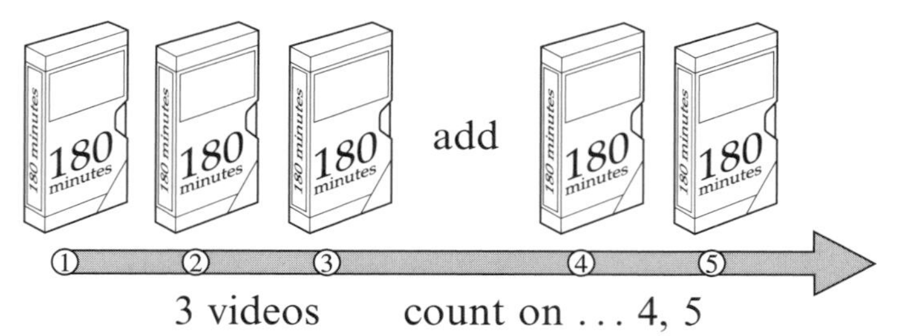

Answer: 5 videos.

Exercise 1

Use cubes to help you.

1 How many pens? and makes ....

2 How many keys? and makes ....

3 How many cubes? and makes ....

4 How many cans? and makes ....

5 How many sweets? and makes ....

Example 2

How many light bulbs altogether?

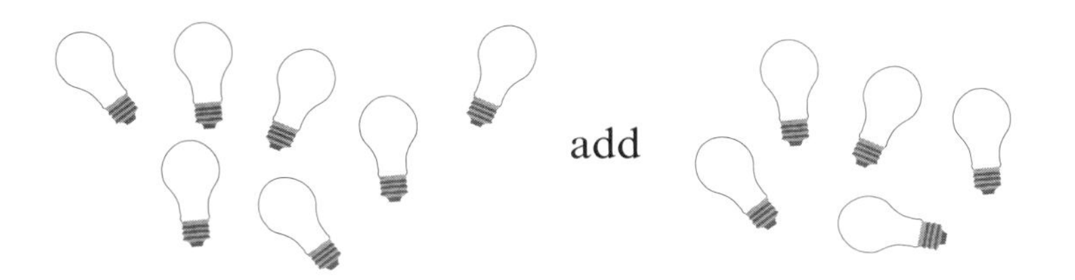

7 light bulbs . . .   count on . . . 8, 9, 10, 11, 12

Answer: 12 light bulbs

Exercise 2

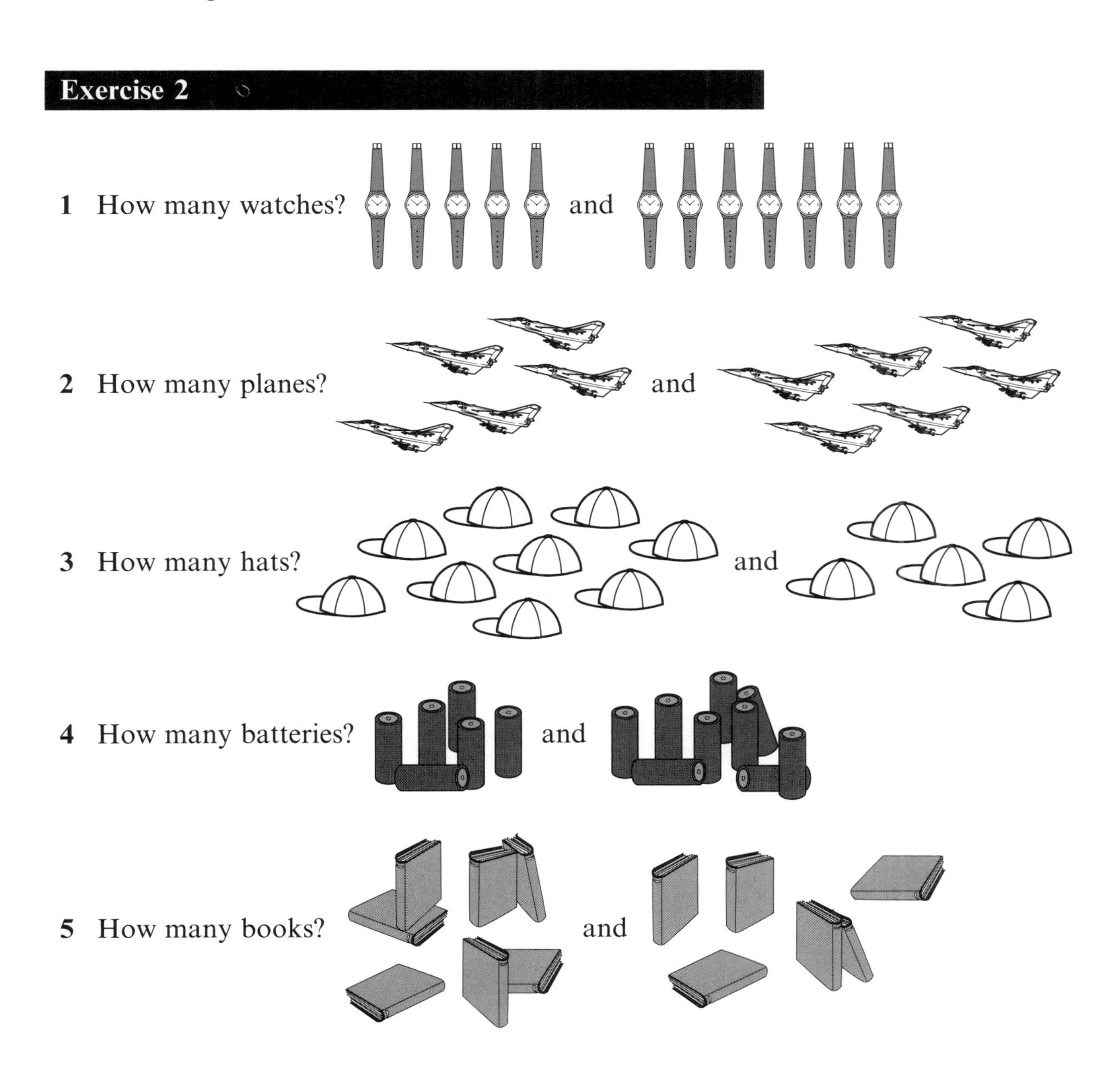

1 How many watches? and

2 How many planes? and

3 How many hats? and

4 How many batteries? and

5 How many books? and

2.5 Adding

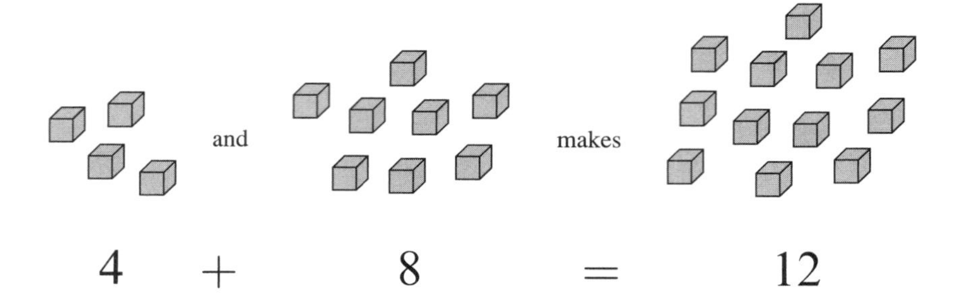

$$4 + 8 = 12$$

Example 1

How many cubes altogether?

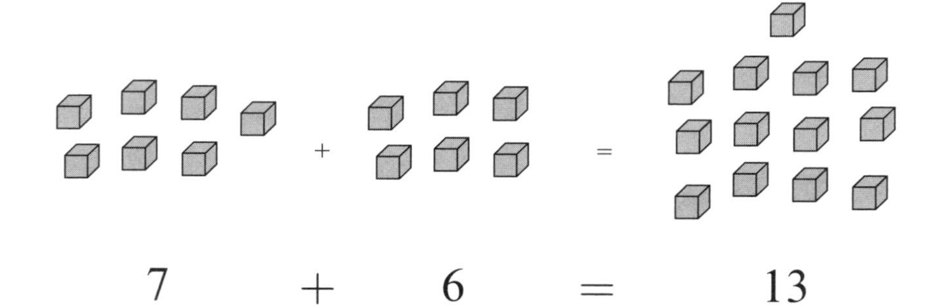

Answer: $7 + 6 = 13$

Exercise 1

1 How many cubes altogether?
Write down and complete the sum.

(a) 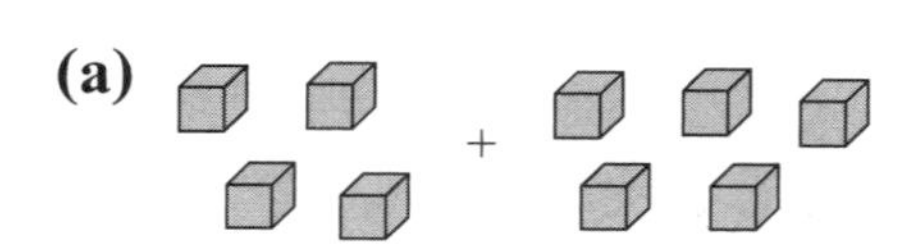

(b) 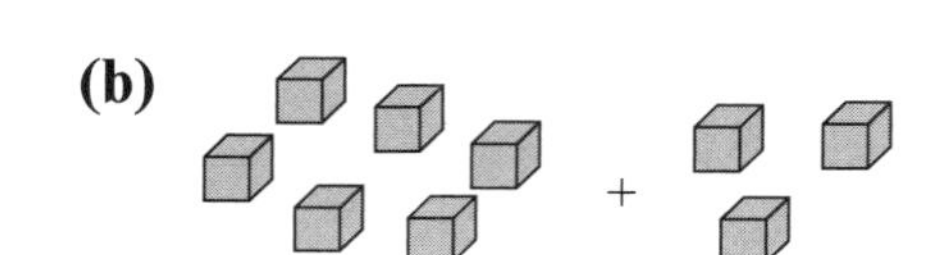

(c)

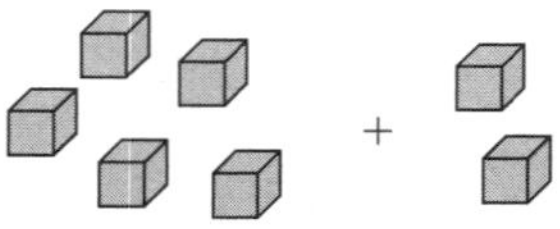

(d) 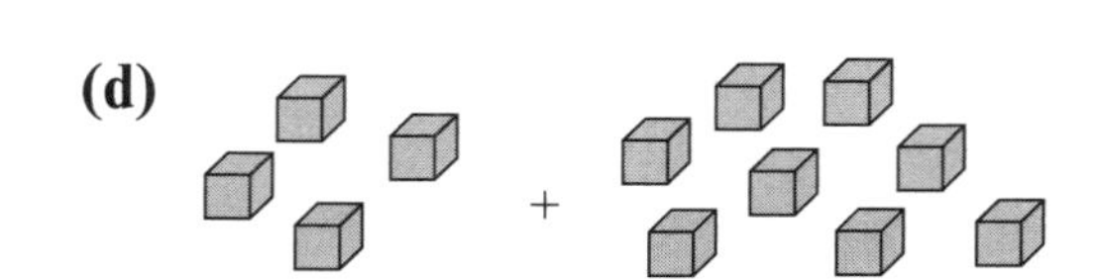

(e)

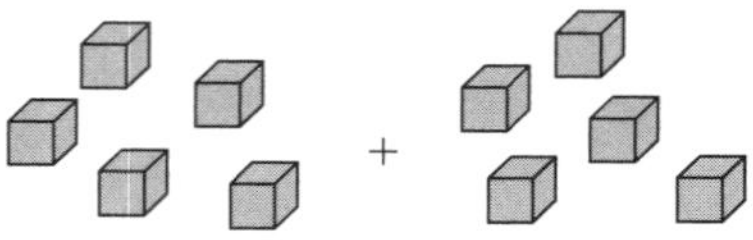

(f)

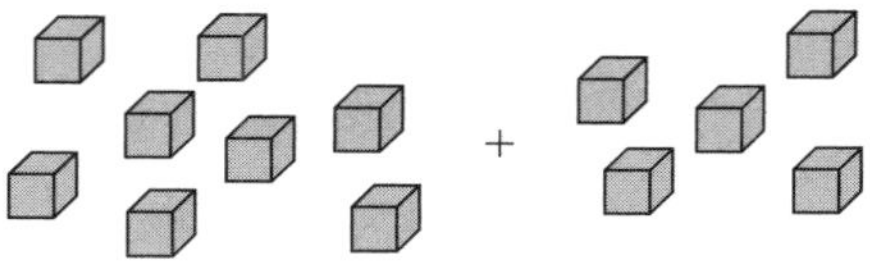

Example 2

Work out $6 + 9$.

Use cubes to help

$$6 + 9 = 15$$

Answer: $6 + 9 = 15$

Exercise 2

1 Use cubes to help work out these sums:

(a) $5 + 9$	**(b)** $6 + 8$	**(c)** $7 + 8$	**(d)** $9 + 4$
(e) $11 + 5$	**(f)** $10 + 4$	**(g)** $8 + 5$	**(h)** $12 + 6$
(i) $9 + 6$	**(j)** $7 + 5$	**(k)** $3 + 11$	**(l)** $8 + 8$
(m) $7 + 12$	**(n)** $14 + 3$	**(o)** $6 + 7$	**(p)** $13 + 4$
(q) $8 + 9$	**(r)** $5 + 12$	**(s)** $2 + 16$	**(t)** $11 + 9$

2.6 Adding two digit numbers

Use cubes to add 12 and 23.

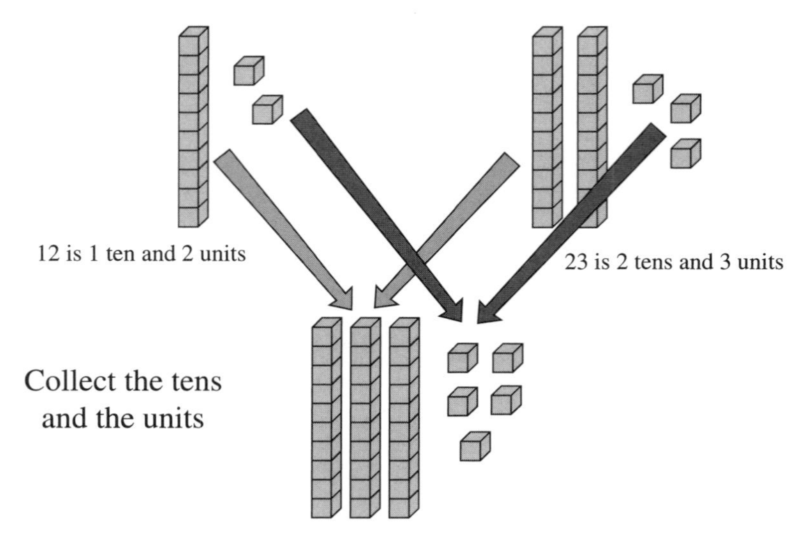
12 is 1 ten and 2 units
23 is 2 tens and 3 units
Collect the tens and the units
3 tens and 5 units is 35

Example 1

1 Complete these sums. Use cubes to help.

(a)

	T	U
	2	3
+	1	4

Answer:

	T	U
	2	3
+	1	4
	3	7

(b)

	T	U
	4	6
+	2	2

Answer:

	T	U
	4	6
+	2	2
	6	8

Exercise 1

Complete these sums.

1

	(a) T	U	(b) T	U	(c) T	U	(d) T	U	(e) T	U
	1	3	2	4	3	5	3	5	4	1
+	2	5	1	4	2	3	4	2	5	5

2

	(a) T	U	(b) T	U	(c) T	U	(d) T	U	(e) T	U
	1	5	3	4	6	1	3	6	5	3
+	1	4	2	2	2	4	1	2	2	4

2.7 Adding – carrying units

Sometimes the units add to 10 or more:

Add 27 cubes and 25 cubes.

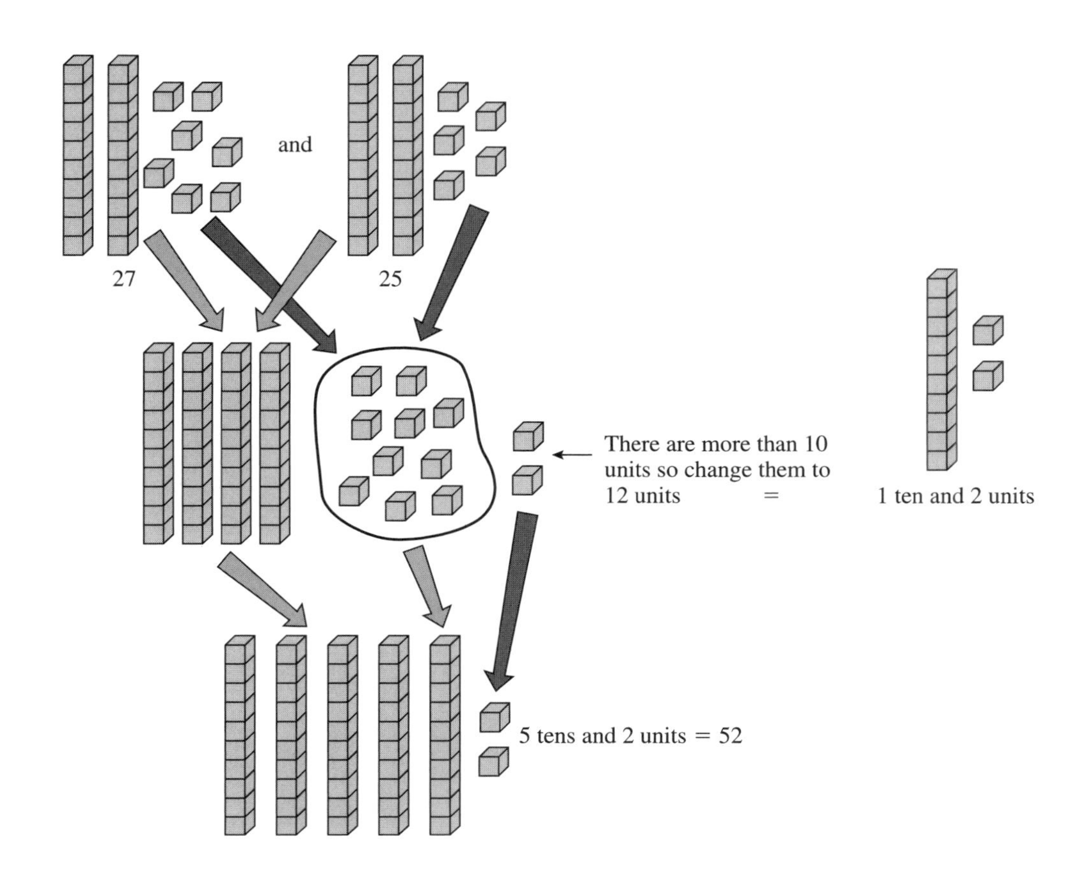

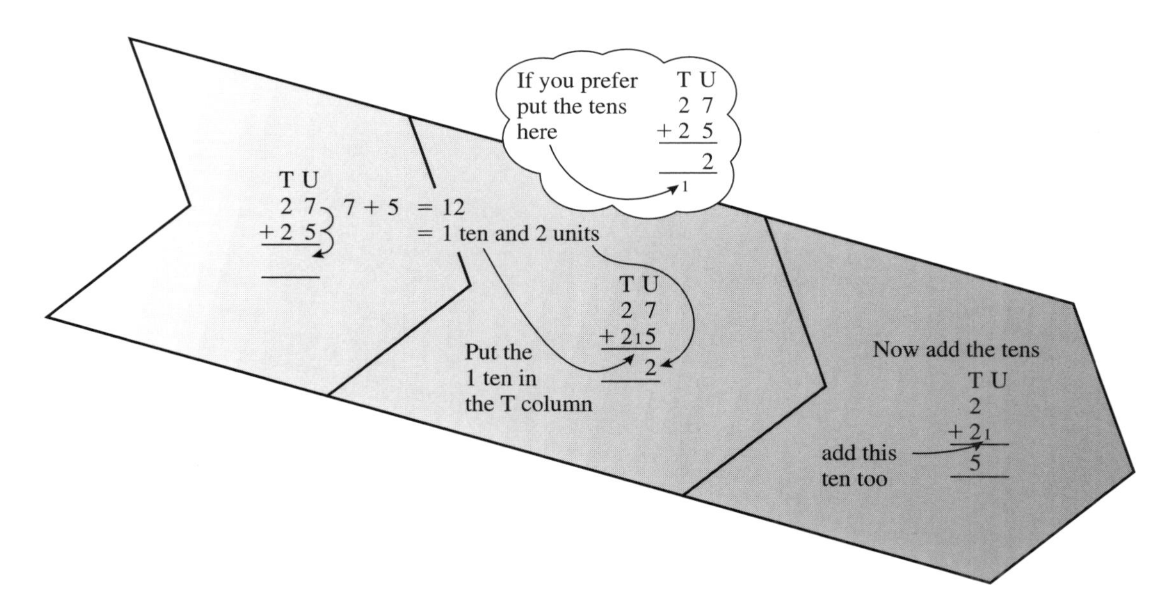

The finished sum looks like this:

$$\begin{array}{cc} T & U \\ 2 & 7 \\ +2_1 & 5 \\ \hline 5 & 2 \\ \hline \end{array}$$

Example 1

Complete:

(a)

	T	U
	2	4
+	1	8

Answer:

	T	U
	2	4
+	2_1 → 1_1	8
	4	2

$4 + 8 = 12$
$= 1$ ten and 2 units

(b)

	T	U
	3	7
+	2	9

Answer:

	T	U
	3	7
+	2_1	9
	6	6

$7 + 9 = 16$
$= 1$ ten and 6 units

Exercise 1

Complete:

1

(a) 34 + 28 = ___
(b) 49 + 15 = ___
(c) 46 + 29 = ___
(d) 27 + 16 = ___
(e) 33 + 48 = ___

(f) 65 + 28 = ___
(g) 37 + 57 = ___
(h) 48 + 25 = ___
(i) 42 + 39 = ___
(j) 24 + 37 = ___

(k) T U: 2 7 + 1 6 = ___
(l) T U: 3 5 + 1 9 = ___
(m) T U: 2 7 + 1 8 = ___
(n) T U: 2 3 + 2 9 = ___
(o) T U: 5 7 + 2 8 = ___

2.8 Carrying tens

Sometimes you have to carry tens into the hundreds column:

Use cubes to add 265 + 154

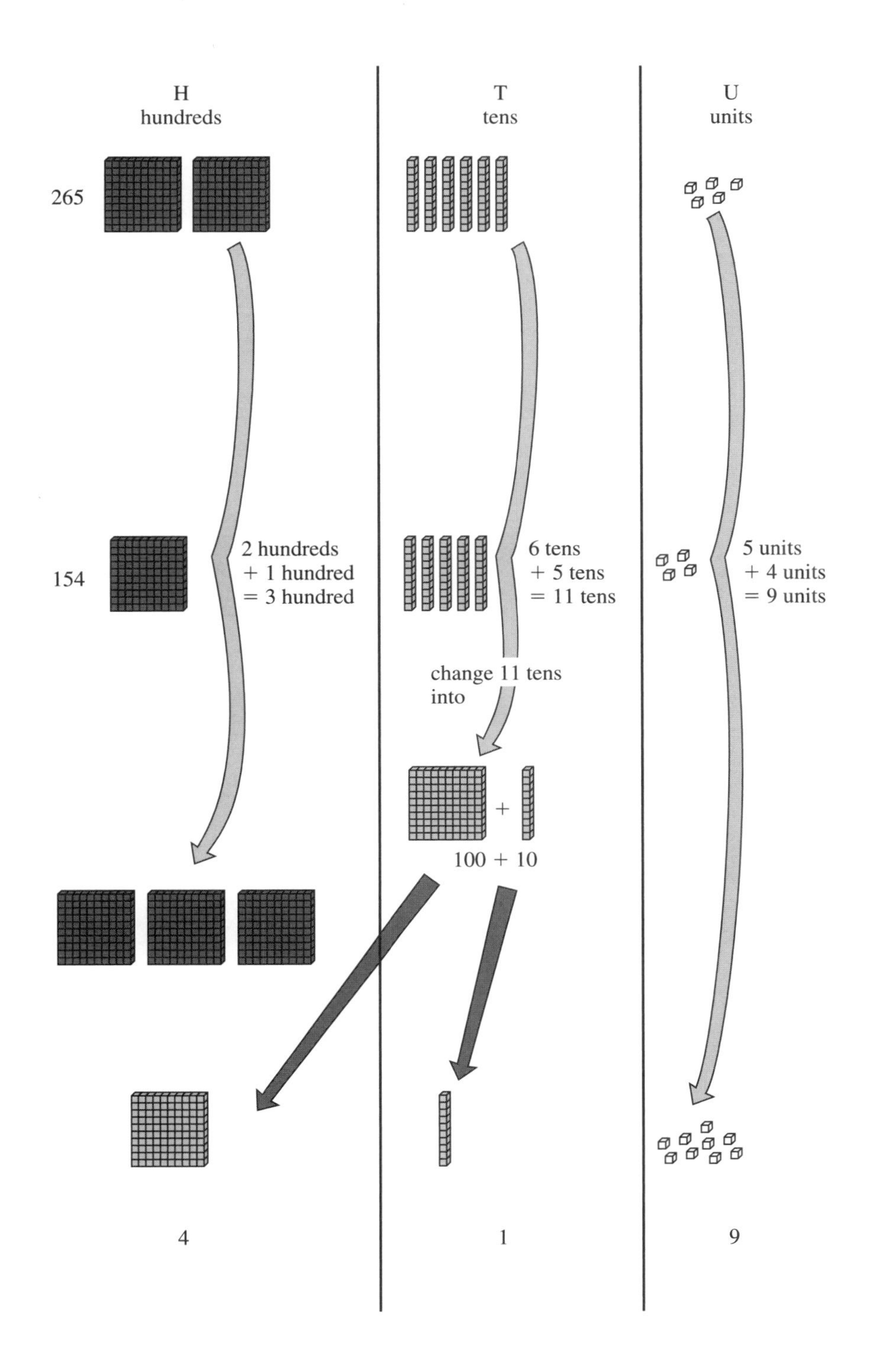

The completed sum looks like this:

	H	T	U
	2	6	5
+	1_1	5	4
	4	1	9

You can add like this:

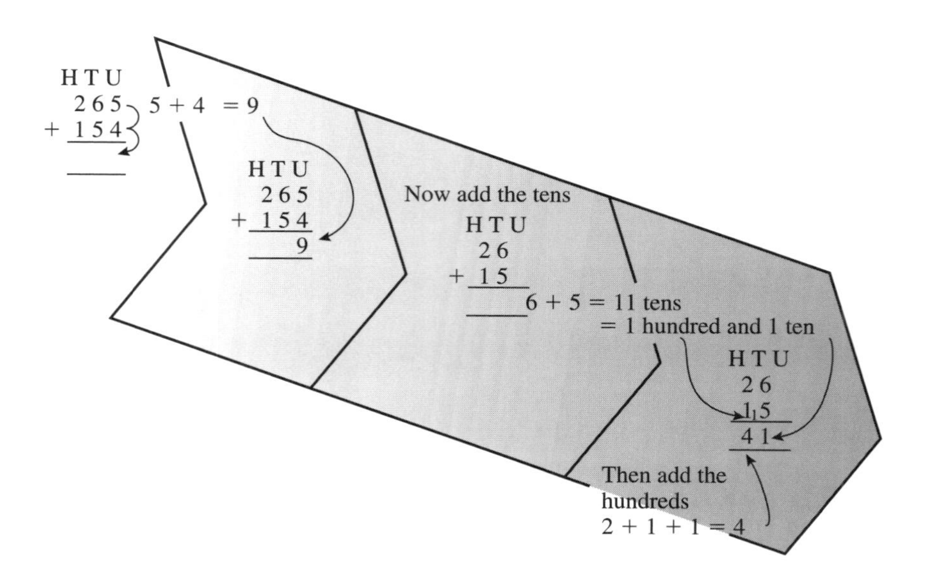

The completed sum looks like this:

	H	T	U
	2	6	5
+	1_1	5	4
	4	1	9

Exercise 1

Complete:

1 138 + 235

2 295 + 347

3 327 + 194

4 648 + 184

5 547 + 269

6 278 + 245

7 349 + 483

8 648 + 397

R2.8

2.9 Subtracting

How many cubes are left?

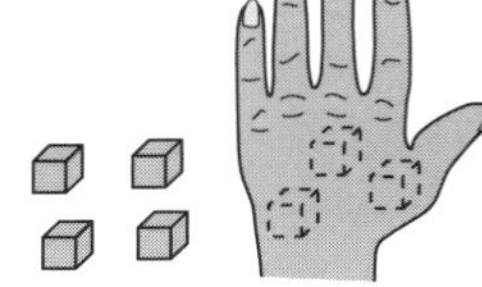

7 take away 3 leaves 4
↓ ↓ ↓ ↓ ↓
$7 - 3 = 4$

Example 1

Work out $6 - 2$

Use cubes

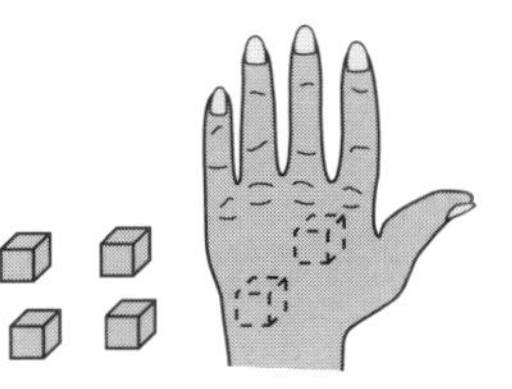

cover 2

Answer: $6 - 2 = 4$

Exercise 1

Use cubes to help you work these out:

1 5 – 2	**2** 4 – 3	**3** 9 – 7	**4** 8 – 1	**5** 10 – 4
6 7 – 4	**7** 8 – 5	**8** 9 – 3	**9** 6 – 4	**10** 7 – 6

Using larger numbers

31 – 6
31 take away 6

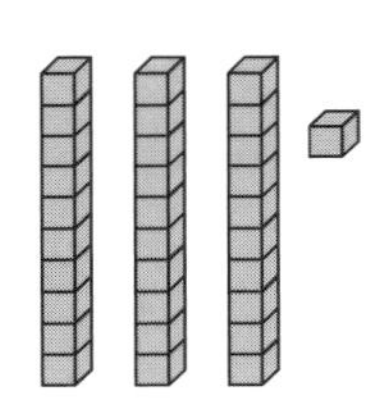

swap a ten for 10 units

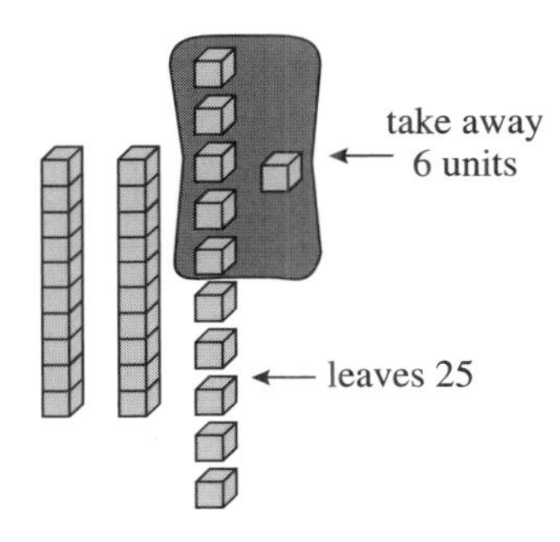

Example 2

Work out $45 - 17$

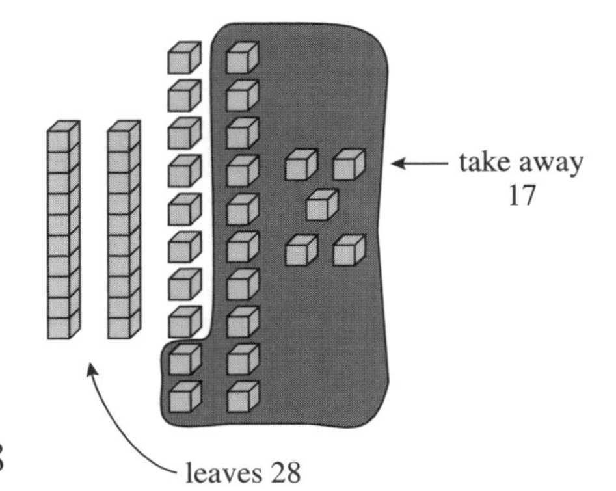

Answer: $45 - 17 = 28$

Exercise 2

Work out:

1 25 – 8	**2** 43 – 15	**3** 33 – 15	**4** 21 – 7	**5** 24 – 15
6 35 – 18	**7** 56 – 27	**8** 46 – 13	**9** 51 – 28	**10** 47 – 25

2.10 Subtraction short cuts

Here are two easy ways to subtract 8 from 25:

First way:

25 − 8 (8 is 5 and 3)

25 − 5 − 3 (easy to subtract 5 from 25 first)

20 − 3 (now subtract 3)

17

Second way:

25 − 8

25 − 10 = 15 (easy to subtract 10 first)

we have taken away 2 too many.
So add 2 back on (8 + 2 = 10)

15 + 2 = 17

So 25 − 8 = 17

Check: 17 + 8 = 25

Example 1

Work out 23 − 9.

First way:

23 − 9

23 − 3 − 6

20 − 6

14

Answer: 14

Second way:

23 − 9
23 − 10 = 13 take away 10
13 + 1 = 14 then add 1

23 − 9 = 14

Exercise 1

Use the way you like best to work out:

1 23 − 7 **2** 15 − 7 **3** 21 − 15 **4** 27 − 15 **5** 25 − 17

6 31 − 18 **7** 28 − 9 **8** 33 − 25 **9** 31 − 17 **10** 21 − 6

2.11 Subtracting hundreds, tens and units

143 − 27

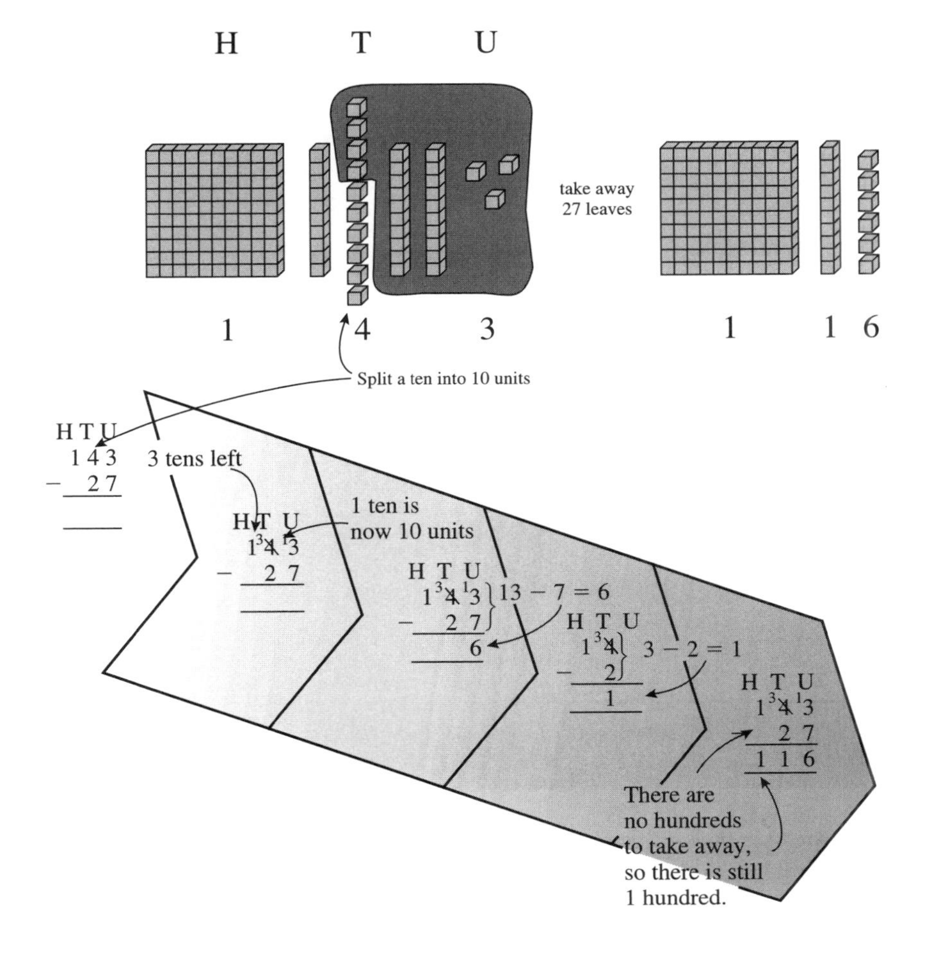

Example 1

Work out 235 − 18

Answer:

	H	T	U
	2	~~3~~²	¹5
−		1	8
	2	1	7

Exercise 1

Work out:

1 343 − 26 **2** 254 − 37 **3** 176 − 48

4 274 − 57 **5** 465 − 48 **6** 284 − 59

7 154 − 36 **8** 247 − 29 **9** 564 − 37

10 281 − 55 **11** 152 − 34 **12** 171 − 35

Answers to Pupils' Book

2 Understanding numbers

Exercise 2A

1 (a) 2 tens (b) 2 units
(c) 2 hundreds (d) 2 units
(e) 2 tens (f) 2 hundreds
2 (a) 7 units (b) 7 units
(c) 7 tens (d) 7 hundreds
(e) 7 tens (f) 7 units
3 (a) 0 tens (b) 0 units
(c) 0 tens (d) 0 units
(e) 0 units (f) 0 tens
4 (a) Lauren 564 Ahmed 58 Nadia 285 Wayne 4
5 (a) accepted (b) rejected
(c) accepted (d) rejected
(e) rejected (f) rejected
6 497, 498, 499
7 (a) Has it got 6 hundreds, has it got 4 tens, has it got more than 7 units?
(b) Has it got 3 hundreds, has it got 9 tens, has it got less than 3 units?
(c) Has it got 8 hundreds, has it got 7 units, has it got more than 5 tens?
(d) Has it got 7 tens, has it got 3 units, has it got more than 7 hundreds?
(e) Has it got 2 tens, has it got 1 unit, has it got more than 6 hundreds?
(f) Has it got 3 hundreds, has it got 2 units, has it got less than 4 tens?
8 Has it got 2 hundreds, has it got 5 tens, has it got more than 2 units, has it got less than 6 units?

Exercise 2B

1 (a) 7 (b) 73 (c) 39 (d) 836
(e) 8 (f) 923 (g) 873 (h) 47
2 (a) 5 (b) 50 (c) 407 (d) 490
(e) 120 (f) 196 (g) 587 (h) 196
3 (a) 6 thousands (b) 60 thousands
(c) 600 thousands (d) 60 thousands
(e) 600 thousands (f) 6 thousands
(g) 60 thousands (h) 6 thousands
4 (a) 5246 (b) 47 396 (c) 364 956
(d) 205 981 (e) 900 215 (f) 26 038
5 (a) rejected (b) accepted
(c) accepted (d) rejected
(e) rejected (f) rejected
(g) accepted (h) rejected
6 (a) Has it got 21 thousands, has it got 5 hundreds, has it got 0 tens, has it got more than 6 units?
(b) Has it got more than 46 thousands, has it got less than 50 thousands, has it got 3 hundreds, has it got 9 tens, has it got 5 units?
(c) Has it got less than 900 thousands has it got more than 896 thousands, has it got 4 hundreds, has it got 2 tens, has it got 3 units?

Exercise 2C

1 4, 25, 43, 81 2 17, 33, 48, 96
3 36, 54, 93, 94 4 15, 24, 38, 56
5 0, 49, 50, 100 6 11, 14, 26, 84
7 42, 51, 69, 98 8 7, 41, 60, 83
9 18, 26, 54, 76 10 11, 38, 54, 87
11 3, 7, 79, 99 12 20, 46, 63, 77
13 (a) Any two from 0, 1, 2, 3, 4
(b) Any two from 5, 6, 7, 8, 9
(c) Any one card from 0, 1, 2, 3, 4 plus any one from 5, 6, 7, 8, 9 except for 0 and 5.
(d) 50 and 05
14 (a) Any three from 5, 6, 7, 8, 9
(b) Any three from 0, 1, 2, 3, 4
(c) Any three from 4, 5, 6, 7, 8

Exercise 2D

1 233, 278, 288, 514, 533
2 407, 428, 849, 858, 876
3 147, 183, 938, 941, 958
4 65, 94, 263, 438, 488
5 91, 381, 392, 629, 684
6 18, 36, 216, 295, 547
7 238, 257, 437, 469, 472, 829, 838
8 485, 492, 548, 559, 576, 763, 782
9 (a) Place the largest digit in the hundreds position, the smallest in the units position.
(b) Place the smallest digit in the hundreds position, the largest in the units position.
10 (a) 259, 952 (b) 378, 873 (c) 127, 721
(d) 479, 974 (e) 249, 942 (f) 139, 931
(g) 148, 841 (h) 467, 764 (i) 234, 432
(j) 578, 875 (k) 377, 773 (l) 408, 840
11 (a) 934 (b) 926 (c) 403
(d) 613 (e) 978 (f) 534
(g) 734 (h) 801 (i) 724
12 (a) 295 (b) 384 (c) 152
(d) 184 (e) 687 (f) 376
(g) 687 (h) 290 (i) 375

Exercise 2E

1 (a) 3, 4 (b) 2, 3 (c) 5, 6
(d) 4, 5 (e) 7, 8 (f) 9, 10
2 (a) 3, 4, 5 (b) 1, 2, 3 (c) 0, 1, 2
(d) 4, 5, 6 (e) 2, 3, 4 (f) 5, 6, 7
3 (a) $0+9, 1+8, 2+7, 3+6, 4+5$
(b) $0+12, 1+11, 2+10, 3+9, 4+8, \ldots 6+6$
(c) $0+10, 1+9, \ldots 5+5$
(d) $0+15, 1+14, 2+13, \ldots 7+8$
(e) $0+18, 1+17, 2+16, \ldots 9+9$
(f) $0+20, 1+19, \ldots 10+10$
4 (a) $5-0, 6-1, 7-2, \ldots 20-15$
(b) $8-0, 9-1, 10-2, 11-3, \ldots 20-12$
(c) $16-0, 17-1, \ldots 20-4$
(d) $20-0$
(e) $1-0, 2-1, 3-2, \ldots 20-19$
(f) $10-0, 11-1, 12-2, \ldots 20-10$
5 There are an infinite number of solutions to each part.
(a) $0+11, 1+10 \ldots 5+6$
(b) $2+1=3, 2+2=4 \ldots 2+18=20$
(c) $20-16=4, 19-15=4 \ldots 4-0=4$
(d) $12-0=12, 12-1=11 \ldots 12-12=0$
(e) $20-5=15, 19-5=14 \ldots 5-5=0$
(f) $0+7=7, 1+7=8 \ldots 13+7=20$
(g) $1+2=0+3, 2+2=1+3 \ldots$
(h) $20-0=10+10, 20-1=10+9 \ldots$
6 Each number from 8 to 20 can be made.
7 Any whole number bigger than 1.
8 5 in the centre. Pairs of numbers adding to 10 opposite each other. For example

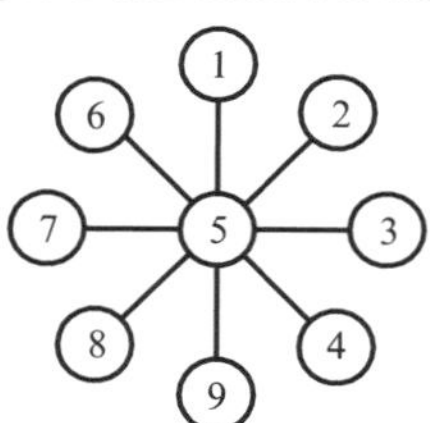

9 (a) (b) (c) (d) (e) (f)

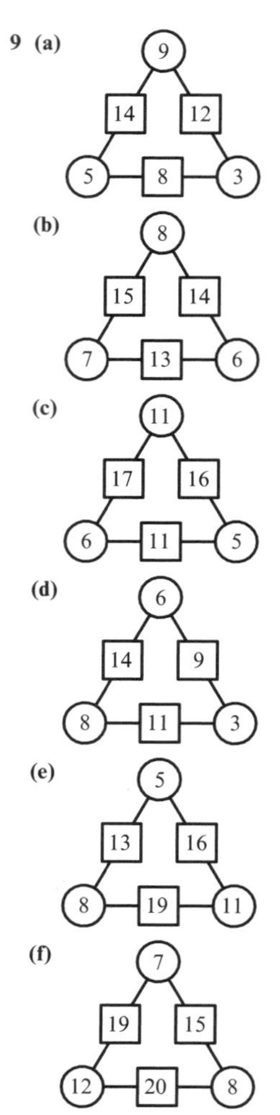

Exercise 2F

2 (a) 36 (b) 55 (c) 22
(d) 44 (e) 97 (f) 84
(g) 44 (h) 67 (i) 74
(j) 15 (k) 62 (l) 57
(m) 46 (n) 62 (o) 44
(p) 16 (q) 84 (r) 64
3 (a) 62 (b) 84 (c) 99
(d) 34 (e) 36 (f) 28
(g) 95 (h) 18 (i) 83
(j) 91 (k) 29 (l) 28
4 (a) 44 (b) 77 (c) 83
(d) 82 (e) 85 (f) 87
(g) 88 (h) 99
5 (a) 65 (b) 59 (c) 17
(d) 36 (e) 6 (f) 17
(g) 19 (h) 1
6 (a) 53 (b) 75 (c) 54
(d) 68 (e) 72 (f) 21
(g) 34 (h) 97
7 47, 57, 67, 58, 68, 78, 69, 79, 89, 72, 82, 92
8 9, 19, 29, 49, 59, 69, 11, 21, 31, 51, 61, 71, 28, 38, 48, 68, 78, 88

Exercise 2G

1 26 2 14 3 24
4 10 5 31 6 21
7 17 8 51 9 42
10 57 11 36 12 29
13 64 14 34 15 35
16 9 17 2 18 10, 2
19 10, 1 20 10, 2

Exercise 2H

1 (a) 57 (b) 48 (c) 58
(d) 56 (e) 79 (f) 97
(g) 87 (h) 97 (i) 49
(j) 97 (k) 89 (l) 77

2 (a) 62 (b) 74 (c) 84 (d) 91
(e) 92 (f) 71 (g) 71 (h) 60
(i) 90 (j) 82 (k) 72 (l) 72

3 (a) 12 if [0] is not chosen,
6 if [0] is chosen
(b) This depends upon the cards chosen
(c) The two largest digits in the tens positions
(d) The two smallest digits in the tens positions if [0] is not chosen.
The two smallest non zero digits in the tens positions if [0] is chosen.

5 The numbers in opposite corners add up to the same total.

Exercise 2I

1 (a) 21 (b) 33 (c) 23 (d) 44
(e) 32 (f) 53 (g) 33 (h) 44
(i) 44 (j) 26 (k) 17 (l) 22

2 (a) 19 (b) 19 (c) 19 (d) 28
(e) 26 (f) 28 (g) 28 (h) 28
(i) 27 (j) 46 (k) 48 (l) 29

3 Lauren 25, 34; Nadia 38, 74;
Ahmed 38, 63; Wayne 25, 63

5 (a) $100 - 23 - 31 - 25 - 19 = 2$
(b) $100 - 18 - 11 - 19 - 17 = 35$

Exercise 2J

1 32 2 63 3 51 4 28
5 (a) 84p (b) 16p 6 8 m
7 (a) 93 (b) 37 8 14 9 24
10 $20 + 18 + 52$, $18 + 32 + 40$,
$28 + 32 + 30$, $40 + 6 + 44$,
$20 + 30 + 40$, $18 + 28 + 44$, $32 + 6 + 52$

Exercise 2K

1 (a) 63 (b) 64 (c) 88 (d) 58
(e) 77 (f) 61 (g) 97 (h) 93
(i) 70 (j) 90 (k) 92 (l) 98

2 (a) 77 (b) 83 (c) 95 (d) 81
(e) 81 (f) 70 (g) 93 (h) 86
(i) 76 (j) 69 (k) 64 (l) 83

3 (a) 84 (b) 96 (c) 89 (d) 94
(e) 93 (f) 90 (g) 92 (h) 82

4 (a) 139 (b) 125 (c) 147 (d) 129
(e) 155 (f) 134 (g) 178 (h) 142
(i) 140 (j) 100 (k) 181 (l) 105

5 (a) 123 (b) 152 (c) 174 (d) 124
(e) 133 (f) 237 (g) 253 (h) 261

6 (a) 393 (b) 692 (c) 841 (d) 1439
(e) 1262 (f) 1241 (g) 1051 (h) 1100
(i) 1000 (j) 1676

7 (a) 667 (b) 392 (c) 423 (d) 543
(e) 273 (f) 620 (g) 803 (h) 600
(i) 743 (j) 844

8 $42 + 35$, $54 + 23$, $53 + 24$, $45 + 32$

9 $46 + 53$, $56 + 43$, $64 + 35$, $65 + 34$

10 (a) 155 (b) 52 (c) $87 + 16 = 103$

11

	largest	*smallest*	*nearest to 100*
(a)	127	78	$49 + 53 = 102$
(b)	127	86	$38 + 58 = 96$
(c)	157	55	$17 + 88 = 105$
(d)	131	78	$36 + 63 = 99$

12 (a) $53 + 25 = 78$ (b) $36 + 52 = 88$ (c) $45 + 37 = 82$
(d) $29 + 34 = 63$ (e) $84 + 12 = 96$ (f) $21 + 48 + 27 = 96$
(g) $27 + 36 + 18 = 81$ (h) $26 + 19 + 48 = 93$ (i) $38 + 27 + 19 = 84$
(j) $16 + 35 + 44 = 95$ (k) $34 + 82 + 63 = 179$ (l) $48 + 63 + 26 = 137$
(m) $96 + 72 + 85 = 253$ (n) $49 + 87 + 35 = 171$ (o) $86 + 49 + 78 = 213$

13 (a) 2662 (b) 2882 (c) 3993 (d) 4884
Yes

Exercise 2L

1 (a) 62 (b) 23 (c) 21 (d) 15
(e) 75 (f) 10 (g) 5 (h) 30
(i) 82 (j) 52 (k) 12 (l) 36

2 (a) 37 (b) 14 (c) 29 (d) 17
(e) 33 (f) 33 (g) 8 (h) 52
(i) 19 (j) 42 (k) 29 (l) 66

3 (a) 144 (b) 364 (c) 354 (d) 424
(e) 740 (f) 203 (g) 200 (h) 42
(i) 50 (j) 4 (k) 6 (l) 12

4 (a) 419 (b) 536 (c) 334 (d) 249
(e) 208 (f) 585 (g) 183 (h) 311
(i) 92 (j) 45 (k) 299 (l) 495
(m) 376 (n) 78 (o) 78

5 (a) 661 (b) 535 (c) 430 (d) 434
(e) 508 (f) 458 (g) 526 (h) 705
(i) 584 (j) 463 (k) 770 (l) 674
(m) 369 (n) 864 (o) 267

6 (a) $478 - 26 = 552$
(b) $429 - 74 = 355$
(c) $476 - 74 = 402$

7 (a) $532 - 96 = 436$
(b) $496 - 99 = 397$
(c) $496 - 96 = 400$

8 (a) $876 - 45 = 831$
(b) $456 - 87 = 369$
(c) $574 - 68 = 506$

Answers to Homeworks

2 Understanding numbers

Exercise 2.1 Links: 2A

1 (a) 3 tens (b) 3 units
(c) 3 hundreds (d) 3 units
(e) 3 hundreds (f) 3 units
(g) 3 tens (h) 3 tens

2 (a) 45 (b) 62 (c) 30 (d) 47
(e) 28 (f) 49 (g) 84 (h) 13

3 (a) 456 (b) 836 (c) 653 (d) 247
(e) 630 (f) 400

4 35, 38, 53, 58, 83, 85 5 90

Exercise 2.2 Links: 2B

1 (a) 3 thousands (b) 30 thousands
(c) 300 thousands (d) 3 thousands
(e) 30 thousands (f) 300 thousands
(g) 3 thousands (h) 3 thousands

2 (a) 26 (b) 2
(c) 236 (d) 40
(e) 193 (f) 391
(g) 103 (h) 35

3 (a) Twenty six thousand four hundred and thirty one
(b) Two thousand five hundred and eighty three
(c) Two hundred and thirty six thousand five hundred and seventy nine
(d) Forty thousand eight hundred and seventy three
(e) One hundred and ninety three thousand seven hundred and two
(f) Three hundred and ninety one thousand two hundred and fifty four
(g) One hundred and three thousand eight hundred and ninety
(h) Thirty five thousand four hundred and four

4 (a) 2703 (b) 308 049
(c) 21 750 (d) 1091

5 90

Exercise 2.3 Links 2C

1 (a), (b) 27, 28, 29, 37, 38, 39, 47, 48, 49, 72, 73, 74, 82, 83, 84, 92, 93, 94
N.B. pupils may have interpreted the question differently and so give 72 ... 94 only.

2

Team	Points
Allstars	71
Gold	64
Bears	48
Egg-heads	38
Top-lot	29

3 (a) Jamie, Gavin, Susie, Florry, Jennifer, Charlie
(b) Charlie

Exercise 2.4 Links: 2D

1 (a) 246, 338, 405, 738, 924
(b) 369, 373, 406, 420, 691
(c) 401, 452, 492, 833, 882
(d) 78, 309, 364, 387, 415

2

City	Distance in miles
London	241
Hull	346
Norwich	354
Newcastle	416
Edinburgh	496
Aberdeen	631

3 Dartmoor
Exmoor
Lake District
Northumberland
North Yorkshire Moors
Yorkshire Dales
Peak District

Exercise 2.5 Links: 2E, 2F, 2G, 2H, 2I

1 (a) $0 + 7$, $1 + 6$, $2 + 5$, $3 + 4$
(b) $0 + 14$, $1 + 13$, $2 + 12$, ... $7 + 7$
(c) $0 + 19$, $1 + 18$, ... $9 + 10$
(d) $0 + 13$, $1 + 12$, ... $6 + 7$
(e) $0 + 16$, $1 + 15$, ... $8 + 8$
(f) $0 + 17$, $1 + 16$, ... $8 + 9$

2 (a) $20 - 17$, $19 - 16$, $18 - 15$, ... $3 - 0$
(b) $20 - 11$, $19 - 10$, ... $9 - 0$
(c) $20 - 14$, $19 - 13$, ... $6 - 0$
(d) $20 - 9$, $19 - 8$, ... $11 - 0$
(e) $20 - 6$, $19 - 5$, ... $14 - 0$
(f) $20 - 13$, $19 - 12$, ... $7 - 0$

3 There are many ways, sometimes infinite, to answer each part.

4 49, 59, 69, 79, 58, 68, 78, 88, 67, 77, 87, 97, 73, 83, 93, 103

5 (a) $16 \xrightarrow{+20} 36 \xrightarrow{+1} 37$, $21 \xrightarrow{+6} 27 \xrightarrow{+10} 37$ etc.
(b) 39 (c) 91 (d) 67

Exercise 2.6 Links: 2J, 2K, 2L

1 £7 2 £12

3 (a) $894 - 320 = 574$
(b) $573 - 541 = 32$
(c) $648 - 397 = 251$

4 (a) 5 [9] 2 − [2] 4 [3] = 3 4 9
(b) [8] 4 [7] − 3 [8] 4 = 4 6 3
(c) 7 [2] [8] − [5] 8 9 = 1 3 9
(d) [4] 6 3 − 2 [0] [7] = 2 5 6

Remediation answers

2.1 Tens and units

Exercise 1

(a) 4 tens 3 units

T	U
4	3

(b) 2 tens 7 units

T	U
2	7

(c) 1 ten 8 units

T	U
1	8

(d) 6 tens 4 units

T	U
6	4

(e) 3 ten 5 units

T	U
3	5

(f) 5 tens 3 units

T	U
5	3

Exercise 2

1 (a) (b) (c) (d) (e) (f) (g) (h) (i) (j)

2.2 Hundreds, tens and units

Exercise 1

1 (a)

H	T	U
3	6	4

(b)

H	T	U
5	2	8

(c)

H	T	U
1	7	6

(d)

H	T	U
2	3	9

(e)

H	T	U
6	4	2

(f)

H	T	U
4	1	5

Exercise 2

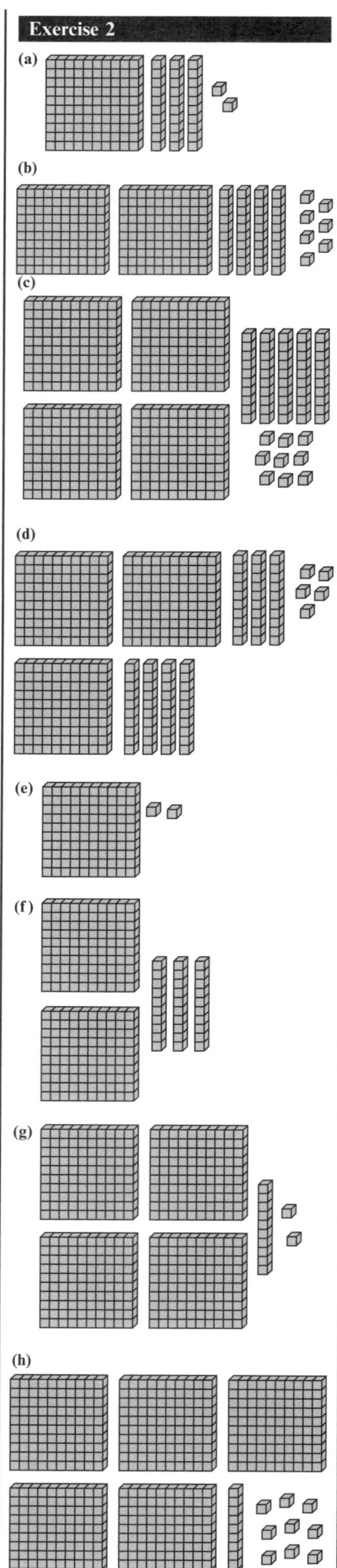

2.3 Thousands

Exercise 1

(a)

Th	H	T	U
1	3	4	7

(b)

Th	H	T	U
5	3	2	5

(c)

Th	H	T	U
2	5	4	3

(d)

Th	H	T	U
3	2	6	7

(e)

Th	H	T	U
4	2	3	0

(f)

Th	H	T	U
2	1	0	5

Exercise 2

(a) (b) (c) (d) (e)

2.4 Adding by counting on

Exercise 1

1 8 2 8 3 9
4 9 5 8

Exercise 2

1 12 2 11 3 14
4 15 5 13

2.5 Adding

Exercise 1

1 (a) 9 (b) 9
(c) 7 (d) 12
(e) 10 (f) 13

Exercise 2

1 (a) 14 (b) 14 (c) 15
(d) 13 (e) 16 (f) 14
(g) 13 (h) 18 (i) 15
(j) 12 (k) 14 (l) 16
(m) 19 (n) 17 (o) 13
(p) 17 (q) 17 (r) 17
(s) 18 (t) 20

2.6 Adding two digit numbers

Exercise 1

1 **(a)** 38 **(b)** 38 **(c)** 58
(d) 77 **(e)** 96
2 **(a)** 29 **(b)** 56 **(c)** 85
(d) 48 **(e)** 77

2.7 Adding – carrying units

1 **(a)** 62 **(b)** 64 **(c)** 75
(d) 43 **(e)** 81 **(f)** 93
(g) 94 **(h)** 73 **(i)** 81
(j) 61 **(k)** 43 **(l)** 54
(m) 45 **(n)** 52 **(o)** 85

2.8 Carrying tens

Exercise 1

1 373 **2** 642 **3** 521 **4** 832
5 816 **6** 523 **7** 832 **8** 1045

2.9 Subtracting

Exercise 1

1 3 **2** 1 **3** 2 **4** 7 **5** 6
6 3 **7** 3 **8** 6 **9** 2 **10** 1

Exercise 2

1 17 **2** 28 **3** 18 **4** 14 **5** 9
6 17 **7** 29 **8** 33 **9** 23 **10** 22

2.10 Subtraction short cuts

Exercise 1

1 16 **2** 8 **3** 6 **4** 12 **5** 8
6 13 **7** 19 **8** 8 **9** 14 **10** 15

2.11 Subtracting hundreds, tens and units

Exercise 1

1 317 **2** 217
3 128 **4** 217
5 417 **6** 225
7 118 **8** 218
9 527 **10** 226
11 118 **12** 136

Unit 3 Number patterns

Content summary

This unit is about sequences. These may be defined numerically, be generated by a number machine, or arise from a sequence of diagrams.
Square numbers, triangle numbers and Fibonacci sequences feature.

NC level

Level 2: Recognise a sequence of numbers.

At about
Level 3: Generate values using a number machine.

Level 4: Square, triangle and Fibonacci numbers.

NA6a

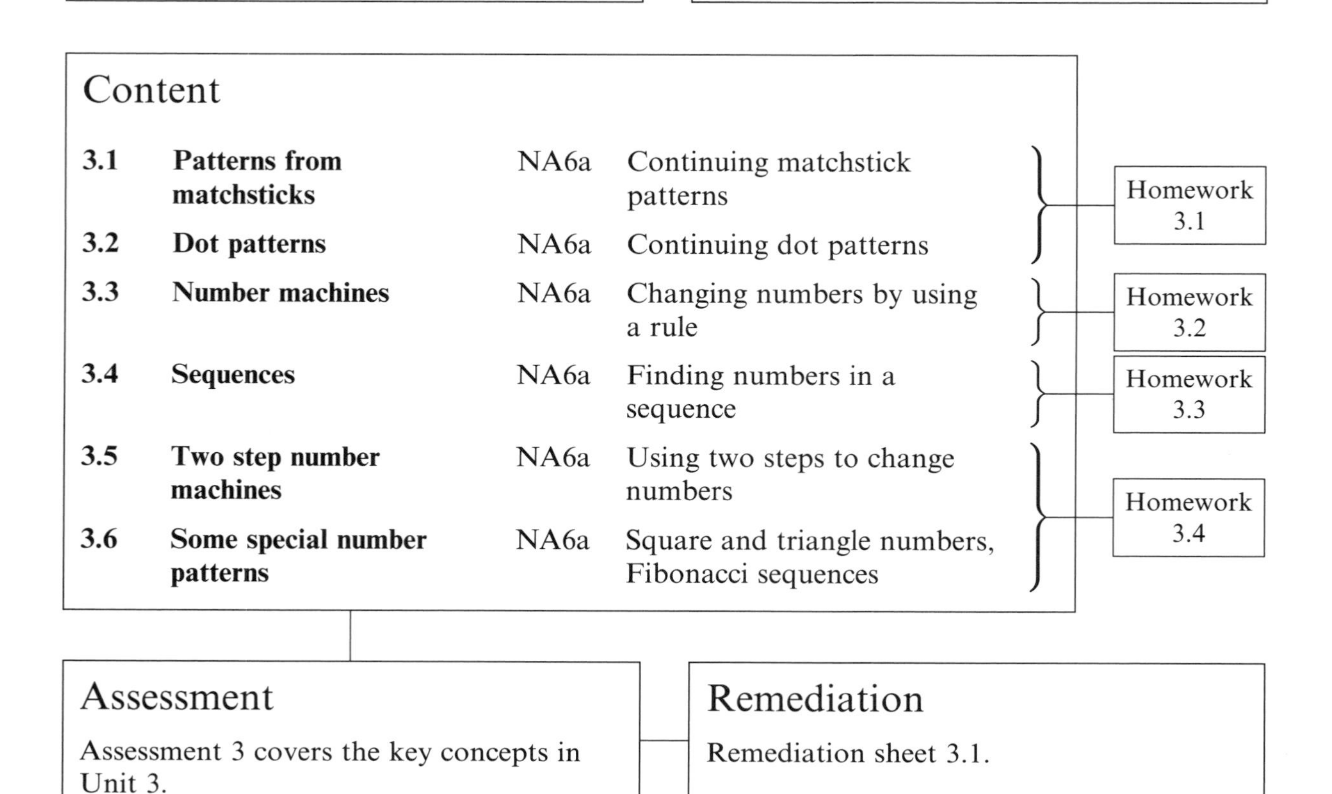

Content

3.1	**Patterns from matchsticks**	NA6a	Continuing matchstick patterns	Homework 3.1
3.2	**Dot patterns**	NA6a	Continuing dot patterns	
3.3	**Number machines**	NA6a	Changing numbers by using a rule	Homework 3.2
3.4	**Sequences**	NA6a	Finding numbers in a sequence	Homework 3.3
3.5	**Two step number machines**	NA6a	Using two steps to change numbers	Homework 3.4
3.6	**Some special number patterns**	NA6a	Square and triangle numbers, Fibonacci sequences	

Assessment

Assessment 3 covers the key concepts in Unit 3.

Remediation

Remediation sheet 3.1.

Assessment

The assessment is marked out of 30. Achievement of 20 or more marks indicates a good understanding of the key concepts.
Marking guidance, answers and links to remediation are provided on page 265.

Equipment

No extra equipment is needed for this chapter.

ICT links

3.1
Use *MicroSmile for Windows Pack 1* to explore patterns from straight lines and circles.

3.3–3.6
Use a spreadsheet to:
- map the changes of numbers for a variety of rules
- generate number sequences:

The Fibonacci Sequence	Triangle Numbers
1	1
1	3
2	6
3	10
5	15
8	21
13	28
21	36
34	45

Remediation

Remediation sheet 3.1 provides extra practice to help with the concept of using number machines.

Questionbank CD

All homeworks and extension questions also appear on the CD.

Pages xvii and xviii of this pack show you how to use the CD to select questions from the Questionbank and further customize them if you wish to.

3 Number patterns

framework teaching objective	§	lesson starter	f/w ref
Generate and describe simple integer sequences.	3.1	Ask pupils to consider a baby creature forming in its mother's womb. 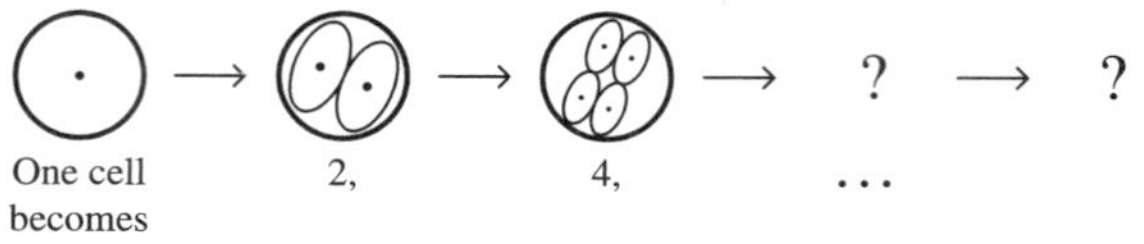 One cell becomes → 2, → 4, → ? → ? … What's happening? 'The baby is growing.' 'The cells are doubling.' Ask pupils to consider a bridge being built with metal struts. 3 struts → 5 struts 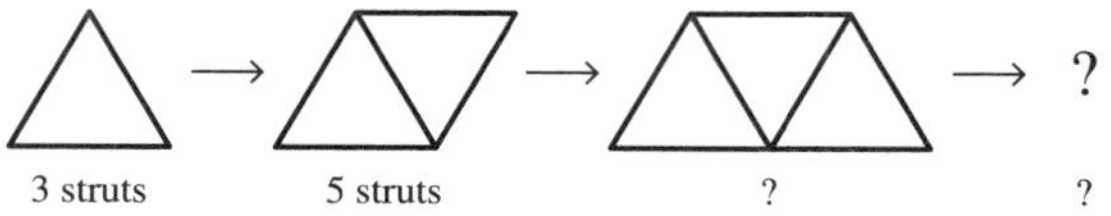 → ? → ? What's happening? 'The bridge is being built.' 'Adding 2.' Does the bridge grow 'as quickly' as the baby? No. The baby's sequence increases at a faster rate. Which makes a sequence increase at a faster rate, multiplying by 2 or adding 2?	144–7
Generate and describe simple integer sequences.	3.4	These 3 robots work only on whole numbers. One is an add robot and two are multiply robots. 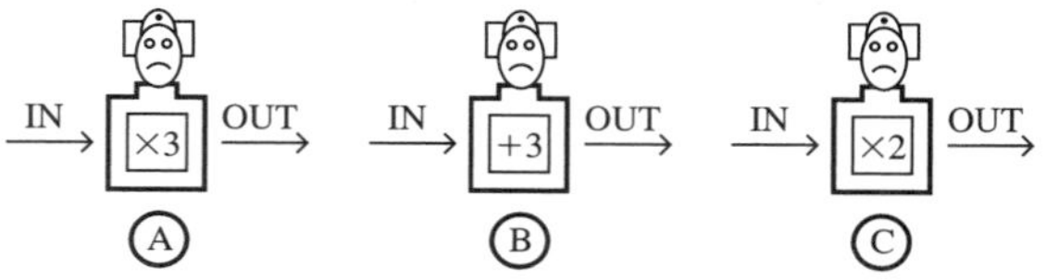 IN → ×3 → OUT (A) IN → +3 → OUT (B) IN → ×2 → OUT (C) Which robot **cannot** make the number 21? Why not? Which two robots **cannot** make the number 25? Why not? Think of a number that all three robots can make. Can Robot B make the number 1? Discuss. Can you think of a **multiply** robot that can make 13? Why not? (A $\times 1$ robot doesn't count!)	144–7

framework teaching objective	**§**	**lesson starter**	**f/w ref**
Generate and describe simple integer sequences.	3.4	Ask pupils to consider how many different ways there are of continuing this sequence? $1 \rightarrow 3 \rightarrow \ldots \rightarrow \ldots$ (*Students should give 'add 2' and 'multiply by 3.'*) What about $1 \rightarrow 3 \rightarrow 4 \rightarrow 7 \rightarrow 11$? What about $1 \rightarrow 3 \rightarrow 7 \rightarrow 15 \rightarrow 31$? Ask pupils what 2 operations you have used for the 3rd sequence? Ask pupils to try to find ways of continuing this sequence: $1 \rightarrow 2 \rightarrow \ldots$?	144–7
Generate and describe simple integer sequences.	3.4	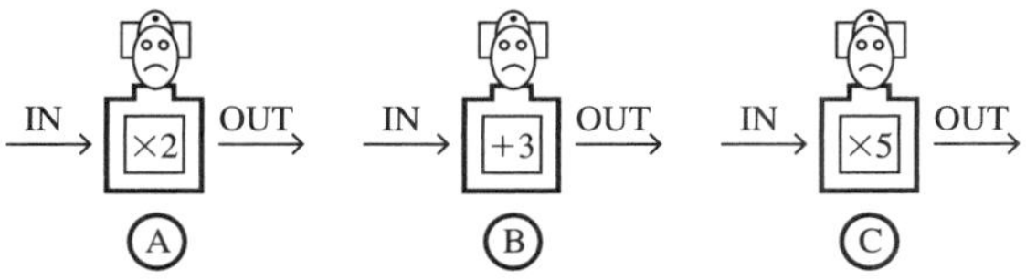 IN → ×2 → OUT (A) IN → +3 → OUT (B) IN → ×5 → OUT (C) I pass the number 4 through all 3 robots. What number comes out at the very end? What happens if the robots change places? Investigate. Which order will give the biggest output? Which orders give the same output?	144–7

3 Number patterns

Exercise 3.1 Links: 3A, 3B

1 Continue these number patterns with another 2 patterns. Write down the rule you used to find the next pattern.

(a) 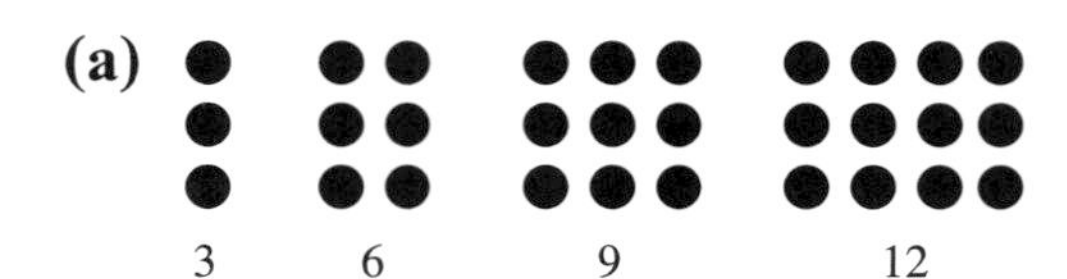

(b) 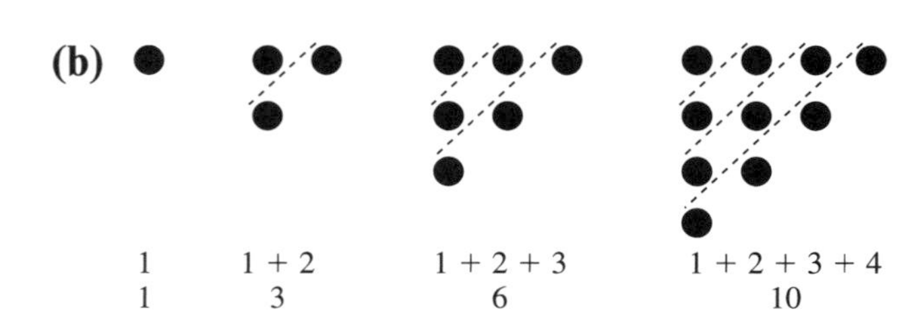

(c) 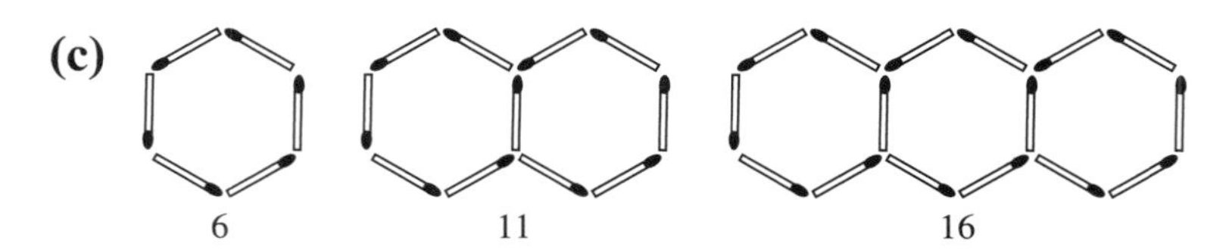

Exercise 3.2 Links: 3C

1 What is the output from each of these number machines?

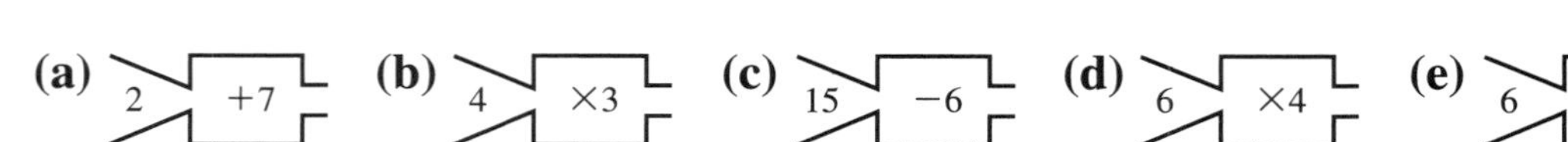

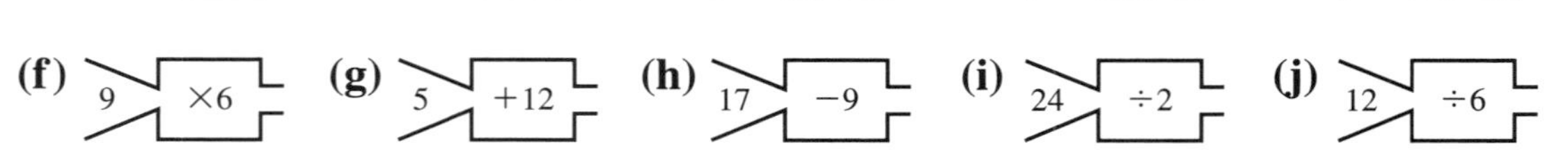

2 Copy and complete the tables to show the outputs.

(a) 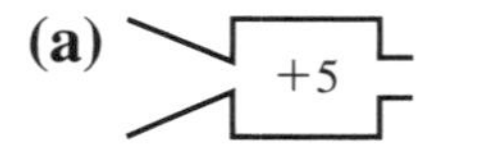

input	output
1	
2	7
3	
4	
5	10
6	

(b) 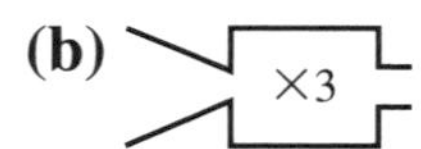

input	output
1	
2	6
3	
4	
5	15
6	

(c) 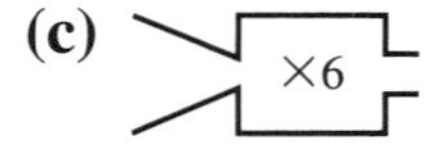

input	output
1	
2	12
3	
4	
5	
6	

Exercise 3.3 Links: 3D, 3E

1 For each sequence:

- Write down the next two numbers.
- Write down the rule that you use to find the next number.

(a) 2, 4, 6, 8, 10, ..., ...

(b) 3, 6, 9, 12, 15, ..., ...

(c) 0, 4, 8, 12, 16, ..., ...

(d) 1, 4, 7, 10, 13, ..., ...

(e) 2, 7, 12, 17, 22, ..., ...

(f) 20, 17, 14, 11, ..., ...

(g) 22, 18, 14, 10, ..., ...

(h) 23, 19, 15, 11, ..., ...

(i) 30, 27, 24, 21, ..., ...

(j) 31, 27, 23, 19, ..., ...

2 Find the missing numbers in these sequences:

(a) 3, 8, 13, 18, 23, ..., ..., 38, ...

(b) 37, 34, 31, 28, ..., ..., 19, ...

(c) 3, 9, 27, ..., ..., 729

(d) 1, 12, 23, 34, ..., ..., 67, ...

Exercise 3.4 Links: 3F, 3G

1 Input the numbers 1, 2, 3, 4 and 5 into these two step machines. Use tables to record your results.

(a) 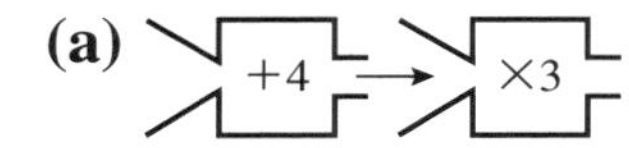

(b) 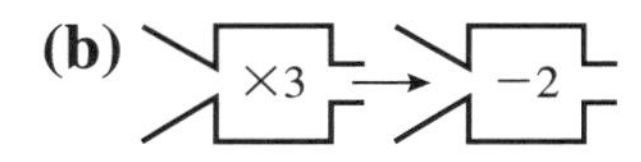

(c) 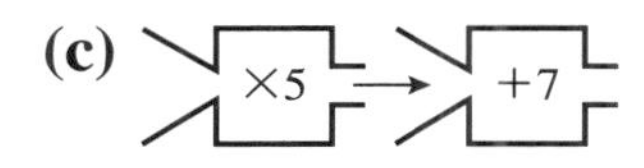

(d) 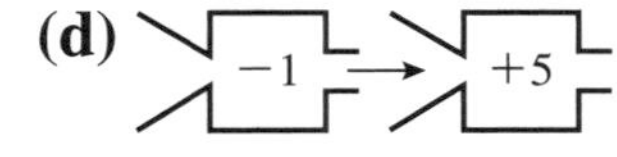

(e) 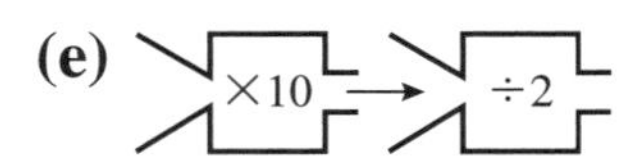

(f) 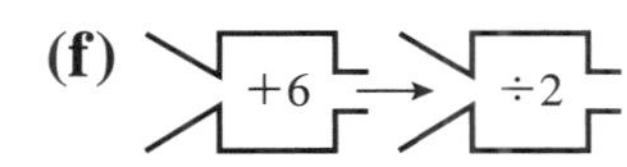

(g) 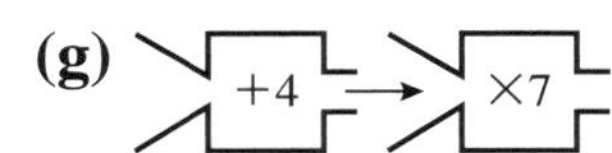

(h) 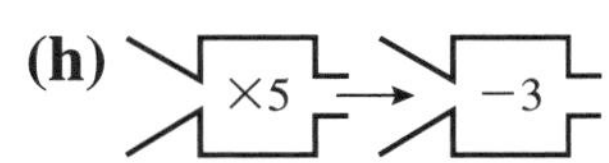

(i) 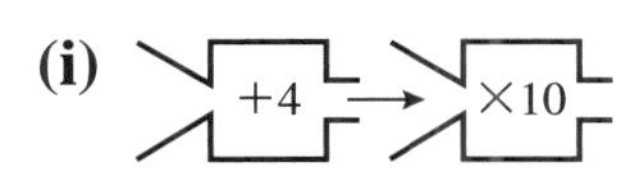

2 Find the next two numbers in these number patterns. Write down the rule you used to find them.

(a) 1, 2, 3, 5, 8, 13, ..., ...

(b) 2, 2, 4, 6, 10, 16, 26, ..., ...

Name ....

3 Number patterns

1 **(a)** Draw the next shape in this pattern.

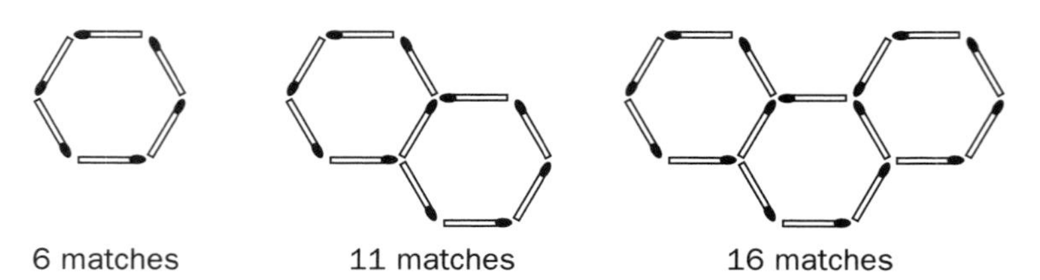

(b) Write down the pattern using numbers 6, 11, 16, ...

(c) Write down the rule to get the next number in the pattern.

.... **(3 marks)**

---

2 **(a)** Draw the next pattern in this series.

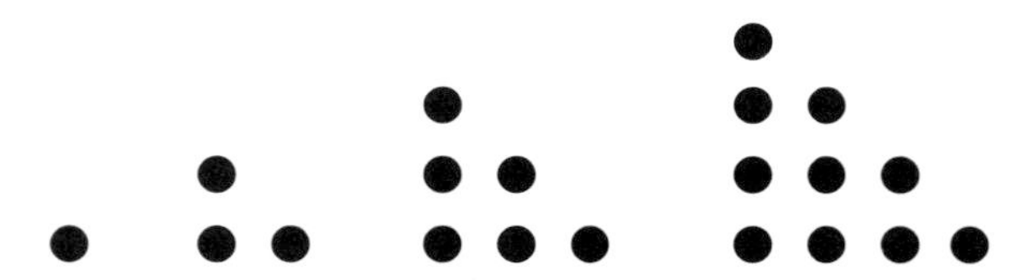

(b) Write down the next two numbers in the pattern.

1, 3, 6, 10, ..., ...

(c) Write down the rule to get the next number in the pattern.

.... **(3 marks)**

---

3 Write down the output numbers for these number machines.

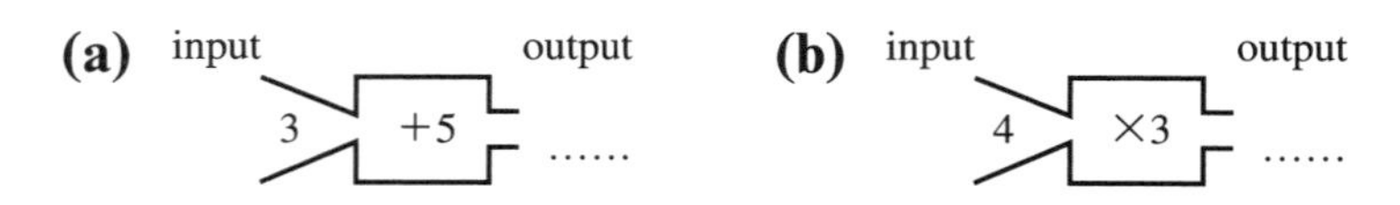

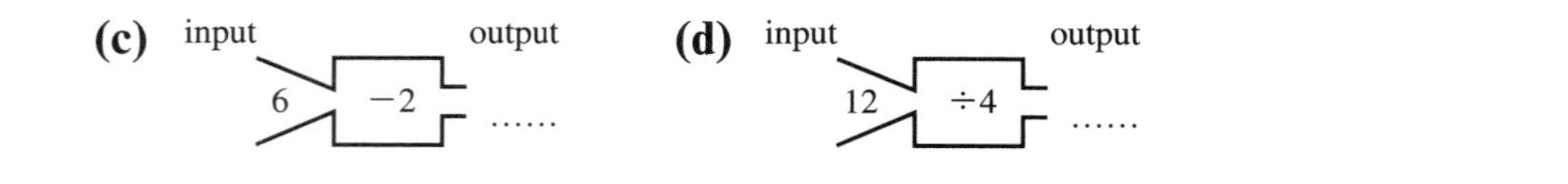

(4 marks)

---

4 Input the numbers 1, 2, 3, 4, 5 and 6 into this number machine.

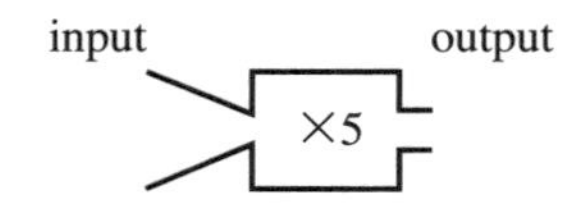

Complete this table of results:

INPUT	OUTPUT
1	
2	
3	
4	
5	
6	

(2 marks)

---

5 Write down the output from these two step number machines.

(a) 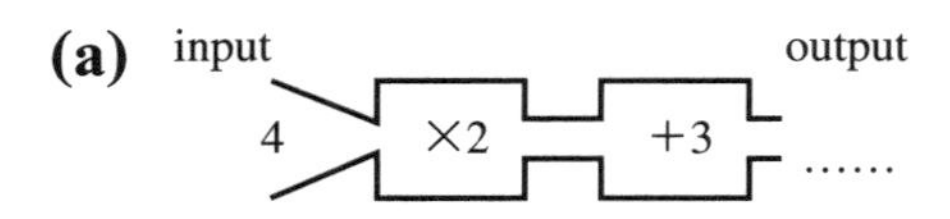

(b) 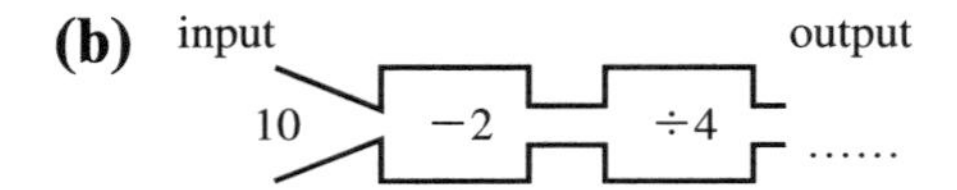

(2 marks)

---

6 **(a)** Write down the next two numbers in these number patterns.

(i) 4, 7, 10, 13, 16, ..., ...

(ii) 42, 38, 34, 30, 26, ..., ...

(b) Write down the rules for finding the next number in the sequences in **(a)**.

(i) ....

(ii) .... **(6 marks)**

---

7 Find the missing numbers in these sequences.

(a) 1, 2, 4, 8, ..., 32, ...

(b) 80, 74, 68, ..., 56, ... **(4 marks)**

8

Write down which numbers in the cloud are:

(a) square numbers

(b) triangular numbers

(c) Fibonacci numbers **(6 marks)**

Unit 3 Number patterns

<table>
<tr><th colspan="3">Question</th><th>Answer</th><th>Marking guidance and remediation sheet links</th><th></th></tr>
<tr><td>1</td><td>(a)</td><td></td><td></td><td>A1</td><td></td></tr>
<tr><td></td><td>(b)</td><td></td><td>21</td><td>A1</td><td></td></tr>
<tr><td></td><td>(c)</td><td></td><td>Add 5</td><td>A1</td><td></td></tr>
<tr><td>2</td><td>(a)</td><td></td><td>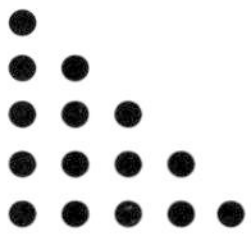</td><td>A1</td><td></td></tr>
<tr><td></td><td>(b)</td><td></td><td>15, 21</td><td>A1 for both</td><td></td></tr>
<tr><td></td><td>(c)</td><td></td><td>Add 7</td><td>A1</td><td></td></tr>
<tr><td>3</td><td>(a)</td><td></td><td>8</td><td>A1</td><td rowspan="5">less than $\frac{4}{6}$ use remediation sheet 3.1</td></tr>
<tr><td></td><td>(b)</td><td></td><td>12</td><td>A1</td></tr>
<tr><td></td><td>(c)</td><td></td><td>4</td><td>A1</td></tr>
<tr><td></td><td>(d)</td><td></td><td>3</td><td>A1</td></tr>
<tr><td>4</td><td></td><td></td><td><table><tr><th>Input</th><th>Output</th></tr><tr><td>1</td><td>5</td></tr><tr><td>2</td><td>10</td></tr><tr><td>3</td><td>15</td></tr><tr><td>4</td><td>20</td></tr><tr><td>5</td><td>25</td></tr><tr><td>6</td><td>30</td></tr></table></td><td>B2 for all correct
B1 for 3 or more correct</td></tr>
<tr><td>5</td><td>(a)</td><td></td><td>11</td><td>A1</td><td></td></tr>
<tr><td></td><td>(b)</td><td></td><td>2</td><td>A1</td><td></td></tr>
<tr><td>6</td><td>(a)</td><td>(i)</td><td>19, 22</td><td>A1, A1</td><td></td></tr>
<tr><td></td><td></td><td>(ii)</td><td>22, 18</td><td>A1, A1</td><td></td></tr>
<tr><td></td><td>(b)</td><td>(i)</td><td>Add 3</td><td>B1</td><td></td></tr>
<tr><td></td><td></td><td>(ii)</td><td>Take away 4</td><td>B1</td><td></td></tr>
</table>

Key to mark scheme
A marks: correct answer
M marks: correct method
B marks: independent work

Page 265 gives a general guidance on use of this assessment scheme with some examples.

Assessment and remediation links

Question		Answer	Marking guidance and remediation sheet links
7	**(a)**	16, 64	B1, B1
	(b)	62, 50	B1, B1
8	**(a)**	4, 9, 16	B1 for 1 correct, B2 for all correct, −1 for any extras
	(b)	6, 10, 21	B1 for 1 correct, B2 for all correct, −1 for any extras
	(c)	5, 21	B1 for 1 correct, B2 for 2 correct, −1 for any extras

Key to mark scheme
A marks: correct answer
M marks: correct method
B marks: independent work

Page 265 gives a general guidance on use of this assessment scheme with some examples.

3.1 Number machines

You use a number machine like this:

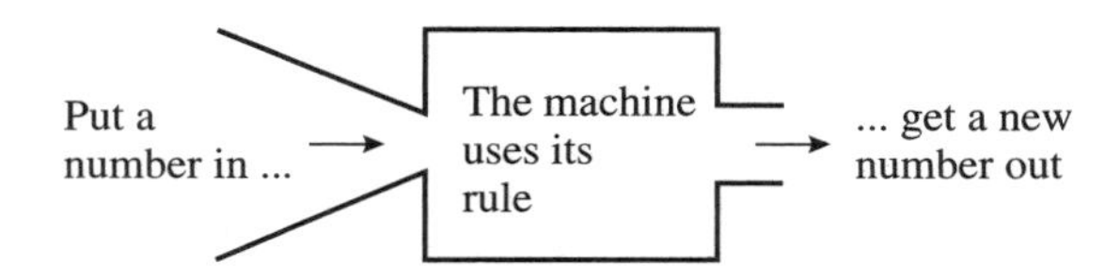

So for an 'add 10' machine:

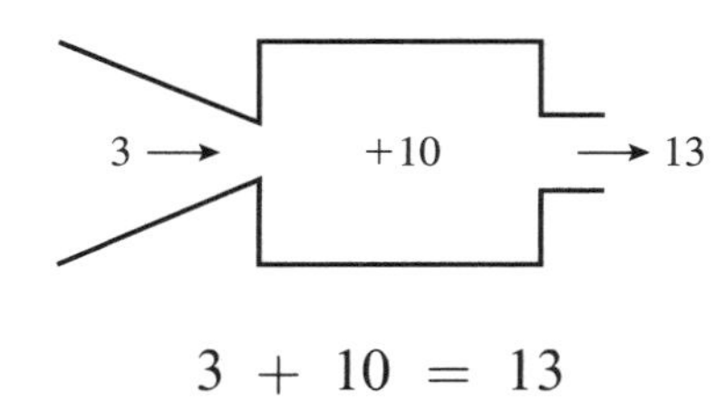

$$3 + 10 = 13$$

Exercise 1

1 Write down the output from these number machines:

(a) 7 → +2 → .....

(b) 8 → +5 → .....

(c) 2 → ×5 → .....

(d) **(e)** **(f)**

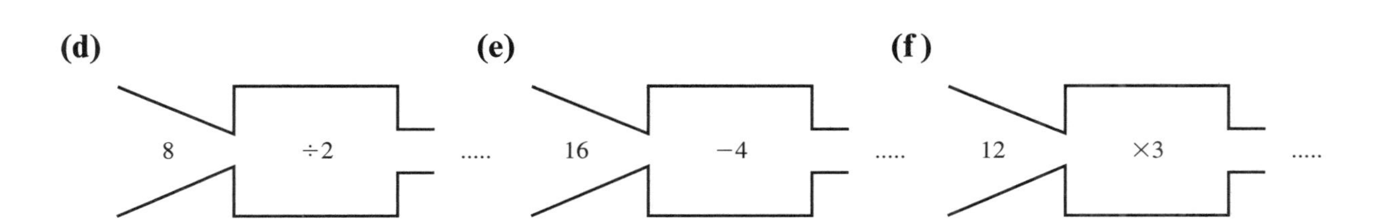

(g) **(h)** **(i)**

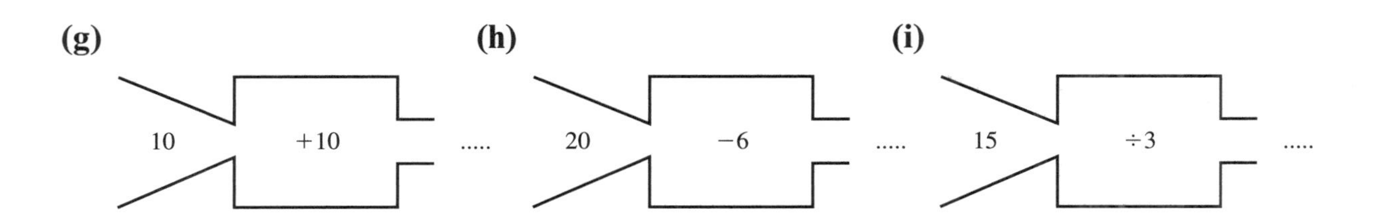

Answers to Pupils' Book

3 Number patterns

Exercise 3A

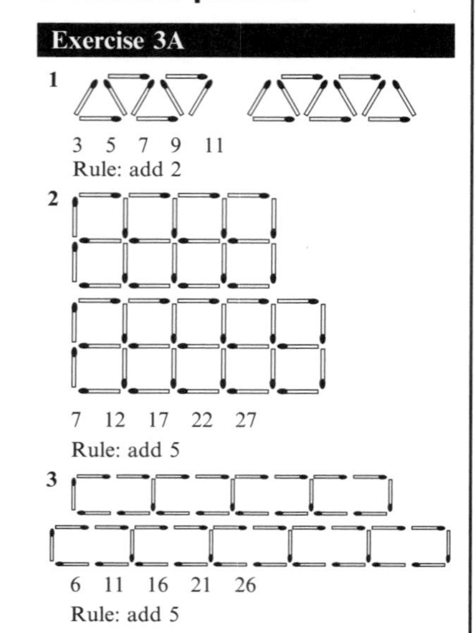

1

3 5 7 9 11

Rule: add 2

2

7 12 17 22 27

Rule: add 5

3

6 11 16 21 26

Rule: add 5

Exercise 3B

1 (a) 2 4 6 8
Rule: add 2

(b) 4 8 12 16
Rule: add 4

(c) 5 10 15 20
Rule: add 5

(d)

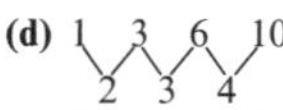

Rule: add 1 more each time *or* increase the gap by 1 more

(e)

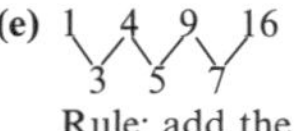

Rule: add the next odd number 3...5...7...9...11

(f)

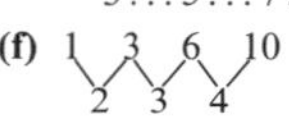

Rule: add 1 more each time

2 (a)

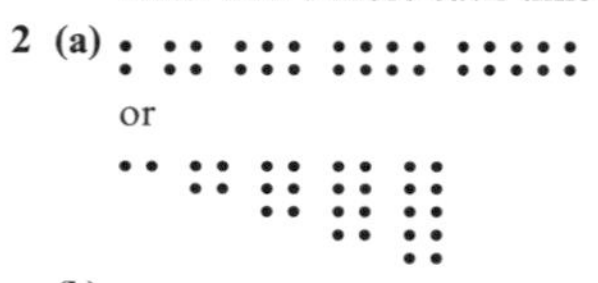

(b)

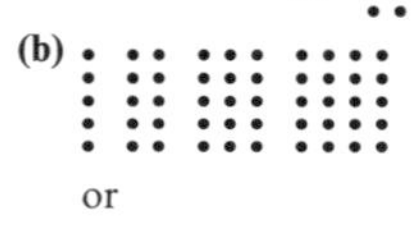

or

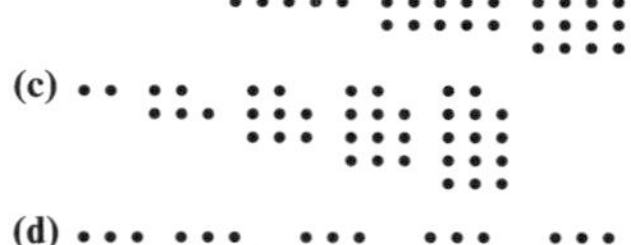

(c)

(d)

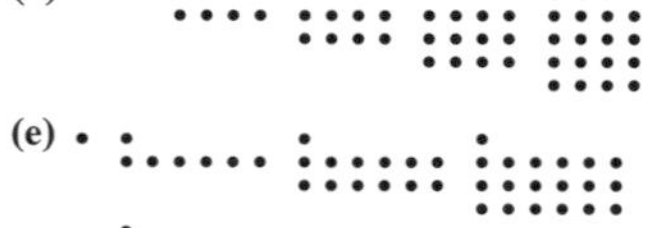

(e)

Exercise 3C

1 (b) 6, 7, 8, 9, 10, 11
(c) counting numbers from 6 to 11
2 (b) 5, 6, 7, 8, 9, 10
(c) counting numbers from 5 to 10
3 (b) 13, 14, 15, 16, 17, 18
(c) counting numbers from 13 to 18
4 (b) 4, 8, 12, 16, 20, 24
(c) numbers in 4× table, multiples of 4, add 4 each time
5 (b) 6, 12, 18, 24, 30, 36
(c) numbers in 6× table, multiples of 6, numbers go up 6 each time
6 (b) 2, 4, 6, 8, 10, 12
(c) numbers in 2× table, even numbers, multiples of 2, numbers go up by 2 each time
7 (b) 3, 6, 9, 12, 15, 18
(c) numbers in 3× table, multiples of 3, numbers go up by 3 each time
8 (b) 1, 2, 3, 4, 5, 6
(c) same output as input, counting numbers 1 to 6
9 (b) 0, 1, 2, 3, 4, 5
(c) counting numbers 0 to 5

Exercise 3D

	(a)	(b)
1	11, 13	add 2
2	15, 18	add 3
3	20, 25	add 5
4	17, 20	add 3
5	6, 7	add 1
6	16, 19	add 3
7	24, 28	add 4
8	50, 60	add 10
9	23, 27	add 4
10	18, 22	add 4
11	35, 42	add 7
12	45, 54	add 9
13	10, 8	take away 2
14	6, 3	take away 3
15	5, 0	take away 5
16	11, 9	take away 2
17	30, 20;	take away 10
18	8, 5	take away 3
19	3, 2	take away 1
20	7, 3	take away 4
21	4, 1	take away 3
22	15, 13	take away 2
23	60, 55	take away 5
24	18, 9	take away 9

Exercise 3E

1 27, 81, 729
2 49, 44, 34
3 72, 60, 36
4 28, 35, 49
5 30, 40, 60
6 26, 22, 14
7 8, 16
8 60, 50, 30
9 15, 19, 27, 31

Exercise 3F

1 9 **2** 16 **3** 11 **4** 10
5 11 **6** 52 **7** 20 **8** 0

9 (b)

Input	Output
1	3
2	5
3	7
4	9
5	11
6	13

(c) odd numbers, output numbers increase by 2

10 (b)

Input	Output
1	2
2	5
3	8
4	11
5	14
6	17

(c) output numbers increase by 3

11 (b)

Input	Output
1	4
2	7
3	10
4	13
5	16
6	19

(c) output numbers increase by 3

12 (b)

Input	Output
1	3
2	8
3	13
4	18
5	23
6	28

(c) output numbers increase by 5

13 (b)

Input	Output
1	3
2	7
3	11
4	15
5	19
6	23

(c) output numbers increase by 4

14 (b)

Input	Output
1	5
2	7
3	9
4	11
5	13
6	15

(c) odd numbers, output numbers increase by 2

15 (b)

Input	Output
1	6
2	11
3	16
4	21
5	26
6	31

(c) output numbers increase by 5

16 (b)

Input	Output
1	5
2	15
3	25
4	35
5	45
6	55

(c) output numbers go up by 10

17 (b)

Input	Output
1	1
2	6
3	11
4	16
5	21
6	26

(c) output numbers increase by 5

18

× 2 + 1

Input	Output
2	5
3	7
5	11
7	15
11	23

× 3 − 1

Input	Output
2	5
3	8
5	14
7	20
11	32

× 3 + 1

Input	Output
2	7
3	10
5	16
7	22
11	34

× 5 − 2

Input	Output
2	8
3	13
5	23
7	33
11	53

× 4 − 1

Input	Output
2	7
3	11
5	19
7	27
11	43

× 2 + 3

Input	Output
2	7
3	9
5	13
7	17
11	25

Exercise 3G

1 **(a)** 1, 9 **(b)** 1, 3, 6 **(c)** 1, 2, 3, 8, 13
2 **(a)** 16 **(b)** 5 **(c)** 36 **(d)** 28 **(e)** 21

Answers to Homeworks

3 Number patterns

Exercise 3.1 Links: 3A, 3B

1 **(a)**

Rule: add an extra column of 3 dots each time.

(b)

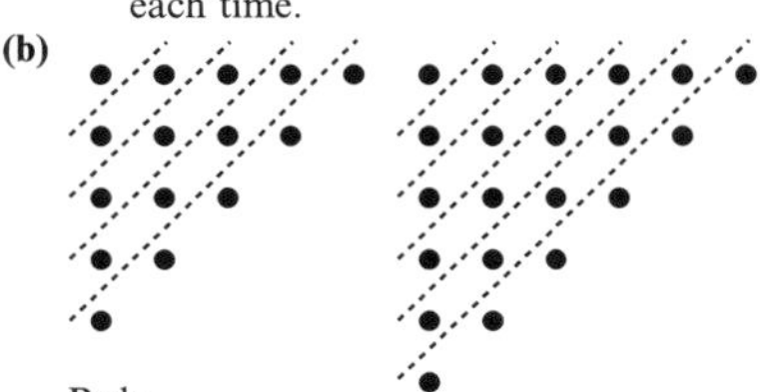

Rule:
- add 1 more ● to each row or
- add the next number of dots (3 then 4 then 5) or
- add a new diagonal row with 1 more dot than before.

(c)

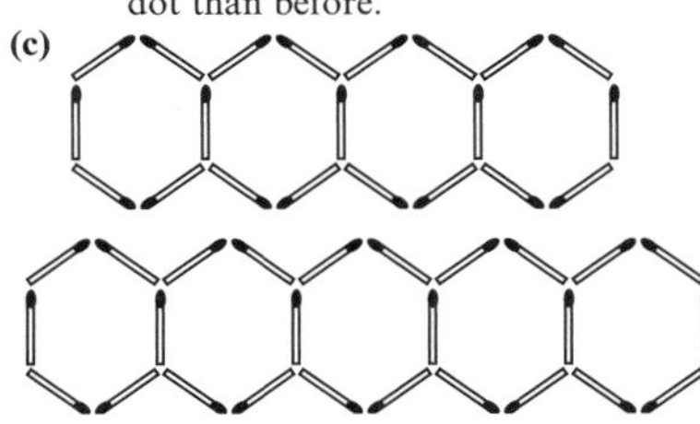

Rule: add another 5 matches each time.

Exercise 3.2 Links: 3C

1 **(a)** 9 **(b)** 12 **(c)** 9 **(d)** 24 **(e)** 2
(f) 54 **(g)** 17 **(h)** 8 **(i)** 12 **(j)** 2

2 **(a)**

Input	Output
1	6
2	7
3	8
4	9
5	10
6	11

(b)

Input	Output
1	3
2	6
3	9
4	12
5	15
6	18

(c)

Input	Output
1	6
2	12
3	18
4	24
5	30
6	36

Exercise 3.3 Links: 3D

1 **(a)** 12, 14; add two
(b) 18, 21; add three
(c) 20, 24; add four
(d) 16, 19; add three
(e) 27, 32; add five
(f) 8, 5; minus three
(g) 6, 2; minus four
(h) 7, 3; minus four
(i) 18, 15; minus three
(j) 15, 11; minus four
2 **(a)** 28, 33, 43
(b) 25, 22, 16
(c) 81, 243
(d) 45, 56, 78

Exercise 3.4 Links: 3F, 3G

1 **(a)**

Input	Output
1	15
2	18
3	21
4	24
5	27

(b)

Input	Output
1	1
2	4
3	7
4	10
5	13

(c)

Input	Output
1	12
2	17
3	22
4	27
5	32

(d)

Input	Output
1	5
2	6
3	7
4	8
5	9

(e)

Input	Output
1	5
2	10
3	15
4	20
5	25

(f)

Input	Output
1	3.5
2	4
3	4.5
4	5
5	5.5

(g)

Input	Output
1	35
2	42
3	49
4	56
5	63

(h)

Input	Output
1	2
2	7
3	12
4	17
5	22

(i)

Input	Output
1	50
2	60
3	70
4	80
5	90

2 **(a)** 1 2 3 5 8 13 21 34
Rule: add the last 2 numbers to get the next number.
(b) 2 2 4 6 10 16 26 42 68
Rule: add the last 2 numbers to get the next number.

Remediation answers

3.1 Number machines

Exercise 1

(a) 9 **(b)** 13 **(c)** 10
(d) 4 **(e)** 12 **(f)** 36
(g) 20 **(h)** 14 **(i)** 5

Unit 4 Probability

Content summary

This unit covers the basic ideas of probability based on likelihood, certain, impossible and the number line 0–1.

NC level

Level 2: Certain and impossible.

Level 3: Order of likelihood.

Level 5: Probability scale 0–1.

H2f H4c H5h

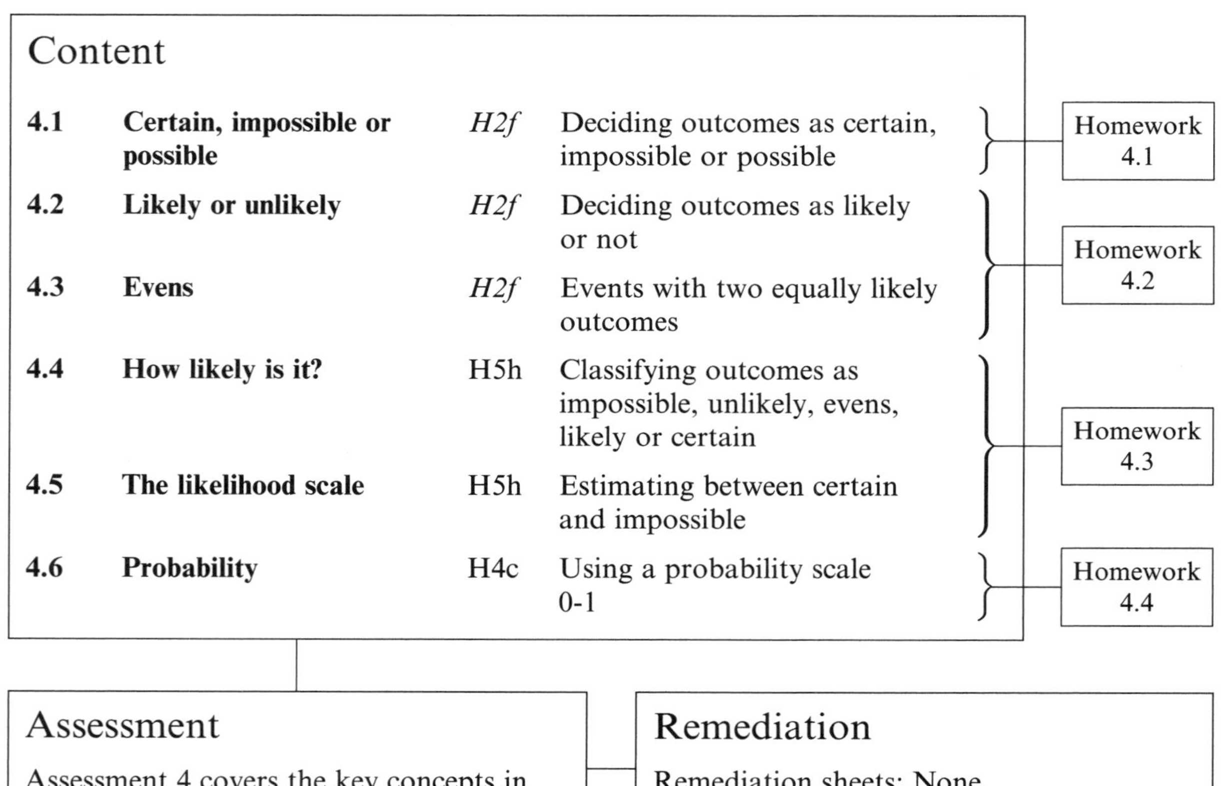

Content

4.1	**Certain, impossible or possible**	*H2f*	Deciding outcomes as certain, impossible or possible	Homework 4.1
4.2	**Likely or unlikely**	*H2f*	Deciding outcomes as likely or not	Homework 4.2
4.3	**Evens**	*H2f*	Events with two equally likely outcomes	
4.4	**How likely is it?**	H5h	Classifying outcomes as impossible, unlikely, evens, likely or certain	Homework 4.3
4.5	**The likelihood scale**	H5h	Estimating between certain and impossible	
4.6	**Probability**	H4c	Using a probability scale 0-1	Homework 4.4

Assessment

Assessment 4 covers the key concepts in Unit 4.

Remediation

Remediation sheets: None.

Assessment

The assessment is marked out of 30.
Achievement of 20 or more marks indicates a good understanding of the key concepts.
Marking guidance, answers and links to remediation are provided on page 265.

ICT links

Use *MicroSmile for Windows Pack 1* to develop an understanding of experimental probability.

Equipment

	Pupils' Book page
Likelihood scales	63
Probability scale	65

Remediation

There are no remediation sheets for this unit.

Questionbank CD

All homeworks and extension questions also appear on the CD.

Pages xvii and xviii of this pack show you how to use the CD to select questions from the Questionbank and further customize them if you wish to.

4 Probability

framework teaching objective	§	lesson starter	f/w ref
Use vocabulary and ideas of probability, drawing on experience.	4.1/ 4.2	'How can the weatherman tell us what the weather will be like tomorrow?' 'Can he see into the future?' 'Is the weatherman always right'? Students should be asked to name types of weather. Write these on the board ... e.g. rain sun windy snow hurricane hail etc. Students should then be asked to place the different weather types on a likelihood scale. impossible — certain (*Evidently the time of year will affect the position of the weather types on the likelihood scale.*)	276–7
Use vocabulary and ideas of probability, drawing on experience.	4.2	Ask pupils to consider this statement: 'It is possible to get hurt playing sport. Some sports have a higher risk of injury than others.' List some sports and ask pupils to think of some more. Rugby Badminton Golf Tennis Football Swimming Gymnastics Dominoes Ask pupils: 'Which are the risky sports?' 'Which are less risky?' 'Which is the least/most dangerous?' Discuss and use the discussion to compile a list of dangerous sports in order of risk. One Saturday, Hammerham town holds a sports festival. At the sports centre, people are playing football, squash, golf and rugby. Why is it useful for the people who run the centre and doctors at the local hospital to think about the likelihood of sporting injuries?	276–7

framework teaching objective	§	lesson starter	f/w ref
Use vocabulary and ideas of probability, drawing on experience.	4.4	Use a line of digit cards numbered 1 to 10. Place them in random order, face down. Turn over the cards one at a time. Ask pupils: 'When I turn the next card, is it likely to be higher or lower? Are there any cards that give an *even* chance of the next card being higher or lower? Why not? To have a good chance of predicting the next card, which cards do I hope to get.' (Very low or very high ones.) Why is 6 a bad card to turn over?	276-7
Find and justify probabilities based on equally likely outcomes in simple contexts.	4.6	Two teams are playing a football match, the Reds and the Blues. To see who kicks off, the captains have to spin a spinner and hope it lands on their teams' colour. The referee has 3 spinners to choose from. 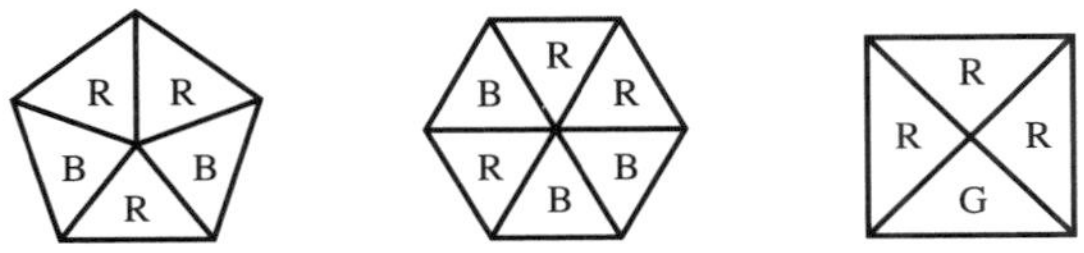 R R B B R — Spinner A; R B R R B B — B; R R R G — C Which spinner does the Blues captain hope the referee will choose? Which spinner gives the Reds the best chance of kicking off? Are any of the spinners fair?	278–81

4 Probability

Exercise 4.1 Links: 4A

1 Say whether each of these outcomes are certain, possible or impossible.

(a) Your best friend will have a birthday next year.

(b) You will be given some chocolate next week.

(c) A dog will have kittens next week.

(d) You will drive a car to school tomorrow.

(e) Your teacher's car will break down next month.

(f) June will be the month after May next year.

2 Write down one outcome which is:

(a) certain

(b) impossible

(c) possible.

Exercise 4.2 Links: 4B, 4C

1 Write down whether these outcomes are likely, unlikely or have an even chance of happening. Give reasons for each answer.

(a) Scoring an odd number with a normal dice.

(b) You will be given some English homework next week.

(c) It will snow on your way to school.

(d) The head teacher will take your next maths lesson.

(e) A coin when tossed will land on 'tails'.

(f) You will see your best friend next weekend.

(g) You will have fish fingers for tea one night next week.

(h) You will catch a bus to school next week.

Exercise 4.3 Links: 4D, 4E

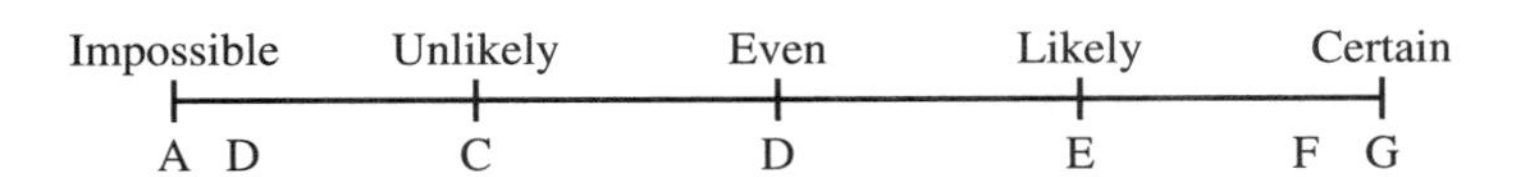

Copy the likelihood scale into your book.
Each letter shows an estimate of an outcome.
Write down a possible outcome for each letter,
e.g. A could be an estimate for the likelihood of a cat having puppies.

Exercise 4.4 Links: 4F

1 Draw a probability scale like the one shown below.

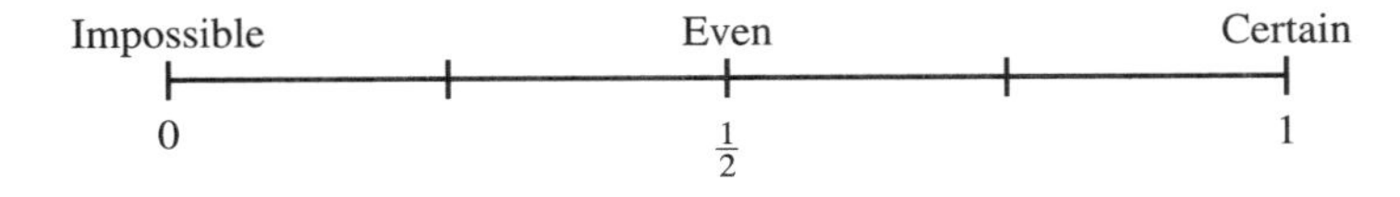

Mark an estimate for the probability of each of the following outcomes on your probability scale.

(a) A coin landing on 'heads'.

(b) A dice landing with 6 on its top face.

(c) You will have a holiday on Mars next year.

(d) You will have maths homework next week.

(e) Sunday will be the day after Saturday next week.

(f) A card taken at random from a normal pack of cards will be a red card.

(g) The next square you draw will have 4 sides.

(h) Manchester United will win their next match.

Name ....

4 Probability

1 Write down whether the outcomes of these events are certain, possible or impossible.

(a) You will throw a six with a normal dice. ....

(b) The sun will rise tomorrow. ....

(c) Next week, Wednesday will be the day after Sunday. ....

(3 marks)

---

2 Write down whether the outcome is likely or unlikely. Give a reason for your answer.

(a) The sun will shine during July. ....

reason ....

(b) You will break your arm tomorrow. ....

reason ....

(4 marks)

---

3 Tick the box that matches the likelihood of these events happening.

Tick **one** for each event.

(a) The next baby to be born will be female.

(b) A piece of balsa wood will float in water.

(c) A steel bar will float in water.

(d) The card at the top of a shuffled pack is an ace.

(e) It will snow in Scotland in January.

impossible	unlikely	evens	likely	certain

(5 marks)

---

4 Which of these outcomes have an even chance of happening?

(a) The next person I meet will be male.

(b) The number on the top of an ordinary dice will be a 6.

(c) A coin when thrown will come down heads. **(3 marks)**

---

5 Impossible unlikely evens likely certain

... ...

On this likelihood scale mark an estimate for each of these outcomes.

(a) The likelihood of a cat living for ever.

(b) The likelihood of the day after Thursday being Friday.

(c) The likelihood of getting a head when you toss a coin.

(d) The likelihood of it snowing in Switzerland in January. **(4 marks)**

6

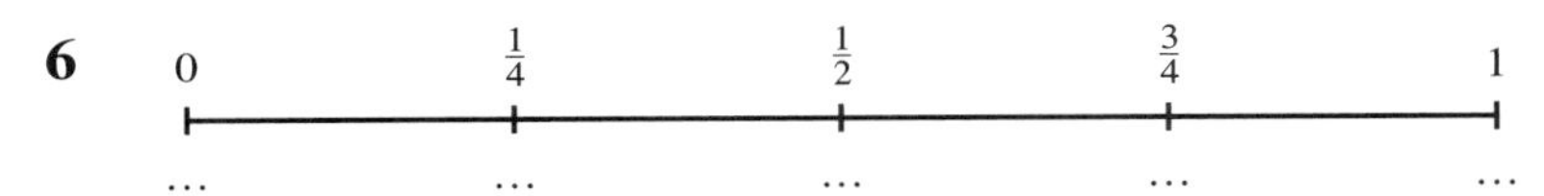

On this probability scale mark an estimate for each of these outcomes. Give a reason for your answer.

(a) The probability that the card on the top of a well shuffled pack will be a spade.

reason ....

(b) The probability that it will rain in London on at least one day next year.

reason ....

(c) The probability that when you roll a dice you will get an even number.

reason ....

(d) The probability that pigs will fly.

reason .... **(8 marks)**

7

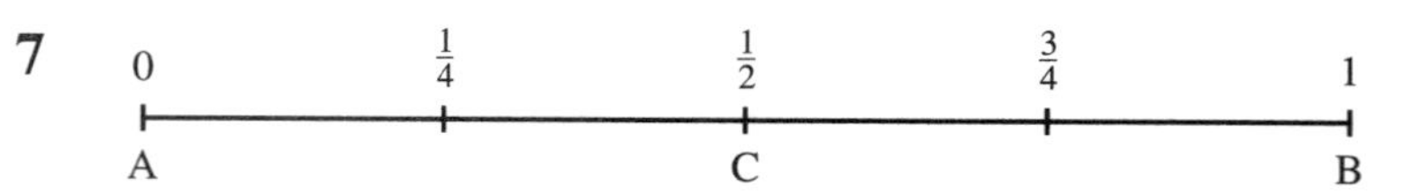

Look at the probability scale.
Outcomes A, B and C have been marked on the scale.
Write down an event that matches these probabilities.

A ....

B ....

C .... **(3 marks)**

Unit 4 Probability

Question	Answer	Marking guidance and remediation sheet links
1 (a)	possible	B1
(b)	certain	B1
(c)	impossible	B1
2 (a)	likely because the sun often shines in July (or summer)	B1 B1
(b)	unlikely because only a few people break their arm each day	B1 B1
3 (a)	evens	B1
(b)	certain	B1
(c)	impossible	B1
(d)	unlikely	B1
(e)	likely	B1
4 (a) & (c)	are evens	B1 for each
(b)	is not evens	B1
5	Impossible, unlikely, evens, likely, certain (a) at Impossible; (c) at evens; (d) at likely; (b) at certain	B1 for each one
6	0, $\frac{1}{4}$, $\frac{1}{2}$, $\frac{3}{4}$, 1 (d) at 0; (a) at $\frac{1}{4}$; (c) at $\frac{1}{2}$; (b) at 1	B1 for each one
(a)	There are four suits in a pack of cards. $\therefore \frac{1}{4}$	B1
(b)	Rain is certain to fall sometime during a whole year in London.	B1

Key to mark scheme
A marks: correct answer
M marks: correct method
B marks: independent work

Page 265 gives a general guidance on use of this assessment scheme with some examples.

Assessment and remediation links

Question		Answer	Marking guidance and remediation sheet links
	(c)	Numbers can be odd or even – there are 3 odd and 3 even numbers on a dice. $\therefore$ probability is $\frac{1}{2}$	B1
	(d)	Pigs do not fly, they are too heavy or do not have wings.	B1
7	**A**	e.g. my dog flies	B1
	B	e.g. Wednesday comes after Tuesday	B1
	C	e.g. a coin comes down heads when thrown	B1

Key to mark scheme
A marks: correct answer
M marks: correct method
B marks: independent work

Page 265 gives a general guidance on use of this assessment scheme with some examples.

Answers to Pupils' Book

4 Probability

Exercise 4A

1. Possible
2. Impossible
3. Possible
4. Possible
5. Certain
6. Possible
7. Impossible
8. Impossible
9. Certain
10. Possible

Exercise 4B

1. Unlikely – breaking a leg is a rare event.
2. Unlikely – famous film stars do not often visit schools.
3. Either – some pupils will always watch Eastenders, others will avoid the program; it may not be on that particular evening.
4. Likely – it is rare that a class achieves full attendance for a week.
5. Likely – it is rare to get a whole month without rain in Spring in England.
6. Likely – there are more number cards than non-number cards.

Exercise 4C

1. Evens – babies are either male or female in roughly equal proportions.
2. Not evens.
3. Not evens.
4. Evens – there are the same number of odd numbers as even numbers on a dice.
5. Evens – there are equal numbers of black and red cards in a pack.

Exercise 4D

1. Likely – it usually rains at sometime during April.
2. Unlikely – the last few champions have been under 30.
3. Unlikely – the F.A. cup has not been won by a non-premier league side since the premier league was created.
4. Evens – roughly the same number of boys and girls are born.
5. Impossible – nights are dark, days are light.
6. Likely – records usually enter the charts high and leave slowly.
7. Impossible – teams from Division 2 cannot win the Division 1 title.
8. Impossible – he died in the 1970s.
9. Unlikely – people are rarely involved in road accidents.
10. Likely – there are a lot of road accidents each day across the world as a whole.

Exercise 4E

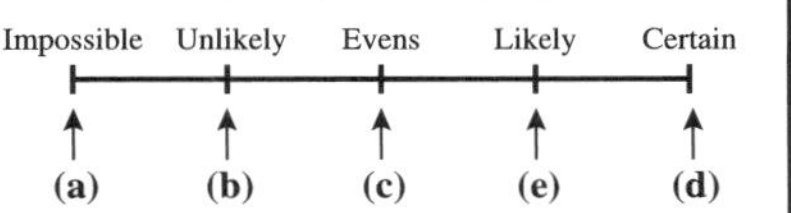

Exercise 4F

1

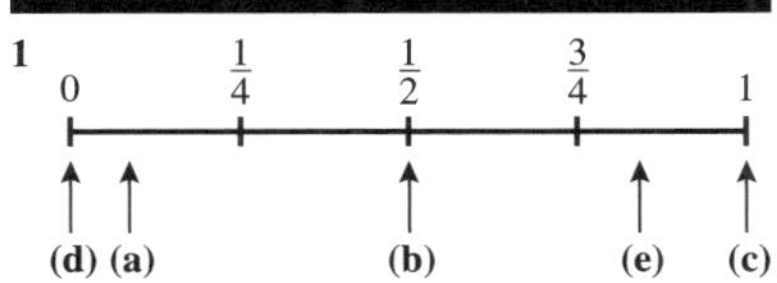

(a) The bus may break down but it is an unusual event.
(b) Babies are either boys or girls in roughly equal numbers.
(c) Ice will always melt if the temperature is above freezing point.
(d) Stones always sink.
(e) Olympic 100 m runners are usually in their 20s.

2

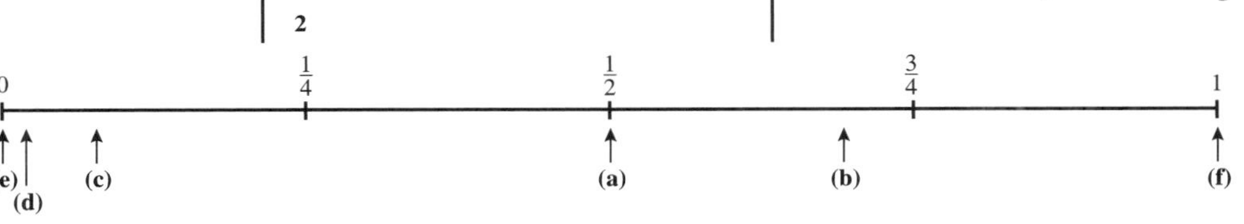

(a) Same number of blacks/reds.
(b) $\frac{4}{13}$ cards in every suite are pictures.
(c) $\frac{4}{52}$ cards are kings.
(d) $\frac{1}{52}$ cards is the Queen of Spades.
(e) There are no blank cards.
(f) All cards are either picture or number cards.

Answers to Homeworks

4 Probability

Exercise 4.1 — Links: 4A

1. (a) certain
   (b) possible
   (c) impossible
   (d) impossible
   (e) possible
   (f) certain

Exercise 4.2 — Links: 4B, 4C

1. (a) evens
   (b) likely
   (c) unlikely
   (d) unlikely
   (e) evens
   (f) likely
   (g) pupils' own answer
   (h) pupils' own answer

Exercise 4.3 — Links: 4D, 4E

Pupils' own answers.

Exercise 4.4 — Links: 4F

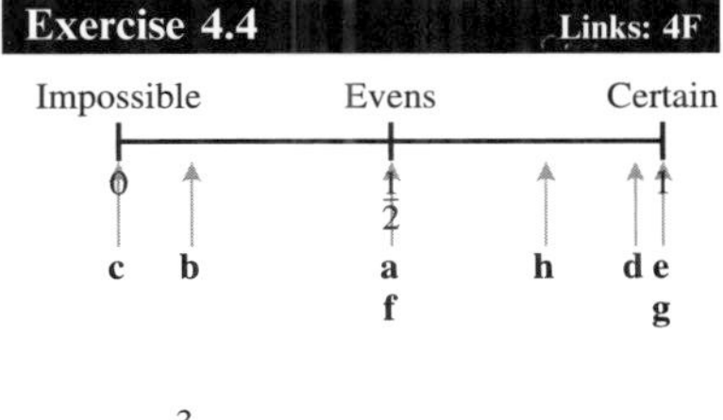

Unit 5 Multiplication and division

Content summary

This unit covers basic multiplication and division of 2 digit numbers, introducing mental and pencil and paper methods and the concepts of odd, even, square numbers, multiples and factors.

Book 1R Unit 5 extends this to multiplication and division of 3 digit by 2 digit and introduces prime numbers and powers beyond squares.

NC level

Level 2: Odd and even numbers.

Level 3: Mental recall to 5 × 5.

Level 4: Place value to multiply and divide by 10, 100. Mental recall to 10 × 10. Mental and written computation with multiplication and division.

N2c *N3b* *N3h* NA2a NA2b NA3a NA3g

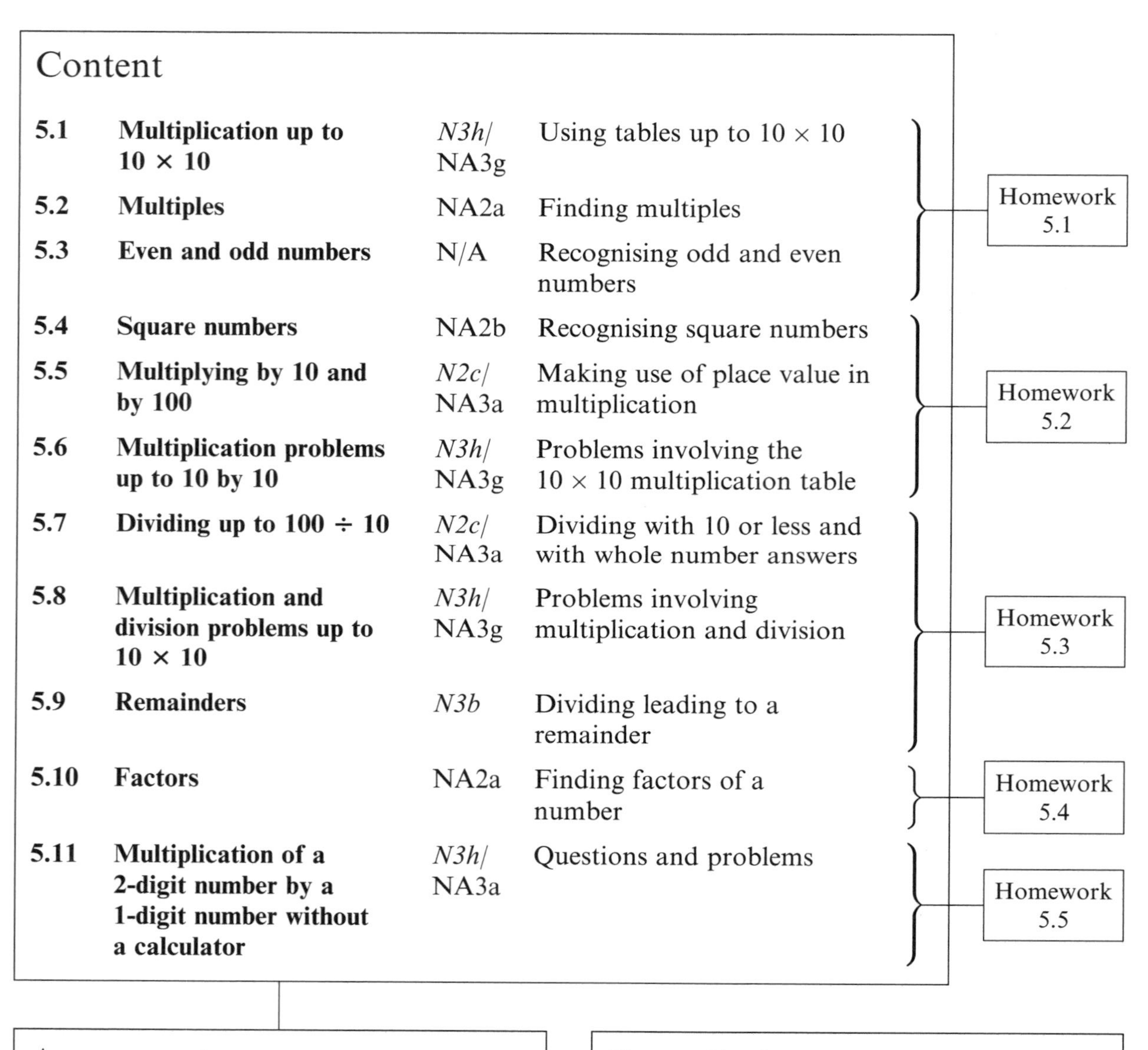

Content

5.1	**Multiplication up to 10 × 10**	*N3h*/ NA3g	Using tables up to 10 × 10	Homework 5.1
5.2	**Multiples**	NA2a	Finding multiples	Homework 5.1
5.3	**Even and odd numbers**	N/A	Recognising odd and even numbers	Homework 5.1
5.4	**Square numbers**	NA2b	Recognising square numbers	Homework 5.2
5.5	**Multiplying by 10 and by 100**	*N2c*/ NA3a	Making use of place value in multiplication	Homework 5.2
5.6	**Multiplication problems up to 10 by 10**	*N3h*/ NA3g	Problems involving the 10 × 10 multiplication table	Homework 5.2
5.7	**Dividing up to 100 ÷ 10**	*N2c*/ NA3a	Dividing with 10 or less and with whole number answers	Homework 5.3
5.8	**Multiplication and division problems up to 10 × 10**	*N3h*/ NA3g	Problems involving multiplication and division	Homework 5.3
5.9	**Remainders**	*N3b*	Dividing leading to a remainder	Homework 5.3
5.10	**Factors**	NA2a	Finding factors of a number	Homework 5.4
5.11	**Multiplication of a 2-digit number by a 1-digit number without a calculator**	*N3h*/ NA3a	Questions and problems	Homework 5.5

Assessment

Assessment 5 covers the key concepts in Unit 5.

Remediation

Remediation sheets 5.1 → 5.3.

Assessment

The assessment is marked out of 30.
Achievement of 20 or more marks indicates a good understanding of the key concepts.
Marking guidance, answers and links to remediation are provided on page 265.

Equipment

	Pupils' Book page
Numbered cards 1–10	68, 69
100 square	72
Dice	69
Square tiles, cubes or squared paper	74, 85

ICT links

5.1–5.4
Use a spreadsheet to generate:
- a 10×10 multiplication table
- multiples of whole numbers
- odd and even numbers
- the first 1000 square numbers.

5.1
Use *Mental Arithmetic from Virtual Image* to practice multiplication and division of whole numbers against the clock.

5.2–5.5
Use *MicroSmile for Windows Pack 4* to investigate the properties of numbers.

Remediation

Multiplication:
Make a practical start by grouping cubes and other objects to help pupils grasp the idea that 'multiplication is quicker than addition'. Learning and practising times tables is appropriate at this stage as a need to know them has been created. Pupils should concentrate on this before going on to paper based and abstract work.

Dividing:
Practically demonstrate division as the opposite of multiplication, starting with the same examples as for multiplication then reversing them. Demonstrate the methods shown in the text using cubes or money.

Note: See the following sheets for further multiplication and division activities.

Questionbank CD

All homeworks and extension questions also appear on the CD.

Pages xvii and xviii of this pack show you how to use the CD to select questions from the Questionbank and further customize them if you wish to.

5 Multiplication and division

framework teaching objective	§	lesson starter	f/w ref
Understand addition, subtraction, multiplication and division as they apply to whole numbers.	5.1	'Which multiplications are easy to remember?' '$2 \times 2 = 4$' '$3 \times 5 = 15$' '$2 \times 4 = 8$' '$4 \times 4 = 16$' How many people remember: $6 \times 7 = ?$ $8 \times 9 = ?$ $11 \times 11 = ?$ $7 \times 8 = ?$ Why are some harder to remember than others? Which times tables are easy to remember? 2×, 5×, 10× Students asked to write as many multiplication facts as they can remember.	82–5
Understand addition, subtraction, multiplication and division as they apply to whole numbers.	5.1	We can use easier multiplication facts to 'put together' harder ones: 7 times table: which ones do we *know*? → $1 \times 7 = 7$ *(5 × 7 can be derived easily either by counting up the 5 times table or halving 10 × 7.)* $2 \times 7 = 14$ $(5 \times 7 = 35)$ $10 \times 7 = 70$ Write these known calculations on the board. Which of these would help me to find $6 \times 7 = ?$ *(5 × 7 = 35 add 7 = 42 for instance)* Which one will help me to find $4 \times 7 = ?$ *(5 × 7 = 35 subtract 7 = 28)* Which one will help me to find $9 \times 7 = ?$ *(10 × 7 = 70 subtract 7 = 63)* Can this method help me with any number multiplied by 9? What is $3 \times 7 = ?$ Could this help me to find $6 \times 7 = ?$ What is $4 \times 7 = ?$ Could this help me to find $8 \times 7 = ?$	82–5

framework teaching objective	§	lesson starter	f/w ref
Understand addition, subtraction, multiplication and division as they apply to whole numbers.	5.6	A new 12 storey office block is being built. Three floors are already complete. There are 6 windows on each floor. How many windows are there in the building so far? (*18*) How many windows will there be: when the 6th floor is complete? (*36*) when the 8th floor is complete? (*48*) when the building is finished? (*72*) What maths do we have to use to work out these answers? (*multiplication and/or addition.*)	82–5
Understand addition, subtraction, multiplication and division as they apply to whole numbers.	5.7/ 5.9	Prize money: £32 is to be shared between 4 friends. What maths do we use to find how much each friend gets? ($32 \div 4 = 8$) Ask pupils to consider a change dispenser machine that gives out £2 coins. How many £2 coins will the machine give me if I put in change equalling £12? What maths did you use? ($12 \div 2 = 6$) How does division help to solve both of these problems? Prize money £*33* is to be shared between 4 friends. Can I use the same maths as before? (*Yes, division but this time with remainders*) What will be left over? What do we often call the leftover part? (*remainder*)	82–5

Strategies for learning times tables to 10 × 10

Learn the two times table first. Make a set of two times table cards with the answers on the back. Work through the cards to see how quickly the answers can be given, turning the cards over to check the answers. Keep any wrongly answered cards to one side and come back to concentrate on these later.

Once pupils are comfortable with the two times table, move on to the four times table. Put the four times table cards out alongside the two times table cards to show that you can get the four times table by doubling the two times table.

Learn the nine times table using fingers:

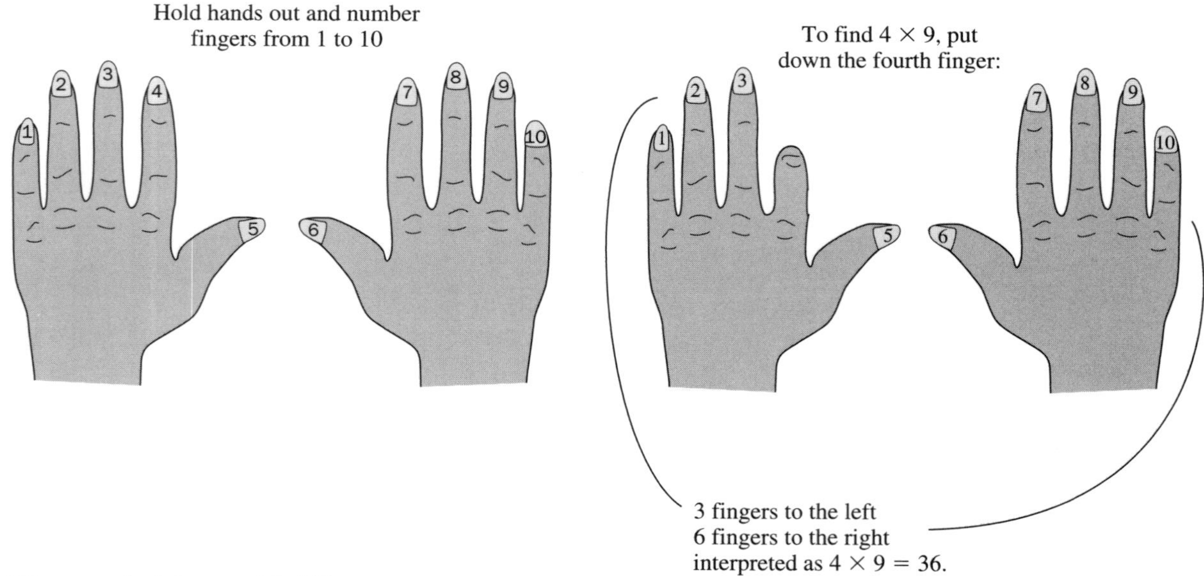

Hold hands out and number fingers from 1 to 10
1
2
3
4
5
6
7
8
9
10
To find 4 × 9, put down the fourth finger:
3 fingers to the left
6 fingers to the right
interpreted as 4 × 9 = 36.

Times table activities

(i) You will need a set of 0 – 9 cards. Decide which times table you are going to practice, shuffle the cards and then turn them over one by one. As each card is turned over the pupil says the answer multiplied by the number of the times table. This could be a good exercise for the pupils to do at home with their parents.

(ii) This activity works best with small groups or pairs. You will need a set of cards marked from 1 × 2 up to 10 × 10 with the answers on the back.
Shuffle the cards and hand out 10 – 15 to each group. Pupils take it in turns to read a card to the person to their left. If the answer is correct the card goes in the middle of the table, if the answer is wrong the answerer has to keep the card. The pupil with the least cards at the end is the winner.

At the end of the activity the pupils should spend some time learning the ones that they got wrong. If it becomes apparent that there is a weakness with a particular times table, use activity **(i)** to give more specific practice.

Once pupils are confident with the activity, improvements can be made by competing against the clock: How many can they do in 30 seconds, how long does it take to do twenty this week, etc.

(iii) Put a times grid on the board:

×	2	5	7	3
6				
8				
7				
2				
9				

Get the pupils to work in groups or pairs as a competition to see who can complete the grid the quickest with the most correct answers.
The outside numbers can be drawn randomly from a set of 0 – 9 cards or chosen by the pupils. Making a larger grid and getting pupils to try and devise a strategy for completing it in the quickest time can extend the activity.

(iv) Activity sheet 11 can be used as an activity and also as an ongoing record of 'multiplications that I can do'. By filling in a chart like this, pupils will find that they can learn multiplications two at a time, increasing their confidence by showing them how little they have left to learn.

Dividing

Once the pupils are confident with times tables they can move on to try some division activities. You can use a similar activity to **(ii)** above, except with division problems on the cards. Also, activity **(iii)** can be used, but it will need to be less random than the multiplication one to get the most benefit from it, e.g.

÷	12	48	24	36
6				
4				
2				

5 Multiplication and division

Exercise 5.1 Links: 5B, 5C

1 Which of these numbers are multiples of 6?
(a) 18 **(b)** 12 **(c)** 15 **(d)** 30 **(e)** 27 **(f)** 20
(g) 48 **(h)** 38 **(i)** 60 **(j)** 56 **(k)** 42 **(l)** 54

2 Which multiples of 8 are between 30 and 70?

3 These numbers are multiples of seven: 84, 91, 98, 105
What are the next four multiples of seven?

4 Write down all the even numbers between 22 and 38.

5 What is the next even number after:
(a) 21 **(b)** 35 **(c)** 43 **(d)** 39 **(e)** 57 **(f)** 76
(g) 46 **(h)** 77 **(i)** 105 **(j)** 125 **(k)** 0 **(l)** 287?

Remember: the next even number **after** 76

6 What is the next odd number after:
(a) 26 **(b)** 42 **(c)** 54 **(d)** 30 **(e)** 82 **(f)** 27
(g) 35 **(h)** 29 **(i)** 108 **(j)** 136 **(k)** 0 **(l)** 576?

Remember: the next odd number **after** 27

7 Which of these multiplications have odd answers and which have even answers?
(a) 2×7 **(b)** 5×4 **(c)** 3×5 **(d)** 8×8
(e) 5×7 **(f)** 5×5 **(g)** 6×10 **(h)** 9×3
(i) 7×6 **(j)** 4×7 **(k)** 7×3 **(l)** 5×8

Exercise 5.2 Links: 5D, 5E, 5F

1 Which of these are square numbers?
(a) 50 **(b)** 4 **(c)** 36 **(d)** 49 **(e)** 100 **(f)** 10
(g) 25 **(h)** 16 **(i)** 44 **(j)** 1 **(k)** 64 **(l)** 81

2 Which of these numbers are multiples of ten?
(a) 90 **(b)** 60 **(c)** 34 **(d)** 450 **(e)** 320 **(f)** 263
(g) 6870 **(h)** 480 **(i)** 2894 **(j)** 590 **(k)** 654 **(l)** 3420

3 Work out:
(a) 47×10 **(b)** 23×100 **(c)** 83×100 **(d)** 94×10
(e) 40×10 **(f)** 30×100 **(g)** 543×10 **(h)** 376×100
(i) 106×100 **(j)** 430×10 **(k)** 200×10 **(l)** 500×100

4 Ted bought 8 packs of fruit juice.
Each pack contained 6 cartons.
How many cartons did Ted buy altogether?

5 Rebecca bought four packs of six batteries. Each pack cost £3.
(a) How many batteries did she buy?
(b) How much did she pay in total?

6 Every day Kath does the following exercises:
7 press ups, 9 step ups, 6 sit ups, 8 stretches and 4 star jumps
How many of each exercise does Kath do in a week?

Exercise 5.3 Links: 5G, 5H, 5K

1 Work out:

(a) $15 \div 5$	**(b)** $28 \div 4$	**(c)** $36 \div 4$
(d) $18 \div 2$	**(e)** $18 \div 3$	**(f)** $24 \div 4$
(g) $21 \div 3$	**(h)** $16 \div 4$	**(i)** $45 \div 5$
(j) $35 \div 5$	**(k)** $30 \div 3$	**(l)** $24 \div 3$

2 Work out:

(a) $24 \div 8$	**(b)** $30 \div 6$	**(c)** $42 \div 6$
(d) $36 \div 9$	**(e)** $48 \div 8$	**(f)** $45 \div 9$
(g) $56 \div 7$	**(h)** $32 \div 8$	**(i)** $27 \div 9$
(j) $18 \div 9$	**(k)** $18 \div 6$	**(l)** $40 \div 10$

3 A farmer put 54 peaches into boxes.
Each box held 6 peaches when full.
How many boxes did he fill?

4 Fiona is organising a party.
She needs 72 glasses which she decides to hire.
The glasses come in boxes of 8.
How many boxes does she need?

5 Each week Marc does the following exercises:

56 press ups
49 sit ups
28 star jumps
63 stretches

He does the same number of exercises each day.
How many of each exercise does he do in a day?

6 A farmer is putting cobs of sweet corn into packs.
He has 73 cobs of sweet corn and each pack holds 4 cobs.
How many packs can he fill?

7 Twenty-six people are going to a night club by mini-cab.
Each mini-cab can take four people.
How many mini-cabs do they need?

8 You have to make 75 hot dogs for a party.
The sausages are sold in packs of ten and the bread rolls in packs of nine.

(a) How many packs of sausages should you buy?
(b) How many packs of bread rolls should you buy?
(c) How many hot dogs could you make?

Exercise 5.4 — Links: 5L

1 What are the factors of:

(a) 12 **(b)** 15 **(c)** 9 **(d)** 21 **(e)** 27 **(f)** 35?

2 True or false:

(a) 2 is a factor of 18 **(b)** 3 is a factor of 29
(c) 5 is a factor of 30 **(d)** 1 is a factor of 9
(e) 6 is a factor of 42 **(f)** 8 is a factor of 58
(g) 7 is a factor of 63 **(h)** 9 is a factor of 69
(i) 8 is a factor of 48 **(j)** 7 is a factor of 28
(k) 10 is a factor of 70 **(l)** 6 is a factor of 54

3 Which number other than 1 is:

(a) a factor of 9 and a factor of 15
(b) a factor of 18 and a factor of 24
(c) a factor of 28 and a factor of 35
(d) a factor of 16 and a factor of 36?

4 Which numbers are:

(a) a factor of 10 but not of 8
(b) a factor of 15 but not of 10
(c) a factor of 6 but not of 9
(d) a factor of 12 but not of 15?

Exercise 5.5 — Links 5M, 5N

1 Work out:

(a) 60×4 **(b)** 40×3 **(c)** 30×5 **(d)** 80×4
(e) 90×5 **(f)** 2×80 **(g)** 3×70 **(h)** 50×4
(i) 5×60 **(j)** 80×5 **(k)** 3×90 **(l)** 4×40

Remember: this is the same as 80×2

2 Work out:

(a) 60×8 **(b)** 30×9 **(c)** 40×8 **(d)** 50×7
(e) 9×60 **(f)** 8×60 **(g)** 80×7 **(h)** 40×7
(i) 70×7 **(j)** 90×7 **(k)** 8×50 **(l)** 9×70

3 Work out:

(a) 23×4 **(b)** 46×3 **(c)** 34×6 **(d)** 62×4
(e) 33×8 **(f)** 7×54 **(g)** 6×47 **(h)** 9×53
(i) 83×6 **(j)** 27×7 **(k)** 9×45 **(l)** 39×5

Remember: this is the same as 54×7

4 In a school there are 8 classes in year 9.
Each class has 28 pupils in it.
How many pupils are there in year 9?

5 Mandy bought nine packs of cola for a school disco.
Each pack contained thirty six cans.
How many cans did she buy?

Name ....

5 Multiplication and division

No calculators to be used in this test.

1 Work out:

(a) $4 \times 5 =$ ....

(b) $6 \times 3 =$ ....

(c) $6 \times 8 =$ ....

(d) $9 \times 4 =$ .... **(2 marks)**

2

From the numbers in the cloud write down:

(a) The multiples of 3 ....

(b) The multiples of 4 .... **(4 marks)**

---

3 5 of these numbers are even numbers.
Put a circle round each even number.

(2 marks)

---

4 5 of the numbers in the cloud are square numbers.
Circle each square number.

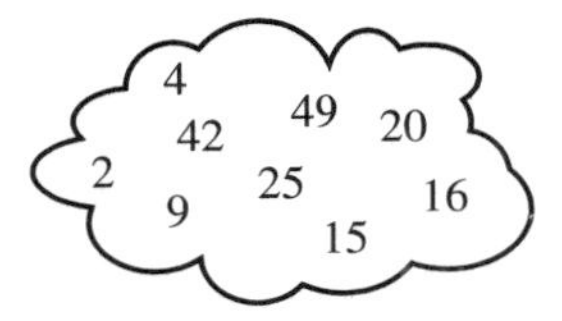

(3 marks)

---

5 Work out:

(a) $24 \times 10 =$ ....

(b) $13 \times 100 =$ ....

(c) $2300 \div 10 =$ ....

(d) $2500 \div 100 =$ .... **(4 marks)**

---

6 Josie bought 8 pencils. Each pencil cost 9 p.
How much did she pay altogether? **(1 mark)**

---

7 Frank bought 6 cassettes costing £8 each.
How much did he spend? **(1 mark)**

---

8 Work out:

(a) $15 \div 3 =$ ....

(b) $24 \div 4 =$ ....

(c) $56 \div 7 =$ .... **(3 marks)**

---

9 Melvyn bought 8 CDs for £40.
How much did each CD cost? **(1 mark)**

---

10 A class of 30 pupils were told to get into teams of 5 by their P.E. teacher.
How many teams were there? **(1 mark)**

---

11 Work out these divisions, giving the remainder.

(a) $19 \div 6 =$ .... r ....

(b) $28 \div 9 =$ .... r ....

(c) $25 \div 4 =$ .... r ....

(d) $24 \div 7 =$ .... r .... **(2 marks)**

---

12 Valerie has 35 eggs to put into egg boxes.
Each egg box will hold 6 eggs.
How many egg boxes can she fill?
How many eggs are left over? **(1 mark)**

---

13 Write down all the factors of 15. **(2 marks)**

---

14 Work out:

(a) $30 \times 7 =$ ....

(b) $23 \times 6 =$ .... **(2 marks)**

---

15 Ian has ordered 6 boxes of pencils.
Each box contains 48 pencils.
How many pencils did Ian order? **(1 mark)**

Unit 5 Multiplication and division

Question		Answer	Marking guidance and remediation sheet links	
1	**(a)**	20	B2, −1 for each wrong answer	less than $\frac{1}{2}$ use remediation sheet 5.1
	(b)	18		
	(c)	48		
	(d)	36		
2	**(a)**	3, 9, 12, 21	B2, −1 for each error but ignore absence of 3	
	(b)	4, 12, 16	B2, −1 for each error	
3		2, 20, 36, 48, 92	B2, −1 for each error	
4		4, 9, 16, 25, 49	B3, −1 for each error	
5	**(a)**	240	A1	
	(b)	1300	A1	
	(c)	230	A1	
	(d)	25	A1	
6		72 p	M1 for 8×9 or A1 for 72	less than $\frac{1}{2}$ use remediation sheet 5.1
7		£48	M1 for 6×8 or A1 for 48	
8	**(a)**	5	A1	less than $\frac{3}{5}$ use remediation sheet 5.3
	(b)	6	A1	
	(c)	8	A1	
9		£5	A1	
10		6	A1	

Key to mark scheme
A marks: correct answer
M marks: correct method
B marks: independent work

Page 265 gives a general guidance on use of this assessment scheme with some examples.

Assessment and remediation links

Question		Answer	Marking guidance and remediation sheet links
11	**(a)**	3 r1	B2, −1 for each wrong answer.
	(b)	3 r1	
	(c)	6 r1	
	(d)	3 r3	
12		5 boxes, 5 eggs left	A1
13		1, 3, 5, 15	B1 for 2 factors B2 for all 4
14	**(a)**	210	A1 } less than $\frac{2}{3}$ use remediation sheet 5.2
	(b)	138	A1
15		288	A1

Key to mark scheme
A marks: correct answer
M marks: correct method
B marks: independent work

Page 265 gives a general guidance on use of this assessment scheme with some examples.

5.1 Multiplying

How many eggs?

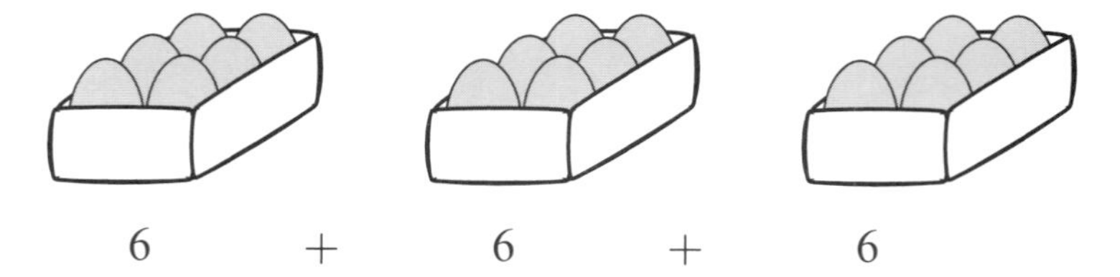

6 + 6 + 6

You can add them:

$6 + 6 + 6$ is the same as 3 lots of 6

This addition can be written as a multiplication: 3×6

and $3 \times 6 = 18$

You can use the 3 times table to find
3 6 18

Example 1

How many cups?

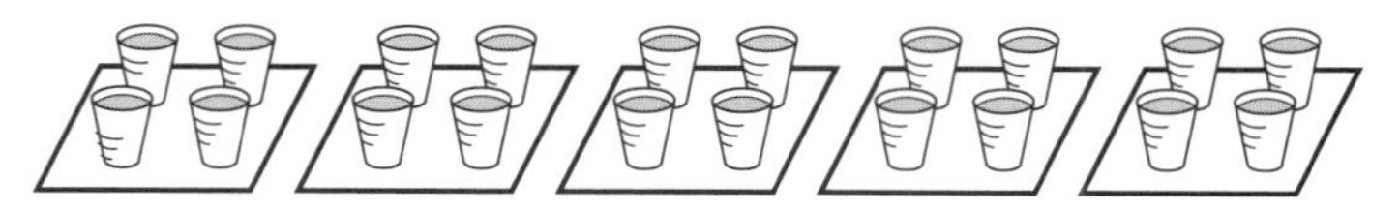

Answer: 5×4 cups $= 20$ cups

Exercise 1

1 How many buns?

2 How many videos?

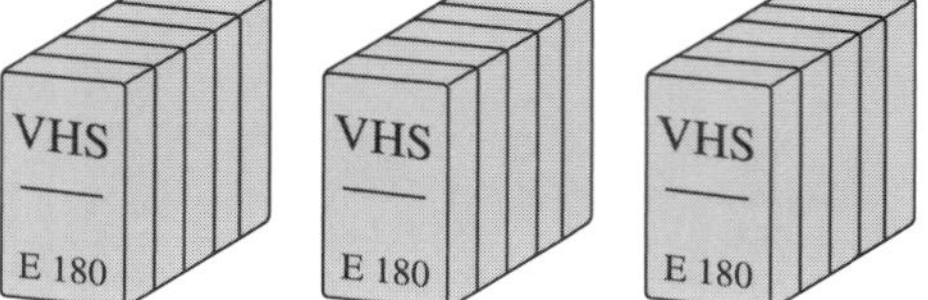

3 How many plates?

4 How many coins?

5.2 More ways to multiply

7 boxes of eggs

12 eggs in each box

7×12 eggs altogether

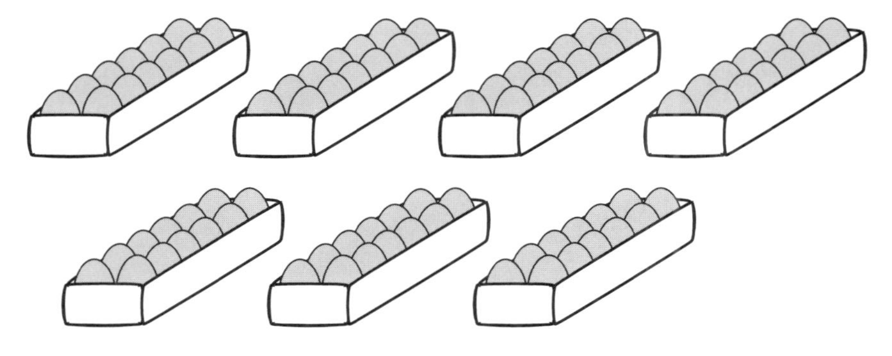

Here are two ways to find 7×12.

First way to multiply

7×12 — Split 12 into 10 and 2: 10 2

Multiply

$7 \times 10 = 70$
$7 \times 2 = 14$
84

add these together

So $7 \times 12 = 84$

Example 1

Work out 6×13

Answer:

$$\begin{aligned} 6 \times 10 &= 60 \\ 6 \times 3 &= 18 \\ & \overline{\;78\;} \end{aligned}$$

Exercise 1

Work out:

1 5×17

2 4×18

3 6×15

4 8×13

5 7×14

6 9×16

7 3×19

8 7×17

9 6×16

10 8×18

11 5×15

12 6×14

13 8×12

14 5×13

15 7×16

16 9×18

17 4×15

18 3×14

19 8×17

20 6×19

Second way

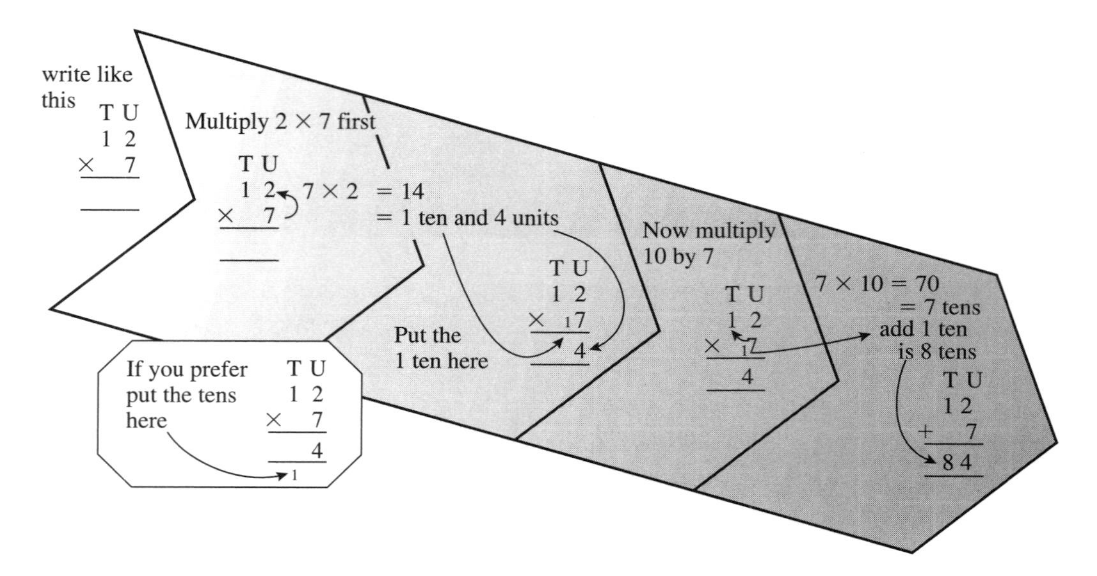

Example 2

Work out 42×6

	H	T	U		
Answer:		4	2	6×2 units	= 12 units = 1 ten and 2 units
		1	6 ×	6×4 tens	= 24 tens
	2	5	2		add 1 ten is 25 tens

Exercise 2

1 27×5 **2** 34×6

3 36×3 **4** 45×7

5 24×7 **6** 32×8

7 28×5 **8** 37×4

9 25×3 **10** 42×9

11 38×6 **12** 24×8

13 33×5 **14** 26×4

15 52×7 **16** 29×3

17 42×8 **18** 67×6

19 43×9 **20** 56×4

5.3 Connecting × and ÷

These calculations are connected:

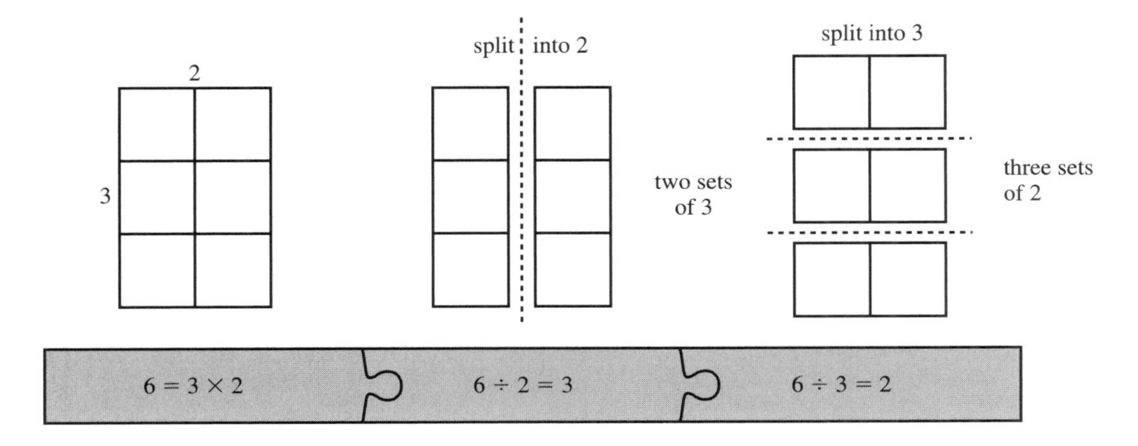

1 Fill in the blanks:

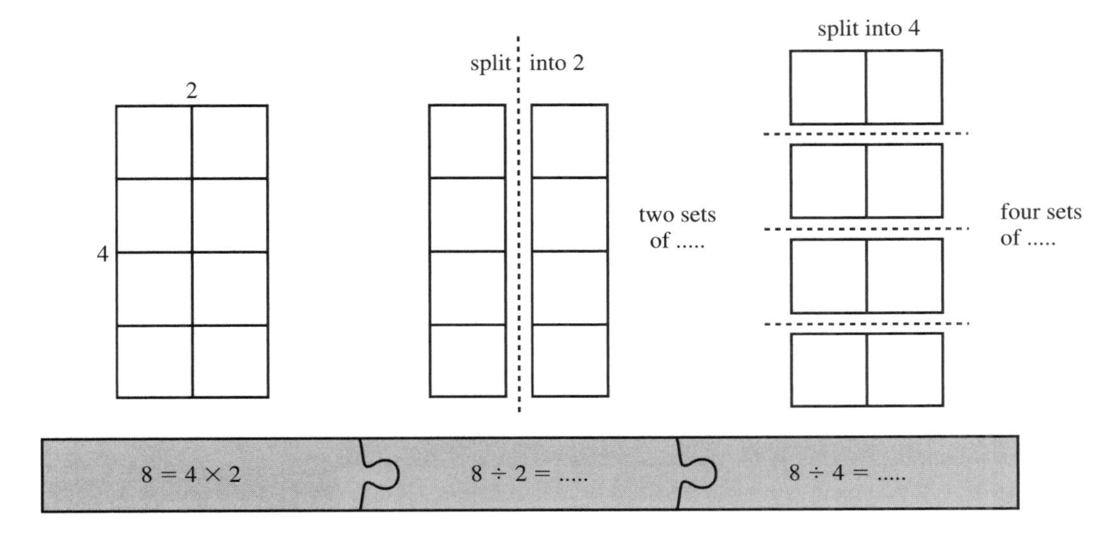

2 Draw pictures here to show:

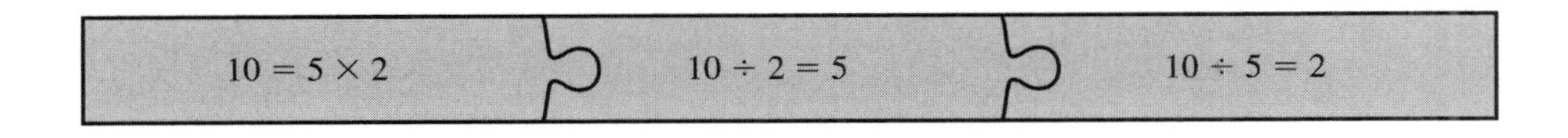

3 Draw pictures here to show:

15 = 5 × 3 | 15 ÷ 3 = 5 | 15 ÷ 5 = 3

These dots and lines show:

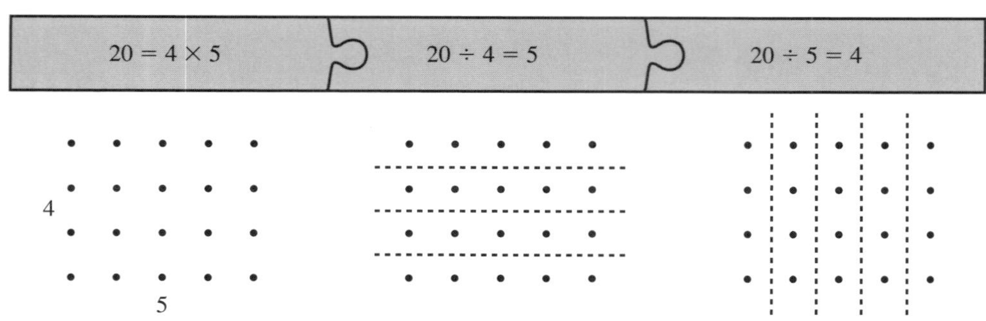

4 Draw lines on these pictures to show:

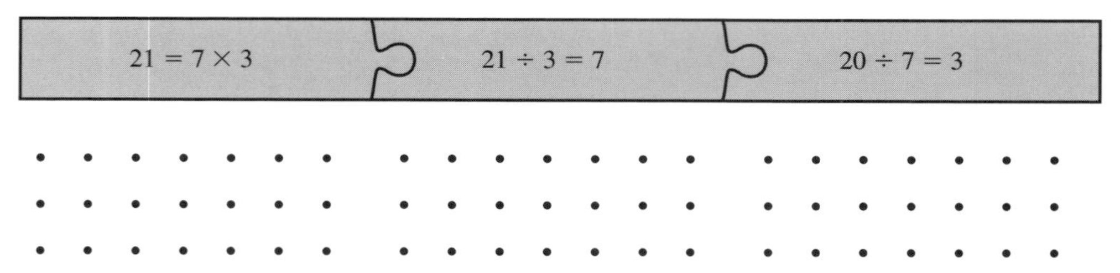

5 Draw dots and lines to show:

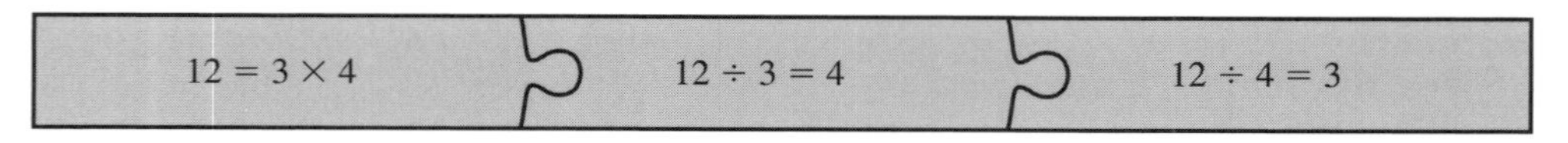

6 Complete these:

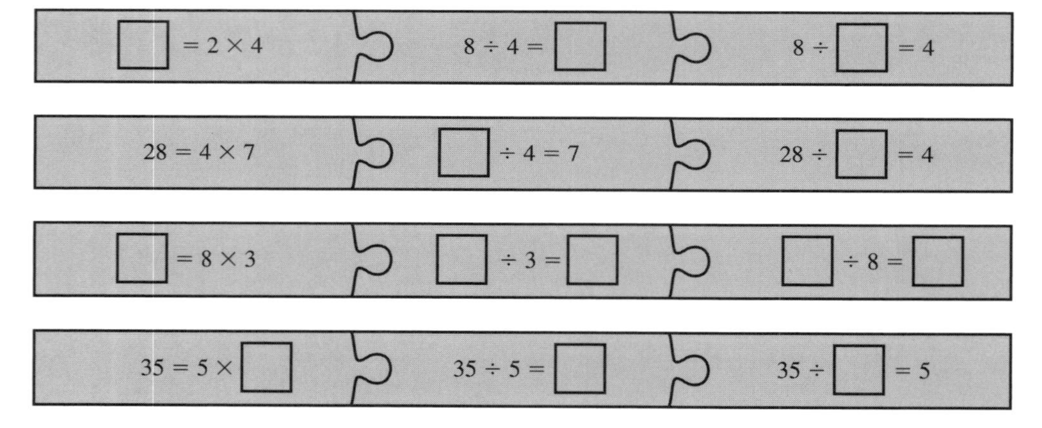

7 Harder questions:

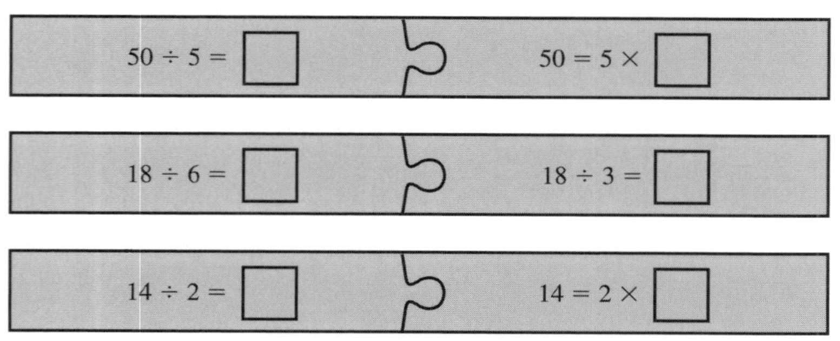

Answers to Pupils' Book

5 Multiplication and division

Exercise 5A

1 (a) 21 (b) 45 (c) 12 (d) 56 (e) 30 (f) 90 (g) 28 (h) 0 (i) 8 (j) 1

Exercise 5B

1 (a) Yes (b) Yes (c) No (d) Yes (e) No (f) No (g) Yes (h) No (i) Yes (j) No (k) Yes (l) Yes
2 (a) No (b) Yes (c) Yes (d) No (e) Yes (f) Yes (g) No (h) Yes (i) No (j) No (k) No (l) Yes
3 (a) 5, 10, 15, 20, 25, ... 75
(b) The last digit is 0 or 5
4 (a) Yes (b) No (c) Yes (d) Yes (e) Yes (f) No (g) Yes (h) Yes (i) No (j) Yes (k) Yes (l) No
5 54, 60, 66, 72, 78
6 63, 70, 77, 84, 91, 98
7 8, 16, 24, 32, 40, 48
8 87, 90, 93, 96
9 72, 76, 80, 84
10 96, 102, 108, 114
11 Jason 14; Ruchi 15; Sophie 16; Tim 12

Exercise 5C

1 (a) Alternate vertical stripes
(b) It is always 0, 2, 4, 6 or 8
(c) It is always 1, 3, 5, 7 or 9
2 2, 4, 6, 8, 10, 12, 14, 16, 18
3 1, 3, 5, 7, 9
4 22, 24, 26, 28, 30
5 62, 64, 66, 68, 70
6 51, 53, 55, 57, 59
7 33, 35, 37, 39
8 (a) 4 (b) 44 (c) 18 (d) 58 (e) 70 (f) 48 (g) 34 (h) 92 (i) 40 (j) 2 (k) 22 (l) 22
9 (a) 5 (b) 29 (c) 19 (d) 39 (e) 65 (f) 73 (g) 49 (h) 9 (i) 57 (j) 41 (k) 25 (l) 25
10 (a) 38 (b) 26 (c) 52 (d) 46 (e) 24 (f) 98
11 (a) 21 (b) 35 (c) 39 (d) 41 (e) 25 (f) 99
12 Jason 14; Ruchi 39; Sophie 48; Tim 51

Exercise 5D

1 No 2 Yes 3 No 4 Yes
5 No 6 No 7 Yes 8 Yes
9 Yes 10 Yes 11 No 12 Yes
13 9, 64, 81

Exercise 5E

1 (a) Yes (b) No (c) No (d) Yes (e) No (f) Yes (g) Yes (h) No (i) Yes (j) No
2 (a) 230 (b) 390 (c) 830 (d) 150 (e) 760 (f) 900 (g) 1540 (h) 3420 (i) 2700 (j) 1090 (k) 1000 (l) 0
3 (a) 3200 (b) 9300 (c) 3800 (d) 400 (e) 8700 (f) 8000 (g) 1500 (h) 1000 (i) 9900 (j) 7300 (k) 10 000 (l) 0

Exercise 5F

1 £15 2 £20 3 28 4 32
5 (a) 18 (b) £24 6 (a) 27 (b) £12
7 $6 \times 9 = 54$ so he has *not* bought enough.
8 (a) $4 \times 8 = 32$ Yes he has bought enough sausages.
(b) $5 \times 6 = 30$ No he has not bought enough bread rolls.
9 63 press ups, 42 sit ups, 49 step ups, 56 stretches, 35 star jumps
10 Jo 20, Adrian 25, Rebecca 28, Marc 27, Ray 24

Exercise 5G

1 (a) 6 (b) 2 (c) 4 (d) 5 (e) 2 (f) 2 (g) 4 (h) 3 (i) 10 (j) 3 (k) 5 (l) 4
2 (a) 9 (b) 7 (c) 6 (d) 6 (e) 9 (f) 8 (g) 9 (h) 9 (i) 7 (j) 7 (k) 8 (l) 8
3 (a) 2 (b) 3 (c) 2 (d) 3 (e) 3 (f) 4 (g) 3 (h) 5 (i) 2 (j) 4 (k) 5 (l) 4
4 (a) 7 (b) 6 (c) 8 (d) 6 (e) 8 (f) 9 (g) 9 (h) 9 (i) 8 (j) 10 (k) 6 (l) 7

Exercise 5H

1 £8 2 8 3 3 min 4 7
5 8 6 £7 7 7
8 (a) 6 min (b) 7 9 (a) 3 (b) 4
10 Karlina 34; Joseph 8; Garth £9; Louise 5

Exercise 5I

1 48p 2 £3 3 9 4 24
5 10 press ups, 5 sit ups, 6 step ups, 9 stretches
6 40 7 6 8 35
9 (a) 12 (b) £24 (c) £2
10 (a) £2 (b) 12 (c) £24

Exercise 5J

1 (a) 5 rem. 1 (b) 5 rem. 1 (c) 3 rem. 2 (d) 3 rem. 2 (e) 3 rem. 2 (f) 5 rem. 1 (g) 7 rem. 4 (h) 7 rem. 1 (i) 8 rem. 1 (j) 7 rem. 2 (k) 6 rem. 1 (l) 9 rem. 3
2 (a) 3 rem. 2 (b) 2 rem. 3 (c) 4 rem. 3 (d) 4 rem. 2 (e) 5 rem. 3 (f) 2 rem. 5 (g) 3 rem. 5 (h) 2 rem. 3 (i) 4 rem. 1 (j) 5 rem. 4 (k) 5 rem. 2 (l) 3 rem. 6

Exercise 5K

1 8 2 5 3 4 4 6 5 7 6 3
7 (a) 7 (b) 9 (c) 54

Exercise 5L

1 (a) 1, 2, 5, 10 (b) 1, 2, 7, 14
(c) 1, 2, 3, 6, 9, 18 (d) 1, 7
(e) 1, 2, 4, 5, 10, 20 (f) 1, 3, 9
(g) 1, 5, 25 (h) 1, 2, 4, 8, 16
(i) 1, 2, 11, 22
(j) 1, 2, 3, 4, 6, 8, 12, 24
(k) 1, 2, 4, 7, 14, 28
(l) 1, 2, 3, 5, 6, 10, 15, 30
2 (a) true (b) true (c) false (d) true (e) true (f) false (g) false (h) true (i) true (j) true (k) true (l) true
3 Sophie 4; Jason 4; Ruchi 7; Tim 3

Exercise 5M

1 (a) 80 (b) 60 (c) 80 (d) 150 (e) 120 (f) 140 (g) 180 (h) 280 (i) 240 (j) 360 (k) 400 (l) 200
2 (a) 210 (b) 168 (c) 350 (d) 240 (e) 360 (f) 420 (g) 540 (h) 420 (i) 560 (j) 720 (k) 640 (l) 630
3 (a) 320 (b) 270 (c) 300 (d) 490 (e) 320 (f) 240 (g) 200 (h) 210 (i) 90 (j) 450 (k) 720 (l) 810

Exercise 5N

1 (a) 72 (b) 74 (c) 104 (d) 81 (e) 85 (f) 72 (g) 78 (h) 192 (i) 228 (j) 225 (k) 252 (l) 180
2 (a) 138 (b) 168 (c) 203 (d) 296 (e) 576 (f) 468 (g) 273 (h) 270 (i) 522 (j) 504 (k) 513 (l) 882
3 92p 4 174
5 168 6 288
7 90

Answers to Homeworks

5 Multiplication and division

Exercise 5.1 — Links: 5B, 5C

1 (a) Yes (b) Yes (c) No (d) Yes (e) No (f) No (g) Yes (h) No (i) Yes (j) No (k) Yes (l) Yes
2 32, 40, 48, 56, 64 3 112, 119, 126, 133
4 24, 26, 28, 30, 32, 34, 36
5 (a) 22 (b) 36 (c) 44 (d) 40 (e) 58 (f) 78 (g) 48 (h) 78 (i) 106 (j) 126 (k) 2 (l) 288
6 (a) 27 (b) 43 (c) 55 (d) 31 (e) 83 (f) 29 (g) 37 (h) 31 (i) 109 (j) 137 (k) 1 (l) 577
7 (a) 14 even (b) 20 even (c) 15 odd (d) 64 even (e) 35 odd (f) 25 odd (g) 60 even (h) 27 odd (i) 42 even (j) 28 even (k) 21 odd (l) 40 even

Exercise 5.2 — Links: 5D, 5E, 5F

1 (a) No (b) Yes (c) Yes (d) Yes (e) Yes (f) No (g) Yes (h) Yes (i) No (j) Yes (k) Yes (l) Yes
2 (a) Yes (b) Yes (c) No (d) Yes (e) Yes (f) No (g) Yes (h) Yes (i) No (j) Yes (k) No (l) Yes
3 (a) 470 (b) 2300 (c) 8300 (d) 940 (e) 400 (f) 3000 (g) 5430 (h) 37 600 (i) 10 600 (j) 4300 (k) 2000 (l) 50 000
4 48
5 (a) 24 (b) £12
6 49 press ups, 63 step ups, 42 sit ups, 56 stretches, 28 star jumps

Exercise 5.3 — Links: 5G, 5H, 5K

1 (a) 3 (b) 7 (c) 9 (d) 9 (e) 6 (f) 6 (g) 7 (h) 4 (i) 9 (j) 7 (k) 10 (l) 8
2 (a) 3 (b) 5 (c) 7 (d) 4 (e) 6 (f) 5 (g) 8 (h) 4 (i) 3 (j) 2 (k) 3 (l) 4
3 9 4 9
5 8 press ups, 7 sit ups, 4 star jumps, 9 stretches
6 18 7 7
8 (a) 8 (b) 9 (c) 80

Exercise 5.4 — Links: 5L

1 (a) 1, 2, 3, 4, 6, 12 (b) 1, 3, 5, 15
(c) 1, 3, 9 (d) 1, 3, 7, 21
(e) 1, 3, 9, 27 (f) 1, 5, 7, 35
2 (a) True (b) False (c) True (d) True (e) True (f) False (g) True (h) False (i) True (j) True (k) True (l) True
3 (a) 3 (b) 2, 3, 6 (c) 7 (d) 2, 4
4 (a) 5, 10 (b) 3, 15
(c) 2, 6 (d) 2, 4, 6, 12

Exercise 5.5 Links: 5M, 5N

1 (a) 240 (b) 120 (c) 150
(d) 320 (e) 450 (f) 160
(g) 210 (h) 200 (i) 300
(j) 400 (k) 270 (l) 160
2 (a) 480 (b) 270 (c) 320
(d) 350 (e) 540 (f) 480
(g) 560 (h) 280 (i) 490
(j) 630 (k) 400 (l) 630
3 (a) 92 (b) 138 (c) 204
(d) 248 (e) 264 (f) 378
(g) 282 (h) 477 (i) 498
(j) 189 (k) 405 (l) 195
4 224 5 324

Remediation answers

5.1 Multiplying

Exercise 1

1 $3 \times 4 = 12$ 2 $5 \times 3 = 15$
3 $8 \times 2 = 16$ 4 $10 \times 4 = 40$

5.2 More ways to multiply

Exercise 1

1	85	2	72
3	90	4	104
5	98	6	144
7	57	8	119
9	96	10	144
11	75	12	84
13	96	14	65
15	112	16	162
17	30	18	42
19	136	20	114

Exercise 2

1	135	2	204
3	108	4	315
5	168	6	256
7	140	8	148
9	75	10	378
11	228	12	192
13	165	14	104
15	364	16	87
17	336	18	402
19	387	20	224

5.3 Connecting × and ÷

1 $8 \div 2 = \underline{4}$ $8 \div 4 = \underline{2}$

2

3

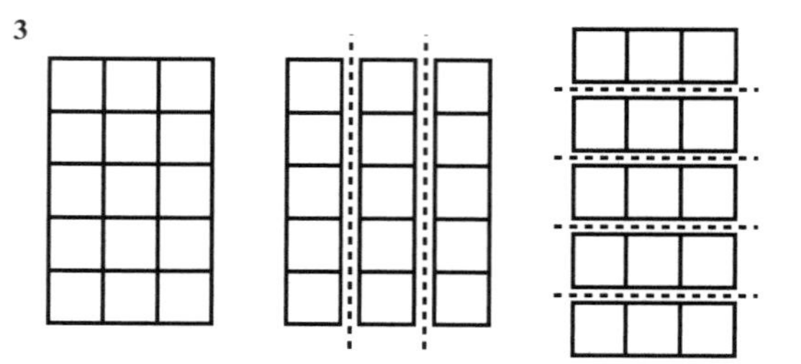

4

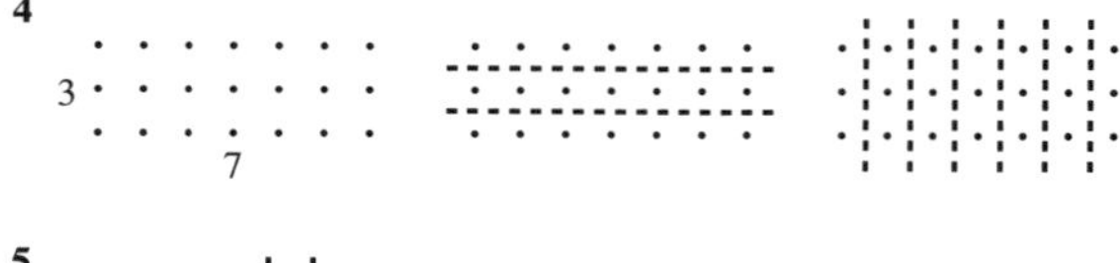

5

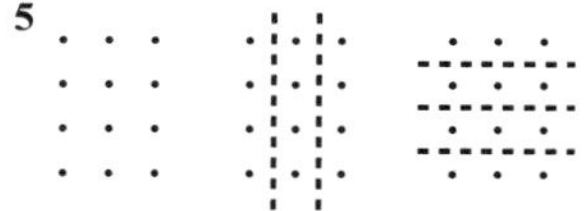

6 (a) [8], [2], [2]
(b) [28], [7]
(c) [24], [24], [8] [24], [3]
(d) [7], [7], [7]

7 (a) [10], [10]
(b) [3], [6]
(c) [7], [7]

1 G

Overview

Unit 6 Decimals

Content summary

This unit takes the number system to 2 decimal places. Two decimal places is reinforced in the context of money. Addition and subtraction without a calculator is included.

Book 1R Unit 6 extends the ideas to 3 decimal places and makes use of place value to multiply and divide by 10, 100 and 1000. Multiplication of decimals by whole numbers is included.

NC level

Level 2:

Level 3: Decimals in the context of money.

Level 4: Add and subtract to two decimal places.

N2i *N3i* NA2d NA3j

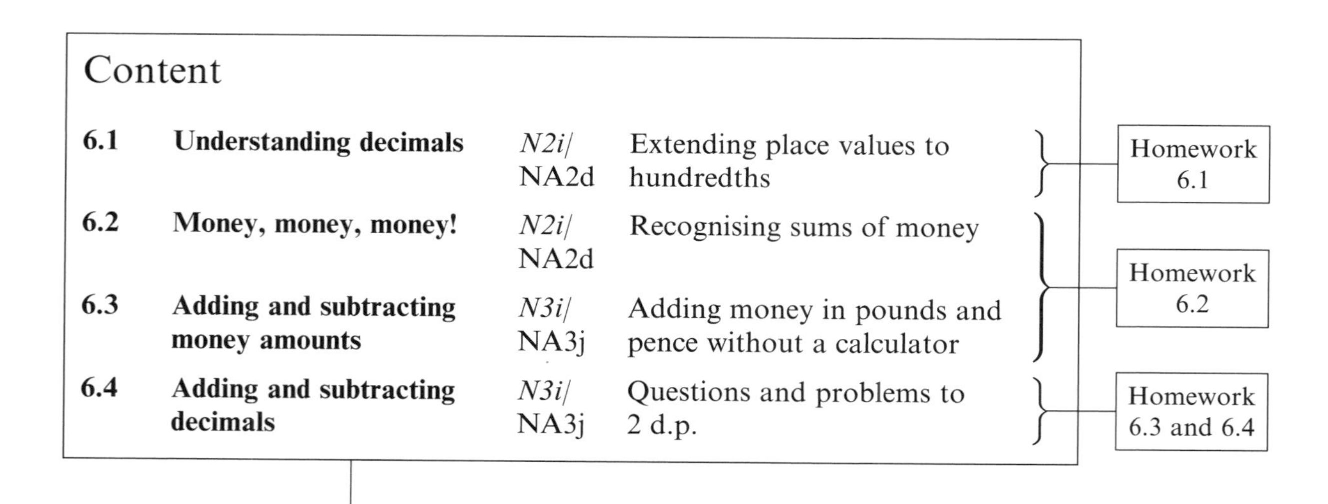

Content

6.1	**Understanding decimals**	*N2i*/ NA2d	Extending place values to hundredths	Homework 6.1
6.2	**Money, money, money!**	*N2i*/ NA2d	Recognising sums of money	Homework 6.2
6.3	**Adding and subtracting money amounts**	*N3i*/ NA3j	Adding money in pounds and pence without a calculator	
6.4	**Adding and subtracting decimals**	*N3i*/ NA3j	Questions and problems to 2 d.p.	Homework 6.3 and 6.4

Assessment

Assessment 6 covers the key concepts in Unit 6.

Remediation

Remediation sheets 6.1 → 6.2.

Assessment

The assessment is marked out of 30. Achievement of 20 or more marks indicates a good understanding of the key concepts.
Marking guidance, answers and links to remediation are provided on page 265.

ICT links

Use *MicroSmile for Windows Pack 3* to investigate decimal places.

6.3 and 6.4
Use *Mental Arithmetic* from *Virtual Image* to practice addition and subtraction of decimals and whole numbers against the clock.

Equipment

	Pupils' Book page
Place value sheets	91ff

Remediation

Decimals:
Practical work can be done using real or plastic money. Show pupils some possible shop labels and ask them to say the price, reinforcing why the decimal point is used. Give plenty of oral work developing the idea of hundredths before moving on to attempt the written work.

Questionbank CD

All homeworks and extension questions also appear on the CD.

Pages xvii and xviii of this pack show you how to use the CD to select questions from the Questionbank and further customize them if you wish to.

6 Decimals

framework teaching objective	§	lesson starter	f/w ref
Understand and use decimal notation and place value.	6.1	Draw a 20 cm by 20 cm square. The class are to identify this as one UNIT. Draw the square cut into ten equal strips What name can we give to these strips? What fraction of the square does one strip equal? Students must devise an appropriate name. If we split a shape into 3 parts what do we call each part? 5 parts? 6 parts? Students must relate name to number of strips needed to 'glue together' to form unit square.	36–9
Understand and use decimal notation and place value.	6.1	Draw 20 cm × 20 cm unit square as above and $\frac{1}{10}$ strips. Draw units and tenths column diagrams. Record the number of squares: U . $\frac{1}{10}$ (i)  3 (ii) 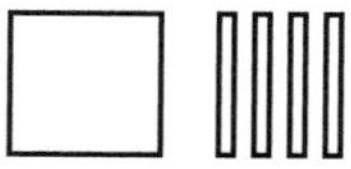 1 . 4 (iii)  0 . 6 Are six lengths enough to make one whole unit? No. That's why we need a zero in the units column. (iv)  1 . 4 How can (ii) and (iv) be the same answer?	36–9

framework teaching objective	§	lesson starter	f/w ref
Understand and use decimal notation and place value.	6.3/ 6.4	'There is a **common mistake** that you can make when adding money.' Add £3.20 and 70p and £5 together. Which bill is correct? A: = £15.20 B: = £8.90 C: = £3.95 (*B is correct*) Can you work out the mistake made in adding bill A and bill C? A: 3.20, 7.0, 5 (middle): 3.20, .70, 5 C: 3.20, 70, 5 Why do the **incorrect** ways of adding 'look' correct? – *'Looks neater'* *'Makes a pattern-triangle.' etc.* How can we use the decimal columns to help us? How can I 'neaten up' the correct way of adding these?' – Add noughts: 3.20 0.70 5.00	36–9

6 Decimals

Exercise 6.1 — Links: 6A, 6B

1 Copy the decimal place value diagram and write in these numbers.

(a) 23.5 **(b)** 8.2 **(c)** 29.7 **(d)** 135.6
(e) 236.4 **(f)** 7.1 **(g)** 40.9 **(h)** 0.3

2 Write down the value of the digit underlined in each of these decimal numbers.

(a) $\underline{2}9.6$ **(b)** $14.\underline{3}$ **(c)** $6.\underline{9}$ **(d)** $\underline{3}21.5$
(e) $18.\underline{4}$ **(f)** $0.\underline{7}$ **(g)** $57\underline{2}.3$ **(h)** $138.\underline{6}$

3 Draw a decimal place value diagram and write in these numbers:

(a) 36.4 **(b)** 8.35 **(c)** 19.3 **(d)** 138.2
(e) 2.53 **(f)** 0.28 **(g)** 251.06 **(h)** 0.08

4 Write down the value of the digit underlined in each of these decimal numbers:

(a) $3\underline{9}.2$ **(b)** $\underline{4}8.3$ **(c)** $16.7\underline{3}$ **(d)** $1.\underline{8}5$
(e) $412.9\underline{8}$ **(f)** $\underline{5}.62$ **(g)** $2\underline{8}5.9$ **(h)** $0.0\underline{8}$

Exercise 6.2 — Links: 6C, 6D

1 Work out the total value of the coins in pounds.

(a) 

(b)   

(c) 

(d) 

(e) 

(f) 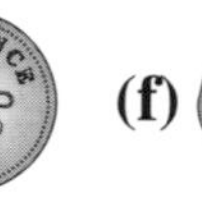  

(g)

(h) 

2 Work these out. Show all your working.

(a) £1.32 + £5.46

(b) £31.25 + £17.63

(c) £53.24 + £25.36

Exercise 6.3 Links: 6E

Work these out. Show all your working.

1 **(a)** 5.4 + 2.3 **(b)** 13.5 + 24.1 **(c)** 34.32 + 25.67

2 **(a)** 25.28 + 32.5 **(b)** 8.63 + 41.2 **(c)** 2.5 + 23.48

3 **(a)** 2.8 + 3.4 **(b)** 5.37 + 2.45 **(c)** 16.63 + 31.54

4 **(a)** 3.6 + 5.82 **(b)** 13.4 + 2.74 **(c)** 5.3 + 12.28 + 31.19

5 **(a)** 2.85 + 9.7 **(b)** 36.5 + 7.83 **(c)** 2.9 + 23.36 + 31.43

6 Leroy uses 4.5 kg of sand and 1.2 kg of cement to make some mortar. Work out the total weight of the sand and the cement.

7 Sharon's empty bag weighs 1.7 kg. How much would her bag weigh with a pencil case weighing 0.4 kg and a book weighing 1.2 kg in it?

8 Tim and Ben walk 3.9 km from Guildford to Compton then 2.6 km from Compton to Puttenham. How far do they walk in total?

9 To make pastry Barbara uses 1.2 kg of flour, 0.35 kg of lard and 0.25 kg of margarine. What is the total weight of the ingredients?

Exercise 6.4 Links: 6F

Work these out. Show all your working.

1 **(a)** £24.79 – £13.25 **(b)** £6.23 – £3.57 **(c)** £20 – £3.76

2 **(a)** 5.9 – 2.6 **(b)** 65.68 – 23.4 **(c)** 56.73 – 4.5

3 **(a)** 1 – 0.3 **(b)** 2.5 – 0.06 **(c)** 3 – 0.02

4 **(a)** 5.7 + 3.5 **(b)** 12.92 – 5.4 **(c)** 16.98 + 7.3

5 **(a)** 38.56 – 16.25 **(b)** 52.5 + 6.72 **(c)** 4.8 – 0.07

6 Ramana travels 5.8 miles to her friend's house. She goes 4.2 miles by bus and then walks the rest of the way. How far, in miles, does she walk?

7 Mark cuts a 1.4 m length of wire from a reel containing 5 metres of wire. Work out the length of wire left over.

8 Ann fills a jug with 0.85 litres of lemonade from a 2 litre bottle. How much lemonade is left in the bottle?

9 Javed's packed rucksack weighed 11.9 kg. How much will it weigh if he removes a torch weighing 0.4 kg and a pair of boots weighing 1.3 kg?

Name ....

6 Decimals

No calculators to be used in this test.

1 Write down the value of the underlined digit in each of these decimal numbers.

(a) $\underline{5}3.2$ ....

(b) $3.0\underline{5}$ ....

(c) $1\underline{9}.01$ .... **(3 marks)**

---

2 Write these numbers in this decimal place diagram.

(a) 5.06

(b) 0.05

(c) 256.5

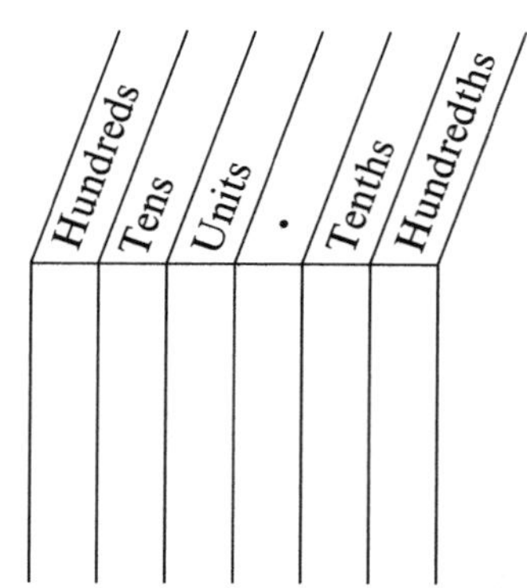

(3 marks)

---

3 Work out the total value of these coins in pounds.

(a)

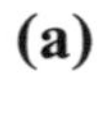

£ ....

(b)

£ .... **(2 marks)**

---

4 Write down the coins you need to make 86 p. Use the least number of coins.

.... **(2 marks)**

---

5 Work out:

(a) £3.46 + £5.37 ....

(b) £10.76 + £5.94 .... **(4 marks)**

---

6 Work out:

(a) 2.4 + 3.9 ....

(b) 3.4 + 51.6 + 5.49 ....

(c) 16.8 + 7.39 + 4 .... **(6 marks)**

---

7 Work out:

(a) 16.9 − 4.7 ....

(b) 25.6 − 13.42 ....

(c) 6 − 3.4 .... **(6 marks)**

---

8 Jason spent £3.45 at a shop.
He paid with a £5 note.
How much change should he receive? .... **(2 marks)**

---

9 Sonal used the following ingredients in a recipe for making jam.

1.25 kg oranges, 2.5 kg sugar and 0.65 kg lemons

Work out the total weight of the ingredients. .... kg **(2 marks)**

Unit 6 Decimals

Question		Answer	Marking guidance and remediation sheet links	
1	**(a)**	50 or 5 tens	A1	less than $\frac{3}{6}$ use remediation sheets 6.1 and 6.2
	(b)	$\frac{5}{100}$ or 5 hundredths	A1	
	(c)	9 or 9 units	A1	
2		Hundreds, Tens, Units, ., Tenths, Hundredths		
	(a)	5 . 0 6	A1	
	(b)	0 . 0 5	A1	
	(c)	2 5 6 . 5	A1	
3	**(a)**	£2.73	A1	
	(b)	£3.49	A1	
4		5 coins 50 p, 20 p, 10 p, 5 p, 1 p	B2 for all correct, B1 for sum of money correct with more than 5 coins.	
5	**(a)**	£3.46 £5.37 £8.83 (carry 1)	M1 for adding A1 for £8.83	
	(b)	£10.76 £ 5.94 £16.70	M1 for 70 p A1 for £16.70	

Key to mark scheme
A marks: correct answer
M marks: correct method
B marks: independent work

Page 265 gives a general guidance on use of this assessment scheme with some examples.

Assessment and remediation links

Question		Answer	Marking guidance and remediation sheet links
6	**(a)**	2.4 3.9 6.3	M1 for correct columns A1 for 6.3
	(b)	3.4 51.6 5.49 60.49	M1 for correct columns A1 for 60.49
	(c)	16.8 7.39 4 28.19	M1 for correct columns A1 for 28.19
7	**(a)**	16.9 − 4.7 12.2	M1 for .2 A1 for 12.2
	(b)	25.60 −13.42 12.18	M1 for .18 A1 for 12.18
	(c)	6.0 −3.4 2.6	M1 for .6 A1 for 2.6
8		5.00 −3.45 1.55	M1 for .55 A1 for £1.55
9		1.25 2.5 0.65 4.40	M1 for correct columns A1 for 4.4 or 4.40

Key to mark scheme
A marks: correct answer
M marks: correct method
B marks: independent work

Page 265 gives a general guidance on use of this assessment scheme with some examples.

1
G

6.1 Decimals: tenths

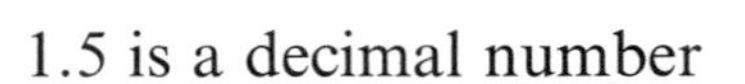

1.5 is a decimal number

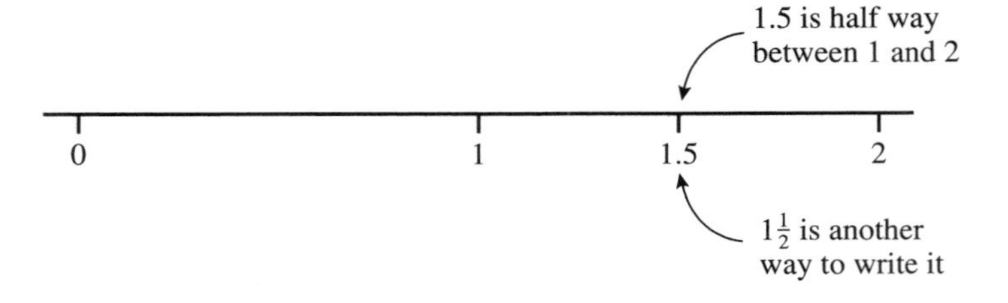

Here are some more numbers **between** 1 and 2:

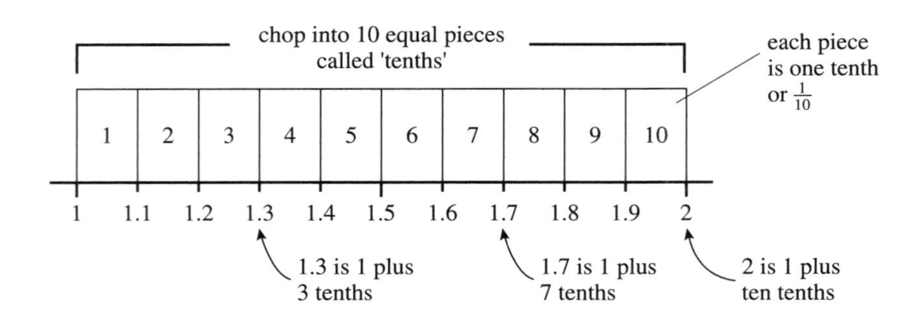

1 Fill in the missing numbers between 2 and 3:

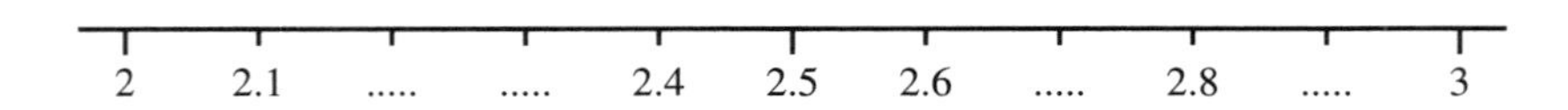

2 Fill in the missing numbers between 7 and 8:

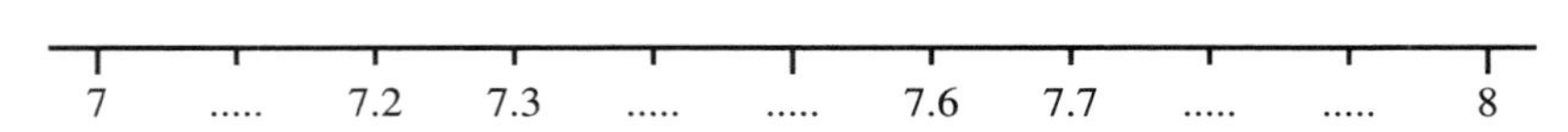

R6.1

3 Fill in the missing numbers between 0 and 1:

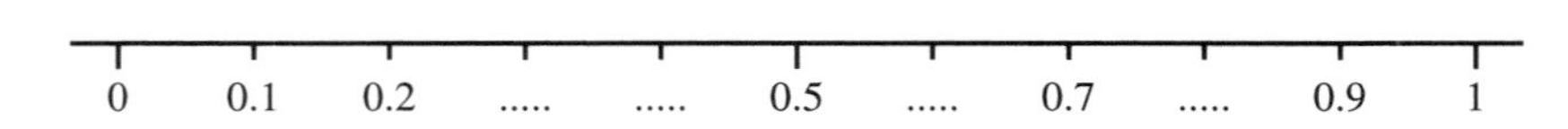

4 Fill in the missing numbers:

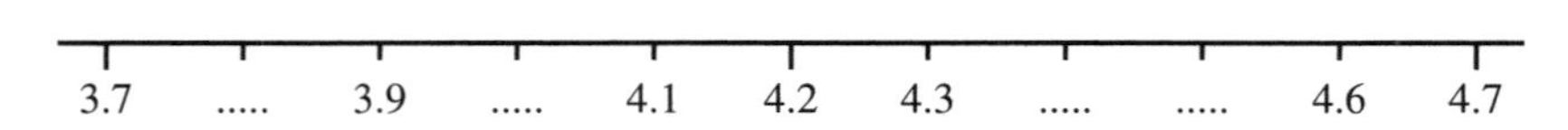

5 Fill in the missing numbers:

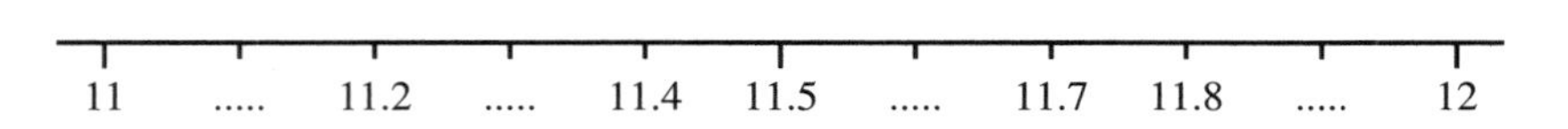

You can write 1.5 in a place value diagram:

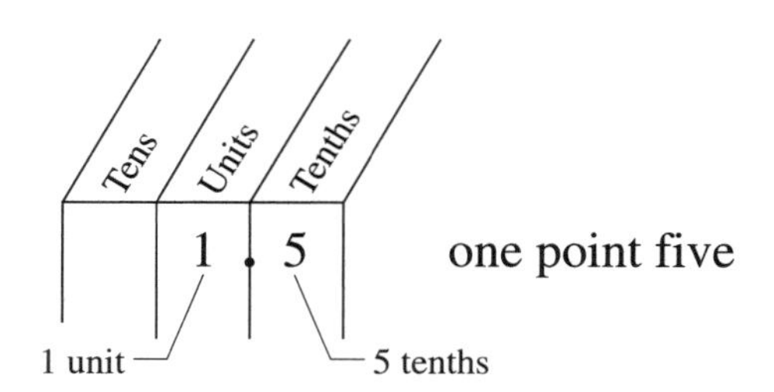

6 Write these numbers in the place value diagrams below:

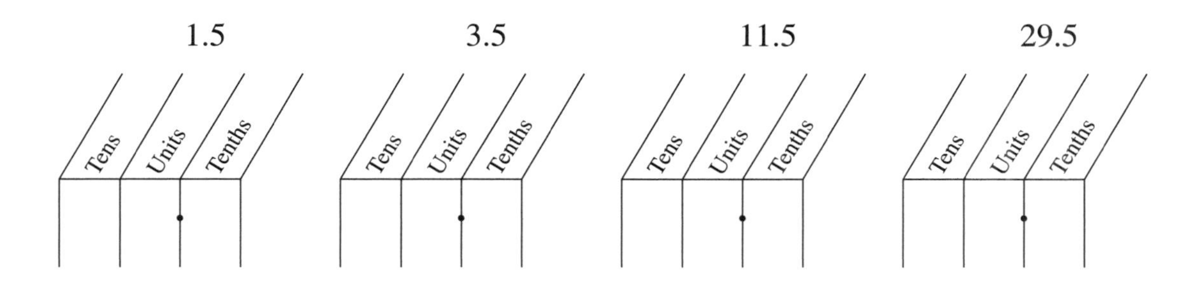

2.3 is larger than 1.9

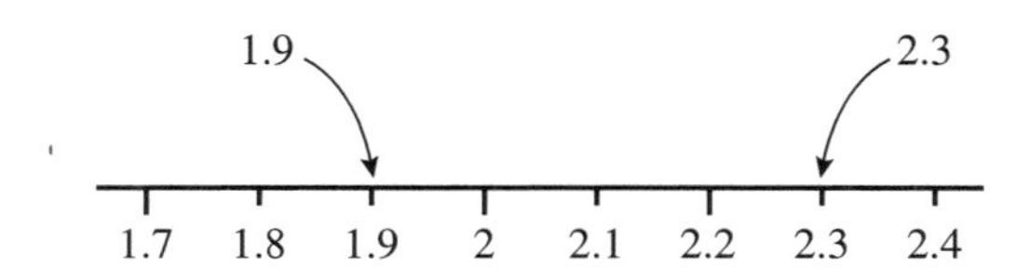

7 Circle the **larger** number in each pair.
The first one is done for you:

(4.3)	or	4.1	2.3	or	3.2
2.7	or	2.6	11.1	or	10.9
1.4	or	4.1	3.9	or	3.7
5	or	4.8	0.3	or	0.9

1
G

6.2 Decimals: hundredths

There are numbers between 1.1 and 1.2

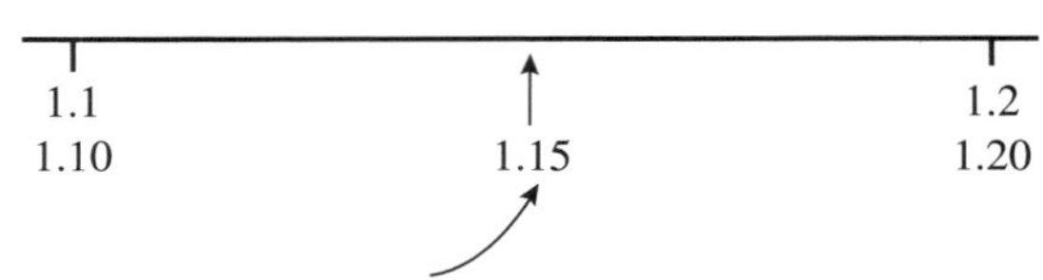

Here are some more numbers between 1.1 and 1.2

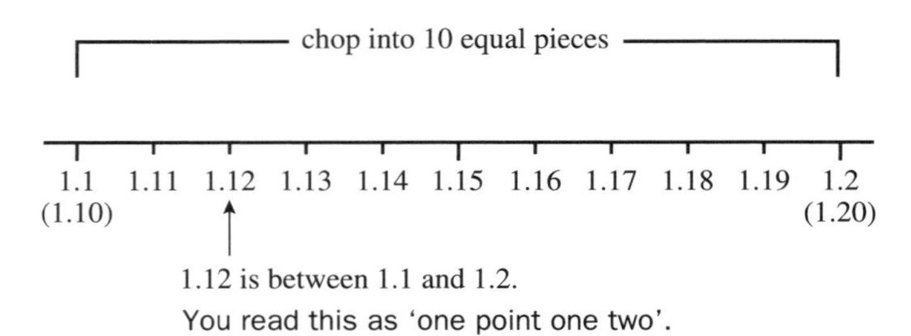

Exercise 1

1 Fill in the missing numbers

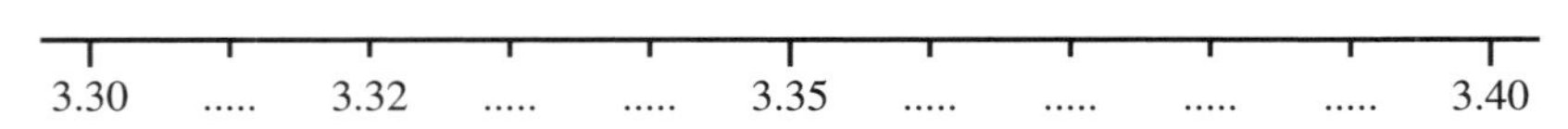

2 Fill in the missing numbers

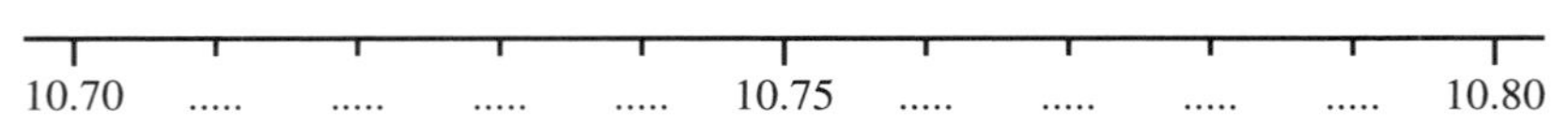

3 Fill in the missing numbers

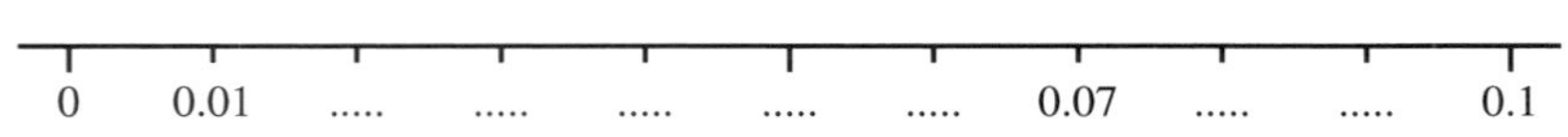

R6.2

You can write numbers like 1.12 and 23.35 in a place value diagram:

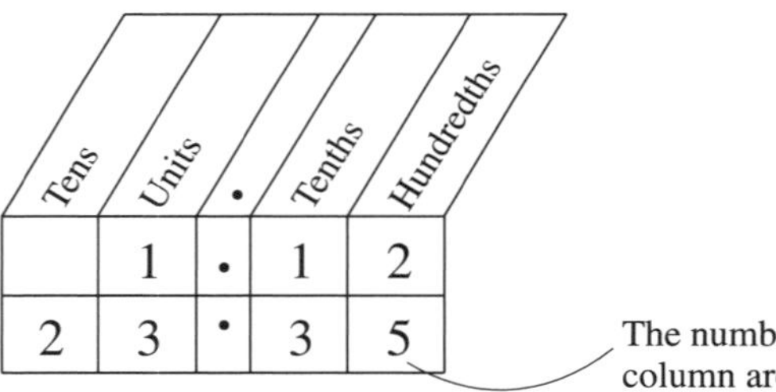

The numbers in this column are called 'hundredths'.

There are 10 hundredths between 1.1 and 1.2:

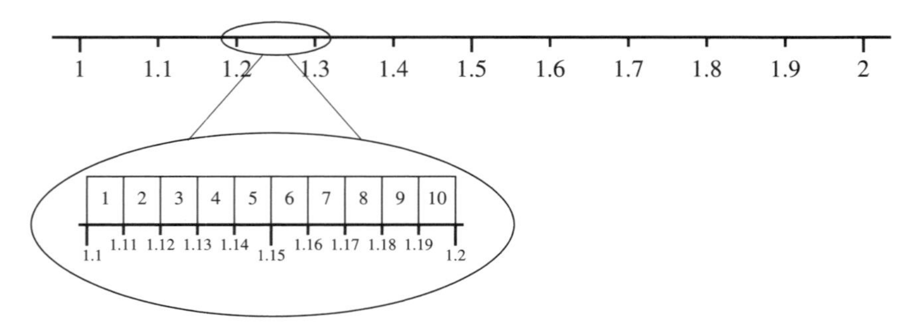

Exercise 2

1 Write these numbers in the decimal place value diagrams below:

1.78, **9.62**, **71.05**, **19.61**

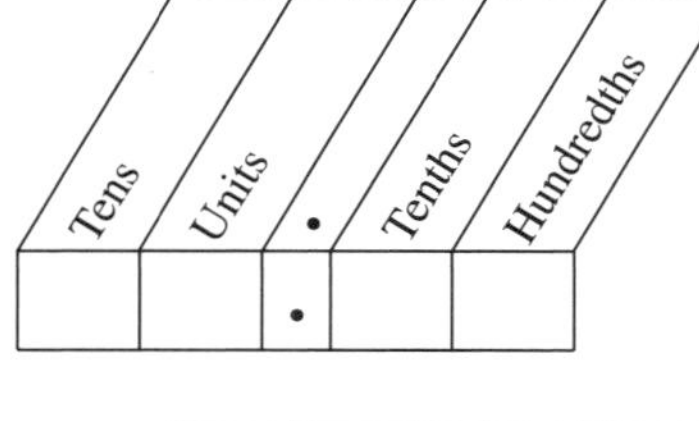

Tens | Units | • | Tenths | Hundredths

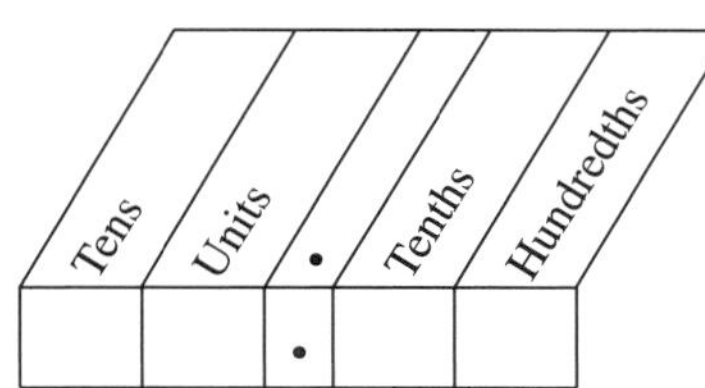

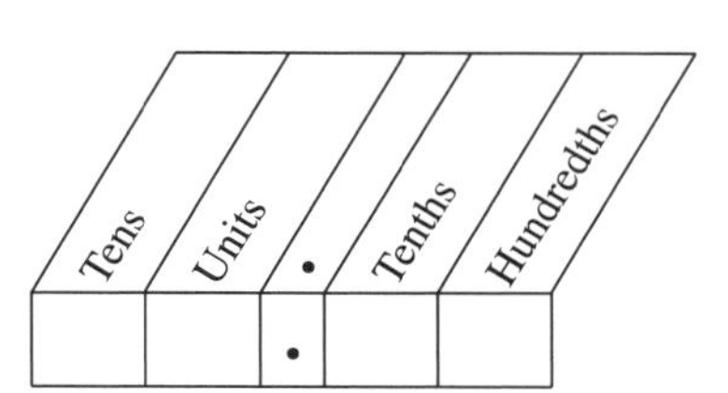

Money in pounds and pence is written like hundredths.
One penny is one hundredth of a pound.

Exercise 3

1 Write down all the money amounts between:

£21.60 and £21.70

2 Circle the larger number in each pair:

(a) 6.32 21.96 **(b)** 17.63 17.59

(c) 76.82 59.86 **(d)** 28.03 28.30

Hint:
Think of each number as an amount of money.

Answers to Pupils' Book

6 Decimals

Exercise 6A

1

	Hundreds	Tens	Units	•	Tenths
(a)		3	9	•	2
(b)			5	•	6
(c)		5	3	•	8
(d)	1	2	9	•	7
(e)	1	3	4	•	5
(f)			9	•	1
(g)		5	0	•	3
(h)			0	•	4

2 **(a)** 3 tens **(b)** 6 units
(c) 8 tenths **(d)** 2 hundreds
(e) 7 tenths **(f)** 3 tenths
(g) 5 units **(h)** 5 tenths

Exercise 6B

1

	Hundreds	Tens	Units	•	Tenths	Hundredths
(a)		2	3	•	4	
(b)			5	•	2	1
(c)		2	8	•	5	
(d)	1	2	3	•	8	
(e)			1	•	2	5
(f)			0	•	3	2
(g)			2	•	0	1
(h)		2	5	•	0	7
(i)			0	•	0	7
(j)	5	2	0	•	0	6
(k)		1	7	•	5	8
(l)			0	•	0	9

2 **(a)** 2 tens **(b)** 3 units
(c) 6 hundredths **(d)** 5 tenths
(e) 3 hundredths **(f)** 9 units
(g) 6 hundreds **(h)** 5 tens
(i) 5 hundredths **(j)** 5 tenths
(k) 2 units **(l)** 4 hundredths
3 **(a)** 1
$0.1 \times 10 = 1$. The digit '1' has moved one place to the left.
(b) 0.1
$0.01 \times 10 = 0.1$. The digit '1' has moved one place to the left.

Exercise 6C

1 **(a)** £1.71 **(b)** £1.42 **(c)** £2.82 **(d)** £1.73
2 **(a)** £2.15 **(b)** £2.31 **(c)** £3.21 **(d)** £1.91
3 **(a)** £2.90 **(b)** £3.10 **(c)** £2.90 **(d)** £1.70
4 **(a)** £0.66 **(b)** £0.97 **(c)** £0.59 **(d)** £0.80
5 **(a)** £0.07 **(b)** £2.80 **(c)** £2.10 **(d)** £0.60
6 **(a)** £1, 50p, 2p
(b) £1, 10p, 1p
(c) £1, 50p, 20p, 10p, 2p, 1p
(d) 20p, 10p, 2p
(e) £1, 50p, 20p, 10p, 5p, 2p, 1p
(f) £1, 20p, 10p, 5p
(g) £1, 50p, 20p
(h) £1, 20p, 10p, 5p, 2p
(i) 5p, 1p
(j) 50p, 20p, 5p
(k) £1, 10p, 5p, 1p
(l) 5p, 2p, 1p
7 **(a)** £1.80 **(b)** £1.05 **(c)** £2.85
8 £1, 50p, 20p, 10p, 5p
£1, 50p, 20p, 10p, 2p, 2p, 1p
£1, 20p, 20p, 20p, 10p, 10p, 5p
£1, 20p, 20p, 20p, 10p, 10p, 2p, 2p, 1p
£1, 50p, 20p, 5p, 2p, 2p, 2p, 2p, 1p, 1p
£1, 50p, 10p, 10p, 5p, 2p, 2p, 2p, 2p, 1p, 1p
£1, 20p, 20p, 20p, 10p, 5p, 2p, 2p, 2p, 2p, 1p, 1p

Exercise 6D

1 £35.38 **2** £15.82 **3** £9.70
4 £27.36 **5** £38.49 **6** £18.75
7 £13.77 **8** £59.85 **9** £20.97
10 £79.79 **11** £18.59 **12** £109.99

Exercise 6E

1 3.7 **2** 76.8 **3** 47.9
4 467.9 **5** 15.9 **6** 20.67
7 29.89 **8** 7.58 **9** 78.77
10 58.79 **11** 13.9 **12** 19.94
13 127.79 **14** 3.87 **15** 8.2
16 6.6 **17** 39.8 **18** 9.8
19 19.98 **20** 19.79
21 15.9 degrees Celsius
22 29.98 cm

Exercise 6F

1 16.2 **2** 3.2 **3** 2.23
4 3.12 **5** 30.1 **6** 163.5
7 102.4 **8** 0.34 **9** 11.41
10 3.45 **11** 12.28 **12** 27.15
13 4.328 **14** 243.25 **15** 8.53
16 243.23 **17** 5.46 **18** 0.6
19 2.42 kg **20** 4.5 degrees Celsius
21 19.4 kg **22** 0.65 metre

Answers to Homeworks

6 Decimals

Exercise 6.1 — Links: 6A, 6B

1

	Hundreds	Tens	Units	•	Tenths	Hundredths
(a)		2	3	•	5	
(b)			8	•	2	
(c)		2	9	•	7	
(d)	1	3	5	•	6	
(e)	2	3	6	•	4	
(f)			7	•	1	
(g)		4	0	•	9	
(h)			0	•	3	

2 **(a)** 2 tens **(b)** 3 tenths
(c) 9 tenths **(d)** 3 hundreds
(e) 4 tenths **(f)** 7 tenths
(g) 2 units **(h)** 6 tenths

3

	Hundreds	Tens	Units	•	Tenths	Hundredths
(a)		3	6	•	4	
(b)			8	•	3	5
(c)		1	9	•	3	
(d)	1	3	8	•	2	
(e)			2	•	5	3
(f)			0	•	2	8
(g)	2	5	1	•	0	6
(h)			0	•	0	8

4 **(a)** 9 units **(b)** 4 tens
(c) 3 hundredths **(d)** 8 tenths
(e) 8 hundredths **(f)** 5 units
(g) 8 tens **(h)** 8 hundredths

Exercise 6.2 — Links: 6C, 6D

1 **(a)** £1.45 **(b)** £1.53 **(c)** £2.71
(d) £1.34 **(e)** £1.40 **(f)** £2.70
(g) £1.01 **(h)** £0.07
2 **(a)** £6.78 **(b)** £48.88 **(c)** £78.60

Exercise 6.3 — Links: 6E

1 **(a)** 7.7 **(b)** 37.6 **(c)** 59.99
2 **(a)** 57.78 **(b)** 49.83 **(c)** 25.98
3 **(a)** 6.2 **(b)** 7.82 **(c)** 48.17
4 **(a)** 9.42 **(b)** 16.14 **(c)** 48.77
5 **(a)** 12.55 **(b)** 44.33 **(c)** 57.69
6 5.7 kg **7** 3.3 kg **8** 6.5 km **9** 1.8 kg

Exercise 6.4 — Links: 6F

1 **(a)** £11.54 **(b)** £2.66 **(c)** £16.24
2 **(a)** 3.3 **(b)** 42.28 **(c)** 52.23
3 **(a)** 0.7 **(b)** 2.44 **(c)** 2.98
4 **(a)** 9.2 **(b)** 7.52 **(c)** 24.28
5 **(a)** 22.31 **(b)** 59.22 **(c)** 4.73
6 1.6 miles **7** 3.6 metres
8 1.15 litres **9** 10.2 kg

Remediation answers

6.1 Decimals: tenths

1 2.2, 2.3 . . . 2.7 . . . 2.9
2 7.1 . . . 7.4, 7.5 . . . 7.8, 7.9
3 0.3, 0.4 . . . 0.6 . . . 0.8
4 3.8 . . . 4.0 . . . 4.4, 4.5
5 11.1 . . . 11.3 . . . 11.6 . . . 11.9
6

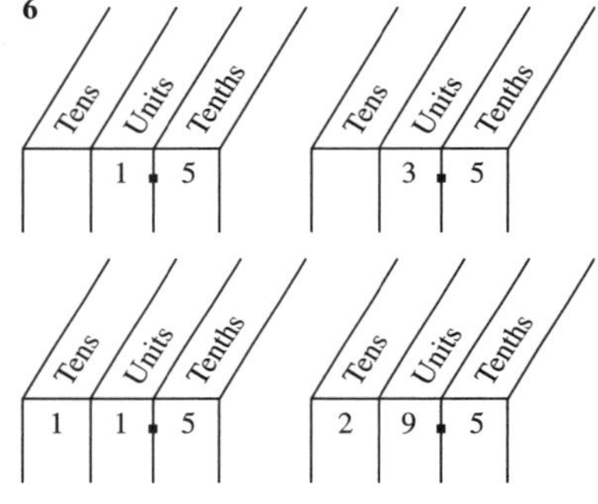

7 3.2, 2.7, 11.1, 4.1, 3.9, 5, 0.9

6.2 Decimals: hundredths

Exercise 1

1 3.31, 3.33, 3.34, 3.36, 3.37, 3.38, 3.39
2 10.71, 10.72, 10.73, 10.74, 10.76, 10.77, 10.78, 10.79

Exercise 2

1

T	U	·	t	h
	1	·	7	8
	9	·	6	2
7	1	·	0	7
1	9	·	6	1

Exercise 3

1 £21.61, 21.62, 21.63, 21.64, 21.65, 21.66, 21.67, 21.68, 21.69
2 **(a)** 21.96 **(b)** 17.63
(c) 76.82 **(d)** 28.30

Unit 7 Measuring

Content summary

This unit is about length and measuring, weighing and reading scales using the metric system. 24 hour clock times, calendars and timetables also feature.

Book 1R Unit 7 covers similar material in more detail and with harder questions
.

NC level

Level 2:

Level 3: Use standard units of length, mass and time.

Level 4: Choose and use appropriate units. Read scales and use timetables.

S4a *S4b* *S4d* S4a S4d H2a

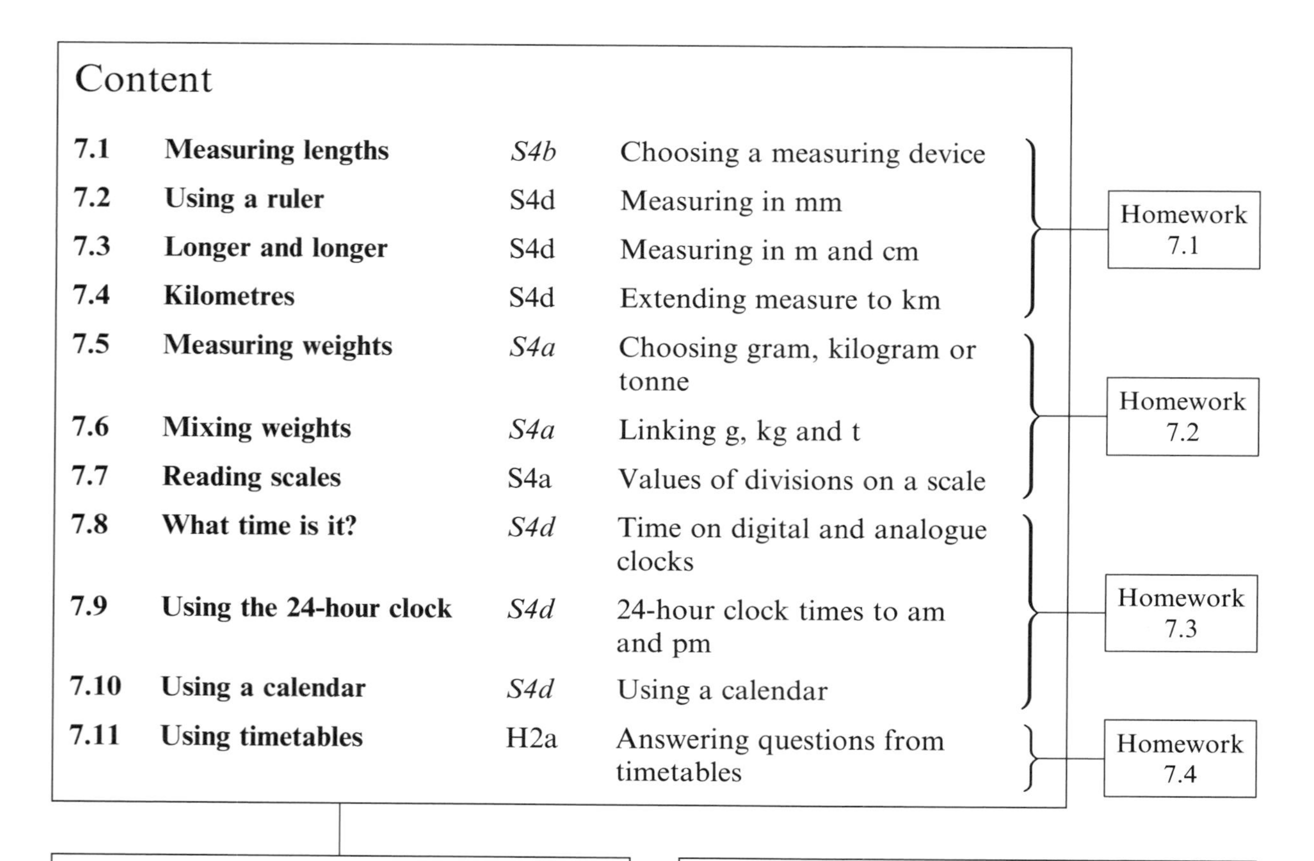

Content

7.1	**Measuring lengths**	*S4b*	Choosing a measuring device	Homework 7.1
7.2	**Using a ruler**	S4d	Measuring in mm	
7.3	**Longer and longer**	S4d	Measuring in m and cm	
7.4	**Kilometres**	S4d	Extending measure to km	
7.5	**Measuring weights**	*S4a*	Choosing gram, kilogram or tonne	Homework 7.2
7.6	**Mixing weights**	*S4a*	Linking g, kg and t	
7.7	**Reading scales**	S4a	Values of divisions on a scale	
7.8	**What time is it?**	*S4d*	Time on digital and analogue clocks	Homework 7.3
7.9	**Using the 24-hour clock**	*S4d*	24-hour clock times to am and pm	
7.10	**Using a calendar**	*S4d*	Using a calendar	
7.11	**Using timetables**	H2a	Answering questions from timetables	Homework 7.4

Assessment

Assessment 7 covers the key concepts in Unit 7.

Extension

Remediation sheets 7.1 → 7.2.

Assessment

The assessment is marked out of 30.
Achievement of 20 or more marks indicates a good understanding of the key concepts.
Marking guidance, answers and links to remediation are provided on page 265.

Equipment

	Pupils' Book page
Rulers	102
Metre rule or measuring tape, counters	103

ICT links

7.1–7.3
Use *The Geometer's Sketchpad* to draw some lines. Estimate their length in inches and centimetres and then check your answers by displaying their correct length.

7.11
Use the web sites listed on page vi to plan a journey by train, aeroplane and train again, from your local railway station to Cities in the USA.

Remediation

Reading scales:
Essentially pupils need to be able to read scales using intervals of 1, 2, 5, and 10. Using actual scales will provide a practical background for the work and help pupils to develop a method for working out 'what each division is worth'.

Time:
Pupils need to have clock faces or photocopies of clock faces to work with. Demonstrate how to count between two times to work out 'How long from ... to ...'

Questionbank CD

All homeworks and extension questions also appear on the CD.

Pages xvii and xviii of this pack show you how to use the CD to select questions from the Questionbank and further customize them if you wish to.

7 Measuring

framework teaching objective	§	lesson starter	f/w ref
Use names and abbreviations of units of measurement to measure, estimate, calculate and solve problems in everyday contexts.	7.1	Draw a 1 m line on the board 'Look about the classroom. Can you see anything that measures roughly 1 metre?' Examples '*Desk,' – its height? Its width? Its length? 'Width of shelves.' 'Height of window.' 'Kimberley.' etc.* Check each suggestion with ruler, tape measure or metre rule. Establish that those suggestions which are not exactly 1 m are not 'wrong' – they are reasonable estimates. Use this as a launching place for a discussion of the difference between reasonable and unreasonable estimates. Ask pupils 'Can you see anything which is **less than** 1 m?' 'Book' – Width? Length? Thickness? *'Height of chair.' 'Pencil.' 'Samantha.'* Ask pupils to consider 2 lists (draw this on the board): less than 1 m | 1 m or above *Students to identify that a 1 m length is not helpful to measure many of the things in the first column, and that a smaller unit is needed – the centimetre.*	228–31
Use names and abbreviations of units of measurement to measure, estimate, calculate and solve problems in everyday contexts.	7.2	Students equipped with plastic rulers. 'Justin draws a 7 cm line in his book'. He measures the line later and finds that it is only 6.6 cm long! What's happened? Has the line shrunk? What mistake has Justin made? *He has measured from the very edge of his ruler – not the zero point.* Why do you think the ruler has that small gap at the edge? *This can lead to a useful discussion about not banging rulers on the desk, thereby breaking bits off and rendering them useless.* *Can also lead to measuring lines with a broken ruler – which starts at 10 cm or 7 cm.*	228–31

framework teaching objective	§	lesson starter	f/w ref
Convert one metric unit to another.	7.3	A wood cutting machine can be programmed to cut lengths of wood as required. It can only be programmed in cm. It does not know what a metre is. 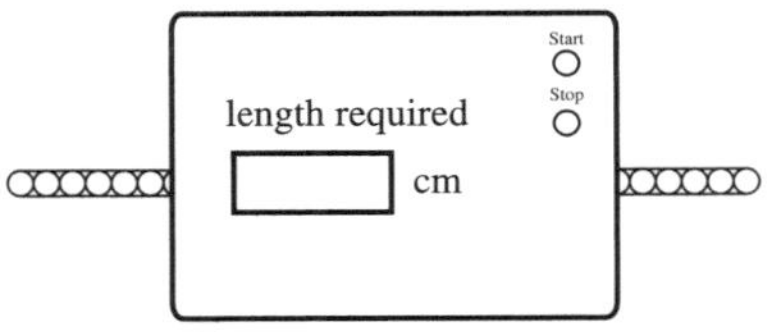 length required [ ] cm Start Stop How can I programme it to cut a 1 m length of wood? – (*100 cm*) How can I programme it to cut a 4 m length? (*400 cm*) A $\frac{1}{2}$ metre length? (*50 cm*) A $6\frac{1}{2}$ m length? (*650 cm*) A 6 m 40 cm length? (*640 cm*)	228–31
Read and interpret scales on a range of measuring instruments.	7.7	Weighing scales Draw the following scales: 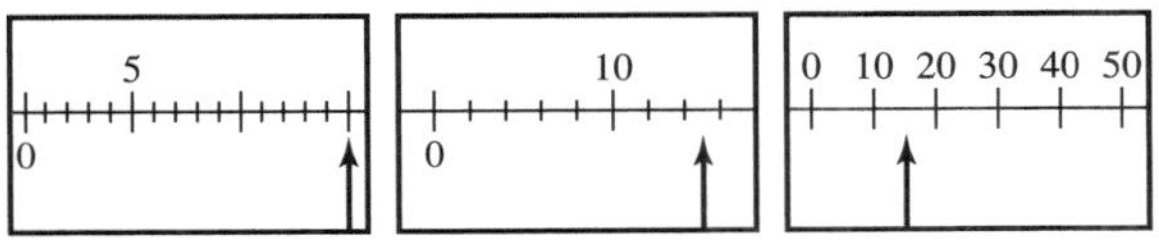 0 5 / 0 10 / 0 10 20 30 40 50 Firouz says: 'Each of these scales points to 15 kg.' Is he right? Why are the scales numbered differently? Which scales will measure very heavy things? Which scale will measure things most accurately?	228–31

7 Measure

Exercise 7.1 Links: 7B, 7C, 7D, 7E

1 Measure these lines in cm.

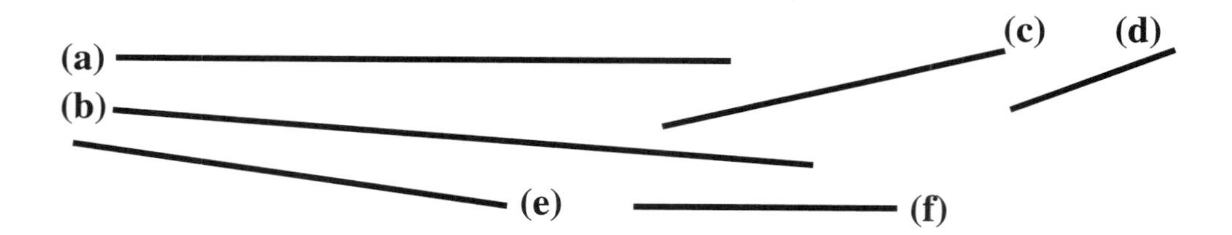

2 Use a ruler and a square corner to draw rectangles with sides.

(a) 2 cm, 3 cm **(b)** 3 cm, 4 cm **(c)** $2\frac{1}{2}$ cm, $4\frac{1}{2}$ cm

3 Put these lengths in order of size.
Start with the smallest.

7 m 69 cm, 705 cm, 75 cm, 6 km, 680 cm, 7 km

Exercise 7.2 Links: 7F, 7G, 7H

1 Put these weights in order of size.
Start with the largest.

350 g, 3 kg, 2800 g, 285 g, 2 kg 900 g, 3050 g

2 **Activity** Measure the height and weight of some packets.
They can be food, washing powder, toys or anything that comes in a packet. Make a table of results.

Item	Height	Weight
Cornflakes packet		

3 What is the reading on these scales?

(a)

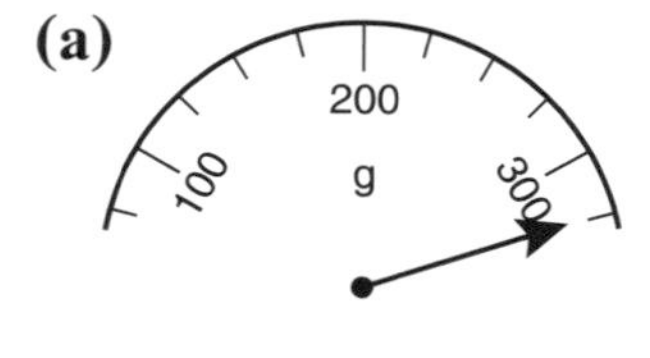

(b)

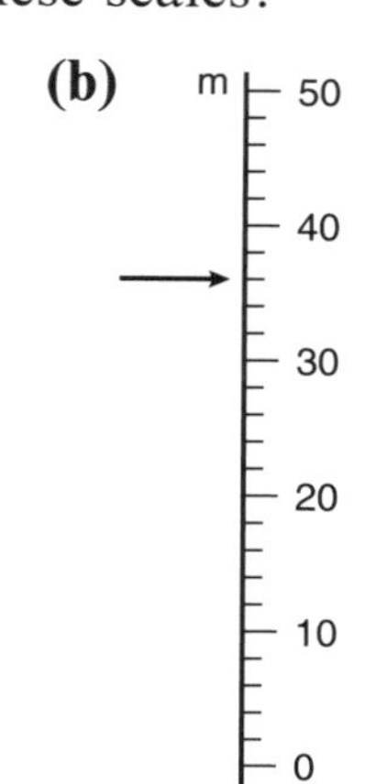

(c)

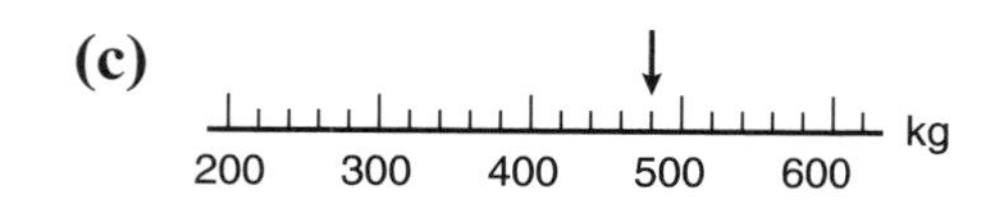

Exercise 7.3 — Links: 7I, 7J, 7K, 7L

1 Write these 24 hour clock times as morning or afternoon times.

(a) 16:15 **(b)** 08:20 **(c)** 11:45 **(d)** 21:00 **(e)** 23:45

2 Write these times as 24 hour clock times.

(a) 2:15 am **(b)** 6:30 pm **(c)** 12:30 am
(d) 8:35 pm **(e)** 6:00 am

3 The 3rd of March is a Saturday.
What day of the week is:

(a) 10th March **(b)** March 20th
(c) 30th March **(d)** 2nd of April?

4 A holiday starts on Saturday 14th June and ends on Saturday 28th June.

(a) How many complete days are there on this holiday?

(b) How many nights are there on the holiday?

Exercise 7.4 — Links: 7M

1 Here is part of a timetable.

East Croydon	07:17	----	----	07:37	----
West Croydon	----	07:26	07:32	----	07:56
Selhurst	07:20	07:30	07:36	07:40	08:00
Thornton Heath	07:22	07:32	07:38	07:42	08:02
Norbury	07:25	07:35	07:41	07:45	08:05
Streatham	----	----	07:46	----	----
Victoria	07:44	07:53	----	08:03	08:23
London Bridge	----	----	08:07	----	----

(a) Which Croydon station must you use for a direct train to London Bridge?

(b) How many trains start from East Croydon between 07:15 and 08:00?

(c) What time does the 07:32 from West Croydon get to Norbury?

(d) How long does the journey from Croydon to London Bridge take?

(e) If you just miss the 07:17 from East Croydon, how long will it be before the next train to Victoria?

Name ....

7 Measuring

1 Match these measuring instruments to the lengths below which need to be measured.

Tape measure **Ruler** **Trundle wheel**

The length of a hockey pitch. Use a ....

The height of a man. Use a ....

The width of this page. Use a .... **(2 marks)**

---

2 **You will need a ruler.**

(a) Measure the length of this line.

________________________ .... cm

(b) Draw a line of length **7 cm** in the space below.

(2 marks)

---

3 **(a)** Write **3 m 24 cm** in centimetres. .... cm

(b) Write **568 cm** in metres and centimetres. .... m .... cm

(c) Write **3 km 200 m** in metres. .... m

(d) Write **3234 m** as a mixed length. .... km .... m **(4 marks)**

---

4 Write these lengths in order of size.
Start with the shortest.

6 m 38 cm **600 cm** **6 km** **623 cm** **6 m 83 cm**

.... **(3 marks)**

---

5 Here are three units of weight.

grams kilograms tonnes

Which of these units would be the most sensible to use to measure the weight of:

(a) a bag of potatoes Use ....

(b) a lorry Use ....

(c) a woman Use ....

(d) a small jar of coffee Use .... **(3 marks)**

---

6 **(a)** Write as mixed weights:

(i) 3750 g .... kg .... g

(ii) 5300 kg .... tonnes .... kg **(2 marks)**

(b) Write **5 tonnes 60 kg** in kilograms .... kg **(1 mark)**

---

7 Put these weights in order of size.
Start with the smallest.

3250 g 4 kg 3 kg 400 g 3 kg 50 g

.... **(2 marks)**

---

8 Mrs Mohammed has used the scales at the supermarket to weigh some apples and some beans.
The diagram below shows the reading on the scales.

(a)

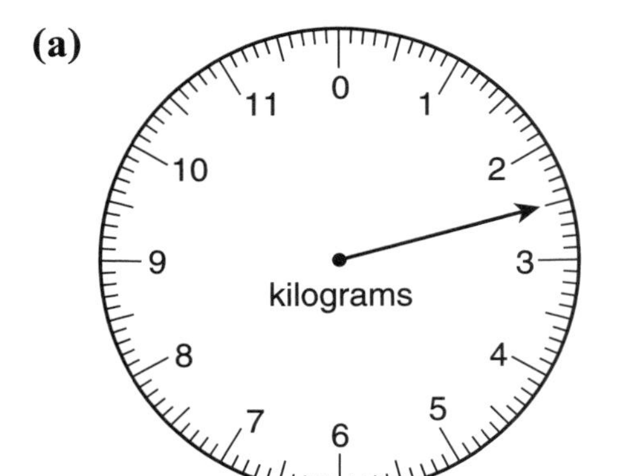

(b)

kg
4
3
2
1
0

What is the weight of the apples on scale **(a)**?
What is the weight of the beans on scale **(b)**? **(2 marks)**

---

9 **(a)** Write down the time shown on the clock below.

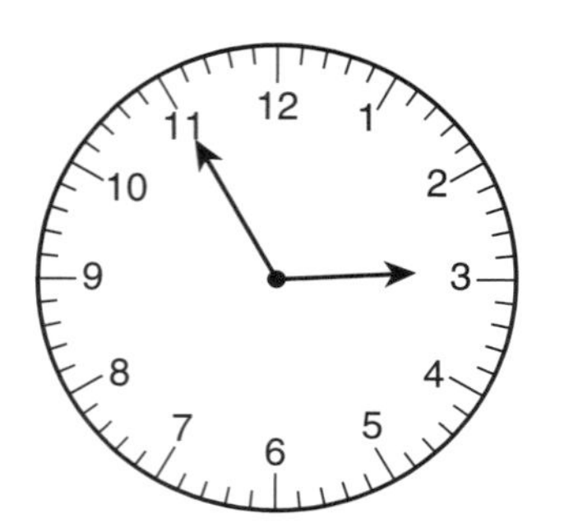

....

(b) On the clock face below show a time of **ten past six**.

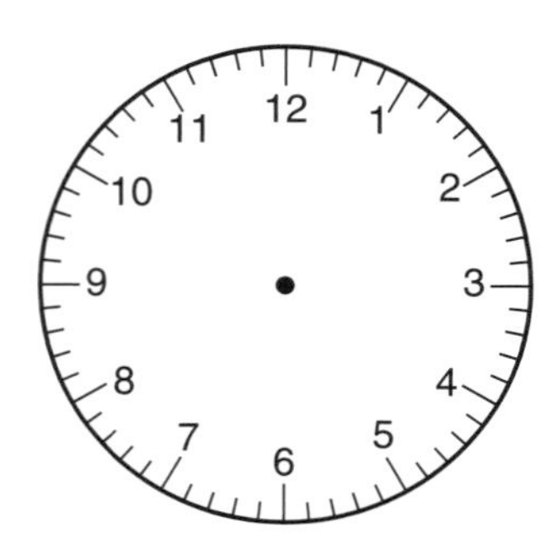

(c) Write the time of **a quarter past seven** on the digital clock below.

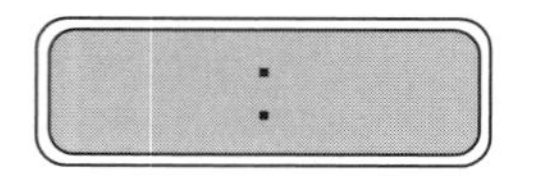

(3 marks)

---

10 **(a)** Write the time of **a quarter to five pm** using the 24 hour clock.

....

(b) A 24 hour clock shows the time of **15:30**.
Write this time as you would say it.

.... **(2 marks)**

---

11 The train should have left Colchester station at half past six.
The train was 40 minutes late.
What time did the train leave Colchester station? .... **(1 mark)**

---

12 Malcolm went on a 17-day holiday.
The first day of the holiday was 23rd August.
What was the date of the last day of the holiday?

August					
M		6	13	20	27
T		7	14	21	28
W	1	8	15	22	29
T	2	9	16	23	30
F	3	10	17	24	31
S	4	11	18	25	
S	5	12	19	26	

....

(1 mark)

---

13 Here is part of a bus timetable.

Park Gates	06:15	06:45	07:15	07:30	07:45
The Station	06:22	06:52	07:22	07:37	07:52
St. Maggs	06:32	07:02	07:32	07:47	----
Lucea Square	06:40	07:10	07:40	07:55	08:10
Terminal	06:55	07:25	07:55	08:10	08:25

(a) At what time should the 07:15 from Park Gates be at Lucea Square?

....

The column for the 07:45 from Park Gates is incomplete.

(b) At what time should the 07:45 from Park Gates be at St. Maggs?

....

(2 marks)

Unit 7 Measuring

Question			Answer	Marking guidance and remediation sheet links
1	**(a)**		Trundle wheel	B1 for 1 correct
	(b)		Tape measure	B2 for all correct
	(c)		Ruler	
2	**(a)**		6 cm	A1
	(b)		7 cm line drawn	A1 ± 0.2 mm
3	**(a)**		324 cm	A1
	(b)		5 m 68 cm	A1
	(c)		3200 m	A1
	(d)		3 km 234 m	A1
4			600 cm, 623 cm, 6 m 38 cm, 6 m 83 cm, 6 km	B1 for 600 cm smallest B3 for all in order B2 for one out of place
5	**(a)**		kilograms	B3 for all correct
	(b)		tonnes	B2 for 2 correct
	(c)		kilogrammes	B1 for 1 correct
	(d)		grams	
6	**(a)**	**(i)**	3 kg 750 g	B1
		(ii)	5 tonnes 300 kg	B1
	(b)		5060 kg	A1
7			3 kg 50 g, 3250 g, 3 kg 400 g, 4 kg	B2 for all correct B1 for one out of order
8	**(a)**		2.5 kg or 2500 g	A1 } less than $\frac{1}{2}$ use remediation sheet 7.1
	(b)		3.5 kg	A1

Key to mark scheme
A marks: correct answer
M marks: correct method
B marks: independent work

Page 265 gives a general guidance on use of this assessment scheme with some examples.

Assessment and remediation links

Question		Answer	Marking guidance and remediation sheet links	
9	**(a)**	Five to three or 2:55 or 14:55	A1	
	(b)	 12 1 2 3 4 5 6 7 8 9 10 11	A1	
	(c)	07:15 or 7:15 or 19:15	A1	
10	**(a)**	16:45	A1	
	(b)	Half past three	A1	
11		Ten past seven or 7:10 or 19:10	A1	less than $\frac{1}{2}$ use remediation sheet 7.2
12		8th September	A1	
13	**(a)**	07:40	B1	
	(b)	08:02	B1	

Key to mark scheme
A marks: correct answer
M marks: correct method
B marks: independent work

Page 265 gives a general guidance on use of this assessment scheme with some examples.

7.1 Reading scales

What is each division on the scale worth?

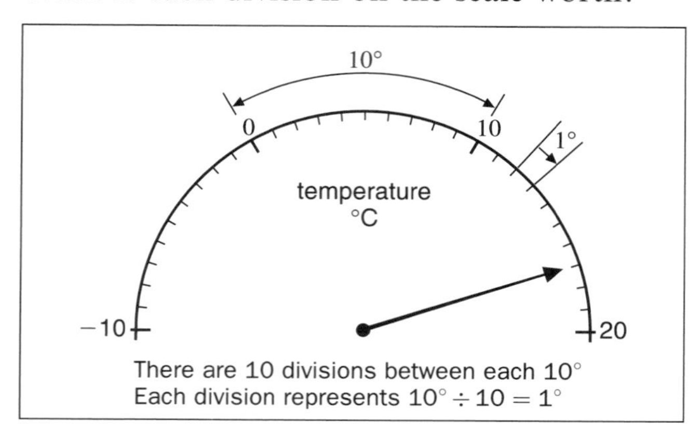

The scale is numbered every 10°.
Each division represents 1°.
The needle is pointing to 17°C.

Exercise 1

Read each scale.
Remember to work out what each division is worth.

(a)

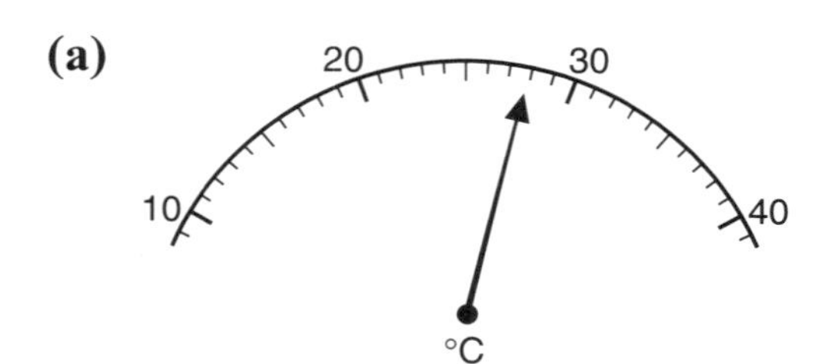

(b)

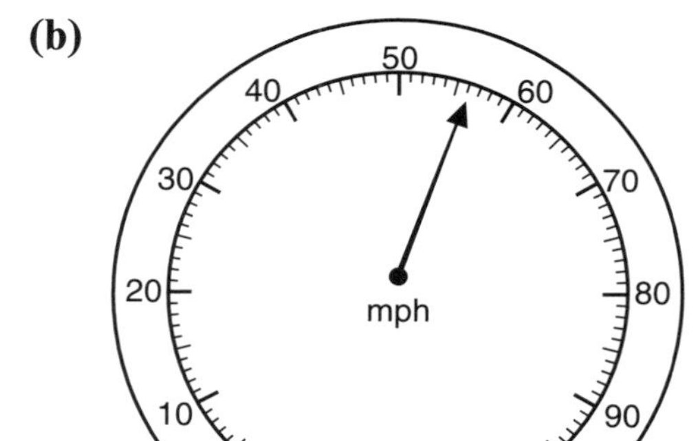

(c)

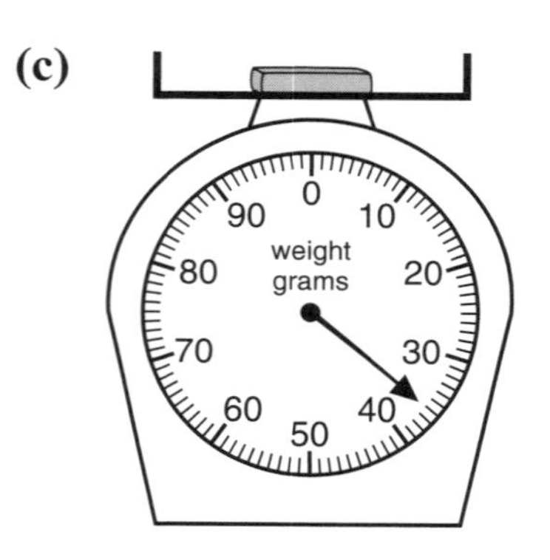

(d)

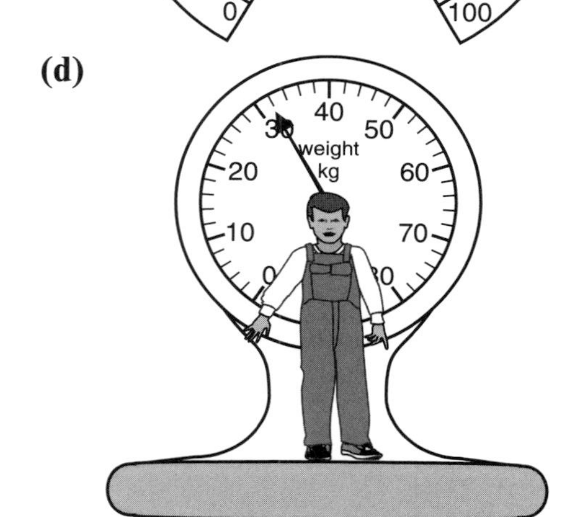

(e)

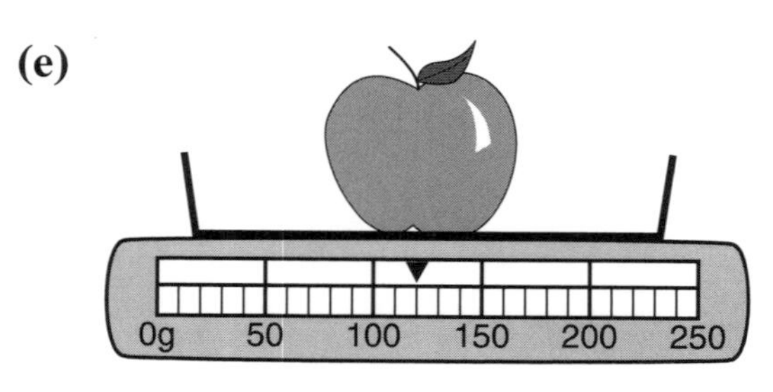

(f)

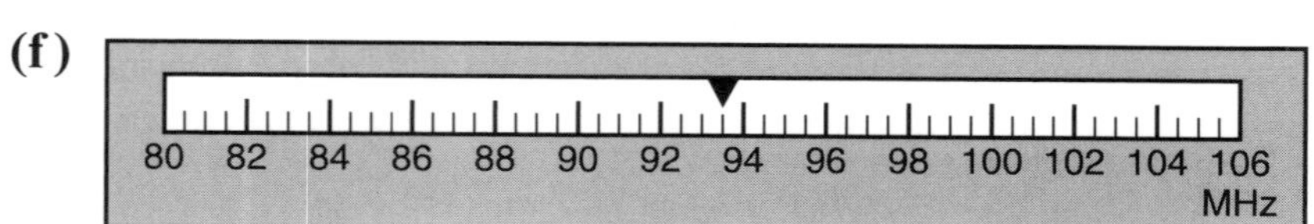

7.2 Time intervals

Use a clockface to help find the difference between two times.

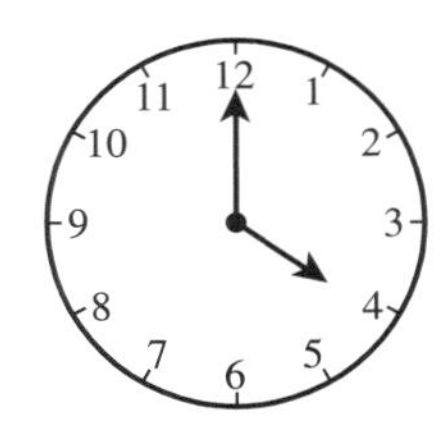

If you get to the station at 10 : 15 and the train leaves at 10 : 40, how long will you wait?

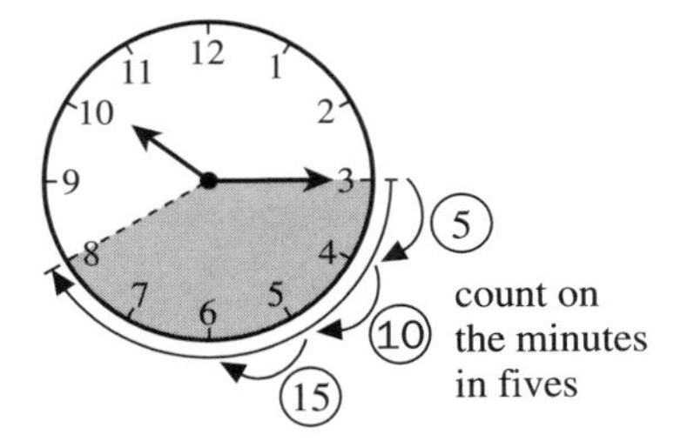

10 : 15 to 10 : 30 is 15 min
10 : 30 to 10 : 40 is 10 min
15 min + 10 min = 25 min

It is useful to count on in 5s when working out time

$1 \times 5 = 5$
$2 \times 5 = 10$
$3 \times 5 = 15$
$4 \times 5 = 20$
$5 \times 5 = 25$
$6 \times 5 = 30$
$7 \times 5 = 35$
$8 \times 5 = 40$
$9 \times 5 = 45$
$10 \times 5 = 50$

A program on television begins at 9 : 45 and finishes at 11 : 00. How long is it on?

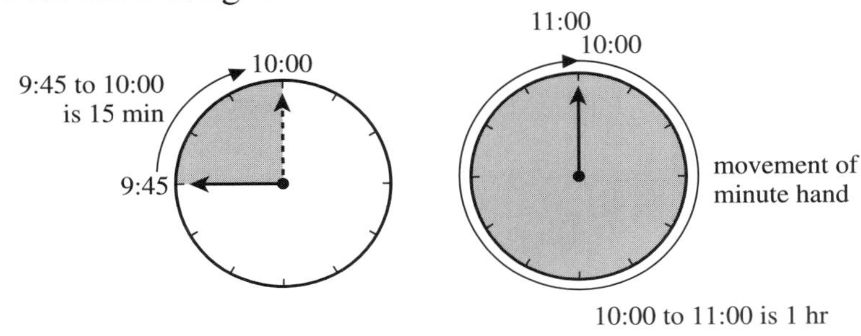

1 hr + 15 min is 1 hr 15 min

Example 1

How long is it from 8 : 30 to 9 : 25?

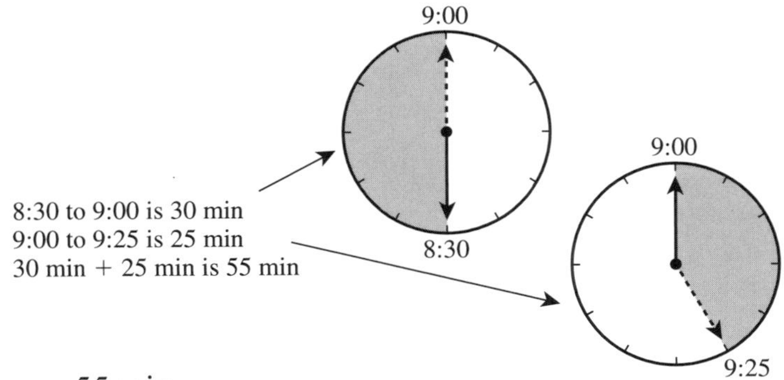

8:30 to 9:00 is 30 min
9:00 to 9:25 is 25 min
30 min + 25 min is 55 min

Answer: 55 min

Exercise 1

How long is it between these times?

(a) 7 : 25 and 7 : 55 **(b)** 6 : 35 and 7 : 05 **(c)** 8 : 25 and 9 : 10

(d) 10 : 30 and 11 : 05 **(e)** 9 : 35 and 10 : 30 **(f)** 11 : 40 and 12 : 15

Answers to Pupils' Book

7 Measuring

Exercise 7A

1 Ruler: **(a)**, **(g)**, **(h)**, **(j)**, **(m)**, **(o)**, **(p)**, **(q)**
Tape: **(d)**, **(e)**, **(k)**, **(l)**, **(n)**, **(s)**
Trundle wheel: **(b)**, **(c)**, **(f)**, **(i)**, **(r)**.
2 cm: **(a)**, **(g)**, **(h)**, **(j)**, **(k)**, **(l)**, **(m)**, **(n)**, **(o)**, **(p)**, **(q)**, **(s)**
m: **(c)**, **(d)**, **(e)**, **(f)**, **(r)**
km: **(b)**, **(i)**

Exercise 7B

1 **(a)** 5 cm **(b)** 3 cm **(c)** 4 cm
(d) 6 cm **(e)** 2 cm
4 **(a)** 5 cm **(b)** 6 cm **(c)** 4 cm
(d) 1 cm **(e)** 9 cm
5 Red: 15 cm Blue: $16\frac{1}{2}$ cm
(Blue is the longer.)

Exercise 7D

1 **(a)** 320 **(b)** 572 **(c)** 812
(d) 1015 **(e)** 2040 **(f)** 1403
2 **(a)** 1 m 50 cm **(b)** 2 m 35 cm
(c) 7 m 58 cm **(d)** 1 m 05 cm
(e) 3 m 07 cm **(f)** 12 m 50 cm
(g) 30 m 56 cm **(h)** 42 m 71 cm
(i) 30 m 08 cm
3 1 m 32 cm, 1 m 48 cm, 2 m 9 cm, 2 m 25 cm, 2 m 30 cm
4 cheetah, leopard, lion, gnu, zebra
5 **(a)** 9 m 3 cm
(b) 9 m 3 cm, 8 m 17 cm, 8 m 9 cm, 7 m 94 cm, 7 m 87 cm, 7 m 81 cm

Exercise 7E

1 **(a)** 3230 **(b)** 21 500 **(c)** 15 370
(d) 2155 **(e)** 10 040 **(f)** 37 020
(g) 1045 **(h)** 2005
2 **(a)** 2 km 125 m **(b)** 4 km 50 m
(c) 14 km 406 m **(d)** 1 km 8 cm
(e) 7 km 30 cm **(f)** 5 km 250 m
(g) 2 km **(h)** 53 km
(i) 12 km 500 m **(j)** 4 km 600 m
3 3000 m, 3 km; 5000 m, 5 km; 1500 m, 1 km 500 m; 10 000 m, 10 km; 4 × 400 m, 1 km 600 m
4 Severn, Thames, Trent, Wye

Exercise 7F

1 tonnes: **(c)**, **(f)**.
kg: **(b)**, **(e)**, **(g)**, **(l)**, **(n)**, **(o)**.
g: **(a)**, **(d)**, **(h)**, **(i)**, **(j)**, **(k)**, **(m)**.

Exercise 7G

1 **(a)** 3000 **(b)** 6200 **(c)** 9420
(d) 3250 **(e)** 8050 **(f)** 10 005
2 **(a)** 6000 **(b)** 4500 **(c)** 3120
(d) 9170 **(e)** 7040 **(f)** 11 009
3 **(a)** 2 kg 750 g **(b)** 3 kg 500 g
(c) 7 kg 570 g **(d)** 1 kg 50 g
(e) 10 kg 25 g **(f)** 4 kg 6 g
(g) 4 t 200 kg **(h)** 6 t 50 kg
(i) 10 t 10 kg
4 1st Fiona; 2nd Inam; 3rd Jenna: 4th Jeremy

Exercise 7H

1 **(a)** 10 g **(b)** 140 g 2 **(a)** 20 g **(b)** 280 g
3 **(a)** 10 g **(b)** 170 g 4 **(a)** 20 g **(b)** 60 g
5 **(a)** 25 g **(b)** 375 g 6 **(a)** 5 g **(b)** 425 g
7 170 kg 8 370 kg

Exercise 7I

1 **(a)** May **(b)** Tim
(c) Trish **(d)** Kunal
(e) Alice **(f)** Petra
2 **(a)** five (minutes) past five
(b) quarter past four
(c) half past two
(d) twenty (minutes) to seven
(e) two (minutes) to one
(f) six (minutes) to twelve
(g) twenty three (minutes) past five
(h) eight (minutes) to ten
(i) two (minutes) to five
(j) eight (minutes) past seven
(k) eighteen (minutes) past twelve
(l) two (minutes) to twelve

Exercise 7J

1 Quarter past four 4:15
Twenty minutes past four 4:20
Twenty five minutes past four 4:25
Half past four 4:30
Twenty five minutes to five 4:35
Twenty minutes to five 4:40
Quarter to five 4:45
Ten minutes to five 4:50
Five minutes to five 4:55
2 **(a)** Quarter past 3 **(b)** 10 to 10
(c) 5 to 12, **(d)** 25 past 2
(e) 5 past 9 **(f)** 3 minutes to 11
(g) 21 minutes to 5 **(h)** 28 minutes to 8.
3 **(a)** 05:15 **(b)** 07:20
(c) 12:30 **(d)** 03:40
(e) 08:55 **(f)** 12:00

Exercise 7K

1 **(a)** 08:00 **(b)** 09:15
(c) 11:20 **(d)** 13:30
(e) 15:45 **(f)** 16:15
(g) 21:15 **(h)** 22:00
(i) 23:15 **(j)** 12:00
(k) 00:00 **(l)** 00:25
2 **(a)** 11:00 am **(b)** 2:40 pm
(c) 5:15 pm **(d)** 8:10 am
(e) 3:50 am **(f)** 9:30 pm
(g) 11:17 pm **(h)** 12:38 am
(i) 12:23 pm **(j)** 12:01 am
3 **(a)** 06:15 **(b)** 14:30
(c) 09:45 **(d)** 17:50
(e) 18:24 **(f)** 00:10

Exercise 7L

1 Ray, Sunday; Sarah, Monday; Mandy, Monday; Michele, Saturday
2 5, 12, 19, 26
3 **(a)** Sunday **(b)** Tuesday
(c) Friday **(d)** Monday
4 **(a)** Saturday October 8th
(b) Saturday March 19th
(c) Wednesday June 8th
(d) Saturday October 23rd

Exercise 7M

1 **(a)** 4 **(b)** 09:25
(c) 11:20 **(d)** 10:15
(e) 09:50
2 **(a)** 12:30 **(b)** 06:00
(c) Canna, Rum, Muck, Eigg
(d) 1 hour
3 **(a)** Freshford, Avoncliff **(b)** 10:11
(c) 07:50, 09:51 **(d)** 09:51

Answers to Homeworks

7 Measure

Exercise 7.1 Links: 7B, 7C, 7D, 7E

1 **(a)** 7 cm **(b)** 8 cm
(c) 4 cm **(d)** 2 cm
(e) 5 cm **(f)** 3 cm
3 75 cm, 680 cm, 705 cm, 7 m 69 cm, 6 km, 7 km

Exercise 7.2 Links: 7F, 7G, 7H

1 3050 g, 3 kg, 2 kg 900 g, 2800 g, 350 g, 285 g
3 **(a)** 325 g **(b)** 36 m
(c) 480 kg

Exercise 7.3 Links: 7I, 7J, 7K, 7L

1 **(a)** 4:15 pm **(b)** 8:20 am
(c) 11:45 am **(d)** 9:00 pm
(e) 11:45 pm
2 **(a)** 02:15 **(b)** 18:30
(c) 00:30 **(d)** 20:35
(e) 06:00
3 **(a)** Saturday **(b)** Tuesday
(c) Friday **(d)** Monday
4 **(a)** 13 days **(b)** 14 nights

Exercise 7.4 Links: 7M

1 **(a)** West Croydon **(b)** 2
(c) 07:41 **(d)** 35 min
(e) 20 min

Remediation answers

7.1 Reading scales

Exercise 1

(a) 28° **(b)** 56 mph
(c) 36 g **(d)** 32 kg
(e) 120 g **(f)** 93.5 MHz

7.2 Time intervals

Exercise 1

(a) 30 min **(b)** 30 min
(c) 45 min **(d)** 35 min
(e) 55 min **(f)** 35 min

Unit 8 Fractions

Content summary

This unit introduces simple fractions. It names fractions to tenths and deals with finding fractions of a quantity and addition of fractions with the same denominator.

Book 1R Unit 8 extends the topic to include mixed numbers, improper and vulgar fractions, equivalent fractions and some addition and subtraction of fractions with different denominators.

NC level

Level 2:

Level 3: Although 'use simple fractions' is NC Level 4 most of the work in the first two sections is about Level 3.

Level 4: Likewise 'finding fractions of quantities' is NC level 5 but the work is at the lower end of this level.

N2c *N2d* NA3c

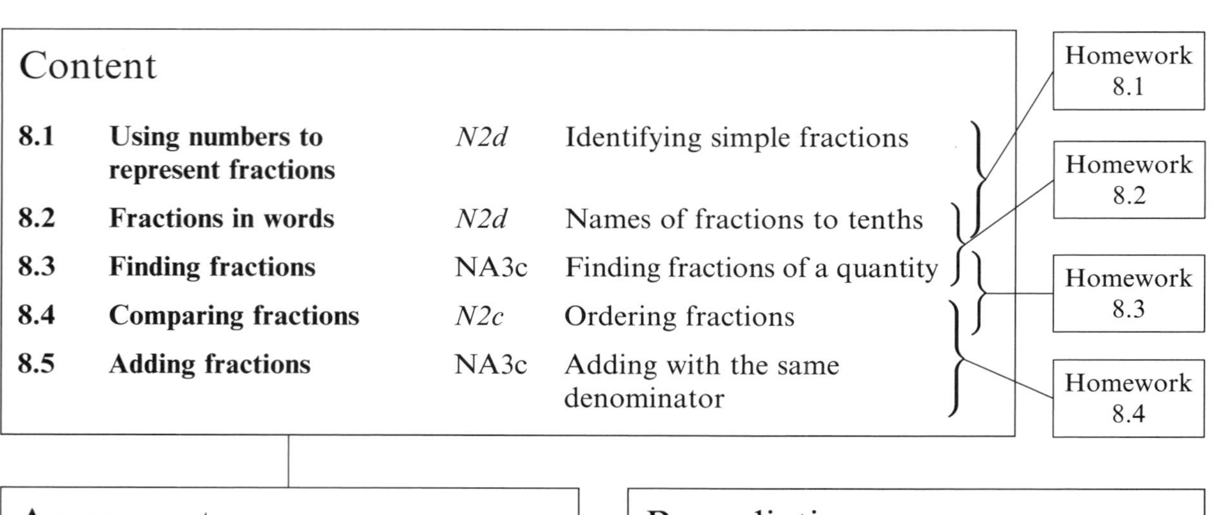

Content

8.1	**Using numbers to represent fractions**	*N2d*	Identifying simple fractions
8.2	**Fractions in words**	*N2d*	Names of fractions to tenths
8.3	**Finding fractions**	NA3c	Finding fractions of a quantity
8.4	**Comparing fractions**	*N2c*	Ordering fractions
8.5	**Adding fractions**	NA3c	Adding with the same denominator

Assessment

Assessment 8 covers the key concepts in Unit 8.

Remediation

Remediation sheet 8.1.

Assessment

The assessment is marked out of 30.
Achievement of 20 or more marks indicates a good understanding of the key concepts.
Marking guidance, answers and links to remediation are provided on page 265.

Equipment

No extra equipment needed for this unit.

ICT links

8.1 and 8.2
Use *MicroSmile for Windows Pack 3* to build fraction walls.

8.4
Use *MicroSmile for Windows Pack 8* to order fractions.

8.3
Use *Mental Arithmetic from Virtual Image* to practice finding a fraction of a quantity.

Remediation

Halves and quarters:
Practically demonstrate halving by splitting groups of cubes or counters into two equally sized groups. Allow the pupils to practice with a number of different objects before moving on to the written work. Once they are confident with halving, extend the method to cover quartering. It may be useful to reinforce times tables at this point.

Questionbank CD

All homeworks and extension questions also appear on the CD.

Pages xvii and xviii of this pack show you how to use the CD to select questions from the Questionbank and further customize them if you wish to.

8 Fractions

framework teaching objective	§	lesson starter	f/w ref
Use fraction notation to describe parts of shapes.	8.1	Two pizzas have been cut into equal slices. Ben Kadiv Each slice is a **fraction** of the whole pizza. How many slices must Ben eat to finish his pizza? Kadir? What fraction can we call one slice of Ben's pizza? One slice of Kadir's? We need two different names. (The names must convey how many slices are needed to complete the whole pizza.) Relate enquiry to fractions that students know – $\frac{1}{2}$, $\frac{1}{4}$. Ben has eaten 3 slices. What fraction of his pizza has he eaten? Kadir has eaten 3 slices of his pizza. Is it the same fraction? Who has eaten more? Annie has cut her pizza into slices. She says: 'I have eaten $\frac{5}{10}$ of my pizza.' What part of the fraction tells us how many slices there are in Annie's pizza?	60–5
Consolidate and extend mental methods of calculation.	8.3/ 8.4	What's $\frac{1}{2}$ of £16? What's $\frac{1}{2}$ of 18 g? What's $\frac{1}{2}$ of 30p? What maths are we using to find $\frac{1}{2}$? (*÷2*) What's $\frac{1}{4}$ of £16? What maths do we use? (*÷4*) How would I work out $\frac{1}{5}$ of 30p? $\frac{1}{6}$ of 30p? Which answer was bigger $\frac{1}{5}$ or $\frac{1}{6}$? Why is $\frac{1}{6}$ smaller than $\frac{1}{5}$?	92–101

framework teaching objective	§	lesson starter	f/w ref
Calculate simple fractions of quantities and measurements.	8.4	£24 is to be shared equally. What is $\frac{1}{3}$ of £24? → £8 $\frac{1}{2}$ of £24? → £12 $\frac{1}{4}$ of £24? → £6 $\frac{1}{8}$ of £24? → £3 Put the answers in size order, **largest** first: $\frac{1}{2}, \frac{1}{3}, \frac{1}{4}, \frac{1}{8}$. Why is $\frac{1}{8}$ smaller than $\frac{1}{2}$? Who would you prefer to share a chocolate bar with, 2 people or 8 people? Jack says: '$\frac{1}{5}$ is bigger than $\frac{1}{4}$' Is he right? Why do you think Jack has made this mistake?	66–9

1 G

8 Fractions

Homework

Exercise 8.1 — Links: 8A, 8B

1 Amarjita has three cats.
Which way should she split the two tins of cat food to make sure all the cats get an equal share?

2 **(a)** What do you call the number on the top of a fraction?
(b) What do you call the number on the bottom of a fraction?

3 Write down the fraction *four fifths* in numbers.
(a) What does the denominator tell you?
(b) What does the numerator tell you?

4 Write down the fraction family for these fractions. The first one has been done for you.

(a) $\frac{2}{3}$ The fraction family name is thirds.

(b) $\frac{1}{5}$ **(c)** $\frac{3}{4}$ **(d)** $\frac{7}{8}$ **(e)** $\frac{1}{6}$

Exercise 8.2 — Links: 8B, 8C

1 Match each fraction to the written name. The first one has been done for you.

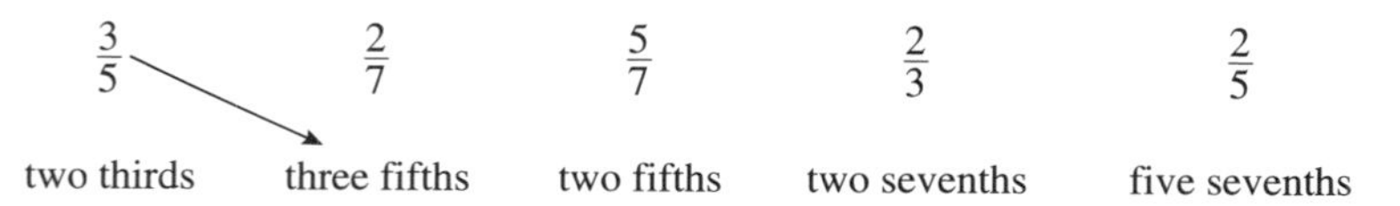

2 What fraction of each of these shapes is shaded?

(a) 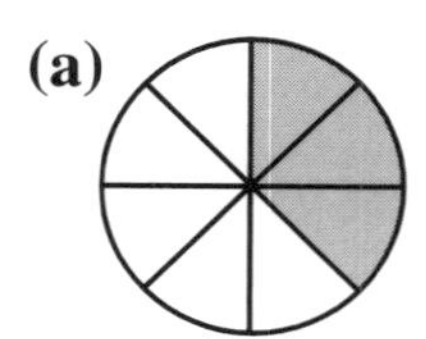
(b) 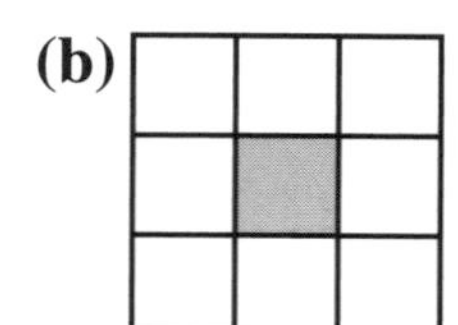
(c) 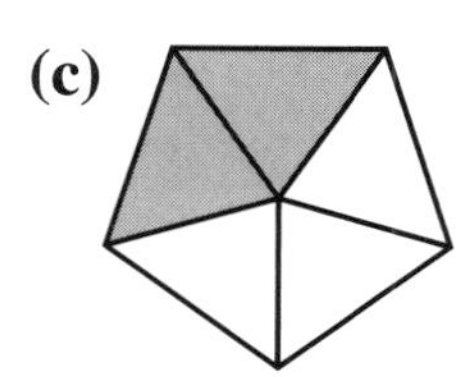

3 Sam is at the seaside. He catches 5 crabs, 2 jellyfish and 3 starfish.
(a) How many sea creatures has Sam caught?
(b) What fraction of his catch is crabs?
(c) What fraction of his catch is not crabs?

4 Find a half of:
(a) 10 **(b)** 16 **(c)** 26 **(d)** 100

Exercise 8.3 — Links: 8C, 8D

1 Half of a number is eight. What is the number?

2 Find one third of:

(a) £12 **(b)** 60p **(c)** 36p **(d)** £21

3 One third of Gina's pocket money is £2. How much does she get?

4 Here are two bags of sweets.

Each bag has 30 sweets in it.

$\frac{1}{2}$ of the sweets in bag A are strawberry.

$\frac{1}{3}$ of the sweets in bag B are strawberry.

(a) Which bag has more strawberry sweets?

(b) Which would you prefer and why?

(c) Which fraction is larger and why?

Exercise 8.4 — Links: 8D, 8E

1 Ravi and Malcolm each have 24 compact discs. Ravi sees that $\frac{1}{8}$ of her compact discs are by boy bands. Malcolm has $\frac{1}{6}$ that are by boy bands. State whether the following sentences are true or false with a reason.

(a) Ravi has more CD's by boy bands than Malcolm.

(b) Malcolm has more CD's by boy bands than Ravi.

(c) They have the same number of boy band CD's.

2 A football match lasts 90 minutes. It was called off after $\frac{1}{3}$ of the game had been played due to bad weather.

(a) How long did they play for?

(b) What fraction of the match was not played?

3 Add the following fractions.

(a) $\frac{1}{7}+\frac{3}{7}$ **(b)** $\frac{3}{8}+\frac{1}{8}$ **(c)** $\frac{3}{10}+\frac{2}{10}$

(d) $\frac{2}{5}+\frac{1}{5}$ **(e)** $\frac{1}{16}+\frac{5}{16}$ **(f)** $\frac{11}{100}+\frac{13}{100}$

Name ....

8 Fractions

1 **(a)** Write down the numerator of $\frac{3}{5}$ ....

(b) Write down the denominator of $\frac{2}{7}$ .... **(2 marks)**

---

2 Write down what fraction of these shapes has been shaded.

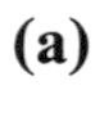

(a)

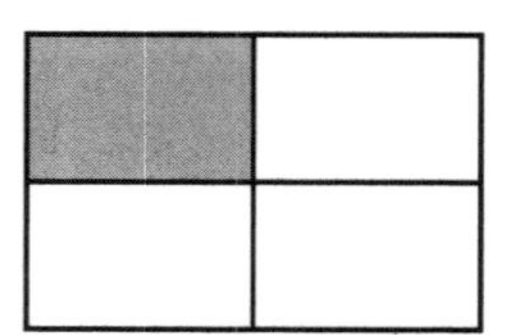

....

(b)

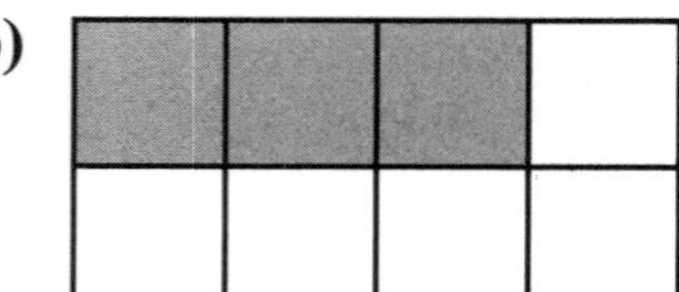

....

(c)

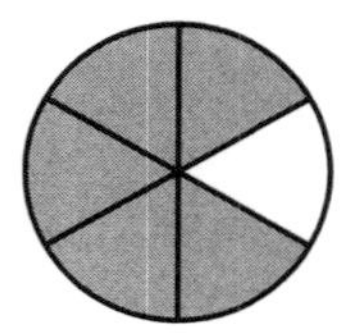

.... **(3 marks)**

---

3 **(a)** Write this fraction in words. $\frac{5}{6}$ ....

(b) Write three fifths using numbers. ....

(c) The numerator of a fraction is 3
The denominator of the fraction is 8
Write down the fraction in numbers. .... **(3 marks)**

---

4 **(a)** Work out half of £6.

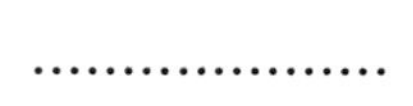

....

(b) Work out $\frac{1}{4}$ of 20.

....

(c) Shade $\frac{2}{5}$ of this rectangle.

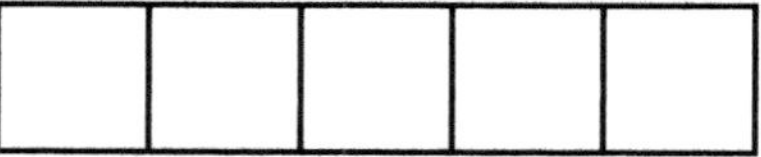

(d) Shade $\frac{3}{8}$ of this shape.

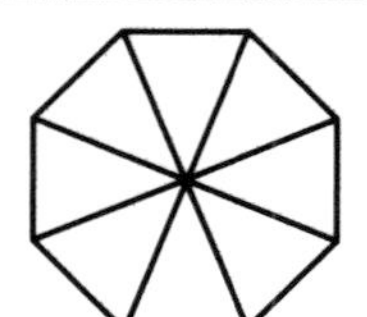

(4 marks)

---

5 **(a)** Work out $\frac{1}{3}$ of £15. ....

(b) Work out $\frac{1}{5}$ of 20. ....

(c) Work out $\frac{1}{8}$ of 40. ....

(d) Reyhana was given a box of 12 chocolates.
She ate $\frac{1}{6}$ of them.
How many chocolates did she eat? .... **(4 marks)**

---

6 Jason is given £24 for his birthday.
He spends $\frac{3}{4}$ of it on some CDs.
How much does he spend on the CDs? .... **(2 marks)**

---

7 Complete the following equivalent fractions.

(a) $\frac{1}{4} = \frac{}{12} = \frac{5}{}$

(b) $\frac{3}{5} = \frac{9}{} = \frac{}{20}$ **(4 marks)**

---

8 Work out.

(a) $\frac{2}{5} + \frac{2}{5}$ ....

(b) $\frac{7}{8} - \frac{3}{8}$ ....

(c) $1\frac{3}{4} + \frac{3}{4}$ ....

(d) $1 - \frac{3}{5}$ .... **(4 marks)**

---

9 Put these fractions in order of size.
Write the smallest one first.

$\frac{1}{2}, \frac{1}{10}, \frac{1}{5}, \frac{1}{7}$ .... **(2 marks)**

---

10 Work out.

(a) $\frac{3}{8} + \frac{1}{2}$ ....

(b) $\frac{5}{6} - \frac{1}{4}$ .... **(2 marks)**

Unit 8 Fractions

Question		Answer	Marking guidance and remediation sheet links	
1	**(a)**	3	A1	
	(b)	7	A1	
2	**(a)**	$\frac{1}{4}$	A1	
	(b)	$\frac{3}{8}$	A1	
	(c)	$\frac{5}{6}$	A1	
3	**(a)**	Five sixths	A1	
	(b)	$\frac{3}{5}$	A1	
	(c)	$\frac{3}{8}$	A1	
4	**(a)**	£3	A1	less than $\frac{6}{8}$ use remediation sheet 8.1 (applies to 4(a)–5(d))
	(b)	5	A1	
	(c)	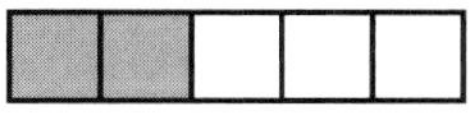	A1 any 2 squares shaded	
	(d)		A1 any 3 segments shaded	
5	**(a)**	£5	A1	
	(b)	4	A1	
	(c)	5	A1	
	(d)	2 chocolates	A1	
6		$24 \div 4 = 6$ $3 \times 6 = £18$	M1 for $24 \div 4$ and $\times 3$ A1 for £18	
7	**(a)**	$\frac{3}{12}$	A1	
		$\frac{5}{20}$	A1	
	(b)	$\frac{9}{15}$	A1	
		$\frac{12}{20}$	A1	

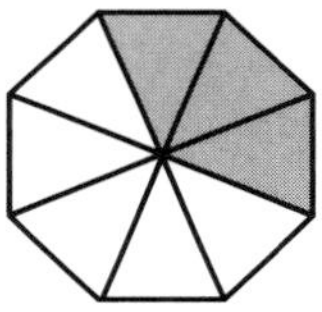

Key to mark scheme
A marks: correct answer
M marks: correct method
B marks: independent work

Page 265 gives a general guidance on use of this assessment scheme with some examples.

Assessment and remediation links

Question		Answer	Marking guidance and remediation sheet links
8	**(a)**	$\frac{4}{5}$	A1
	(b)	$\frac{4}{8}$ or $\frac{2}{4}$ or $\frac{1}{2}$	A1
	(c)	$2\frac{1}{2}$	A1 accept $1\frac{6}{4}$
	(d)	$\frac{2}{5}$	A1
9	**(a)**	$\frac{1}{10}, \frac{1}{7}, \frac{1}{5}, \frac{1}{2}$	A2 A1 for one out of place
10	**(a)**	$\frac{7}{8}$	A1
	(b)	$\frac{7}{12}$	A1

Key to mark scheme
A marks: correct answer
M marks: correct method
B marks: independent work

Page 265 gives a general guidance on use of this assessment scheme with some examples.

8.1 Finding halves and quarters

To find half you divide into 2 equal parts.

6 counters

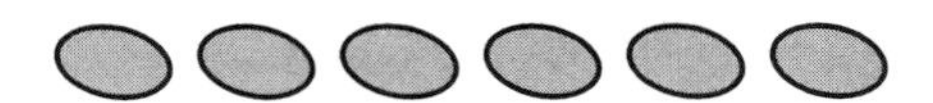

split into 2 groups the same

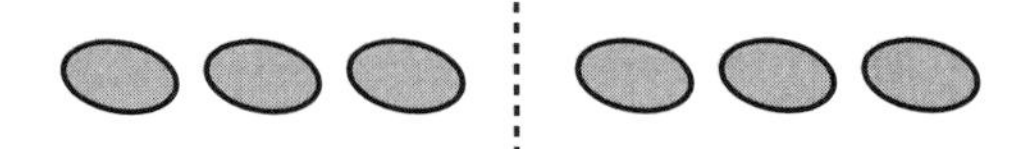

Each group has
3 counters.
Half of 6 is 3.   Check: 3 and 3 is 6.

Example 1

Work out half of 10

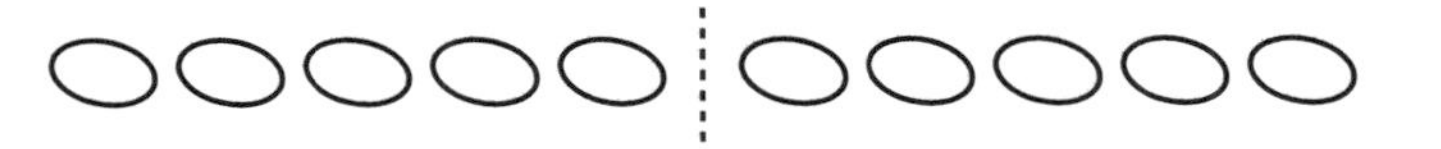

10 counters split into
2 groups the same.

Answer 5.

Exercise 1

Work out half of:

(a) 8	**(b)** 16	**(c)** 14	**(d)** 20
(e) 30	**(f)** 4	**(g)** 26	**(h)** 32

To find a quarter divide into 4 equal parts.

8 counters

split into half

then into half again

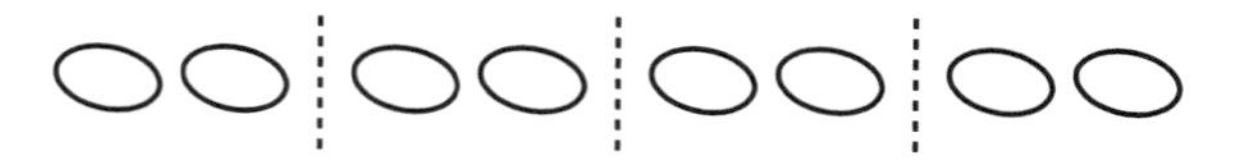

8 counters split into 4 groups the same.

Quarter of 8 is 2. Check: 2 and 2 and 2 and 2 is 8.

Example 2

Work out a quarter of 12

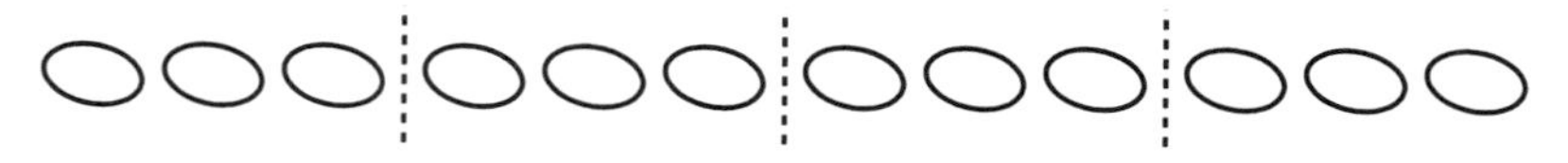

12 counters split into 4 groups the same.

Answer 3.

Exercise 2

Work out a quarter of:

(a) 20 **(b)** 4 **(c)** 32 **(d)** 40
(e) 24 **(f)** 16 **(g)** 28 **(h)** 36

Answers to Pupils' Book

8 Fractions

Exercise 8A

1 **(a)** 2 **(b)** 4 **(c)** 3 **(d)** 7 **(e)** 5 **(f)** 12
2 **(a)** 2 **(b)** 10 **(c)** 6 **(d)** 8 **(e)** 7 **(f)** 16
3 **(a)** 3, 2, $\frac{2}{3}$ **(b)** 5, 1, $\frac{1}{5}$ **(c)** 8, 2, $\frac{2}{8}(=\frac{1}{4})$ **(d)** 6, 1, $\frac{1}{6}$ **(e)** 9, 3, $\frac{3}{9}(=\frac{1}{3})$ **(f)** 16, 3, $\frac{3}{16}$
4 **(a)** $\frac{1}{4}$ **(b)** $\frac{1}{3}$ **(c)** $\frac{2}{4}(=\frac{1}{2})$ **(d)** $\frac{1}{6}$ **(e)** $\frac{1}{5}$ **(f)** $\frac{2}{8}(=\frac{1}{4})$
5 **(a)** $\frac{1}{25}$ **(b)** $\frac{7}{25}$ **(c)** $\frac{18}{25}$
6 **(a)** $\frac{2}{6}=\frac{1}{3}$ **(b)** $\frac{4}{6}=\frac{2}{3}$

Exercise 8B

1 **(a)** one third **(b)** two thirds **(c)** three fifths **(d)** one tenth **(e)** five sixths **(f)** three quarters **(g)** five sevenths **(h)** three eighths
2 **(a)** $\frac{3}{4}$ **(b)** $\frac{1}{2}$ **(c)** $\frac{2}{5}$ **(d)** $\frac{3}{10}$ **(e)** $\frac{5}{8}$ **(f)** $\frac{1}{6}$
3 **(a)** half, $\frac{1}{2}$ **(b)** five eighths, $\frac{5}{8}$ **(c)** three quarters, $\frac{3}{4}$ **(d)** three eighths, $\frac{3}{8}$
5 **(a)** one half **(b)** one quarter **(c)** one sixth
6 one half
7 four twelfths, $\frac{4}{12}=\frac{1}{3}$
8 **(a)** $\frac{460}{1000}=\frac{23}{50}$ **(b)** $\frac{540}{1000}=\frac{27}{50}$

Exercise 8C

1 **(a)** 7 **(b)** 9 **(c)** 8 **(d)** 8
2 **(a)** 5 biscuits **(b)** £6 **(c)** 4 kg **(d)** 16 hours **(e)** 6p
3 2 km
4 **(a)** 50 cartons of orange juice **(b)** 15 cartons of pineapple
5 **(a)** 5 **(b)** 6
6 £1.00
7 72 books

Exercise 8D

1 $\frac{1}{10}$ of 100 m = 10 m.
$\frac{1}{5}$ of 100 m = 20 m.
Jill has run furthest.
2 Gina uses 25 tiles.
Diana uses 20 tiles.
Gina uses the most tiles.
3 Amy gets £10.
Mary gets £18.
Tom gets £62. Tom gets the most.
4 **(a)**
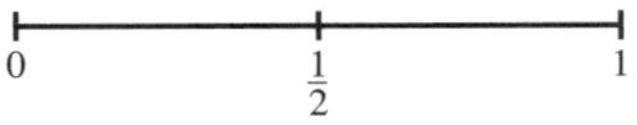

(b)
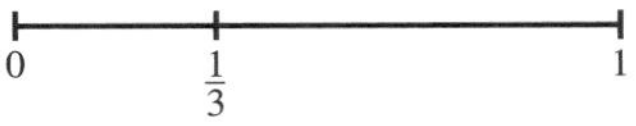

(c)

(d)

(e) $\frac{1}{5}, \frac{1}{4}, \frac{1}{3}, \frac{1}{2}$.

Exercise 8E

1 **(a)** $\frac{3}{5}$ **(b)** $\frac{4}{10}=\frac{2}{5}$ **(c)** $\frac{7}{9}$ **(d)** $\frac{3}{3}=1$ **(e)** The answer is 1 whole.
2 **(a)** $\frac{5}{8}$ **(b)** $\frac{8}{10}(=\frac{4}{5})$ **(c)** $\frac{6}{7}$ **(d)** $\frac{10}{13}$ **(e)** $\frac{13}{20}$ **(f)** $\frac{13}{15}$ **(g)** $\frac{22}{40}(=\frac{11}{20})$ **(h)** $\frac{19}{50}$ **(i)** $\frac{51}{100}$ **(j)** $\frac{4}{8}(=\frac{1}{2})$ **(k)** $\frac{4}{5}$ **(l)** $\frac{9}{10}$ **(m)** $\frac{14}{20}(=\frac{7}{10})$ **(n)** $\frac{4}{4}=1$ whole **(o)** $\frac{6}{4}=1\frac{2}{4}=1\frac{1}{2}$

Answers to Homeworks

8 Fractions

Exercise 8.1 — Links: 8A, 8B

1 Each tin divided into 3 equal parts.
2 **(a)** numerator **(b)** denominator
3 $\frac{4}{5}$
(a) The fraction family is fifths
(b) The fraction has 4 of these fifths
4 **(b)** fifths **(c)** quarters **(d)** eighths **(e)** sixths

Exercise 8.2 — Links: 8B, 8C

1 ($\frac{2}{3}$ two thirds) ($\frac{2}{7}$ two sevenths) ($\frac{2}{5}$ two fifths) ($\frac{5}{7}$ five sevenths)
2 **(a)** $\frac{3}{8}$ **(b)** $\frac{1}{9}$ **(c)** $\frac{2}{5}$
3 **(a)** 10 **(b)** $\frac{5}{10}=\frac{1}{2}$ **(c)** $\frac{1}{2}$ or $\frac{5}{10}$
4 **(a)** 5 **(b)** 8 **(c)** 13 **(d)** 50

Exercise 8.3 — Links: 8C, 8D

1 16
2 **(a)** £4 **(b)** 20p **(c)** 12p **(d)** £7
3 £6
4 **(a)** Bag A
(b) Pupils' own answers.
(c) $\frac{1}{2}$ is larger than $\frac{1}{3}$ because it is the whole contents divided into 2 equal parts, and $\frac{1}{3}$ is a whole divided into 3.

Exercise 8.4 — Links: 8D, 8E

1 **(a)** False **(b)** True **(c)** False
2 **(a)** 30 min **(b)** $\frac{2}{3}$
3 **(a)** $\frac{4}{7}$ **(b)** $\frac{4}{8}(=\frac{1}{2})$ **(c)** $\frac{5}{10}(=\frac{1}{2})$ **(d)** $\frac{3}{5}$ **(e)** $\frac{6}{16}(=\frac{3}{8})$ **(f)** $\frac{24}{100}(=\frac{6}{25})$

Remediation answers

8.1 Finding halves and quarters

Exercise 1

(a) 4 **(b)** 8 **(c)** 7 **(d)** 10 **(e)** 15 **(f)** 2 **(g)** 13 **(h)** 16

Exercise 2

(a) 5 **(b)** 1 **(c)** 8 **(d)** 10 **(e)** 6 **(f)** 4 **(g)** 7 **(h)** 9

Unit 9 Perimeter, area and volume

Content summary

This unit develops the ideas of perimeter area and volume to the point of obtaining them by counting. Areas of irregular shapes on grids are covered.

Book 1R Unit 10 extends the ideas to the use of simple formulae and appropriate units. Some work is done on triangles and composite shapes. The concept of capacity is introduced.

NC level

Level 4: Although perimeter, area and volume by counting is NC Level 4 the topic is accessed at an easier point of entry than Level 4.

S4e S4g

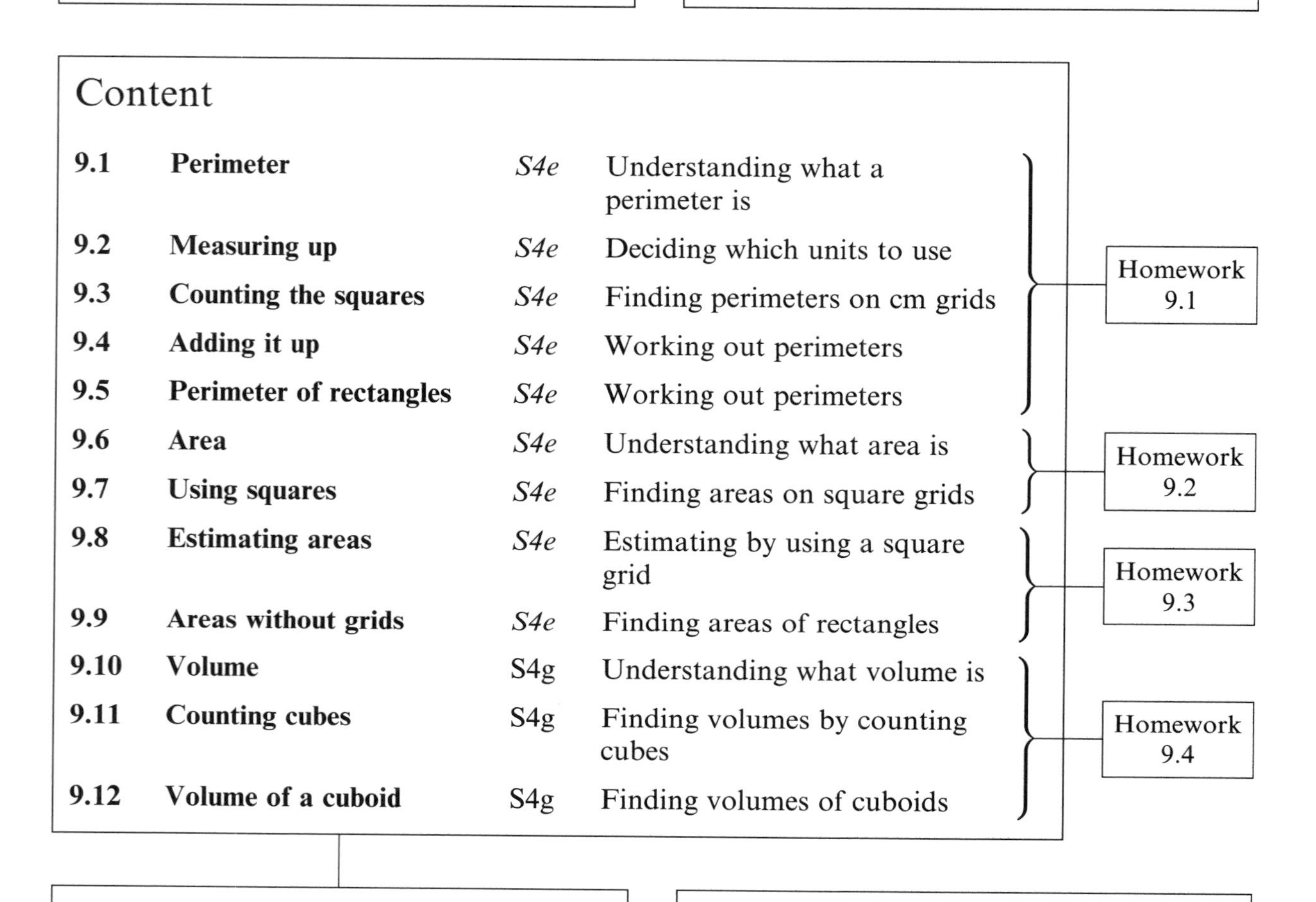

Content

9.1	**Perimeter**	*S4e*	Understanding what a perimeter is	Homework 9.1
9.2	**Measuring up**	*S4e*	Deciding which units to use	Homework 9.1
9.3	**Counting the squares**	*S4e*	Finding perimeters on cm grids	Homework 9.1
9.4	**Adding it up**	*S4e*	Working out perimeters	Homework 9.1
9.5	**Perimeter of rectangles**	*S4e*	Working out perimeters	Homework 9.1
9.6	**Area**	*S4e*	Understanding what area is	Homework 9.2
9.7	**Using squares**	*S4e*	Finding areas on square grids	Homework 9.2
9.8	**Estimating areas**	*S4e*	Estimating by using a square grid	Homework 9.3
9.9	**Areas without grids**	*S4e*	Finding areas of rectangles	Homework 9.3
9.10	**Volume**	S4g	Understanding what volume is	Homework 9.4
9.11	**Counting cubes**	S4g	Finding volumes by counting cubes	Homework 9.4
9.12	**Volume of a cuboid**	S4g	Finding volumes of cuboids	Homework 9.4

Assessment

Assessment 9 covers the key concepts in Unit 9.

Remediation

Remediation sheets 9.1 → 9.3.

Assessment

The assessment is marked out of 30.
Achievement of 20 or more marks indicates a good understanding of the key concepts.
Marking guidance, answers and links to remediation are provided on page 265.

ICT links

9.1–9.9
Use *The Geometer's Sketchpad* to draw some rectangles, triangles and non-uniform shapes. Estimate their area in square inches and square centimetres and then check your answers by displaying their correct area.

Equipment

	Pupils' Book page
Rulers	137
Squared paper	146

Remediation

Perimeter and area:
At this level it is best to split perimeter and area as pupils can often confuse the two. Encourage pupils to make use of the word perimeter for a boundary: the perimeter fence of a playground, a garden fence, etc. Use multilink for practical work but take care to only count the edges on the boundary rather than the number of cubes used.

Move on to area once the pupil's knowledge of perimeter is sound. For extra practice pupils can draw 'islands' on tracing paper and work out approximate areas. They should try to draw one smaller and one bigger than those given to encourage comparisons of area by eye – 'bigger than', 'smaller than'.

Questionbank CD

All homeworks and extension questions also appear on the CD.

Pages xvii and xviii of this pack show you how to use the CD to select questions from the Questionbank and further customize them if you wish to.

9 Perimeter, area and volume

framework teaching objective	§	lesson starter	f/w ref
Calculate the perimeter and area of shapes made from rectangles.	9.1	A rectangular hole in the pavement. How can we make sure that people don't fall into the hole? *'We can put a metal guard around the edges'.* (2 m, 5 m) How long will the metal guard be along the top edge? (*2 m*) How long will the metal guard be along the right edge? (*5 m*) I have 10 m of metal guard in the van. Do I have enough. What maths do we use? 2 + 2 + 5 + 5 Is there a short cut? What do we call the length 'all the way around' the shape?	234–7
Calculate the perimeter and area of shapes made from rectangles.	9.6	There are two shelves in a classroom. One measures 20 cm by 3 cm. Which is the length? Which is the width? Another shelf measures 10 cm by 8 cm. Zeinab says: 'I can fit more onto the first shelf because it's longer.' Is Zeinab right? What name do we give to 'how much space' there is in a shape? How do I work out the area of the two shelves?	234–7

framework teaching objective	§	lesson starter	f/w ref
Calculate the area of shapes made from rectangles.	9.8	Draw three squares on the board and add red 'dots' like so: 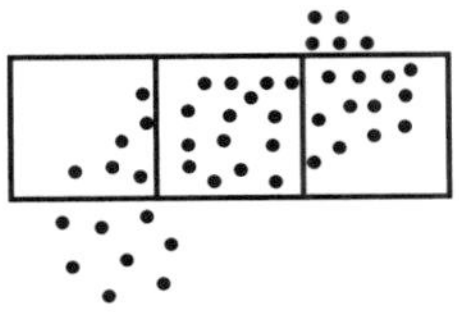 Are there enough red 'dots' on the board to 'dot in' the 3 squares? Now draw four squares with dots: 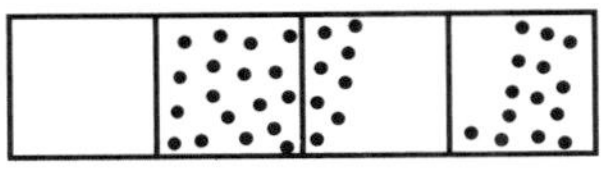 How many **complete** squares could I dot in? Each of these plots is $1\ m^2$. What **area** is covered in grass? path grass 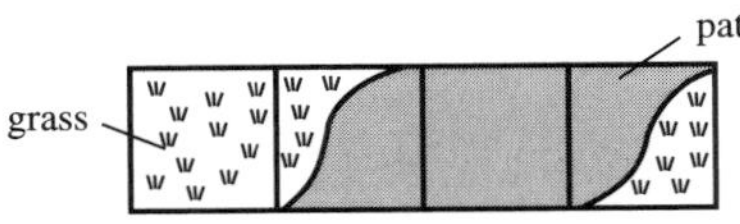	234–7
Know and use the formula for volume of a cuboid.	9.10	Two tanks. Length by width by height Tank A 8 cm by 5 cm by 12 cm Tank B 10 cm by 6 cm by 5 cm Sophie says: 'I can fit more water into tank B because it's longer and wider than tank A'. Chantelle says: 'I can fit more water into tank A because it's taller than tank B'. Who is right? How do we find out? What 3 measures do I need to find the volume?	238–41

9 Perimeter, area and volume

Exercise 9.1 **Links: 9A, 9B, 9C, 9D, 9E**

1 Here are the names of four flat shapes.
List them in order of the length of their perimeter.
Start with the smallest.

A domino, a table cloth, a postage stamp, an envelope

2 Which standard unit of length would be most sensible for measuring the perimeter of:

(a) an athletics field **(b)** a postage stamp **(c)** a county?

3 Each of these shapes has been drawn on centimetre squared paper.

Work out the perimeter of each shape.

(a)

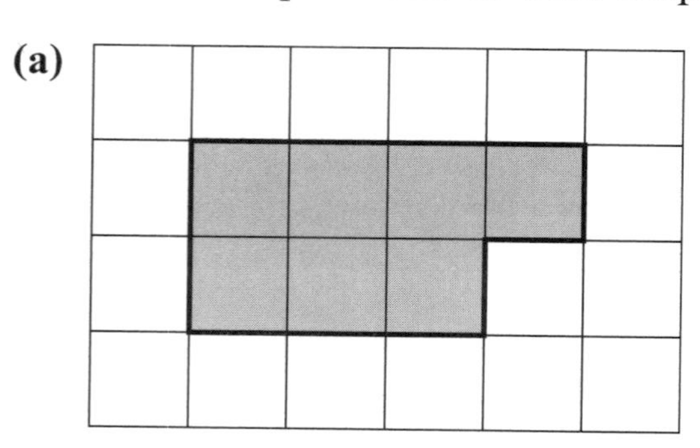

(b)

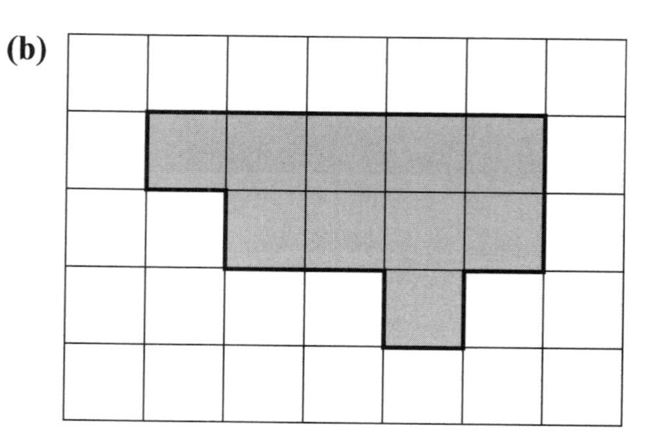

4 Work out the perimeters of each of these shapes.

(a)

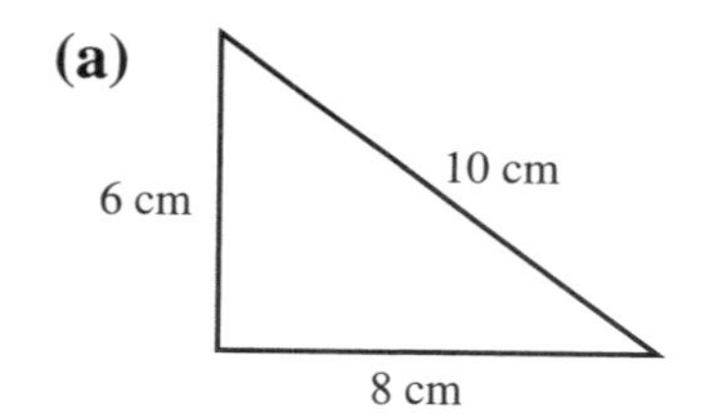

(b)

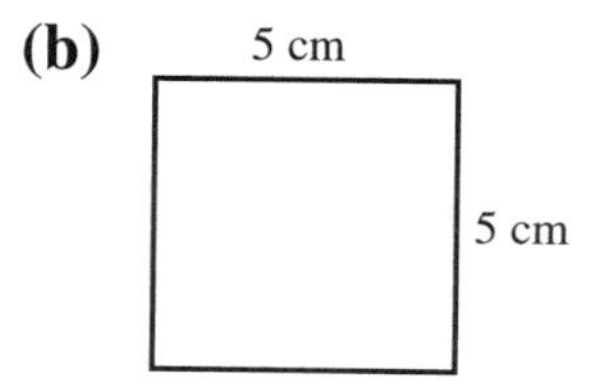

(c)

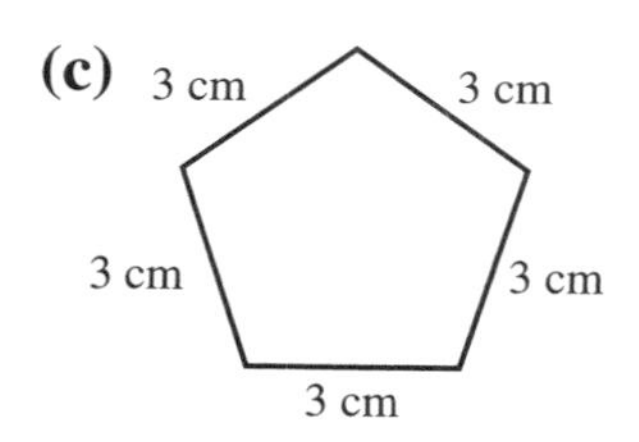

(d)

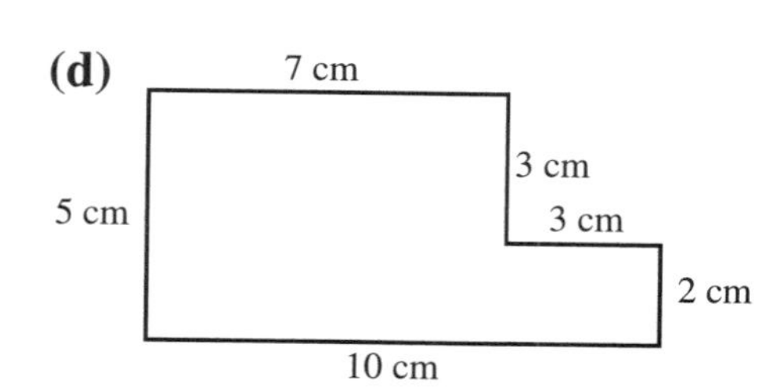

5 Find the perimeter of:

(a) A field which is a rectangle measuring 200 m by 150 m.

(b) A rectangular carpet measuring 4 m by 3 m.

(c) A rectangular sheet of paper measuring 25 cm by 15 cm.

Remember: Always give the units in your answers

Exercise 9.2 — Links: 9F, 9G

1 Here are the names of four flat shapes.
List them in order of the size of their area.
Start with the smallest.

A page of this book, a football pitch,
a county in England, a postage stamp.

2 Which units of area would you use to measure the area of:

(a) a postage stamp **(b)** the floor of a room
(c) a page of this book **(d)** Ireland?

3 These shapes are drawn on centimetre squared paper.

Work out the area of each shape.

(a)

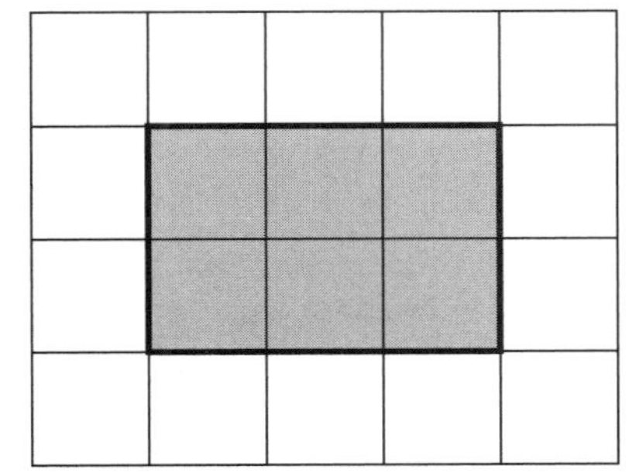

(b)

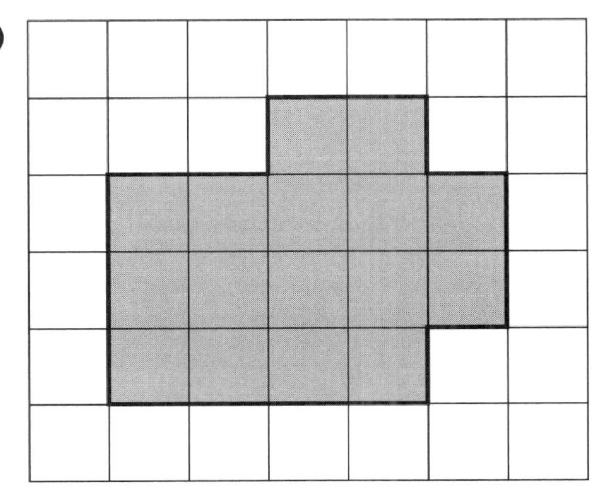

(c)

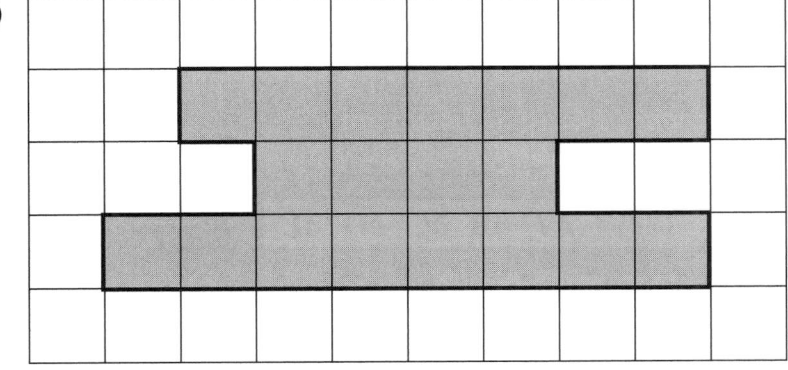

4 Pat has laid this patio in her garden.
Each slab is a square with 1 metre sides.

(a) Work out the perimeter of the patio.

(b) Work out the area of the patio.

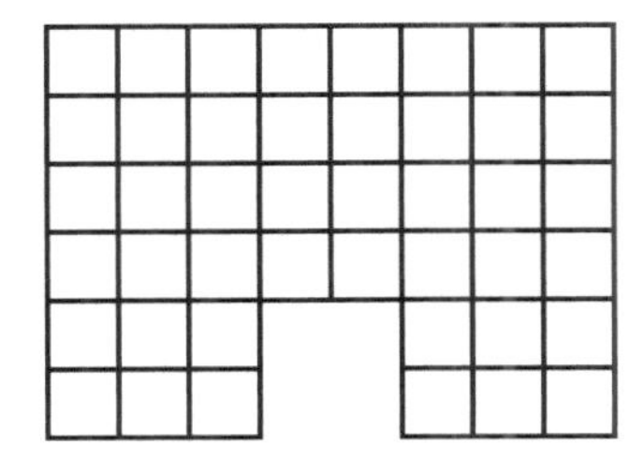

Exercise 9.3 Links: 9H, 9I

1 Each of these shapes has been drawn on centimetre squared paper.
Estimate the area of each shape.

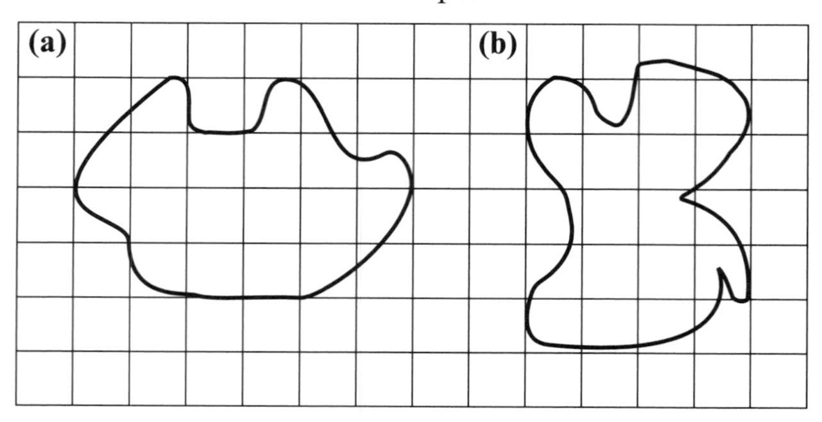

2 Work out the area of each of these rectangles.

(a)

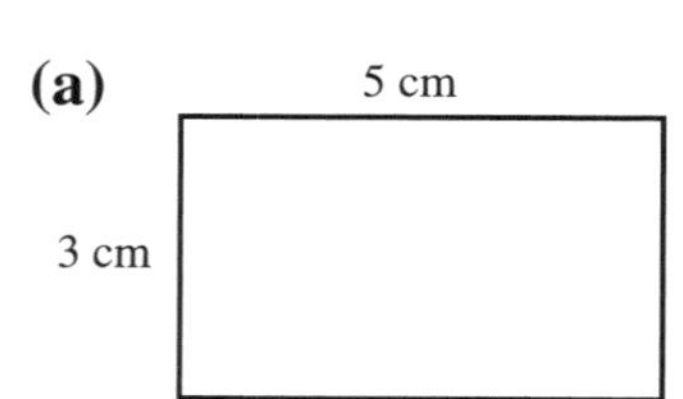

(b)

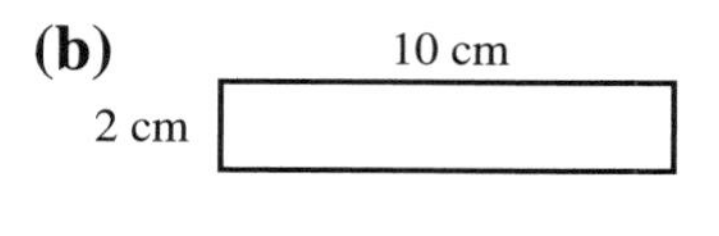

(c)

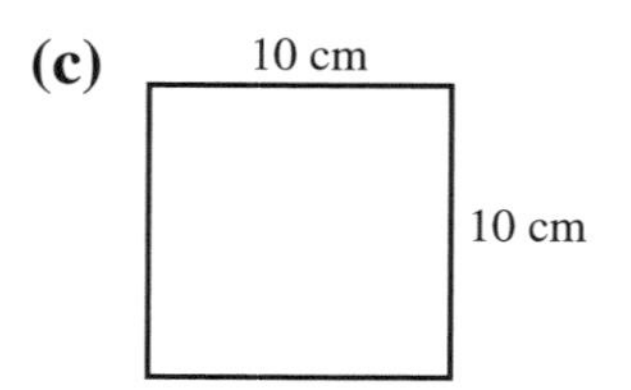

(d)

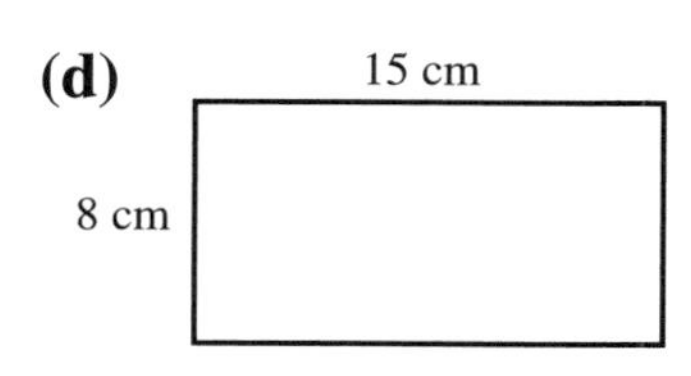

3 A rectangular fence measures 2 m by 15 m.
Work out:

(a) the perimeter of the fence

(b) the area of the fence.

4 A square lawn has sides of length 7 metres.
Work out:

(a) the perimeter of the lawn

(b) the area of the lawn.

5 Which of these shapes has the greater area, and by how much?
Show all your working.

Shape A: A square with side of length 10 cm

Shape B: A rectangle measuring 8 cm by 12 cm

Exercise 9.4 Links: 9J, 9K, 9L

1 List these solid objects in order of volume size.
Start with the smallest.

An apple, a pin, a mountain, a woman

2 Work out the volume of these shapes made from centimetre cubes.

(a)

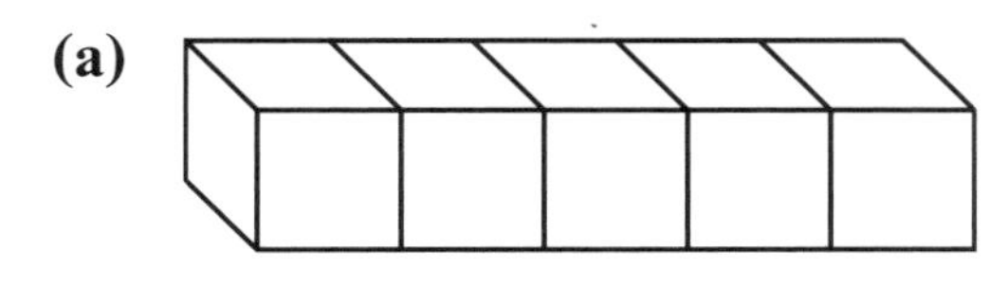

(b)

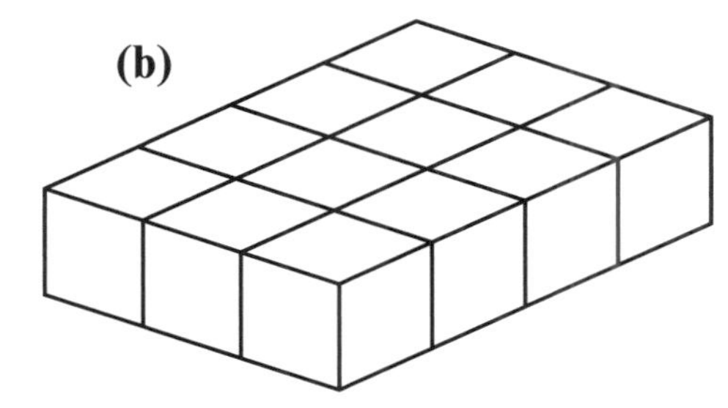

3 Each of these shapes has been made with centimetre cubes.
Find the volume of each shape.

(a)

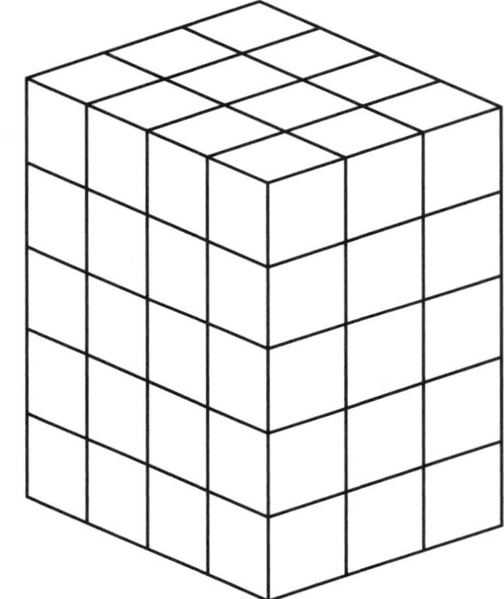

(b)

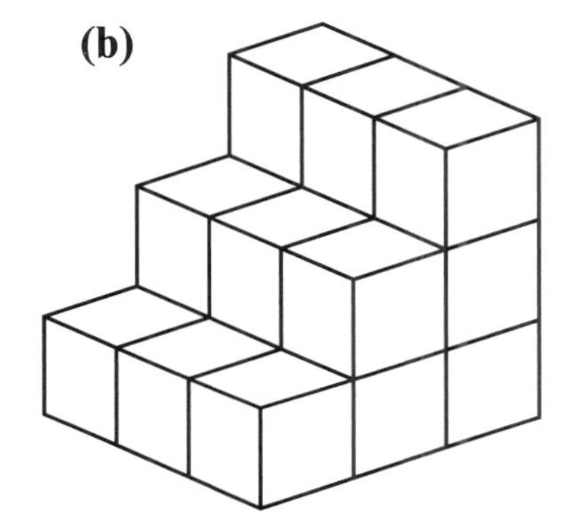

4 Anne-Marie wants to make this cuboid.

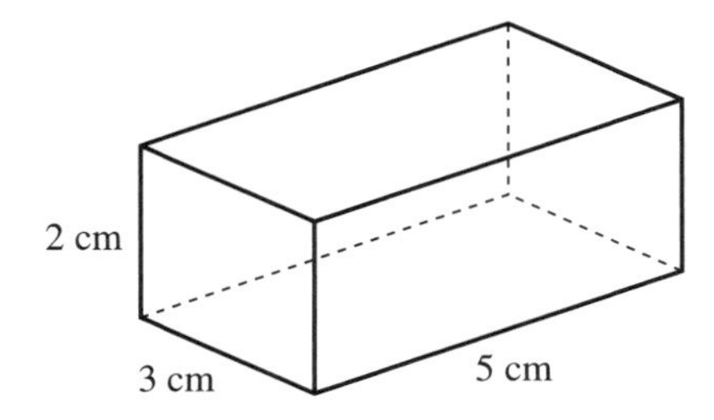

She is going to use centimetre cubes.
How many centimetre cubes will she need?

Name ....

9 Perimeter, area and volume

1 Look at these four shapes.

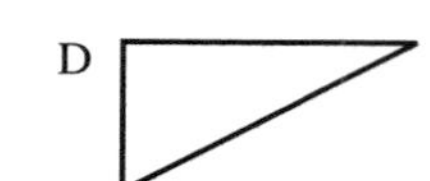

List them in order of perimeter size.
Start with the smallest. .... **(2 marks)**

---

2 Which would be the most sensible units of length to use to measure:

(a) the perimeter of this page ....

(b) the perimeter of a tennis court? .... **(2 marks)**

---

3 Each of these shapes has been drawn on cm^2 paper.
Work out the perimeter of each shape.

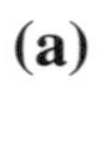
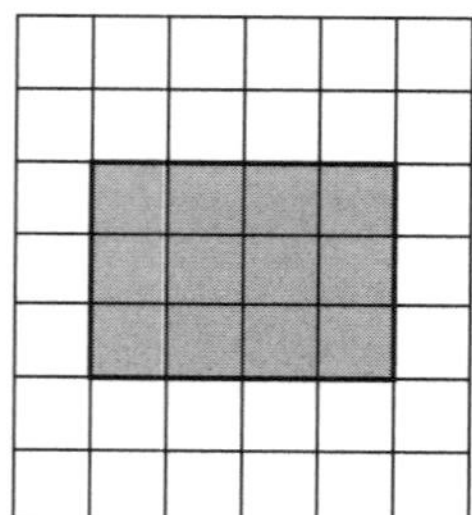

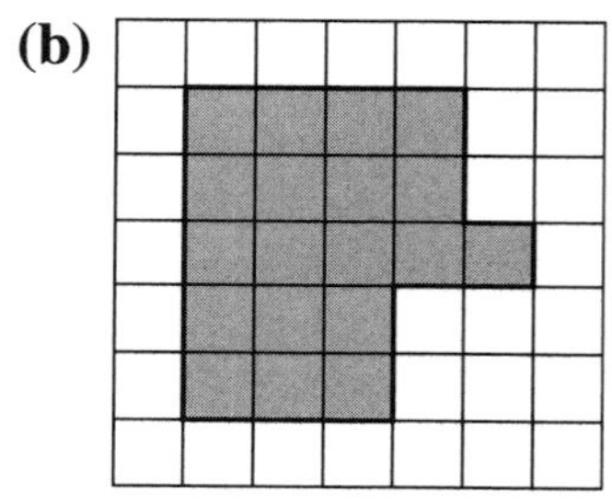

Perimeter = ... cm   Perimeter = ... cm **(2 marks)**

---

4 Work out the perimeter of each of these shapes.
Show your working.

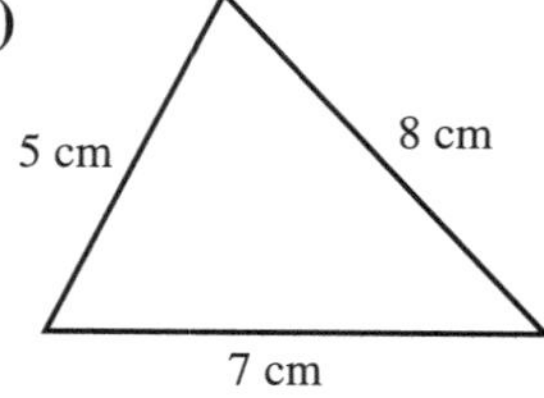

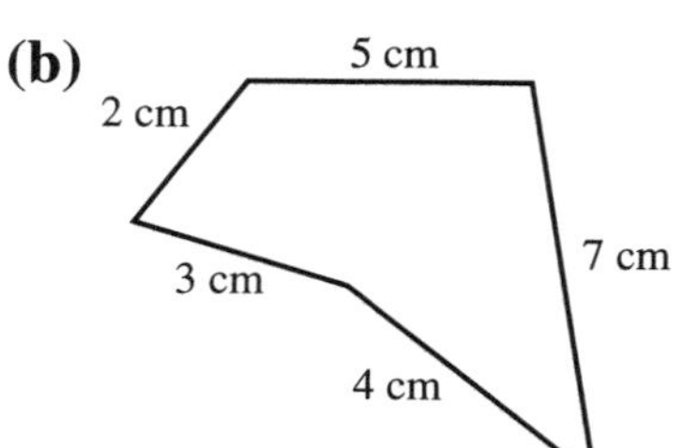

Perimeter = ... cm   Perimeter = ... cm **(4 marks)**

---

5 **Show your working in each part of this question.**

(a) Work out the perimeter of this rectangle.

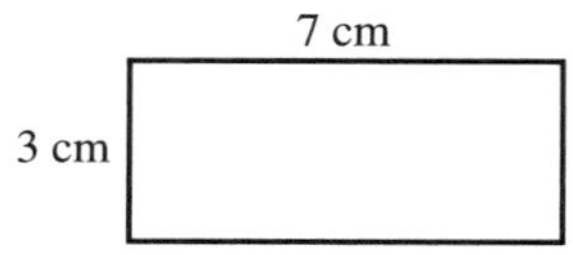

7 cm

3 cm

.... cm

(b) A rectangular floor space has a length of 8 metres and a width of 5 metres.
Work out the perimeter of the floor. .... m **(4 marks)**

---

6 In the space below sketch three flat shapes in order of **area** size.
The first shape should have the smallest area.

(2 marks)

---

7 Each of the shapes below has been draw on cm^2 paper.

(a) Work out the area of this shape.

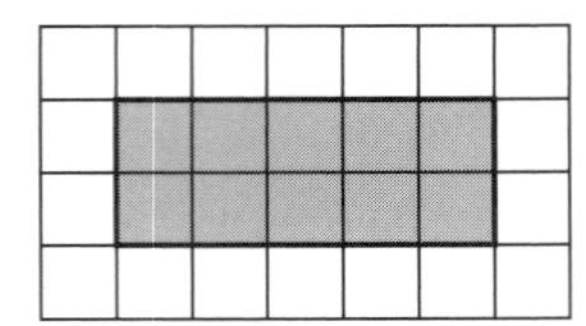

.... cm^2

(b) Work out the area of this shape.

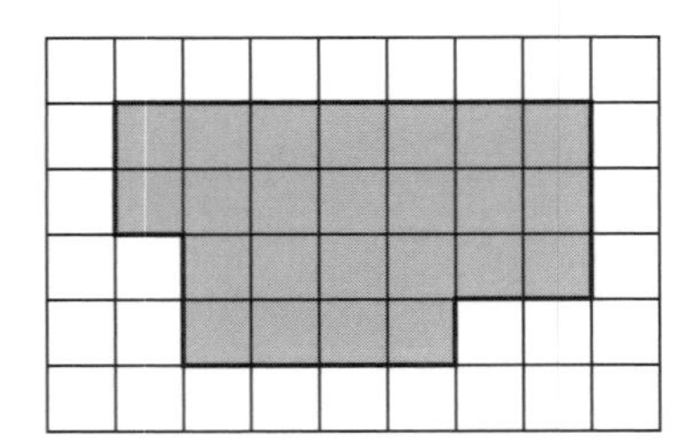

.... cm^2

(c) Estimate the area of this shape.
Show your working.

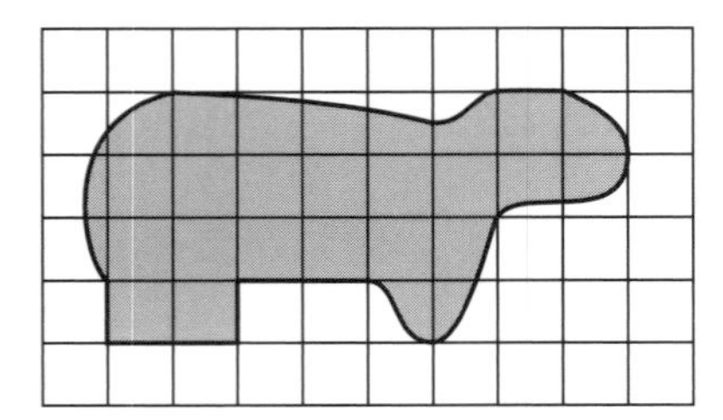

.... cm^2 **(4 marks)**

---

8 **Show your working in both parts of this question.**

(a) Work out the area of this rectangle.

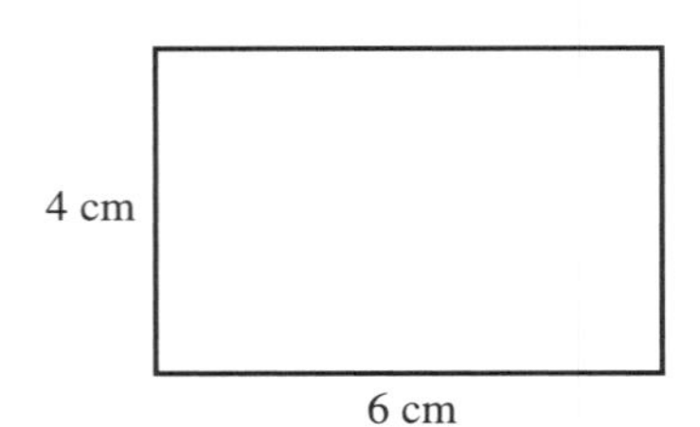

.... cm^2

(b) A rectangular carpet measures 5 metres by 4 metres.
Work out the area of this carpet.

.... **(4 marks)**

---

9 Write these solid objects in order of volume.
Start with the smallest.

A potato **A man** **A sugar cube**

.... **(2 marks)**

---

10 The shapes drawn below have been made out of cm^3 cubes.
Find the volume of each shape.

(a)

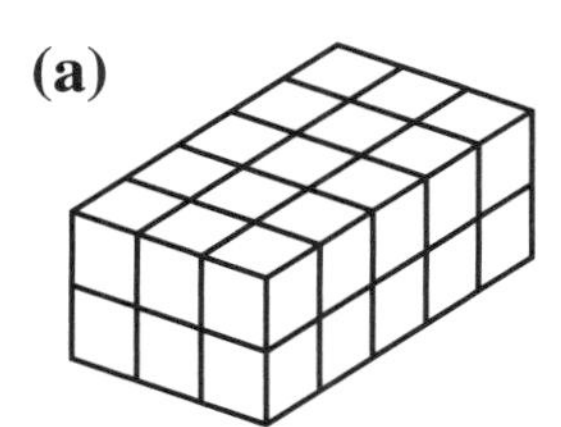

(b)

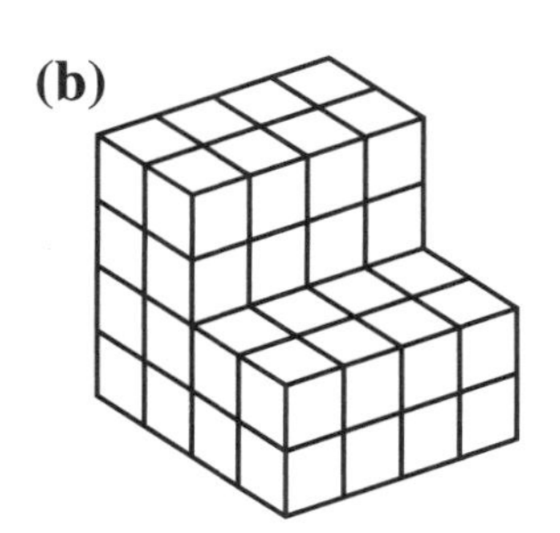

Volume = ... cm^3 Volume = ... cm^3 **(2 marks)**

---

11 **Show your working.**
The diagram shows a cuboid.
Work out the volume of this cuboid.

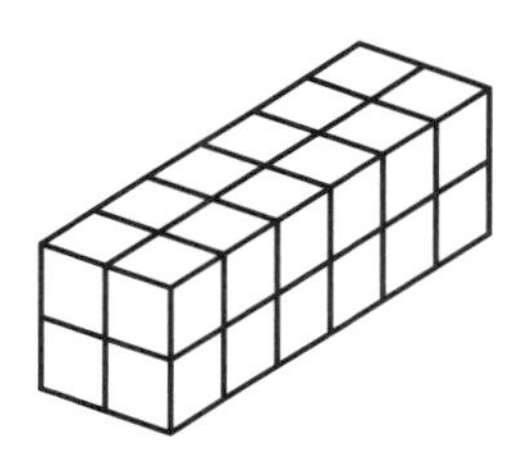

.... cm^3 **(2 marks)**

Unit 9 Perimeter, area and volume

Question		Answer	Marking guidance and remediation sheet links	
1		C, B, D, A	B2 all correct B1 one out of place	
2	**(a)**	cm	A1	
	(b)	m	A1	
3	**(a)**	14 cm	A1	
	(b)	20 cm	A1	
4	**(a)**	20 cm	M1 for $5 + 8 + 7$, A1 for 20	less than $\frac{6}{8}$ use remediation sheet 9.1
	(b)	21 cm	M1 for $5 + 7 + 4 + 3 + 2$, A1 for 21 cm	
5	**(a)**	20 cm	M1 for $7 + 3 + 7 + 3$, A1 for 20	
	(b)	26 m	M1 for $8 + 5 + 8 + 5$ or $2(8 + 5)$, A1 for 26	
6		3 shapes drawn (2-D)	B2 for 3 2-D shapes in order of area B1 for 1 shape out of order or reversed order	
7	**(a)**	10 cm^2	A1	less than $\frac{6}{8}$ use remediation sheets 9.2 → 9.3
	(b)	24 cm^2	A1	
	(c)	23 cm^2	B2 for 22, 23, 24 B1 for 21 or 25	
8	**(a)**	24 cm^2	M1 for 6×4, A1 for 24 cm^2	
	(b)	20 m^2	M1 for $5 \times 4 = 20$, A1 for 20 m^2	

Key to mark scheme
A marks: correct answer
M marks: correct method
B marks: independent work

Page 265 gives a general guidance on use of this assessment scheme with some examples.

Assessment and remediation links

Question		Answer	Marking guidance and remediation sheet links
9		Sugar cube, potato, man	B2 for all correct B1 for 1 out of order
10	**(a)**	$30\,\text{cm}^3$	A1
	(b)	$48\,\text{cm}^3$	A1
11		$2 \times 2 \times 6 = 24\,\text{cm}^3$	M1 for $2 \times 2 \times 6$, A1 for $24\,\text{cm}^3$

Key to mark scheme
A marks: correct answer
M marks: correct method
B marks: independent work

Page 265 gives a general guidance on use of this assessment scheme with some examples.

9.1 Perimeters

Remember the **perimeter** is the measurement all around the outside.

This garden has a fence all along each side. The lengths of the sides are

15 m
10 m
5 m
20 m

10 m, 15 m, 5 m and 20 m

So the perimeter of the garden is 10 m + 15 m + 5 m + 20 m = 50 m

Example 1

Find the perimeter of this shape.

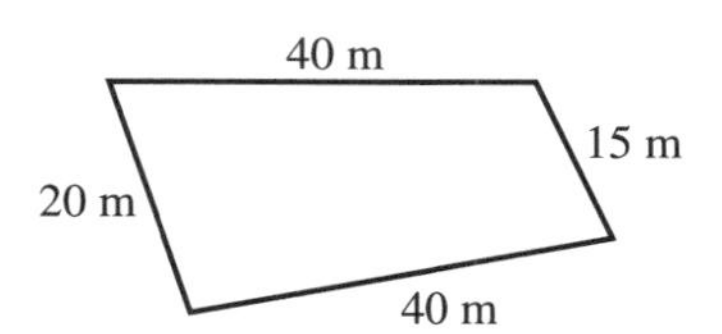

Answer: 40 + 15 + 40 + 20 = 115 m.

Exercise 1

Find the perimeters of these shapes.

(a) 10 m, 15 m, 20 m, 20 m

(b) 30 m, 40 m, 50 m, 40 m

(c) 70 m, 60 m, 85 m

(d) 4 m, 4 m, 5 m, 4 m, 3 m

(e) 112 m, 200 m, 70 m, 100 m, 70 m

(f)

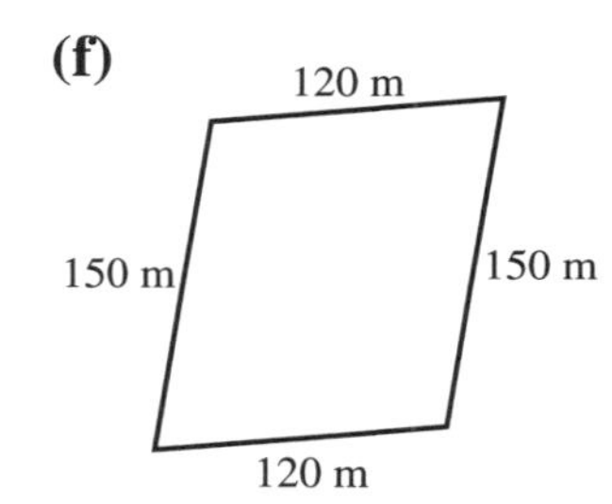

(g) 75 m, 50 m, 120 m

(h)

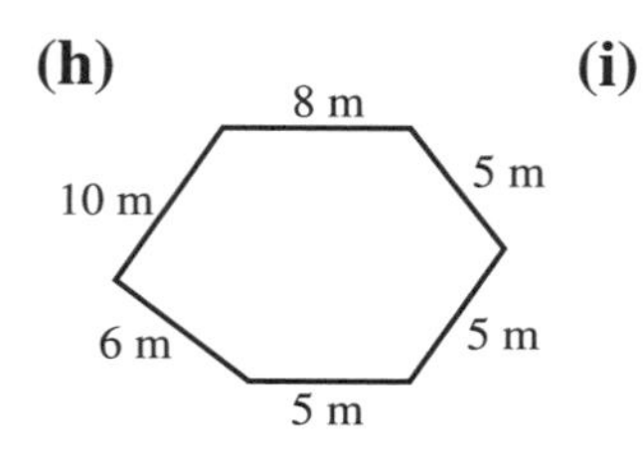

(i)

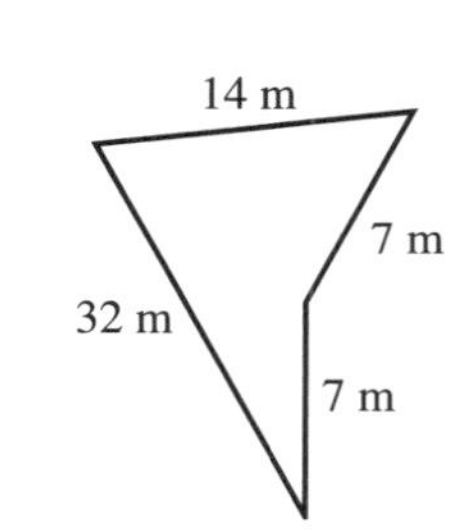

This perimeter fence surrounds the playground.

300 metres of fencing were needed.

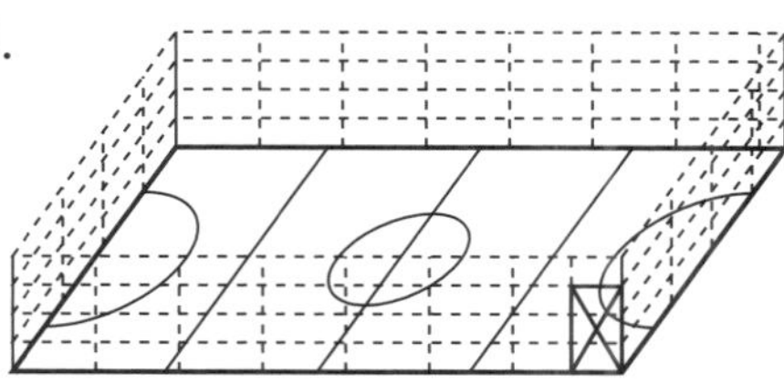

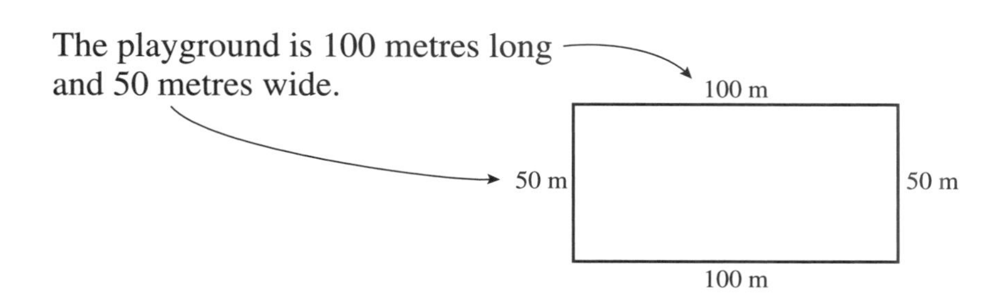

The perimeter is $100 + 50 + 100 + 50 = 300$ metres.

Example 2

What is the length of this perimeter fence?

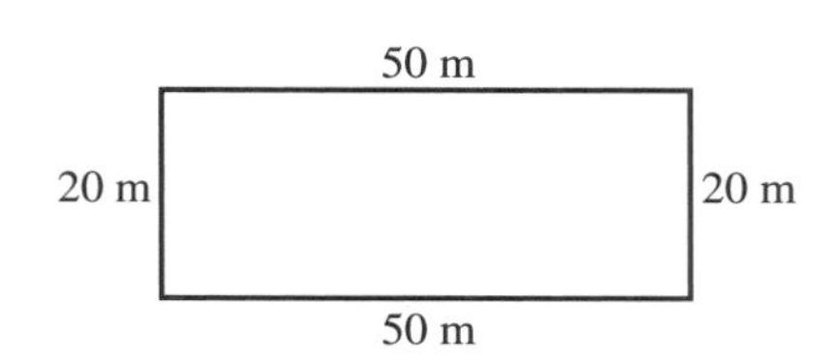

Answer: $50 + 20 + 50 + 20 = 140$ metres.

Exercise 2

Find the lengths of these perimeter fences.

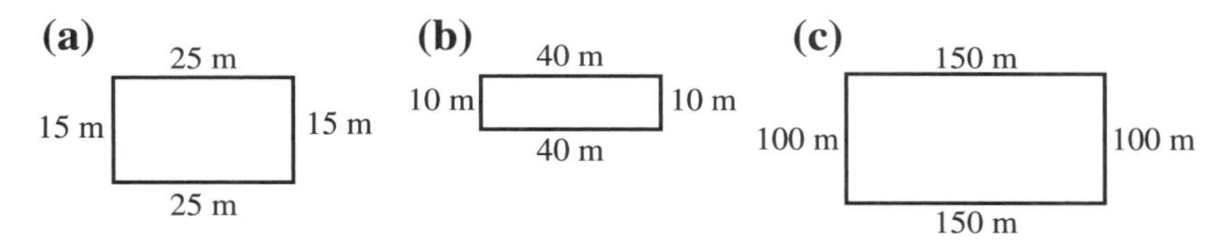

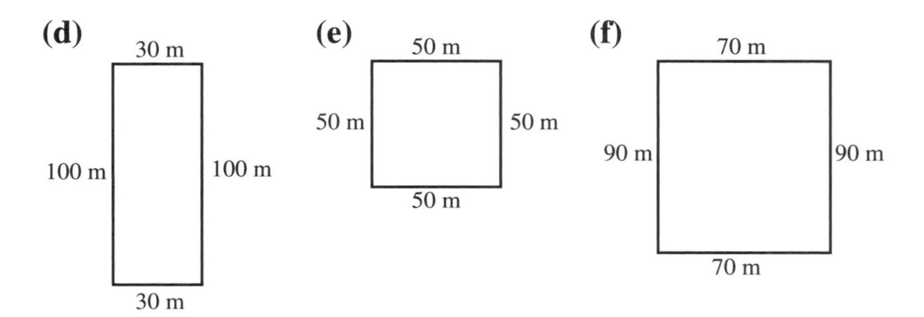

9.2 Area

The area of a flat shape is the amount of space it covers.

Example 1

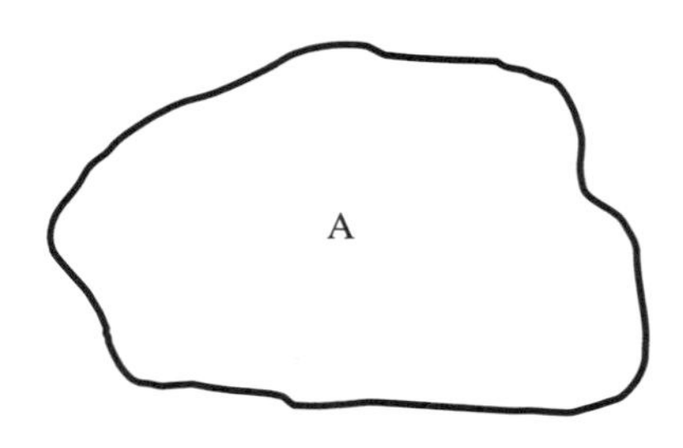

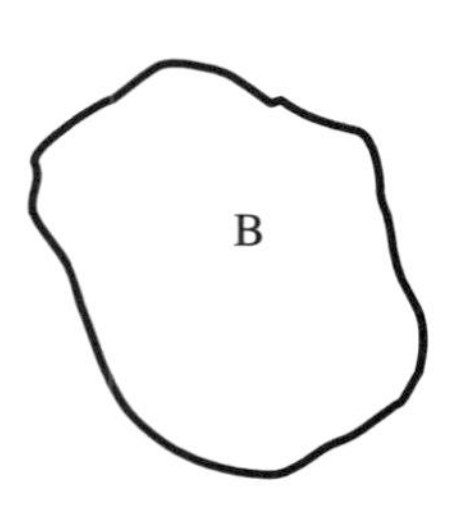

Trace the two shapes and cut them out. Put B on top of A.
You can see shape A is larger than shape B.
(Save your tracing to use later).

Shape A covers more space.
Shape A has the largest area.

Exercise 1

1 Write down which shape is larger, A or B.
To help, trace each pair and cut them out.

(a) 

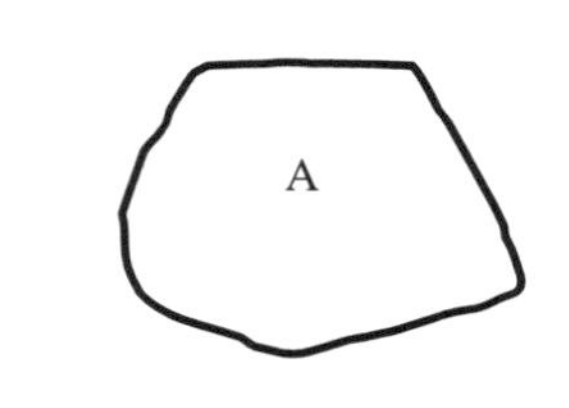

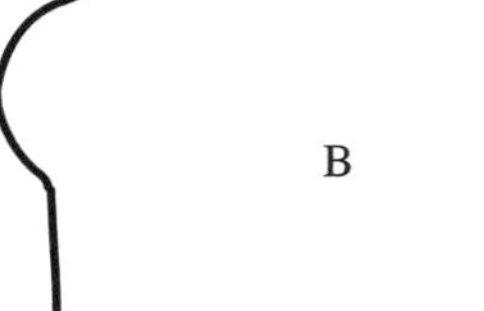

(b)

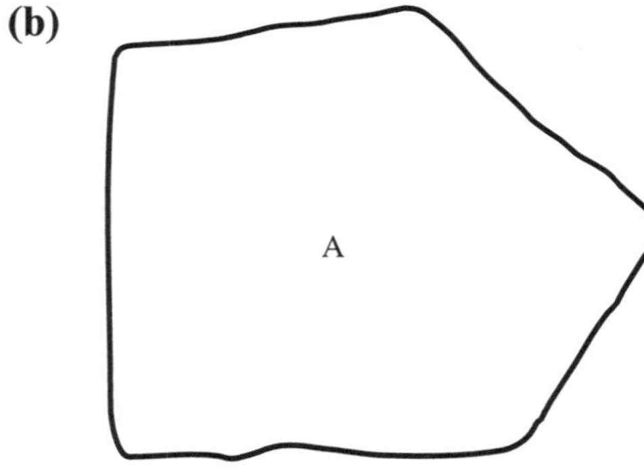

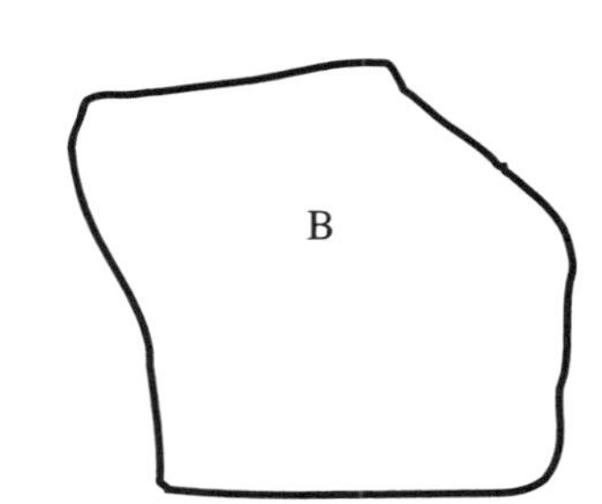

(c)

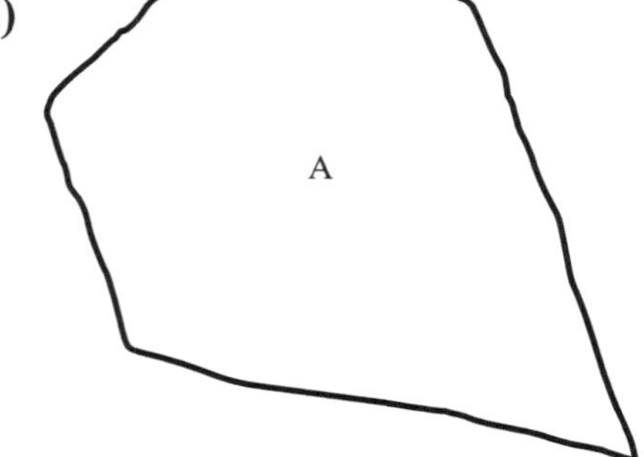

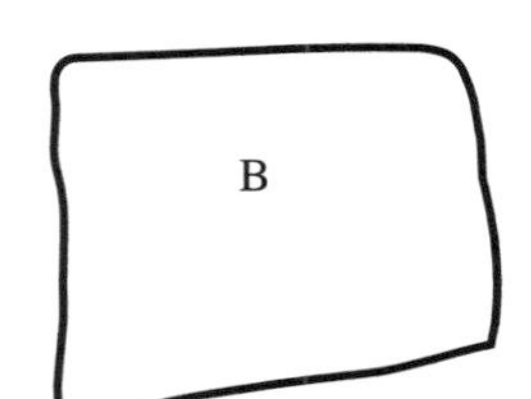

9.3 Area by counting squares

To find the area of a shape use 1 cm squared paper.
Trace the shape and put it on the squared paper like this:
Put a dot in the **whole** squares and the squares that are **half or more**.

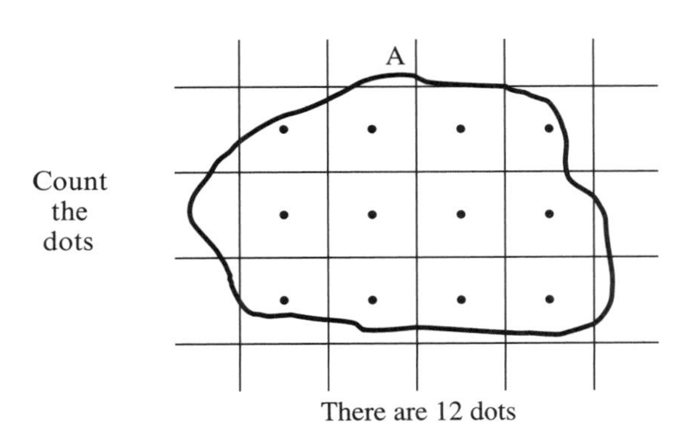

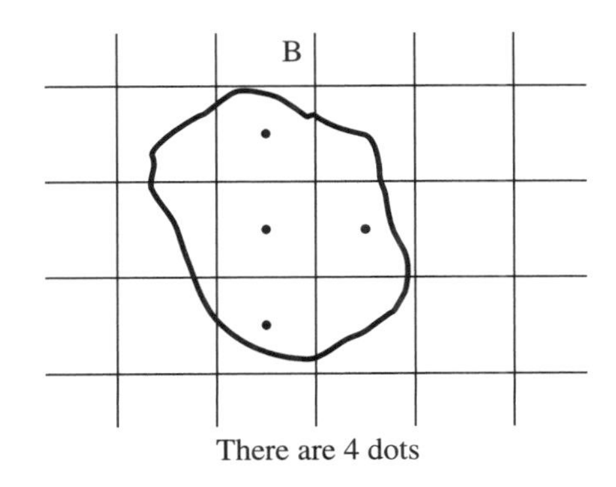

This shows that shape A has area: 12 cm squares or 12 cm^2 for short
and shape B has area: 4 cm squares or 4 cm^2.

Exercise 1

1 Find the area of each shape.

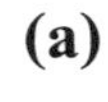
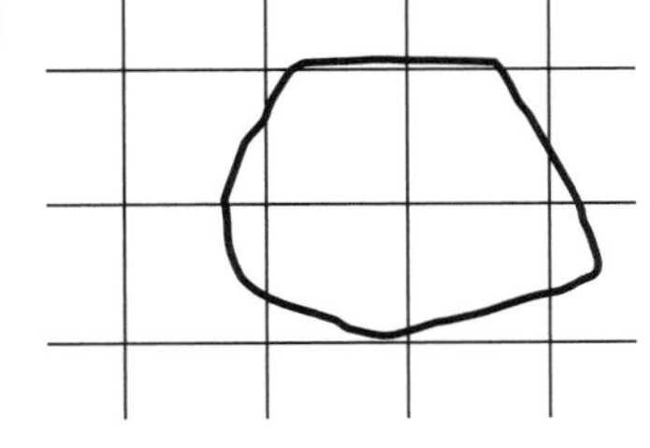

(b)

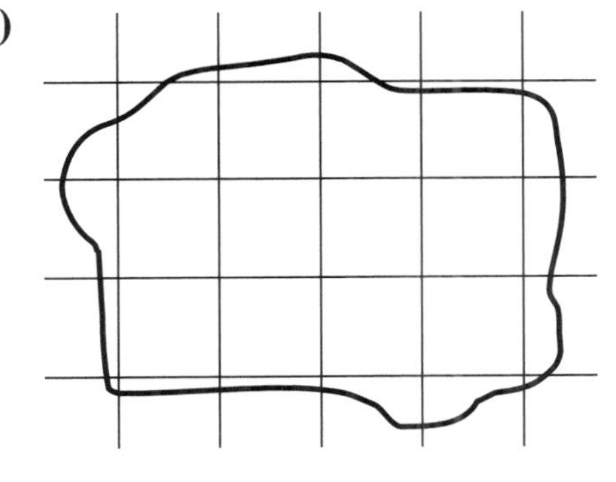

(c)

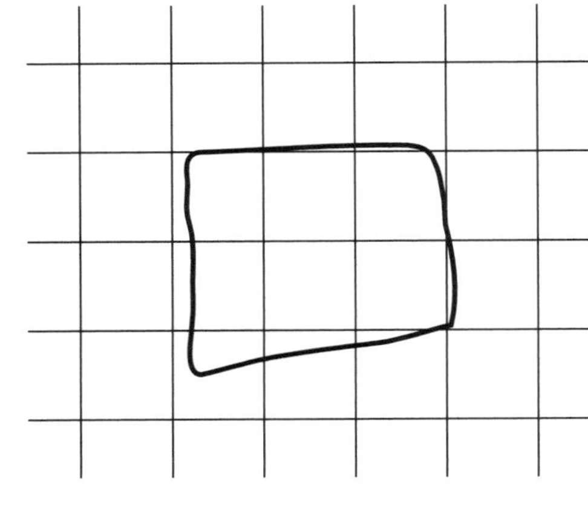

(d)

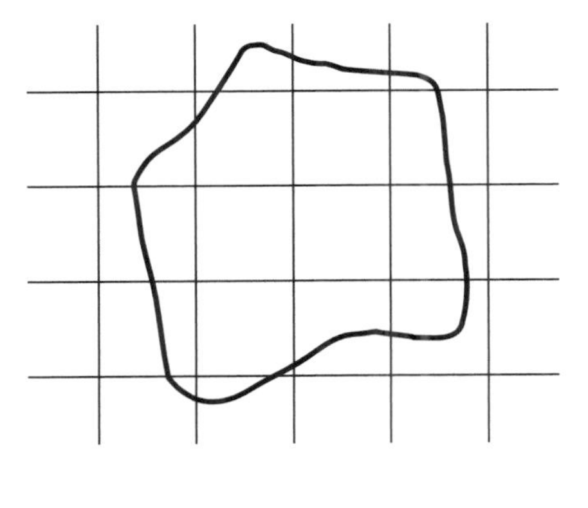

(e)

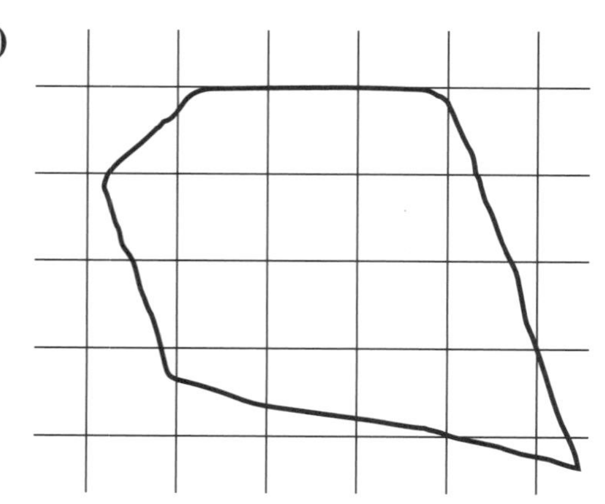

(f)

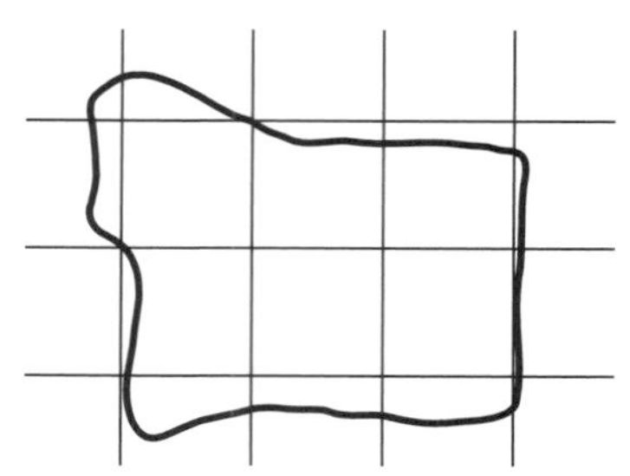

(g)

(h)

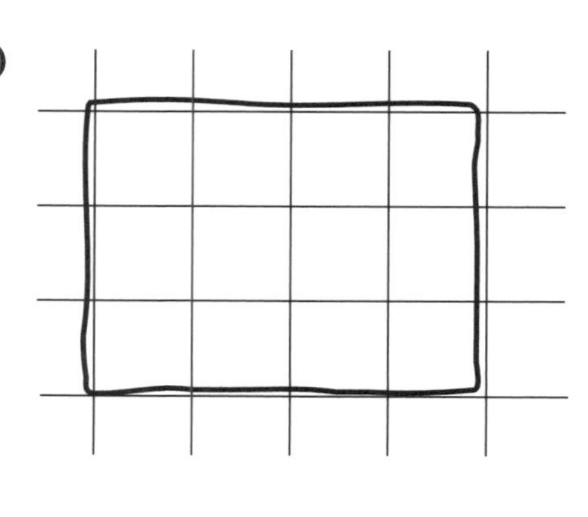

Example 1

What is the area of this sticker?

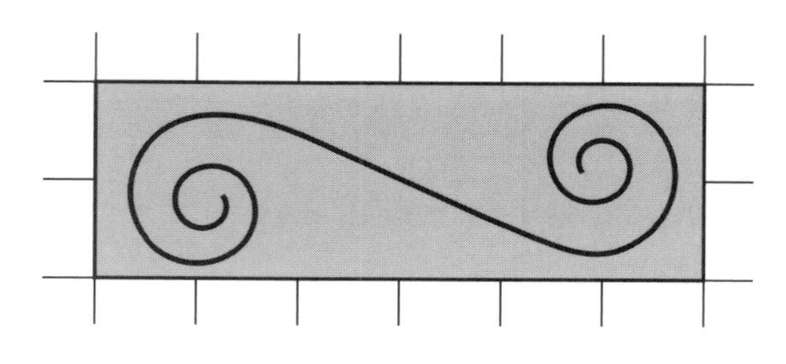

It is 6 squares wide and 2 squares high, like this:

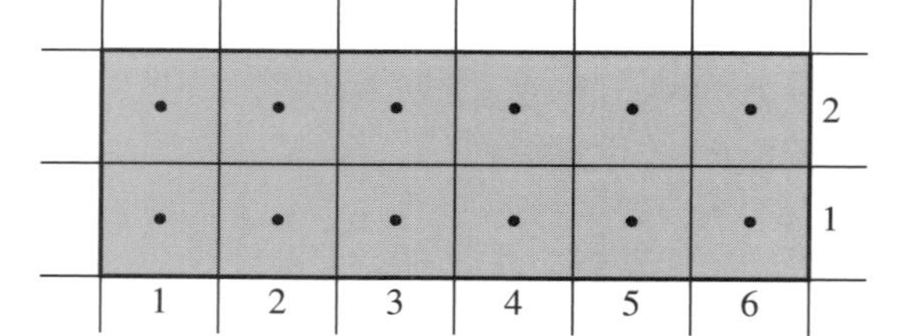

Answer: 12 cm^2.

Exercise 2

1 Find the area of each sticker.
Use cm^2 in your answers.

(a)

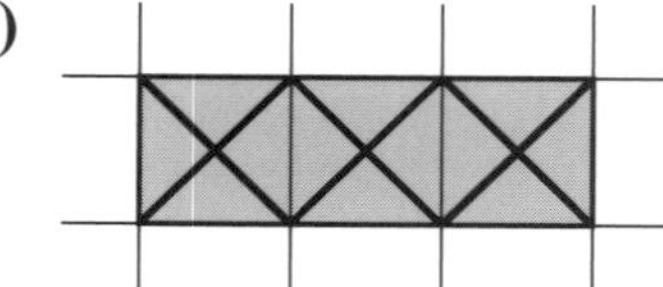

(b)

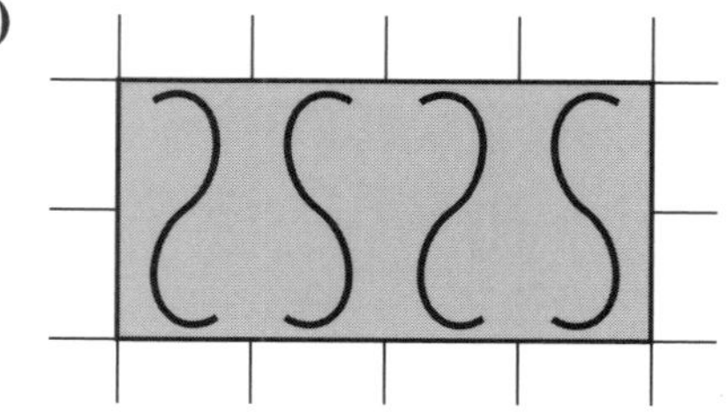

(c)

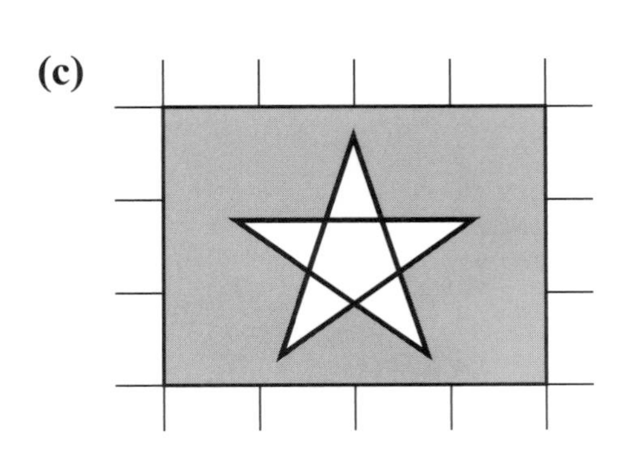

(d)

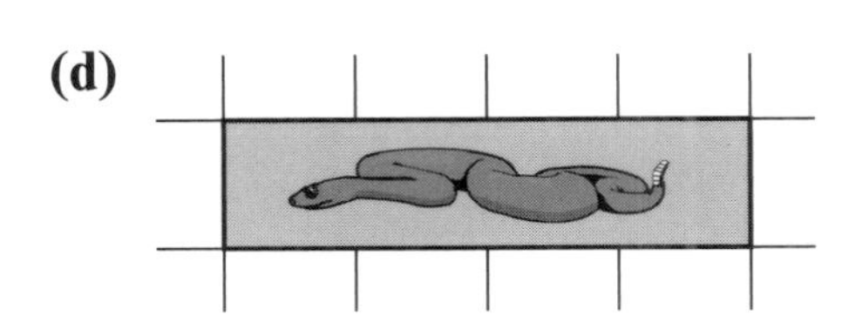

(e)

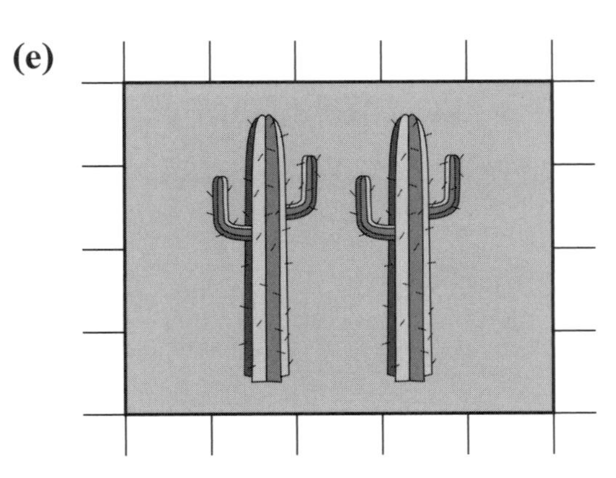

(f)

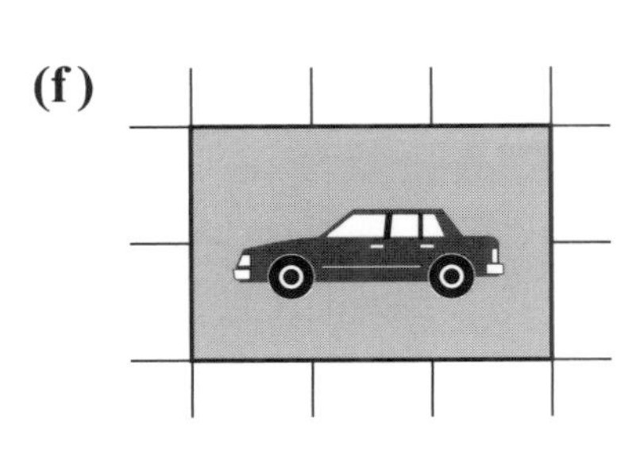

(g)

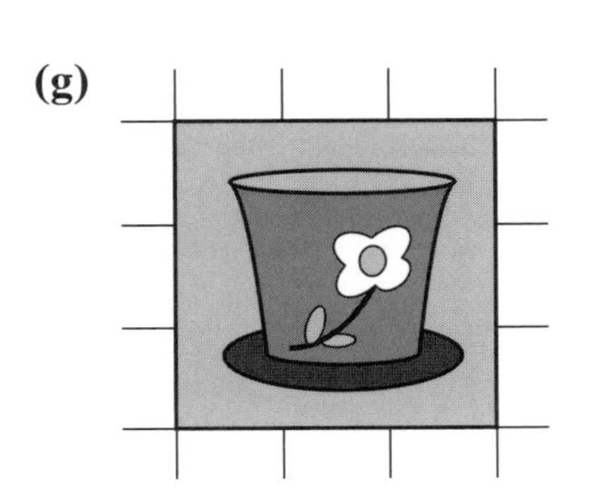

(h)

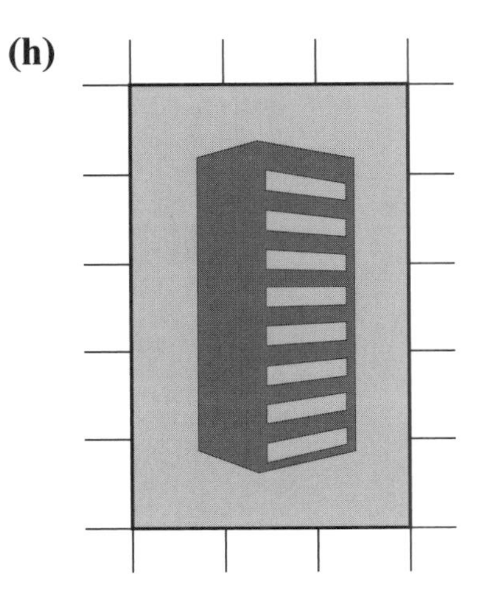

Answers to Pupils' Book

9 Perimeter, area and volume

Exercise 9A

1 (a) A (b) B
2 (a) C (b) B (c) B, D, A, E, C
3 page of book, table top, floor of room, tennis court, football pitch

Exercise 9B

1 cm 2 m 3 cm 4 m
5 km 6 m 7 m 8 cm

Exercise 9C

1 (a) 10 cm (b) 12 cm (c) 18 cm
(d) 4 cm (e) 18 cm (f) 16 cm
(g) 18 cm (h) 20 cm
2 (a) 12 cm (b) 20 cm (c) 16 cm

Exercise 9D

1 16 cm 2 13 m 3 20 cm 4 18 m
5 22 m 6 22 cm 7 16 cm 8 18 m

Exercise 9E

1 16 m
2 (a) 18 m (b) 1000 m (c) 160 m
(d) 60 cm (e) 70 m (f) 40 cm

Exercise 9F

1 (a) A (b) B
2 (a) D (b) B (c) D, A, C, E, B
3 page of book, table top, floor of room, tennis court, football pitch

Exercise 9G

1 (a) 7 cm^2 (b) 5 cm^2 (c) 14 cm^2
(d) 10 cm^2 (e) 28 cm^2 (f) 20 cm^2
2 (a) 8 cm^2 (b) 19 cm^2 (c) 14 cm^2
(d) 10 cm^2

Exercise 9H

1 32 cm^2
2 (a) 24 cm^2 (b) 13 cm^2 (c) 19 cm^2

Exercise 9I

1 (a) 2, 5, 10 cm^2
(b) 3, 6, 18 cm^2
(c) 4, 5, 20 cm^2
(d) 3, 4, 12 cm^2
2 (a) 3, 7, 21 cm^2
(b) 2, 8, 16 cm^2
(c) 2, 3, 6 cm^2
(d) 4, 6, 24 cm^2

Exercise 9J

1 (a) B (b) A
2 (a) A (b) C
3 marble, tennis ball, football, hot air balloon
4 (a) Washing up bowl
(b) washing up bowl, milk carton, teacup, teaspoon

Exercise 9K

1 10 cubic cm 2 8 cubic cm
3 16 cubic cm 4 7 cubic cm
5 14 cubic cm 6 7 cubic cm
7 14 cubic cm

Exercise 9L

1 (a) 6 (b) 4 (c) 24 cubic cm
2 (a) 12 (b) 4 (c) 48 cubic cm
3 (a) 15 (b) 6 (c) 90 cubic cm
4 (a) 8 (b) 5 (c) 40 cubic cm
5 (a) 4 (b) 6 (c) 24 cubic cm
6 (a) 10 (b) 3 (c) 30 cubic cm
7 (a) 30 (b) 3 (c) 90 cubic cm
8 (a) 28 (b) 3 (c) 84 cubic cm

Answers to Homeworks

9 Perimeter, area and volume

Exercise 9.1 Links: 9A, 9B, 9C, 9D, 9E

1 postage stamp, domino, envelope, table cloth
2 (a) metres
(b) centimetres or millimetres
(c) kilometres
3 (a) 12 cm (b) 16 cm
4 (a) 24 cm (b) 20 cm
(c) 15 cm (d) 30 cm
5 (a) 700 m (b) 14 m (c) 80 cm

Exercise 9.2 Links: 9F, 9G

1 postage stamp, page of this book, football pitch, county of England
2 (a) cm^2 (b) m^2 (c) cm^2 (d) km^2
3 (a) 6 cm^2 (b) 16 cm^2 (c) 19 cm^2
4 (a) 32 m (b) 44 m^2

Exercise 9.3 Links: 9H, 9I

1 (a) 17 cm^2 (b) 15 cm^2
2 (a) 15 cm^2 (b) 20 cm^2
(c) 100 cm^2 (d) 120 cm^2
3 (a) 34 m (b) 30 m^2
4 (a) 28 m (b) 49 m^2
5 Shape A 100 cm^2, Shape B 96 cm^2, so Shape A by 4 cm^2

Exercise 9.4 Links: 9J, 9K, 9L

1 a pin, an apple, a woman, a mountain
2 (a) 5 cm^3 (b) 12 cm^3
3 (a) 60 cm^3 (b) 18 cm^3
4 30 centimetre cubes.

Remediation answers

9.1 Perimeters

Exercise 1

(a) 65 m (b) 160 m
(c) 215 m (d) 20 m
(e) 552 m (f) 540 m
(g) 245 m (h) 39 m
(i) 60 m

Exercise 2

(a) 80 m (b) 100 m
(c) 500 m (d) 260 m
(e) 200 m (f) 320 m

9.2 Area

Exercise 1

(a) B (b) A (c) A

9.3 Area by counting squares

Exercise 1

(a) 4 cm^2 (b) 12 cm^2
(c) 6 cm^2 (d) 8 cm^2
(e) 6 cm^2 (f) 6 cm^2
(g) 15 cm^2 (h) 12 cm^2

Exercise 2

(a) 3 cm^2 (b) 8 cm^2
(c) 12 cm^2 (d) 4 cm^2
(e) 20 cm^2 (f) 6 cm^2
(g) 9 cm^2 (h) 15 cm^2

Unit 10 Formulae and equations

Content summary

This unit shows how to use and write simple word formulae. Equations are introduced through the method of balances and there is some work on simple equations using ☐ as the unknown.

Book 1R Unit 11 makes use of the algebra learned in Unit R9 to begin more formal work on equations. Inverse number machines also feature.

NC level

Level 2: The work on simple equations using ☐ as the unknown is about Level 2.
Balances are about Level 3.

Level 4: Although 'word formulae' is NC Level 4 those used in this unit are at the easy end of this level.

N4d Na5d

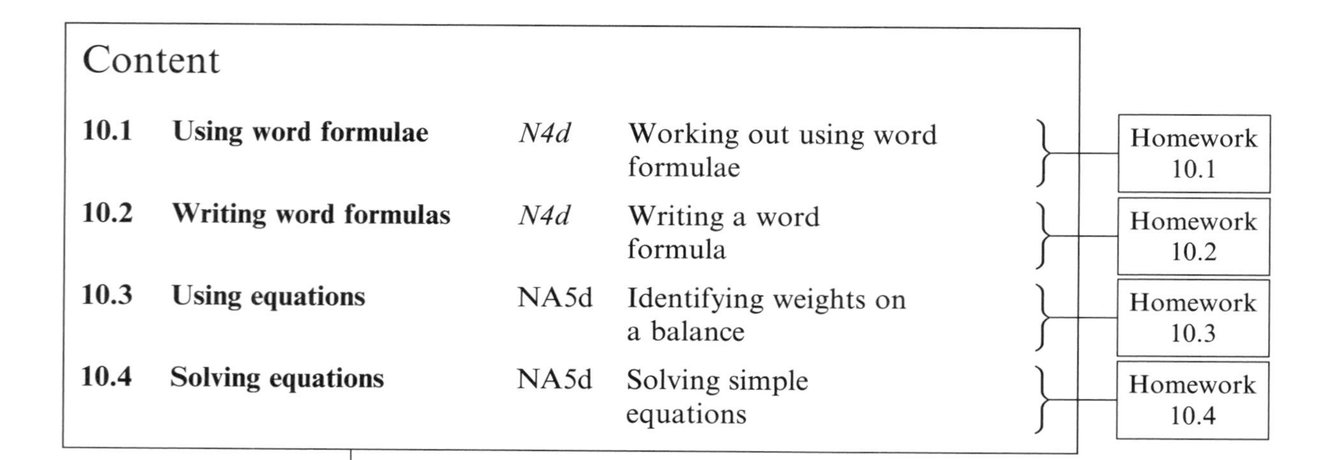

Content

10.1	**Using word formulae**	*N4d*	Working out using word formulae	Homework 10.1
10.2	**Writing word formulas**	*N4d*	Writing a word formula	Homework 10.2
10.3	**Using equations**	NA5d	Identifying weights on a balance	Homework 10.3
10.4	**Solving equations**	NA5d	Solving simple equations	Homework 10.4

Assessment

Assessment 10 covers the key concepts in Unit 10.

Remediation

Remediation sheet 10.1.

Assessment

The assessment is marked out of 30.
Achievement of 20 or more marks indicates a good understanding of the key concepts.
Marking guidance, answers and links to remediation are provided on page 265.

ICT links

10.1 and 10.2
Enter some formulae into a spreadsheet and use the formulae to generate some outputs from various inputs.

Equipment

No extra equipment needed for this chapter.

Remediation

Formulae and equations:
A practical start to using formulae can be using objects (e.g. apples) and linking the price of one to the price of more than one. Using lots of different objects (rulers, pens, pencils, etc.) at various prices can vary this activity.

Questionbank CD

All homeworks and extension questions also appear on the CD.

Pages xvii and xviii of this pack show you how to use the CD to select questions from the Questionbank and further customize them if you wish to.

10 Formulae and equations

framework teaching objective	§	lesson starter	f/w ref
Use simple formulae from maths and other subjects, and in simple cases, derive a formula	10.1	Reg delivers daffodil bulbs to gardeners. Each bulb costs 7p. Reg says: 'I've noticed that no matter how many bulbs a customer wants, I use the same type of maths every time to work out the total cost. What maths does Reg use? (*multiply by 7*) What is the cost of 4 bulbs? (*28p*) 9 bulbs? (*63p*) 6 bulbs? (*42p*) A customer places an order. What information does Reg need before he can work out the total cost? (*The number of bulbs required.*) What will he do with this number? (*multiply by 7*) What maths sentence will Reg use to explain how to find the total cost to his assistant, Tony? 'Total cost = number of bulbs × 7'	138–43
Construct and solve simple linear equations.	10.3	A set of marble bags. There are the same number in each bag. We call this number n. Romaine says: 'I have used 10 marbles to fill these bags'. n n = 10 marbles How many marbles are there in each bag? (*5*) n n n = 18 marbles What does n equal here? (*6*) Lisa says: 'I have used 15 marbles. I have put some into bags but there are 3 left over.' n n = 15 marbles How many marbles are there in each bag? (*6*)	122–5

10 Formulae and equations

Exercise 10.1 — Links: 10A

1 Andrew buys some pencils. He uses the formula

$$\text{Cost of pencils} = \text{Cost of one pencil} \times \text{number of pencils bought}$$

The cost of one pencil is 10p. Work out the cost of 2 pencils.

2 Narinder buys some sweets. She uses the formula

$$\text{Cost of sweets} = \text{Cost of one sweet} \times \text{number of sweets bought}$$

The cost of one sweet is 8p. Work out the cost of 4 sweets.

3 Jo buys some apples. She uses the formula

$$\text{Cost of apples} = \text{Cost of one apple} \times \text{number of apples bought}$$

The cost of one apple is 20p. Work out the cost of 4 apples.

4 Louise uses the formula to work out the cost of tapes.

$$\text{Cost of tapes} = \text{Cost of one tape} \times \text{number of tapes bought}$$

One tape costs £3. Work out the cost of 8 tapes.

Exercise 10.2 — Links: 10B

1 Write down a word formula to work out the cost of apples.
Use your word formula to work out the cost of 4 apples at 20p each.

2 Write down a word formula to work out the cost of bars of chocolate.
Use your word formula to work out the cost of 4 bars at 30p each.

3 Write down a word formula to work out the cost of peaches.
Use your word formula to work out the cost of 3 peaches at 20p each.

4 Write down a word formula to work out the cost of cans of beans.
Use your word formula to work out the cost of 3 cans of beans at 21p each.

5 Write down a word formula to work out the cost of jars of coffee.
Use your word formula to work out the cost of 3 jars of coffee at £3 each.

Exercise 10.3 Links: 10C

1 These scales all balance.
Find what must go in the box.

(a)

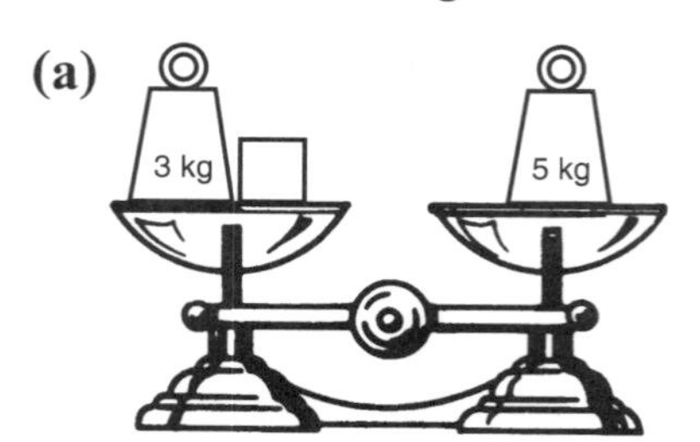

(b)

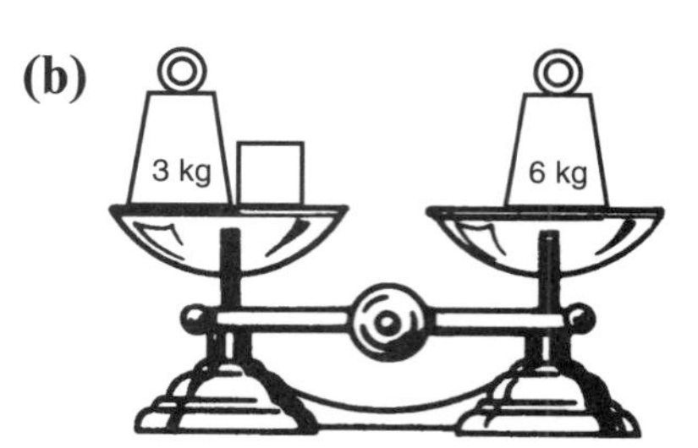

(c)

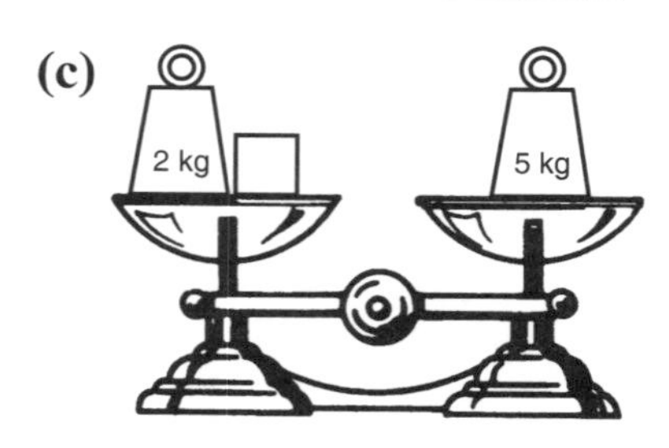

(d)

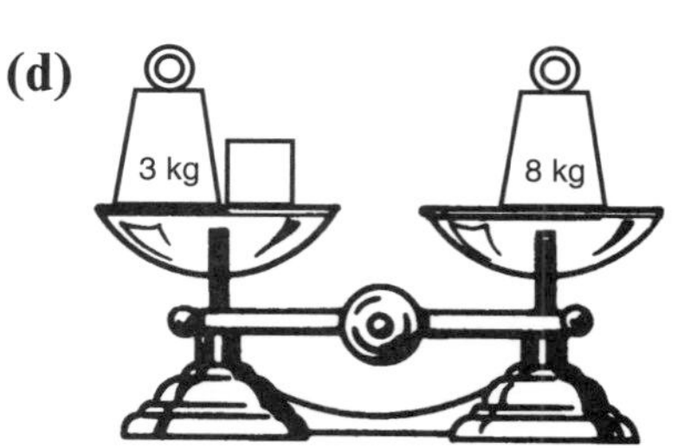

(e)

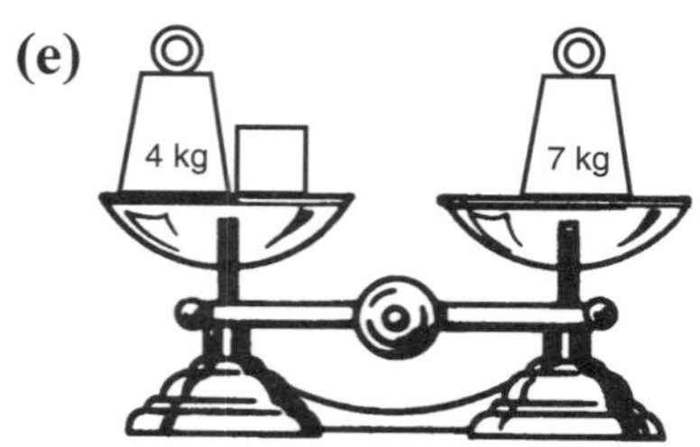

(f)

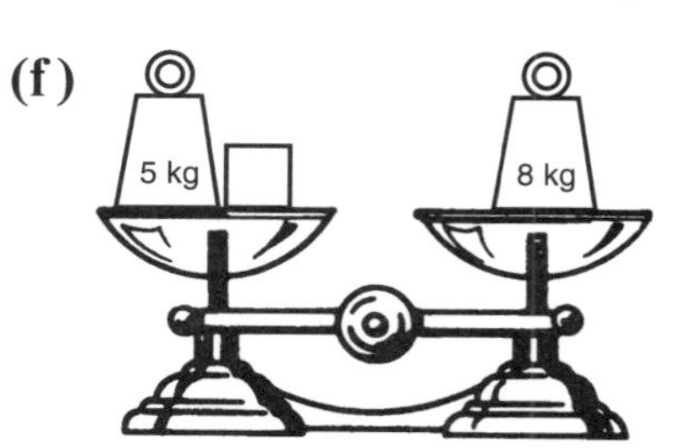

Exercise 10.4 Links: 10D

1 Use your number facts to complete these number statements.

(a) $2 + \square = 5$ **(b)** $2 + \square = 6$ **(c)** $3 + \square = 7$

(d) $4 + \square = 5$ **(e)** $7 - \square = 4$ **(f)** $7 - \square = 3$

(g) $5 - \square = 3$ **(h)** $\square + 3 = 8$ **(i)** $\square + 5 = 8$

(j) $\square + 6 = 10$ **(k)** $\square - 4 = 5$ **(l)** $\square - 2 = 2$

(m) $\square - 4 = 3$ **(n)** $3 \times \square = 12$ **(o)** $2 \times \square = 10$

(p) $6 \times \square = 12$ **(q)** $5 \times \square = 25$ **(r)** $\square \times 4 = 8$

(s) $\square \times 3 = 12$ **(t)** $\square \times 3 = 18$ **(u)** $12 \div \square = 3$

(v) $12 \div \square = 4$ **(w)** $15 \div \square = 3$ **(x)** $\square \div 2 = 6$

(y) $\square \div 5 = 4$ **(z)** $\square \div 4 = 6$

Name ....

10 Formulae and equations

1 Wayne buys 3 cakes. He uses the formula

Cost of cakes = Cost of one cake × Number of cakes bought

The cost of one cake is 20 p.
Work out the cost of

(a) 3 cakes .... p

(b) 8 cakes .... p **(4 marks)**

---

2 Sharon buys 4 sweets. She uses the formula

Cost of sweets = Cost of one sweet × Number of sweets bought

The cost of one sweet is 5 p.
Work out the cost of

(a) 4 sweets .... p

(b) 25 sweets .... p **(4 marks)**

---

3 David goes for a walk. He uses the formula

Distance travelled = Speed × Hours walked

David walks for 3 hours at a speed
of 4 miles per hour.

How far did he walk? .... miles **(2 marks)**

---

4 Write down a formula to work out the cost of apples.

Use your formula to work out the cost of 4 apples at
20 p each.

....

.... p **(4 marks)**

---

5 Write down a formula to work out the cost of chocolate bars.
Use your formula to work out the cost of 5 chocolate bars at 36 p each.

£ .... **(4 marks)**

---

6 These scales all balance.
Find what must go in the box

(a)

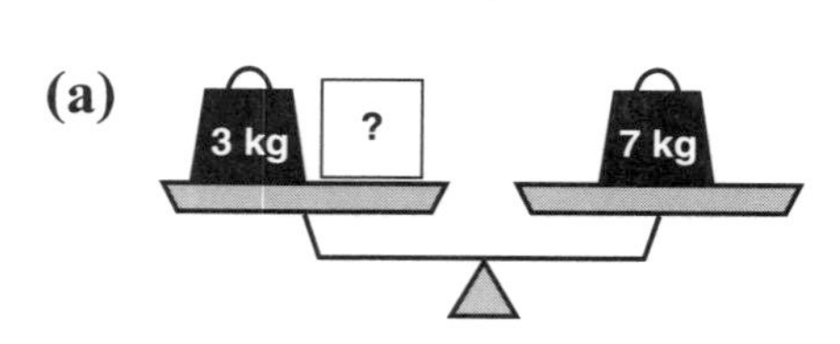

....

(b)

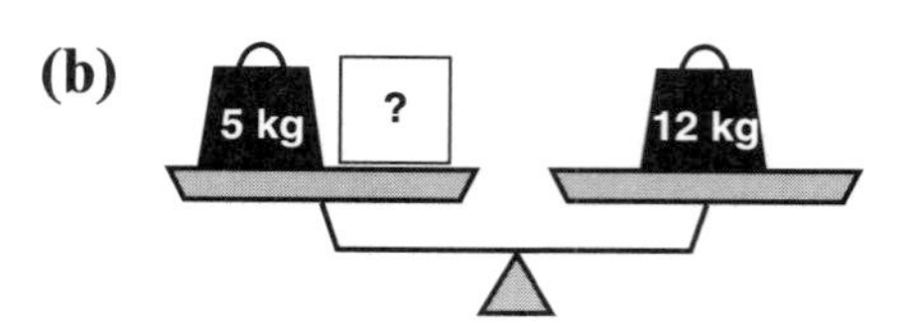

....

(c)

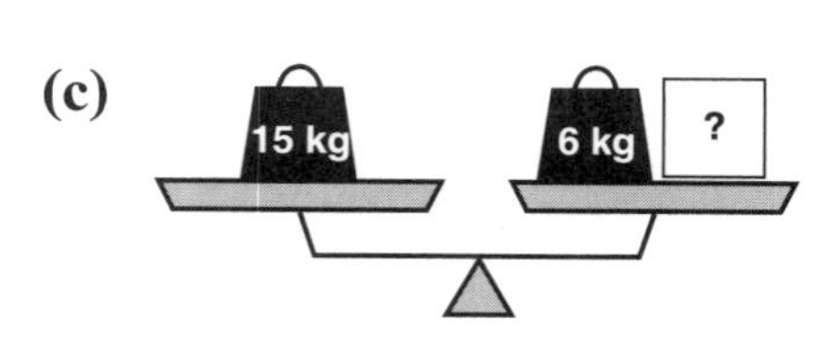

....

(d)

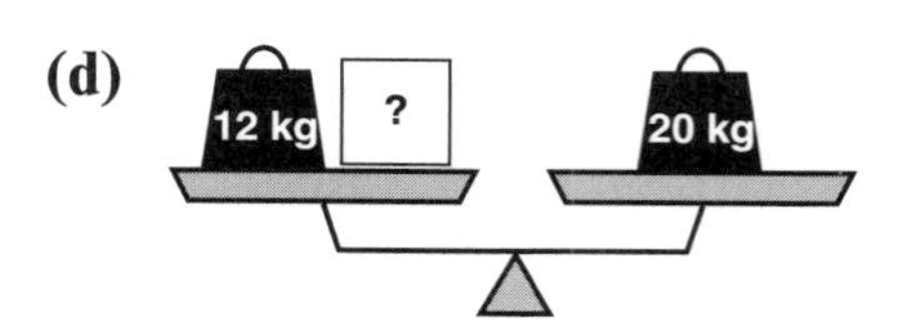

.... **(4 marks)**

---

7 Solve these equations.
Write the answer in the box.

(a) $\square + 3 = 5$ **(b)** $4 + \square = 7$

(c) $\square - 2 = 6$ **(d)** $15 - \square = 6$

(e) $3 \times \square = 12$ **(f)** $\square \times 6 = 18$

(g) $\square \div 3 = 7$ **(h)** $12 \div \square = 2$ **(8 marks)**

Assessment

Unit 10 Formulae and equations

Question		Answer	Marking guidance and remediation sheet links	
1	**(a)**	60 p	M1 for 3 × 20, A1 for 60	
	(b)	160 p	M1 for 8 × 20, A1 for 160 p	
2	**(a)**	20 p	M1 for 5 × 4, A1 for 20	
	(b)	125 p	M1 for 5 × 25, A1 for 125 p	
3		12 miles	M1 for 4 × 3, A1 for 12	
4		Cost of apples = cost of one apple × number bought. cost = 4 × 20 = 80 p	B1 for cost of apples = or cost = B1 for cost of one apple × number bought M1 for 4 × 20 A1 for 80 p	
5		Cost of chocolate bars = cost of one bar × number bought. cost = 5 × 36 = £1.80	B1 for cost = or cost of choc bars = B1 for cost of one bar × number bought M1 for 5 × 36 A1 for £1.80	
6	**(a)**	4 kg	A1	less than $\frac{8}{12}$ use remediation sheet 10.1
	(b)	7 kg	A1	
	(c)	9 kg	A1	
	(d)	8 g	A1	
7	**(a)**	2	A1	
	(b)	3	A1	
	(c)	8	A1	
	(d)	9	A1	
	(e)	4	A1	
	(f)	3	A1	
	(g)	21	A1	
	(h)	6	A1	

Key to mark scheme
A marks: correct answer
M marks: correct method
B marks: independent work

Page 265 gives a general guidance on use of this assessment scheme with some examples.

10.1 Sums that go together

These sums go together:

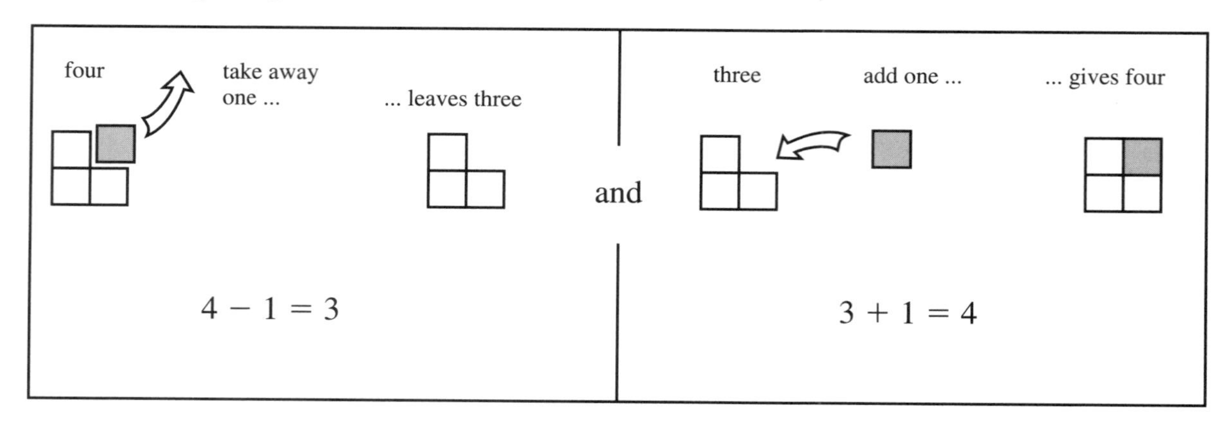
four
take away one ...
... leaves three
and
three
add one ...
... gives four
4 − 1 = 3
3 + 1 = 4

Example 1

Fill in the missing number:

$$7 - \square = 3$$

If $7 - \square = 3$ then $3 + \square = 7$

$$3 + \boxed{4} = 7$$

Exercise 1

Fill in the missing numbers:

(a) $10 - \square = 7$ (b) $9 - \square = 6$ (c) $15 - \square = 10$

(d) $35 - \square = 25$ (e) $66 - \square = 55$ (f) $74 - \square = 63$

(g) $51 - \square = 37$ (h) $31 - \square = 10$ (i) $31 - \square = 9$

(j) $31 - \square = 15$ (k) $45 - \square = 23$ (l) $56 - \square = 12$

(m) $40 - \square = 17$ (n) $100 - \square = 75$ (o) $100 - \square = 25$

R10.1

Answers to Pupils' Book

10 Formulae and equations

Exercise 10A

1 30p **2** 48p **3** 30p **4** 45p
5 60p **6** £15.00 **7** £35.00 **8** £80.00
9 £2.10 **10** £35.00 **11** £1.20

Exercise 10B

1 cost of apples = cost of one apple × number of apples bought
£1.00

2 cost of cans of orange drink = cost of one can × number of cans bought
£1.35

3 cost of chocolate bars = cost of one bar × number of bars bought
70p

4 cost of buns = cost of one bun × number of buns bought
£1.00

5 cost of apples = cost of one apple × number of apples bought
60p

6 cost of peaches = cost of one peach × number of peaches bought
60p

7 cost of kiwifruit = cost of one × number bought
60p

8 cost of cans of beans = cost of one can × number of cans bought
84p

9 cost of packets of cereals = cost of one packet × number of packets bought
£1.60

10 cost of jars of coffee = cost of one jar × number of jars bought
£6.00

11 cost of cups of tea = cost of one cup × number of cups bought
£2.40

12 cost of ice cream = cost of one ice cream × number of ice creams bought
£5.00

13 cost of pencils = cost of one pencil × number of pencils bought
£1.50

Exercise 10C

1 1 kg **2** 3 kg
3 5 kg **4** 7 kg
5 2 kg **6** 5 kg
7 7 kg **8** 3 kg
9 6 kg **10** 7 kg

Exercise 10D

1 4 **2** 3 **3** 4
4 3 **5** 4 **6** 2
7 5 **8** 2 **9** 3
10 2 **11** 4 **12** 7
13 8 **14** 5 **15** 6
16 7 **17** 2 **18** 4
19 4 **20** 3 **21** 4
22 4 **23** 3 **24** 7
25 2 **26** 3 **27** 4
28 3 **29** 8 **30** 12
31 18 **32** 20

Answers to Homeworks

10 Formulae and equations

Exercise 10.1 Links: 10A

1 20p **2** 32p
3 80p **4** £24.00

Exercise 10.2 Links: 10B

1 cost of apples = cost of one apple × number of apples bought
80p

2 cost of chocolate bars = cost of one bar × number of bars bought
£1.20

3 cost of peaches = cost of one peach × number of peaches bought
60p

4 cost of cans of beans = cost of one can × number of cans bought
63p

5 cost of jars of coffee = cost of one jar × number of jars bought
£9.00

Exercise 10.3 Links: 10C

1 **(a)** 3 kg **(b)** 3 kg
(c) 3 kg **(d)** 5 kg
(e) 3 kg **(f)** 3 kg

Exercise 10.4 Links: 10D

1 **(a)** 3 **(b)** 4
(c) 4 **(d)** 1
(e) 3 **(f)** 4
(g) 2 **(h)** 5
(i) 3 **(j)** 4
(k) 9 **(l)** 4
(m) 7 **(n)** 4
(o) 5 **(p)** 2
(q) 5 **(r)** 2
(s) 4 **(t)** 6
(u) 4 **(v)** 3
(w) 5 **(x)** 12
(y) 20 **(z)** 24

Remediation answers

10.1 Sums that go together

Exercise 1

(a) 3 **(b)** 3
(c) 5 **(d)** 10
(e) 11 **(f)** 11
(g) 14 **(h)** 21
(i) 22 **(j)** 16
(k) 22 **(l)** 44
(m) 23 **(n)** 25
(o) 75

Unit 11 Positive and negative numbers

Content summary

This unit introduces negative numbers through temperature going on to make use of a vertical number line to find differences and the result of changes in temperature.

Book 1R Unit 12 goes on to a more abstract consideration of positive and negative making use of 'counting on' and 'counting back' methods to add and subtract positive and negative numbers.

NC level

Level 3: Recognise and use negative numbers in context.

Level 5: Order negative numbers.

N2c NA2a S4a

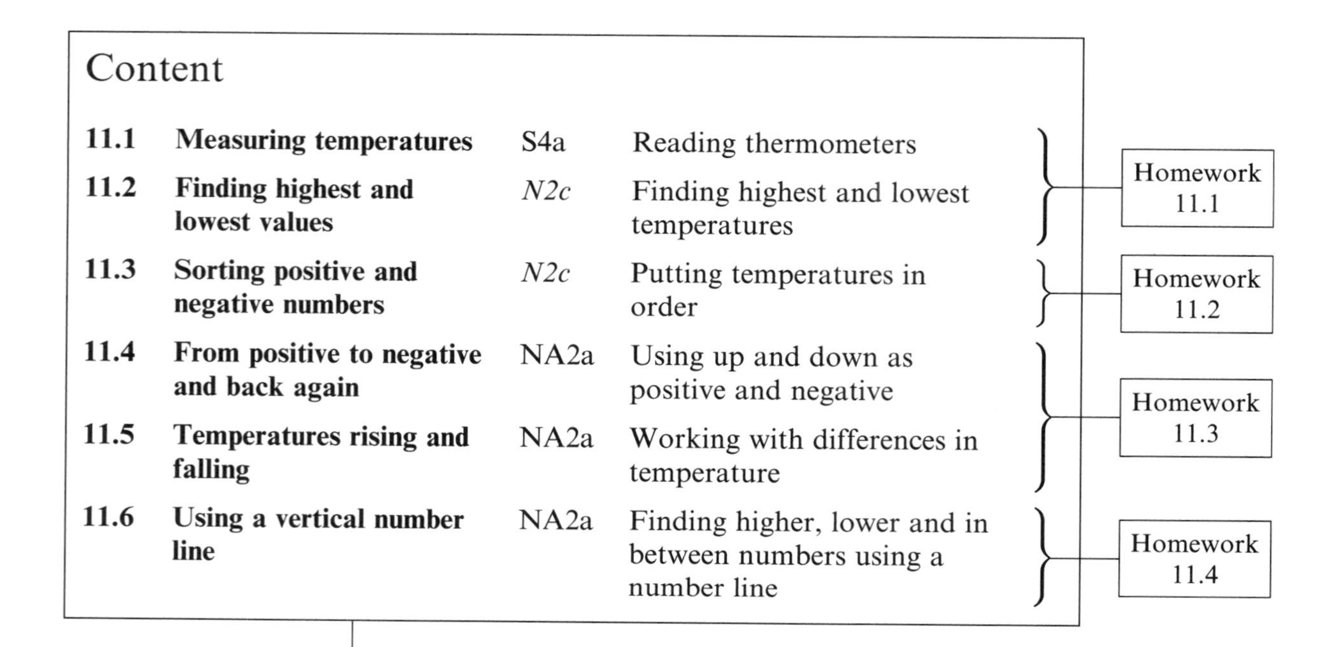

Content

11.1	**Measuring temperatures**	S4a	Reading thermometers	Homework 11.1
11.2	**Finding highest and lowest values**	*N2c*	Finding highest and lowest temperatures	
11.3	**Sorting positive and negative numbers**	*N2c*	Putting temperatures in order	Homework 11.2
11.4	**From positive to negative and back again**	NA2a	Using up and down as positive and negative	Homework 11.3
11.5	**Temperatures rising and falling**	NA2a	Working with differences in temperature	
11.6	**Using a vertical number line**	NA2a	Finding higher, lower and in between numbers using a number line	Homework 11.4

Assessment

Assessment 11 covers the key concepts in Unit 11.

Remediation

Remediation sheet 11.1.

Assessment

The assessment is marked out of 30.
Achievement of 20 or more marks indicates a good understanding of the key concepts.
Marking guidance, answers and links to remediation are provided on page 265.

Equipment

	Pupils' Book page
Activity sheet 8	163
Number line	171–173
Dice and counters	174

ICT links

Use *Numbers You Need: Negative Numbers* from *BT* to view animations and receive audio instructions on the number line. Answer multiple choice questions on the various topics.

Use the database, *Keyplus* to search for world temperatures. Use the database to sort in ascending or descending order and search for temperatures above or below specified values.

Use *MicroSmile for Windows pack 3* to investigate the ordering of negative numbers.

Remediation

Negative numbers:
The counter moving up and down the stairs should help to develop the concept of moving up and down relative to a starting point. The work in the text could be done as a class or group practical activity rather than writing down answers.

Questionbank CD

All homeworks and extension questions also appear on the CD.

Pages xvii and xviii of this pack show you how to use the CD to select questions from the Questionbank and further customize them if you wish to.

11 Positive and negative numbers

framework teaching objective	§	lesson starter	f/w ref
Understand negative numbers as positions on a number line; order, add and subtract positive and negative integers in context.	11.1	When water freezes it can be bad news. What things happen if it freezes overnight? Examples of answers might be: (*'If the "wetness" on the ground freezes, it can harm plants and small animals.'* *'A car uses water and if it freezes, the car might not start.'*) Why do you think we have decided to call the temperature at which water freezes 0°C? 'zero degrees Celsius?' Examples of answers might be: (*'Temperatures above 0 mean that we won't have frost.'* *Temperatures below 0 mean that we will.'*)	48–51
Understand negative numbers as positions on a number line; order, add and subtract positive and negative integers in context.	11.2	Nathaniel says: '10°C is warmer than 2°C. 10 is bigger than 2.' Jason says: −10°C is **colder** than −2°C. So −10 is **smaller** than −2.' Who is right? We use negative numbers to show just how cold things are. The thermometer falls down the number line reaching smaller and smaller numbers. Which is colder: −4°C or −9°C? : −10°C or −20°C? Which is smaller: −10 or −20? : −19 or −20?	48–51
Understand negative numbers as positions on a number line; order, add and subtract positive and negative integers in context.	11.3	Which is the coldest place to be? Leeds (−1°C) Bradford (−5°C) Keighley (−2°C) York (−3°C) (*'Bradford −5°C*) Does this mean −5 is the smallest number? Aaron says: '−5 can't be the smallest. 5 is bigger than 1, 2 or 3'. How can we explain to Aaron that −5 is smaller? Is there a diagram we can draw to help Aaron understand? (*Students should be encouraged to devise vertical number line.*)	48–51

framework teaching objective	§	lesson starter	f/w ref
Understand negative numbers as positions on a number line; order, add and subtract positive and negative integers in context.	11.5	The temperature falls as night draws in. Why is this? In Fulham the temperature is 7°C at 4 pm. By midnight it has fallen to −2°C. By how many degrees has it fallen? Aaron says: 'I don't feel ready to work it out in my head.' Is there a diagram that we can draw to help Aaron? (*Again students should devise a number line.*) How can I show on the number line how many degrees the temperature has fallen by? What maths do we use when the temperature falls? (*minus, subtract*) when the temperature rises (*add*).	48–51

11 Positive and negative numbers

Exercise 11.1 Links: 11A, 11B

1 Write down each temperature in words and figures.

(a)

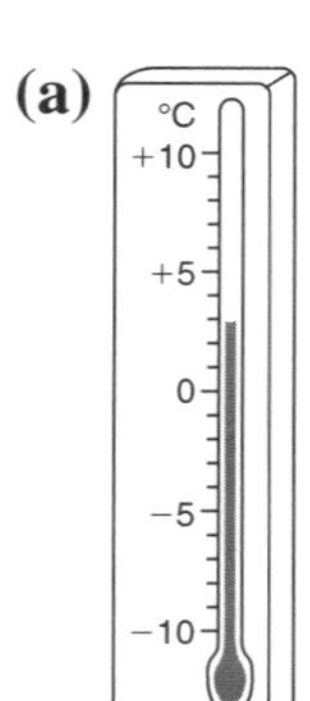

(b)

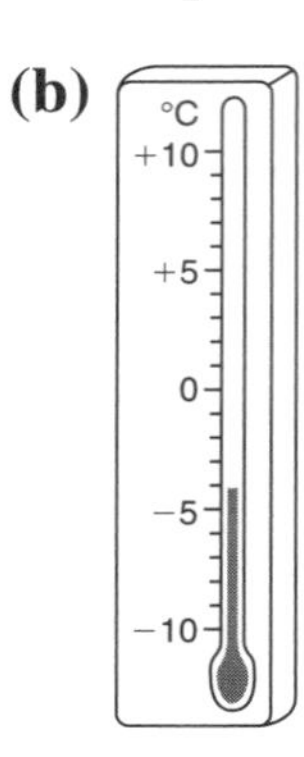

(c)

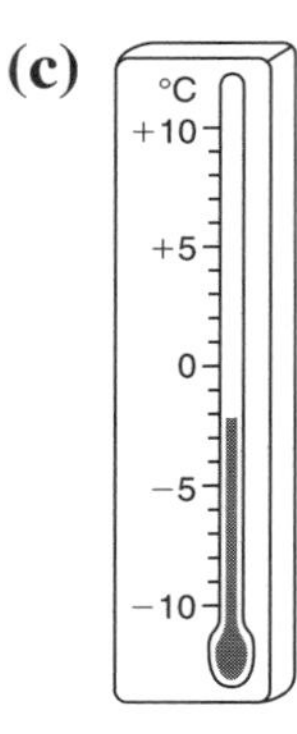

(d)

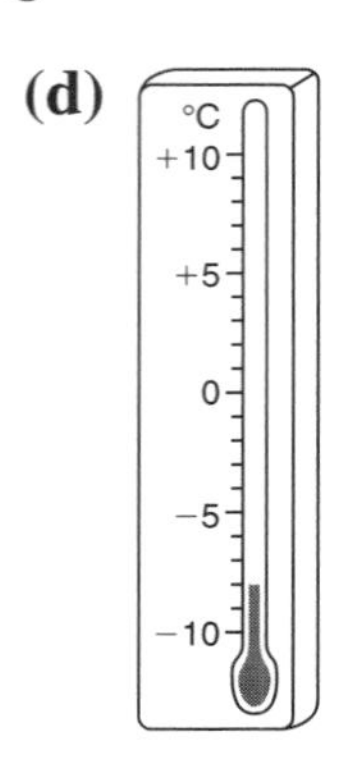

2 Write down the lower of the two temperatures:

(a) −6 °C and 4 °C **(b)** 1 °C and −3 °C

(c) −5 °C and −1 °C **(d)** −4 °C and −9 °C

3 Write down the highest temperature in each list:

(a) +2 °C, +5 °C, −4 °C, −7 °C, 0 °C, +1 °C.

(b) −3 °C, −5 °C, 0 °C, −7 °C, −9 °C, −2 °C.

(c) −3 °C, −8 °C, −6 °C, −5 °C, −7 °C, −2 °C.

Exercise 11.2 Links: 11C

1 Write the temperatures in °C for each map in order of size, starting with the lowest:

(a)

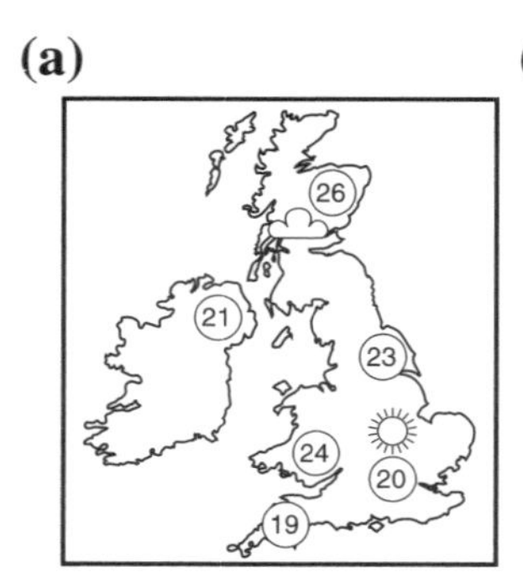

(b)

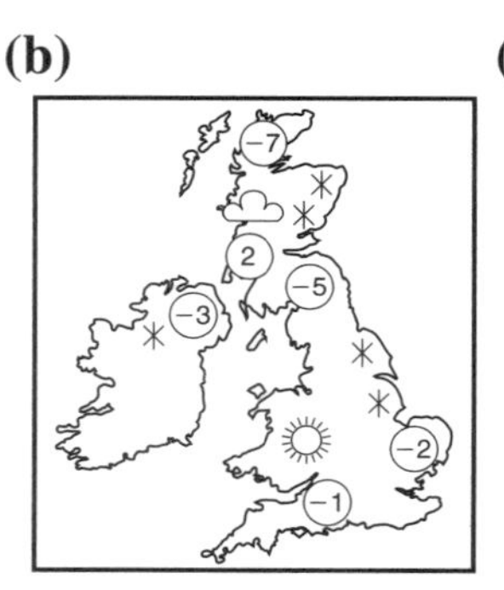

(c)

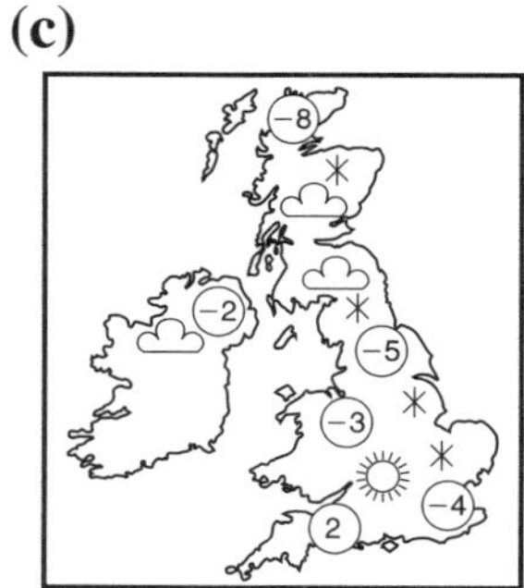

2 Write down these temperatures in order of size, starting with the lowest.

(a) 1 °C, −4 °C, 3 °C, −5 °C, −7 °C

(b) −2 °C, −6 °C, −4 °C, −1 °C, 3 °C

3 Write down these temperatures in order of size, starting with the highest.

(a) −4 °C, 0 °C, 5 °C, −8 °C, 6 °C

(b) −7 °C, −9 °C, −3 °C, −2 °C, −6 °C

Exercise 11.3 Links: 11D, 11E

Use a sketch like this to help you answer questions **1**, **2** and **3**.

4
3
2
1
0
−1
−2

1 The picture shows all the floors that a lift stops at in a block of flats.
Write down the floor the lift gets to if:
(a) it starts at floor 4 and goes down 2 floors
(b) it starts at floor −2 and goes up 5 floors
(c) it starts at floor 2 and goes down 4 floors
(d) it starts at floor −2 and goes up 1 floor.

2 How many floors does the lift go up if it goes from:
(a) floor −1 to floor 3 **(b)** floor −1 to floor 1
(c) floor −2 to floor −1 **(d)** floor −2 to floor 3?

3 How many floors does the lift go down if it goes from:
(a) floor 3 to floor 0 **(b)** floor 2 to floor −1
(c) floor −1 to floor −2 **(d)** floor 4 to floor −2?

4 The temperature in Preston at midnight was −4 °C.
By noon the temperature had gone up to 3 °C.
Work out the rise in the temperature.

5 The temperature in Shetland at noon was −2 °C.
By midnight the temperature had fallen by 6 °C.
What was the temperature at midnight?

Exercise 11.4 Links: 11F

Hint: use a vertical number line to help you.

1 Which is the higher number in each pair?
(a) −4, +2 **(b)** +3, −4 **(c)** −2, +5
(d) −3, +2 **(e)** −6, −4 **(f)** −2, −9

2 Write down all the whole numbers between:
(a) −2 and 3 **(b)** −8 and −2 **(c)** −7 and 2
(d) −9 and −2 **(e)** −3 and −8

3 Write down the result of these:
(a) Start at −6 and go up 2.
(b) Start at −3 and go up 5.
(c) Start at +2 and go down 6.
(d) Start at +3 and go down 7.
(e) Start at −2 and go down 5.
(f) Start at −9 and go up 4.

4 Write down the next two numbers in each pattern:
(a) 5, 3, 1, −1, ... **(b)** 8, 5, 2, −1, ...
(c) 13, 10, 7, 4, ... **(d)** 15, 11, 7, 3, ...
(e) −9, −7, −5, −3, ... **(f)** −10, −6, −2, 2, ...
(g) −11, −8, −5, −2, ... **(h)** −25, −19, −13, −7, ...
(i) −10, −7, −4, −1, ...

Name ....

11 Positive and negative numbers

1 Write down the temperature shown on each thermometer.

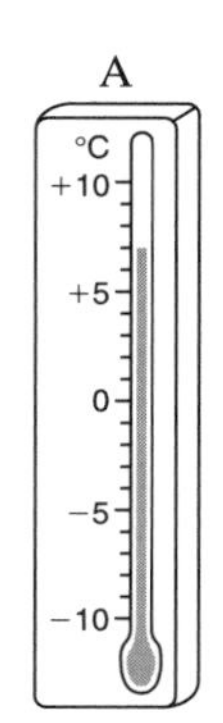

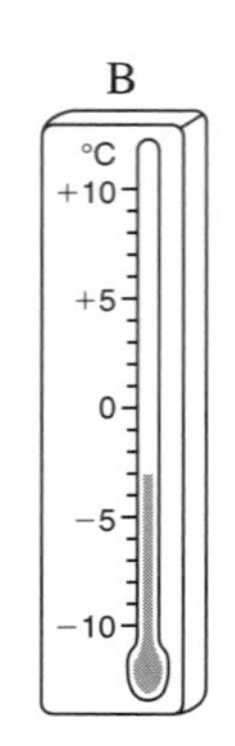

A .... °C

B .... °C **(2 marks)**

---

2 The temperature in five cities were:

Aberdeen	London	Paris	Vienna	Moscow
−3 °C	**0 °C**	**+2 °C**	**+1 °C**	**−5 °C**

(a) Which city had the highest temperature? ....

(b) What was the lowest temperature? .... °C **(2 marks)**

---

3 Look at this weather map.

−3°
Scotland
−11°
Moscow
0°
Paris
12°
Southern
Spain
10°
Italy

(a) Write down the highest temperature. .... °C

(b) Write down the lowest temperature. .... °C **(2 marks)**

---

4 Complete the labelling of the number line.

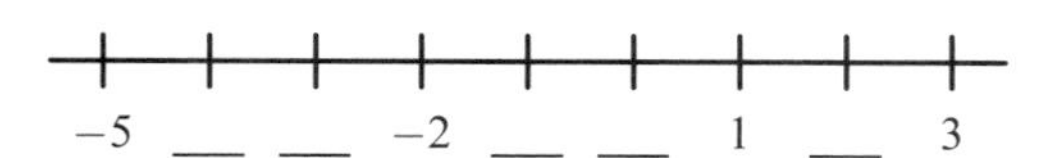

(2 marks)

---

5 Write down these temperatures in order of size, starting with the lowest.

−6 °C 2 °C −7 °C 0 °C 4 °C

....

(2 marks)

---

6 The diagram shows the floor indicator inside a lift.

4
3
2
1
0
−1
−2

(a) Emma gets into the lift at floor −2.
She goes up 3 floors and then gets out of the lift.
At what floor does she get out? ....

(b) Carl gets into the lift at the top.
He goes down 5 floors and then gets out.
At what floor does he get out? ....

(2 marks)

---

7 Use the vertical number line for these questions.

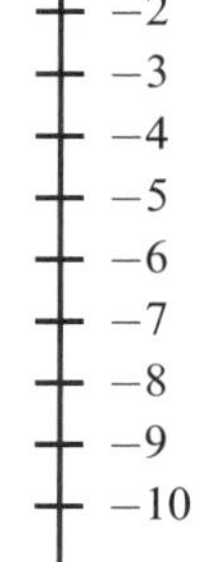

(a) Start at number −3 and go up 8.
What number do you end up at? ....

(b) Start at number 4 and go down 5.
What number do you end up at? ....

(c) You move up 5 places to end up at number 3.
Where did you start? ....

(d) Start at number −3 and move down 10.
What number do you end up at? ....

(4 marks)

---

8 The levels on a staircase are labelled from -3 to 6.

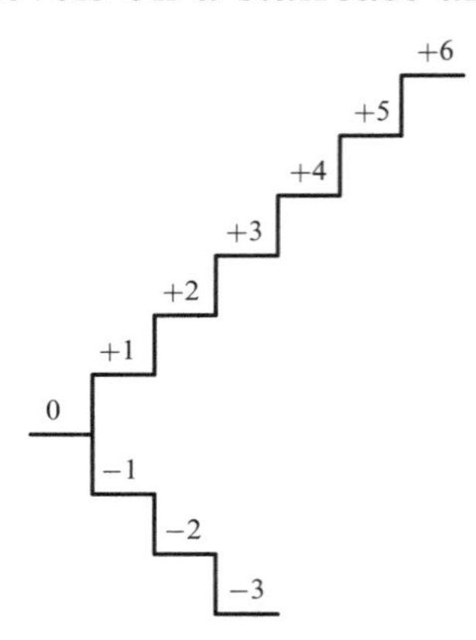

(a) How many levels are there on the staircase? ....

(b) Sumreen starts at level -2.
She climbs up 6 levels before she stops.
At what level does she stop? ....

(c) Aleya starts at level 5.
She walks down 7 levels before she stops.
At what level does she stop? .... **(3 marks)**

---

9 Write down all the whole numbers between -3 and 4.

.... **(1 mark)**

---

10 The temperature in Belfast at midnight was $-4\,°C$.
By noon the next day the temperature had gone up to $3\,°C$. Work out the rise in temperature. .... °C **(2 marks)**

---

11 The temperature in Exeter at midnight was $-3\,°C$.
By noon the next day the temperature had risen by $12\,°C$. Work out the temperature in Exeter at noon. .... °C **(2 marks)**

---

12 The temperature at the top of a mountain is $-12\,°C$.
The temperature at the bottom of the mountain is $3\,°C$.
Work out the rise in temperature between the top and the bottom of the mountain. .... °C **(2 marks)**

---

13 Write down the next two numbers in each of these patterns.

(a) 11, 8, 5, 2, ..., ... and .....

(b) 1, 0, -2, -5, ..., ... and ..... **(4 marks)**

Unit 11 Positive and negative numbers

Question		Answer	Marking guidance and remediation sheet links	
1		A 7°C B −3°C	B1 B1	
2	**(a)**	Paris	A1	
	(b)	−5	A1	
3	**(a)**	12°C	A1	
	(b)	−11°C	A1	
4		−4, −3, −1, 0, 2	B2 for all correct B1 for 2 correct	
5		−7°C, −6°C, 0°C, 2°C, 4°C	B2 for all correct B1 for one error	
6	**(a)**	Floor 1	A1	less than $\frac{6}{9}$ use remediation sheet 11.1 (questions 6–8)
	(b)	Floor −1	A1	
7	**(a)**	5	A1	
	(b)	−1	A1	
	(c)	−2	A1	
	(d)	−13	A1	
8	**(a)**	10 levels	A1	
	(b)	+4	A1	
	(c)	−2	A1	
9		−2, −1, 0, 1, 2, 3	A1	
10		7°C	M1 for 3 − −4, A1 for 7	
11		9°C	M1 for −3 + 12, A1 for 9	
12		15°C	M1 for 3 − −12, A1 for 15	
13	**(a)**	−1, −4	A1, A1	
	(b)	−9, −14	A1, A1	

Key to mark scheme
A marks: correct answer
M marks: correct method
B marks: independent work

Page 265 gives a general guidance on use of this assessment scheme with some examples.

11.1 From positive to negative

Here is a way to practice using positive (+) and negative (−) numbers:

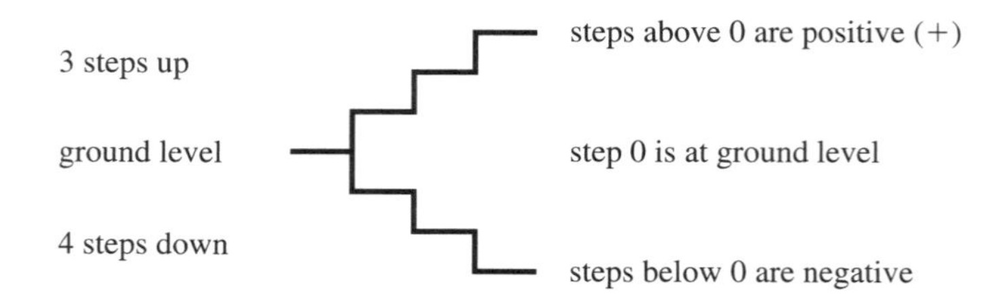

Move a counter up and down the steps to help you.

This counter is at 0
It is at ground level.

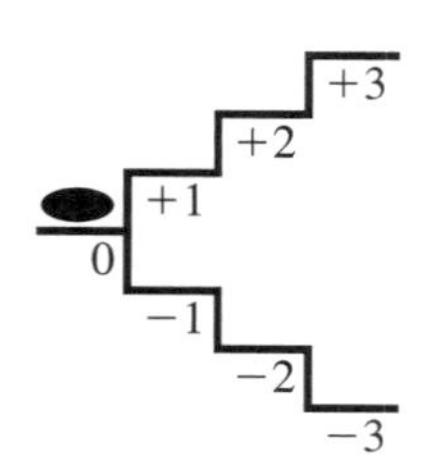

This counter is at +2
It is 2 steps above 0

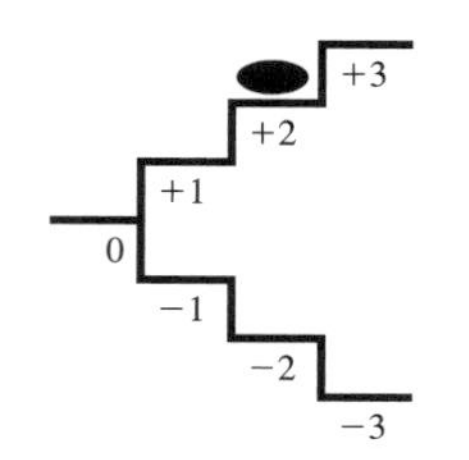

This counter is at −3
It is 3 steps below 0

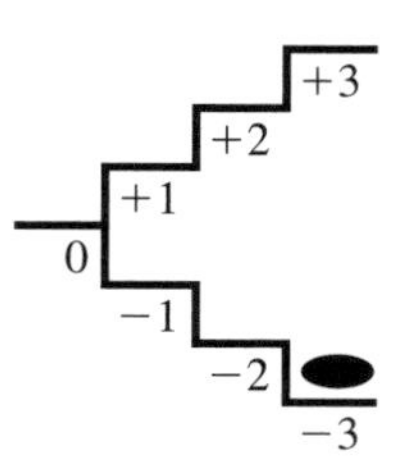

Example 1

Put a counter on step +2
Move it up 2 steps.
What step is it on now?
It is on step +4
(or 4 steps above 0).

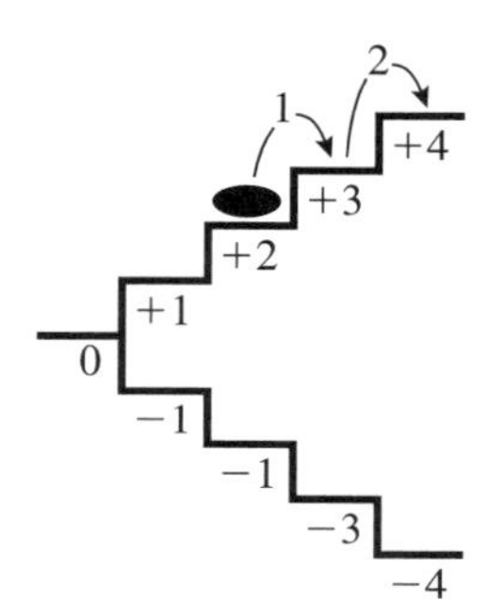

Example 2

Put a counter on step +3.
Move it down 5 steps.
What step is it on now?
It is on step −2
(or 2 steps below 0).

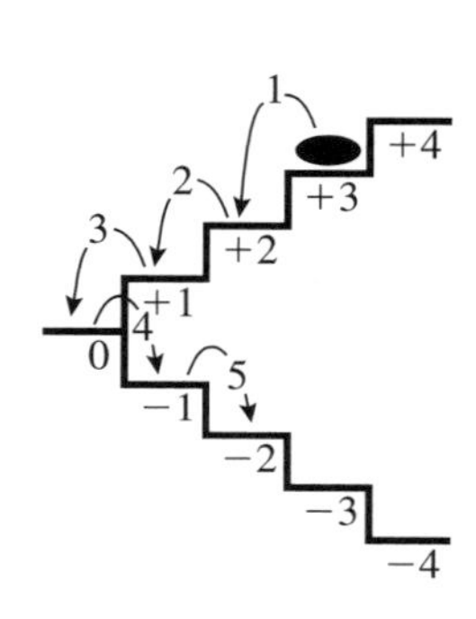

Example 3

Put a counter on step −3
Move it up 4 steps.
What step is it on now?
It is on step +1
(or 1 step above 0).

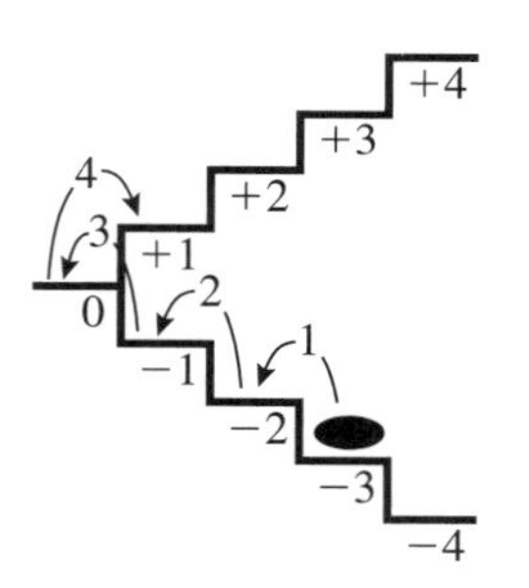

Exercise 1

1 Put a counter on step +1. Move it up 3 steps.
What step is it on now?

2 Put a counter on step −1. Move it down 4 steps.
What step is it on now?

Answers to Pupils' Book

11 Positive and negative numbers

Exercise 11A

1 (a) Positive eight degrees Celsius
(b) +8 °C
2 (a) Negative five degrees Celsius
(b) −5 °C
3 (a) Positive four degrees Celsius
(b) +4 °C
4 (a) Negative three degrees Celsius
(b) −3 °C
5 (a) Negative nine degrees Celsius
(b) −9 °C
6 (a) Nought degrees Celsius
(b) 0 °C
7 (a) Negative one degree Celsius
(b) −1 °C
8 (a) Positive two degrees Celsius
(b) +2 °C
9 (a) Negative two degrees Celsius
(b) −2 °C
10 (a) Negative four degrees Celsius
(b) −4 °C
11 (a) Negative six degrees Celsius
(b) −6 °C
12 (a) Negative eight degrees Celsius
(b) −8 °C

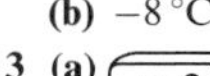

13 (a) (b) (c)

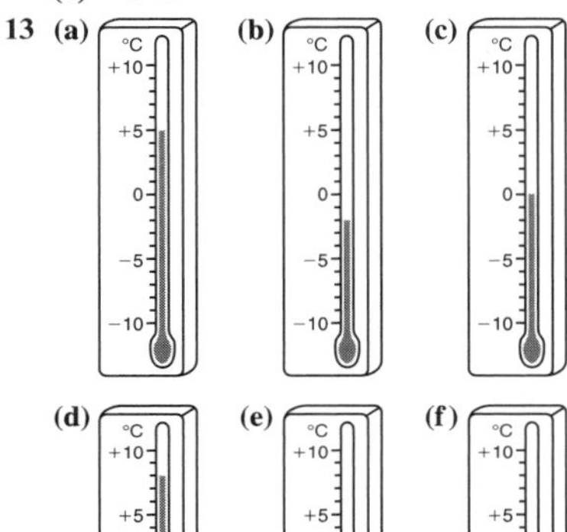

(d) (e) (f) (g) (h) (i) (j) (k) (l)

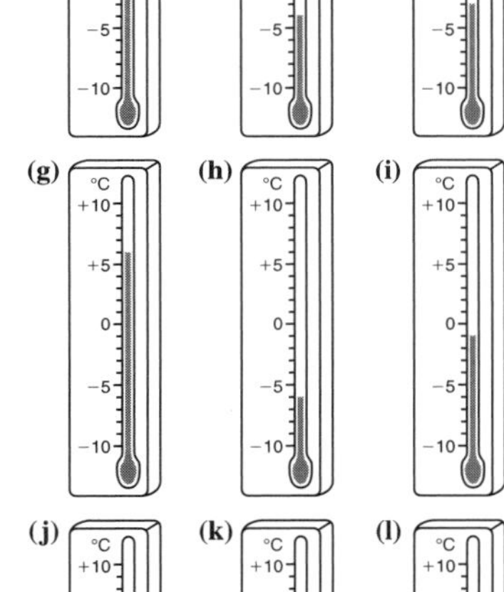

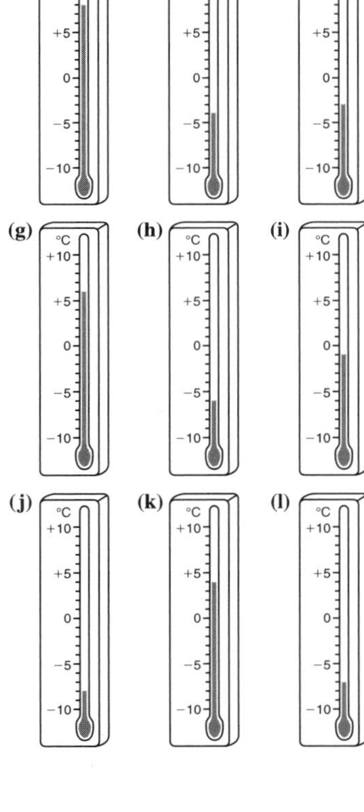

Exercise 11B

1 (a) 4 °C (b) −2 °C (c) 0 °C
(d) 2 °C (e) 3 °C (f) 1 °C
(g) −5 °C (h) 5 °C (i) −1 °C
2 (a) 0 °C (b) −1 °C
(c) Newcastle (d) Folkestone
3 (a) 11 °C (b) −12 °C
4 (a) 0 °C (b) −5 °C
5 (a) 5 °C (b) 8 °C (c) 3 °C
(d) 5 °C (e) 4 °C (f) −3 °C
6 (a) 1 °C (b) 0 °C (c) −5 °C
(d) −4 °C (e) −1 °C (f) −10 °C
7 (a) +10 °C (b) +5 °C (c) 0 °C
(d) −1 °C
8 (a) −6 °C (b) −7 °C (c) −7 °C
(d) −8 °C

Exercise 11C

1 (a) −4 °C, −3 °C, −1 °C, 2 °C, 3 °C
(b) −8 °C, −6 °C, −5 °C, −3 °C, −2 °C, 0 °C
(c) −4 °C, −3 °C, −2 °C, −1 °C, 0 °C, 2 °C, 5 °C
2 21 °C, 15 °C, 5 °C, 4 °C, 2 °C, −3 °C, −5 °C, −11 °C, −12 °C
3 (a) 10 °C, 4 °C, 0 °C, −2 °C, −3 °C, −6 °C
(b) 4 °C, 2 °C, 1 °C, −3 °C, −6 °C, −7 °C
(c) 2 °C, 0 °C, −1 °C, −3 °C, −5 °C, −8 °C
(d) 0 °C, −1 °C, −3 °C, −4 °C, −7 °C, −10 °C
4 (a) −8 °C, −4 °C. −3 °C, 0 °C, 1 °C, 5 °C
(b) −9 °C, −4 °C, −1 °C, 2 °C, 5 °C, 8 °C
(c) −10 °C, −5 °C, −4 °C, 1 °C, 3 °C, 6 °C
(d) −8 °C, −5 °C, −2 °C, −1 °C, 3 °C, 6 °C

Exercise 11D

1 (a) floor 2 (b) floor 1
(c) floor 2 (d) floor −2
(e) floor −2 (f) floor −2
(g) floor −1 (h) floor 2
2 (a) 4 floors (b) 4 floors
(c) 4 floors (d) 1 floor
(e) 5 floors (f) 6 floors
3 (a) 2 floors (b) 3 floors
(c) 4 floors (d) 6 floors
(e) 1 floor (f) 4 floors

Exercise 11E

1 5 °C 2 4 °C 3 3 °C 4 −8 °C
5 Rise: 8 °C, 8 °C, 4 °C
Noon next day: 5 °C, 1 °C, 4 °C
6 Fall: 4 °C, 7 °C, 7 °C
2 am next day: −9 °C, −2 °C, −10 °C

Exercise 11F

1 (a) +4 (b) +2 (c) +3 (d) +4
(e) +6 (f) +2 (g) −4 (h) −3
2 (a) −2 (b) −3 (c) −2 (d) −4
(e) +2 (f) −7 (g) −6 (h) −8
(i) −4
3 (a) −2, −1, 0, 1
(b) −4, −3, −2, −1, 0
(c) −6, −5, −4, −3
(d) −3, −2, −1, 0, 1, 2, 3, 4
(e) −5, −4, −3, −2, −1, 0, 1, 2
(f) −7, −6, −5, −4
(g) −3, −4
(h) −5
(i) 0, 1, 2, 3
4 (a) −2 (b) 2 (c) 4 (d) 7 (e) 0 (f) 3
5 −4 6 −5

7 (a) −5, −8 (b) −7, −11
(c) −1, −3 (d) 0, −2
(e) −10, −13 (f) −9, −11
(g) −1, 2 (h) 5, 9
(i) −4, −9 (j) 3, 8

Answers to Homeworks

11 Positive and negative numbers

Exercise 11.1 Links: 11A, 11B

1 (a) Positive three degrees Celsius +3°C
(b) Negative four degrees Celsius −4 °C
(c) Negative two degrees Celsius −2 °C
(d) Negative eight degrees Celsius −8 °C
2 (a) −6 °C (b) −3 °C
(c) −5 °C (d) −9 °C
3 (a) +5 °C (b) 0 °C
(c) −2 °C

Exercise 11.2 Links: 11C

1 (a) 19 °C, 20 °C, 21 °C, 23 °C, 24 °C, 26 °C
(b) −7 °C, −5 °C, −3 °C, −2 °C, −1 °C, 2 °C
(c) −8 °C, −5 °C, −4 °C, −3 °C, −2 °C, 2 °C
2 (a) −7 °C, −5 °C, −4 °C, 1 °C, 3 °C
(b) −6 °C, −4 °C, −2 °C, −1 °C, 3 °C
3 (a) 6 °C, 5 °C, 0 °C, −4 °C, −8 °C
(b) −2 °C, −3 °C, −6 °C, −7 °C, −9 °C

Exercise 11.3 Links: 11D, 11E

1 (a) floor 2 (b) floor 3
(c) floor −2 (d) floor −1
2 (a) 4 floors (b) 2 floors
(c) 1 floor (d) 5 floors
3 (a) 3 floors (b) 3 floors
(c) 1 floor (d) 6 floors
4 7 °C
5 −8 °C

Exercise 11.4 Links: 11F

1 (a) +2 (b) +3
(c) +5 (d) +2
(e) −4 (f) −2
2 (a) −1, 0, 1, 2
(b) −7, −6, −5, −4, −3
(c) −6, −5, −4, −3, −2, −1, 0, 1
(d) −8, −7, −6, −5, −4, −3
(e) −4, −5, −6, −7
3 (a) −4 (b) +2 (c) −4
(d) −4 (e) −7 (f) −5
4 (a) −3, −5 (b) −4, −7
(c) 1, −2 (d) −1, −5
(e) −1, 1 (f) 6, 10
(g) 1, 4 (h) −1, 5
(i) 2, 5

Remediation answers

11.1 From positive to negative

Exercise 1

1 +4 2 −5

Unit 12 Graphs

Content summary

This unit begins with reading and plotting coordinates in the first quadrant. Then simple line graphs which show relationships are interpreted and constructed.

Book 1R Unit 13 works in all 4 quadrants, naming equations for lines parallel to the axes and then simple diagonal cases. Working out coordinates from an equation (including use of a table) and conversion graphs feature.

NC level

Level 4: Use and plot points in the first quadrant.
Construct and interpret line graphs. However, the work is more akin to Level 3.

N4e NA6f

Content

12.1	**Reading coordinates**	*N4e*	Naming a marked coordinate	Homework 12.1
12.2	**Plotting coordinates**	*N4e*	Plotting coordinates	Homework 12.2
12.3	**Using graphs to show relationships**	NA6f	Reading from a line graph	Homework 12.3–12.4

Assessment

Assessment 12 covers the key concepts in Unit 12.

Remediation

Remediation sheets: None.

Assessment

The assessment is marked out of 30. Achievement of 20 or more marks indicates a good understanding of the key concepts.
Marking guidance, answers and links to remediation are provided on page 265.

Equipment

	Pupils' Book page
Squared paper	177–8, 183
Counters	179

ICT links

12.1 and 12.2
Use *Geomat for Windows* to create shapes from sets of coordinates.
Use *MicroSmile for Windows Pack 5* to look at coordinates in an investigative way.

12.3
Use a spreadsheet to plot the relationship between given values,. Use the line graphs produced to read off some values.

Remediation
There is no remediation for this unit.

Questionbank CD

All homeworks and extension questions also appear on the CD.

Pages xvii and xviii of this pack show you how to use the CD to select questions from the Questionbank and further customize them if you wish to.

12 Graphs

framework teaching objective	§	lesson starter	f/w ref
Find co-ordinate of points determined by geometric information.	12.1	Draw a horizontal number line. 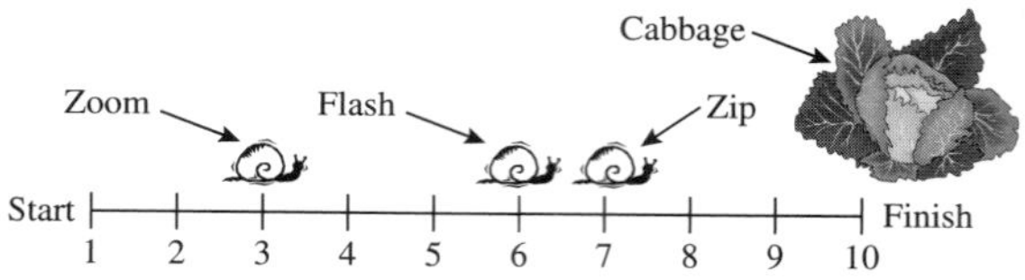 Cabbage Zoom Flash Zip Start 1 2 3 4 5 6 7 8 9 10 Finish 3 snails set off on a race. To see who's going to win, I've drawn a line along the course to show the position of each snail after 10 minutes. So, for example (draw on the snails) 'Zoom is at 3.' Where's Flash and Zip? Who's moved furthest across? But hang on. Do snails always travel in straight lines? Students encouraged to expand the number line to include the snail's deviations. 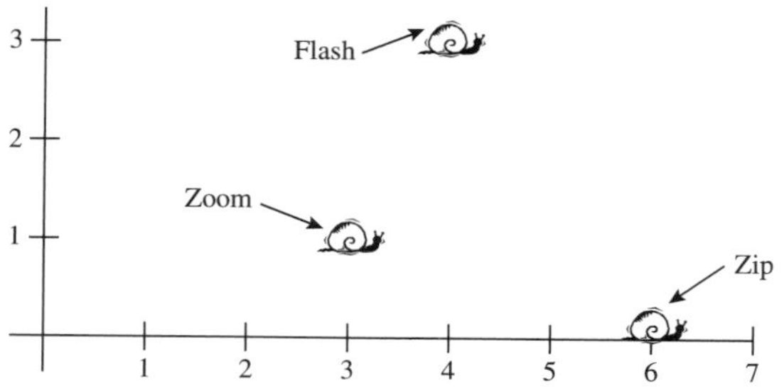 3 2 1 Flash Zoom Zip 1 2 3 4 5 6 7 How far across have they moved? How far 'up' have they moved? How do I write Zip's position? What if they move off the line in the 'down' direction?	218–19

framework teaching objective	§	lesson starter	f/w ref
Generate co-ordinate pairs that satisfy a simple linear rule; plot the graphs of simple linear functions.	12.3	Sometimes it helps to make a drawing to remember important ideas. Draw a horizontal line 100 mm long. Mark each 10 mm interval. 0 10 mm 20 mm 30 mm 40 mm etc. At each point, we'll draw a vertical line to show how long the mm measure is in cm. Try 10 mm. How many cm is that? (*1 cm*) Draw a 1 cm vertical line at the 10 mm point. 1 cm 0 10 mm Students complete series of 10 vertical lines which increase by 1 cm. How can I show that 15 mm = 1.5 cm? How can I show (choose several other conversions). What line can I draw to show **all** the possible conversions from mm into cm?	164–7

12 Graphs

Exercise 12.1 **Links: 12A, 12B**

Look at the grid. It shows the layout of stalls at the school fete.

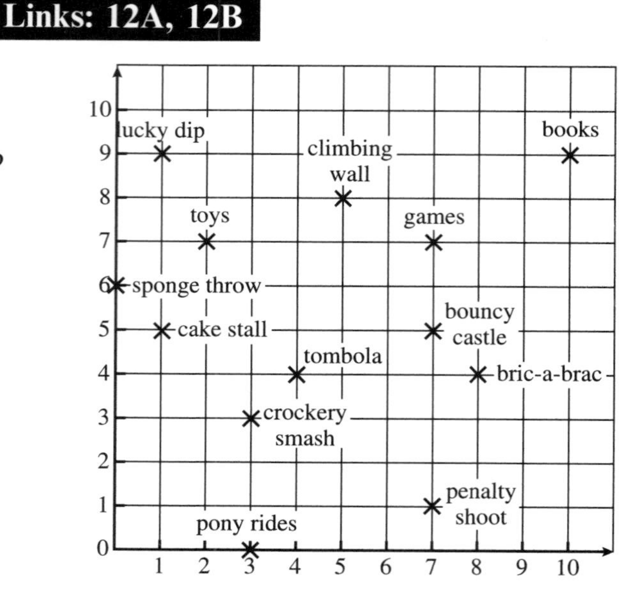

1 What is at each of these coordinates?

(a) (3, 0) **(b)** (8, 4)
(c) (10, 9) **(d)** (5, 8)
(e) (1, 9)

2 What are the coordinates of:

(a) crockery smash
(b) tombola
(c) bouncy castle
(d) toys
(e) sponge throw
(f) penalty shoot

3 13 stalls are shown on the grid. 11 have been used in questions **1** and **2**.
What are the 2 missing stalls and what are their coordinates?

4 The organisers wish to place rubbish bins around the field. They will place them half way between stalls.
Find the coordinates of bins placed half way between these stalls.

(a) cake stall, lucky dip
(b) penalty shoot, bouncy castle
(c) bouncy castle, games
(d) tombola, bric-a-brac

5 Draw a coordinate grid. Number each axis from 0 to 10. Plot these points on your grid.

(6, 5), (10, 5), (9, 7), (6, 7), (6, 9), (5, 10), (4, 9), (4, 7), (1, 7), (0, 5), (4, 5), (4, 2), (3, 2), (2, 0), (8, 0), (7, 2), (6, 2).

Joint each point to the last point you plotted. Join the last point to the first to make a shape. Shade the shape. You should get an aeroplane.

Exercise 12.2 Links: 12B, 12C

1 Draw three coordinate grids. Number each axis from 0 to 10.
For each set of points:
Plot the points. Join them up in order to make a shape.

(a) (1, 5), (1, 1), (9, 1), (9, 5), (1, 5), (3, 7), (7, 7), (9, 5)

(b) (7, 7), (10, 7), (10, 10), (1, 10), (1, 7), (4, 7), (4, 4), (1, 4), (1, 1), (10, 1), (10, 4), (7, 4), (7, 7)

(c) (0, 0), (10, 0), (10, 9), (9, 9), (9, 8), (8, 8), (8, 9), (7, 9), (7, 5), (0, 5), (0, 0)

2 Question **1(c)** should look like a church.
Add windows by plotting and joining the following sets of points.

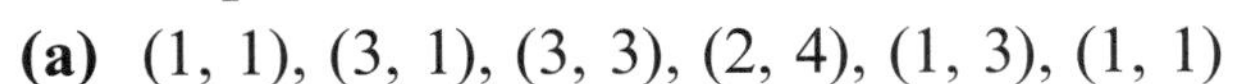

(a) (1, 1), (3, 1), (3, 3), (2, 4), (1, 3), (1, 1)

(b) (5, 4), (6, 3), (6, 1), (4, 1), (4, 3), (5, 4)

(c) (7, 1), (9, 1), (9, 3), (8, 4), (7, 3), (7, 1)

3 Two teams take turns to put a counter on a grid.
Counters can only be put in an empty position.
You cannot put one counter on top of another.

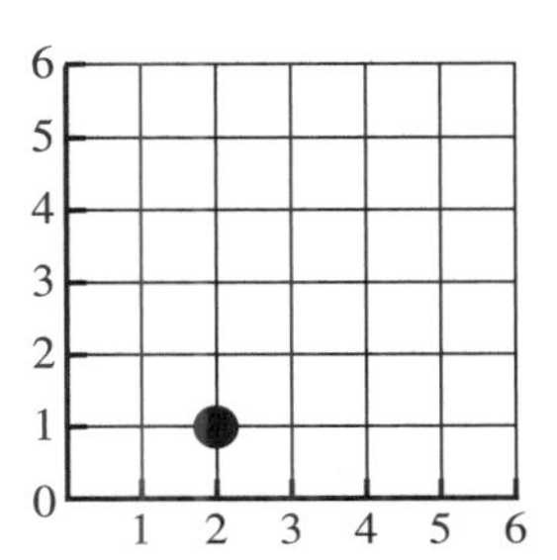

To win the game, get four of your counters in a straight line. The line can be horizontal (across), vertical (up) or diagonal (slanted).

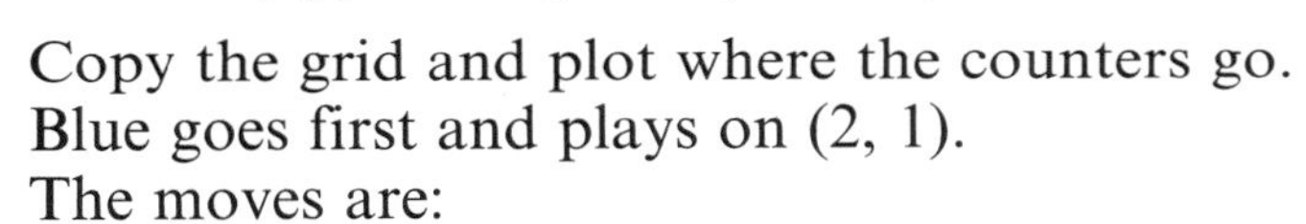

Copy the grid and plot where the counters go.
Blue goes first and plays on (2, 1).
The moves are:

Blue (2, 1) — (2, 2) — (3, 2) — (5, 2) — (3, 3) — (4, 1)
White (3, 1) — (2, 3) — (4, 2) — (4, 3) — (5, 3) —

Where should white place the next counter to win?

1 G

Exercise 12.3 Links: 12D

1 The owner of a garden centre charges £3 for 2 metres of rope. The graph helps him to work out how much to charge for other lengths. Use the graph to find:

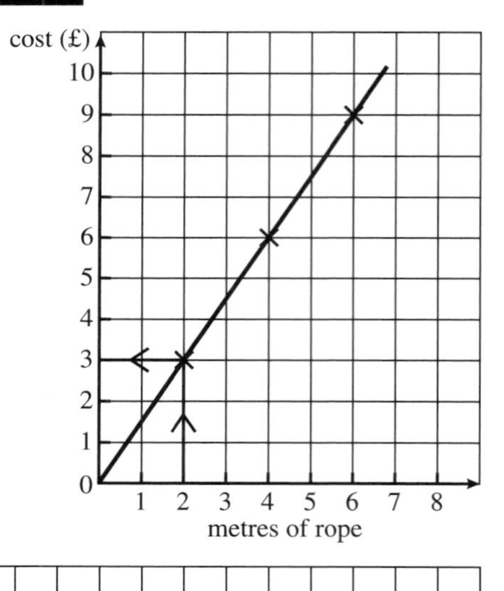

(a) the cost of 6 metres
(b) the cost of 4 metres
(c) the cost of 5 metres
(d) the cost of 1 metre
(e) how much rope can you buy for £7
(f) how much rope can you buy for £7.50
(g) how much rope can you buy for £2

2 The graph shows the cost of packets of crisps at the school tuck shop.

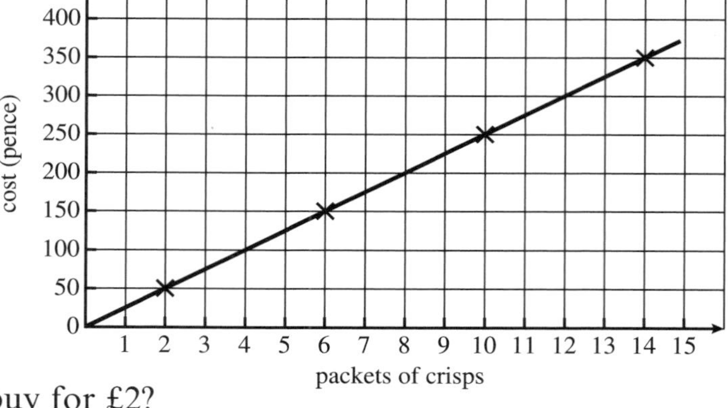

(a) How much do 4 packs cost?
(b) How much do 10 packs cost?
(c) How much do 14 packs cost?
(d) What is the cost of 1 pack?
(e) How many packs can you buy for £2?
(f) How many packs can you buy for £3?
(g) How much do 7 packs cost?

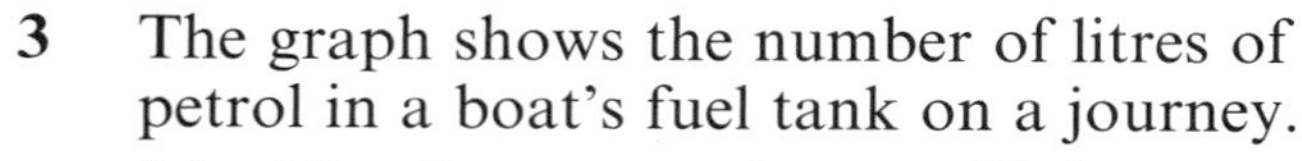

3 The graph shows the number of litres of petrol in a boat's fuel tank on a journey.

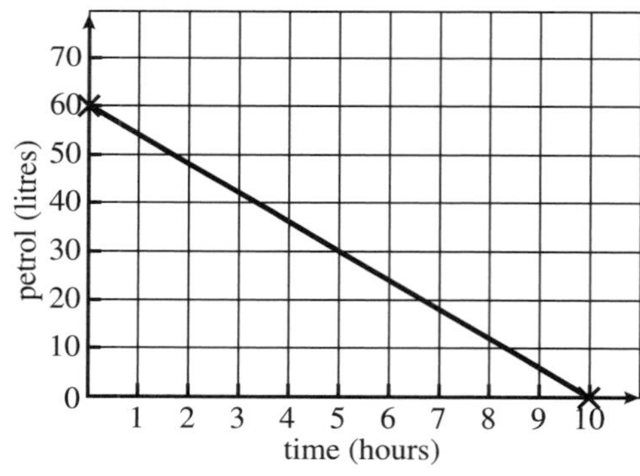

(a) After how many hours will the boat run out of fuel?
(b) How much fuel was there at the start?
(c) After how long was the tank half full?

4 The graph shows the cost of disco tickets.

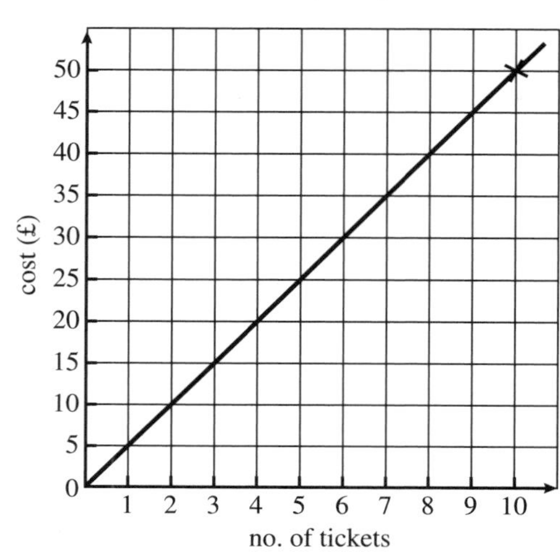

(a) How much would 1 ticket cost?
(b) How much would 8 tickets cost?
(c) How much would 5 tickets cost?
(d) How many tickets could you buy for £45?
(e) How many tickets could you buy for £30?

Homework

Exercise 12.4 Links: 12E

1 Some children are guiding a floor robot through an obstacle course. It has to pass over each marker.

To reach the first marker it goes:
start at (1, 9) move to (1, 8) → (1, 7) → (1, 6)

Part of its path to the second marker is:
start at (1, 6) → (2, 6) → (3, 6) → (4, 6) →

Complete the path to marker 2.

Write down the coordinate routes to reach the other markers.

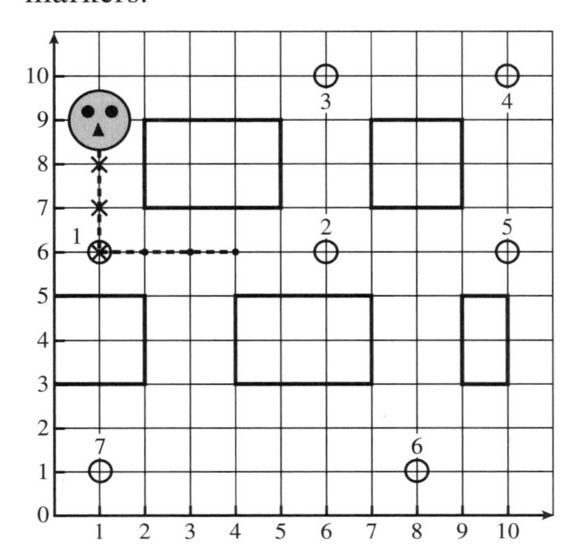

2 Write down a coordinate route to take the robot from marker 7 (1, 1) back to its start at (1, 9).

3 **(a)** There are 3 exits to this maze. One is at (9, 0). What are the coordinates of the other 2?

(b) Sanjay is at (9, 7). He wishes to get out of the maze at (9, 0). His first 3 moves are: (10, 7) → (11, 7) → (12, 7) Write down his remaining moves.

(c) Mina is lost! Guide her to exit C. (First move (1, 2) → (1, 3))

(d) Neema enters at B and exits at A. Make a list of her moves.

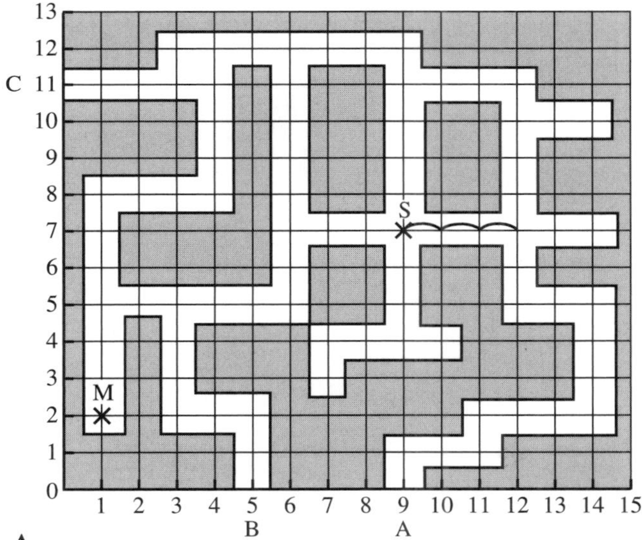

Name ....

12 Graphs

1 Here is the map of an island drawn on a coordinate grid.

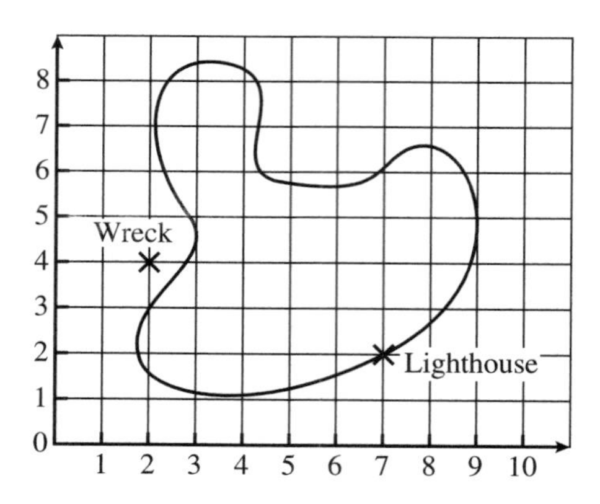

(a) Write down the coordinates of the

(i) wreck (.........., ...)

(ii) lighthouse (.........., ...)

(b) Mark and label the position of the

(i) tall tree at (4, 3)

(ii) treasure at (4, 7). **(6 marks)**

---

2 Here is the map of a town drawn on a coordinate grid.

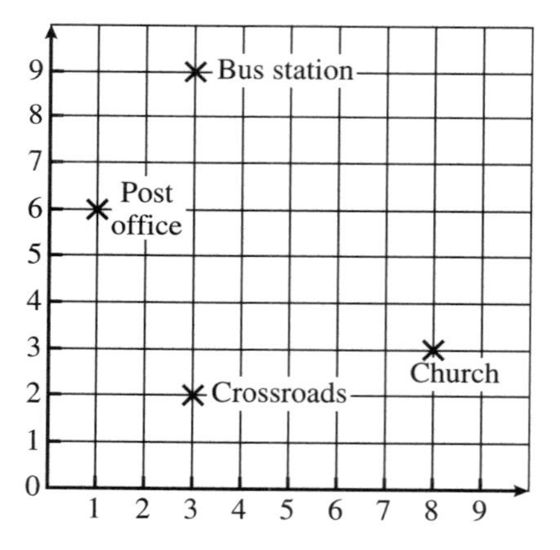

(a) Write down the coordinates of the

(i) crossroads (.........., ...)

(ii) post office (.........., ...)

(b) Mark and label the position of the

(i) cinema at (7, 4)

(ii) garage at (4, 8). **(6 marks)**

---

3 **(a)** On the coordinate grid plot and label the points:

A (1, 0) B (0, 4) C (2, 6)

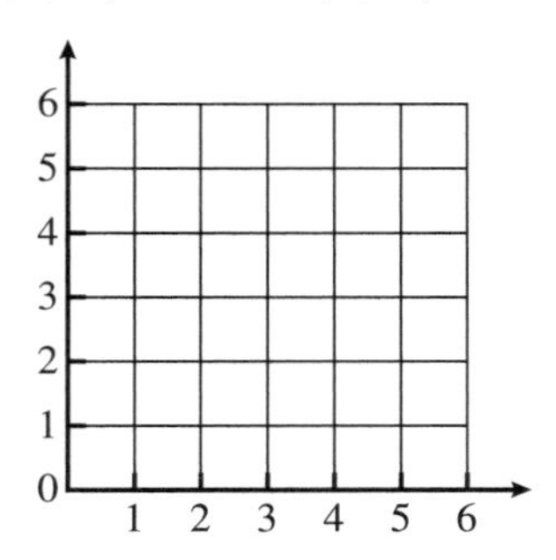

(b) Join ABC and then plot the point D so that ABCD is a parallelogram.

(c) Write down the coordinates of point D. ....

(6 marks)

---

4 Number each axis on the grid from 0 to 8.
Plot these points on the grid.

(1, 7)

(7, 6)

(4, 1)

(1, 1)

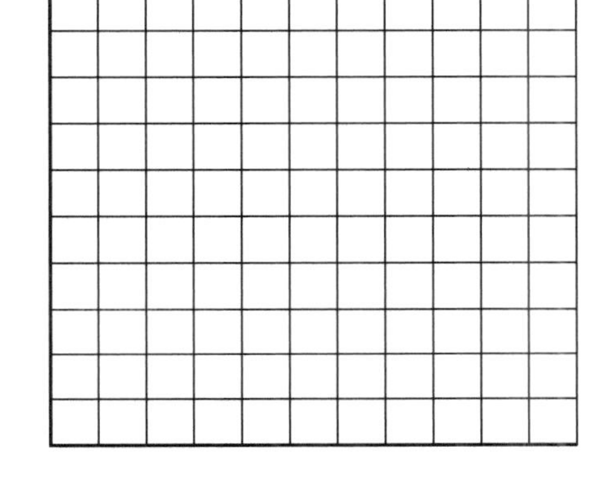

Join all the points in order. **(6 marks)**

---

5 Here is a graph to work out the cost of packets of sweets.

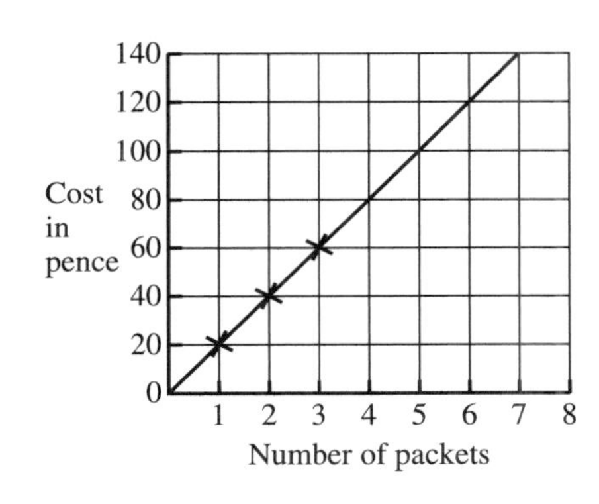

(a) What is the cost of 1 packet of sweets? .... p

(b) How many packets can you buy for 60 p? .... packets

(c) How much would 6 packets cost? .... **(3 marks)**

---

6 This graph is used to work out the cost of cinema tickets.

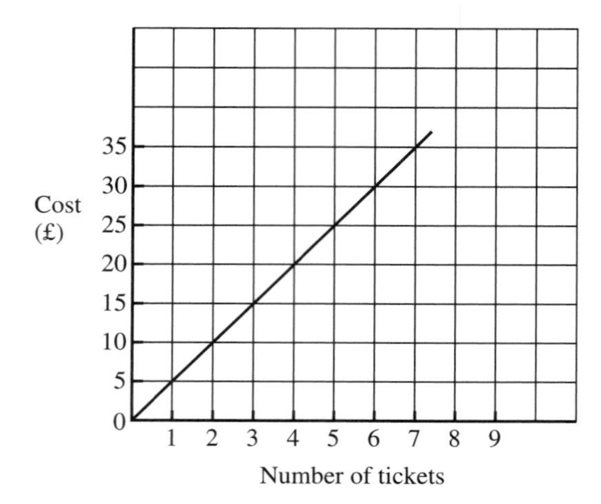

(a) How much does 1 ticket cost? ....

(b) How many tickets can you buy with £15? ....

(c) How much do 6 tickets cost? .... **(3 marks)**

Unit 12 Graphs

Question		Answer	Marking guidance and remediation sheet links
1	**(a) (i)**	(2, 4)	(B1, B1)
	(ii)	(7, 2)	(B1, B1)
	(b) (i)	tall tree at (4, 3)	B1
	(ii)	treasure at (4, 7)	B1
2	**(a) (i)**	(3, 2)	(B1, B1)
	(ii)	(1, 6)	(B1, B1)
	(b) (i)	cinema at (7, 4)	B1
	(ii)	garage at (4, 8)	B1
3	**(a)**	A plotted at (1, 0) B plotted at (0, 4) C plotted at (2, 6)	B1 B1 B1
	(b)	D plotted at (3, 2) and ABCD joined	B1
	(c)	(3, 2)	(B1, B1)
4		x-axis labelled 0–8 y-axis labelled 0–8 (1, 7) plotted (7, 6) plotted (4, 1) plotted (1, 1) plotted and all points joined in order	B1 B1 B1 B1 B1 B1
5	**(a)**	20 p	A1
	(b)	3 packets	A1
	(c)	£1.20 or 120 p	A1
6	**(a)**	£5	A1
	(b)	3 tickets	A1
	(c)	£30	A1

Key to mark scheme
A marks: correct answer
M marks: correct method
B marks: independent work

Page 265 gives a general guidance on use of this assessment scheme with some examples.

Answers to Pupils' Book

12 Graphs

Exercise 12A

1 **(a)** church **(b)** windmill
(c) lighthouse **(d)** harbour
(e) cliffs
2 **(a)** (6, 5) **(b)** (8, 2)
(c) (2, 1) **(d)** (2, 3)
(e) (9, 1) **(f)** (1, 2)
3 **(a)** exit **(b)** elephants **(c)** cafe
(d) camels **(e)** giftshop
4 **(a)** (6, 5) **(b)** (7, 4) **(c)** (8, 3)
(d) (1, 1) **(e)** (3, 1)
5 (2, 3) (2, 5) (4, 8) (8, 8) (10, 5) (10, 3) (8, 1) (7, 3) (6, 0) (5, 3) (4, 1)

Exercise 12B

2

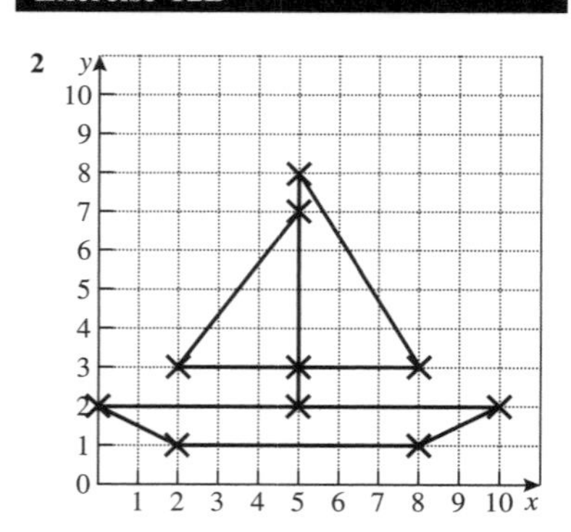

3 **(a)** square **(b)** triangle
(c) parallelogram.

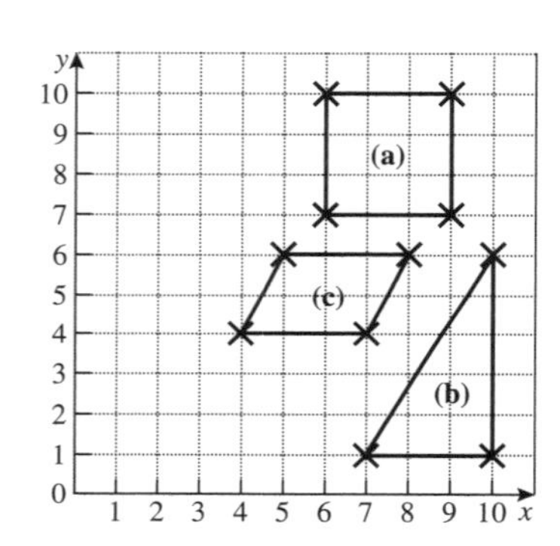

4

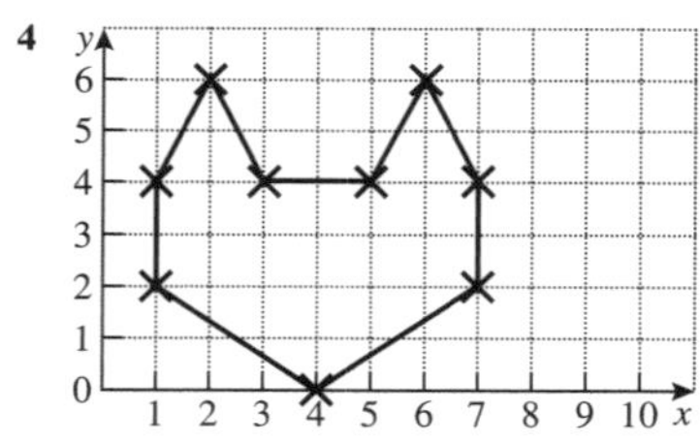

5 **(a)** (5, 5) **(b)** (2, 10) **(c)** (10, 4)

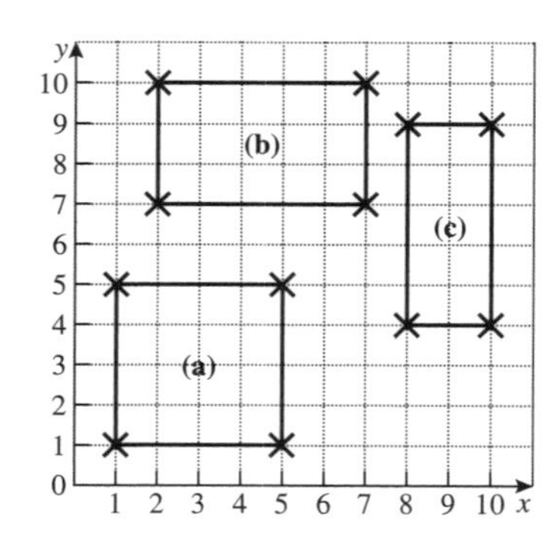

Exercise 12C

1 yellow to win on next move (5, 0)
winning line: (5, 0) (5, 1) (5, 2) (5, 3)
2 Yellow to play (1, 2) or (5, 2)
Winning line: (1, 2) (2, 2) (3, 2) (4, 2) or (2, 2) (3, 2) (4, 2) (5, 2)
Blue to play (4, 1) or (6, 0)
Winning line: (3, 1) (4, 1) (5, 1) (6, 1) or (6, 0) (6, 1) (6, 2) (6, 3).

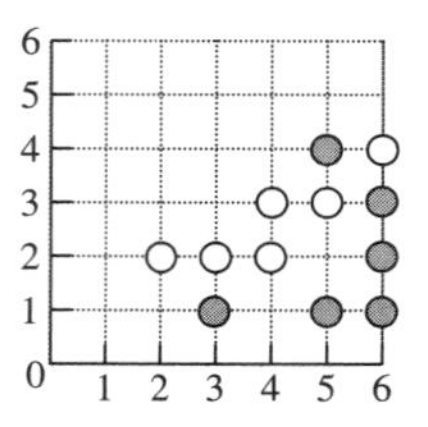

Exercise 12D

1 **(a)** 225p (£2.25) **(b)** 6 packets
2 **(a)** £35 **(b)** £20 **(c)** 9 tickets
3 **(a)** 15p **(b)** 4 bags **(c)** 105p (£1.05)
4 **(a)** 120p (£1.20) **(b)** 180p (£1.80)
5 **(a)** 75p **(b)** 15p **(c)** 7
6 **(a)** 6 hours **(b)** 120 litres
7 **(a)** £12 **(b)** £9
(c) 8 miles **(d)** 5 miles

Exercise 12E

1 (1, 3) → (2, 3) → (3, 3) → (4, 3) → (5, 3) → (5, 4) → (6, 4) → (7, 4) → (7, 3) → (8, 3)
2 (9, 1) → (8, 1) → (8, 2) → (8, 3) → (8, 4) → (7, 4) → (6, 4) → (6, 3) → (5, 3) → (4, 3) → (3, 3) → (3, 2) → (3, 1) → (4, 1) → (5, 1) → (5, 0)
3 **(a)** (2, 5) (3, 5) (4, 5)
(b) (8, 1) (8, 2) (8, 3) (8, 4)
(c) (1, 1) (1, 2) and (5, 0) (6, 0)

Answers to Homeworks

12 Graphs

Exercise 12.1 Links: 12A, 12B

1 **(a)** pony rides **(b)** bric-a-brac
(c) books **(d)** climbing wall
(e) lucky dip
2 **(a)** (3, 3) **(b)** (4, 4)
(c) (7, 5) **(d)** (2, 7)
(e) (0, 6) **(f)** (7, 1)
3 games (7, 7) cake stall (1, 5)
4 **(a)** (1, 7) **(b)** (7, 3)
(c) (7, 6) **(d)** (6, 4)

5

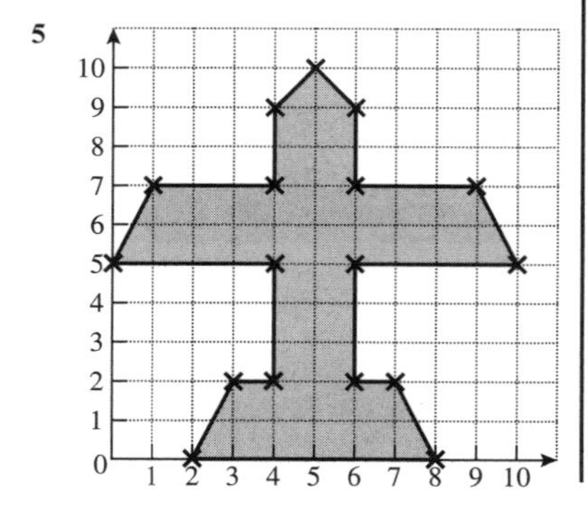

Exercise 12.2 Links: 12B, 12C

1 **(a)**

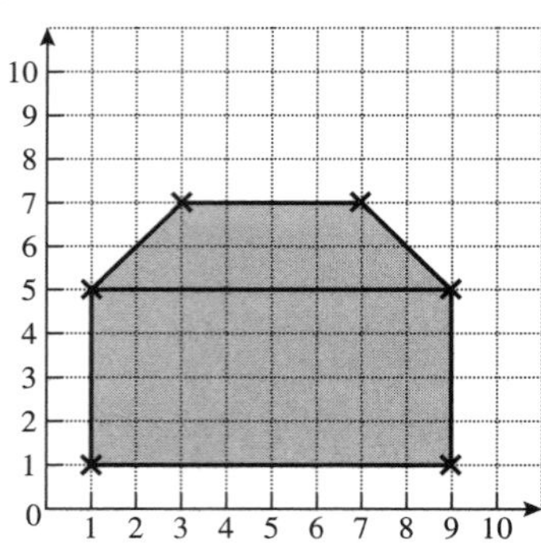

(b)

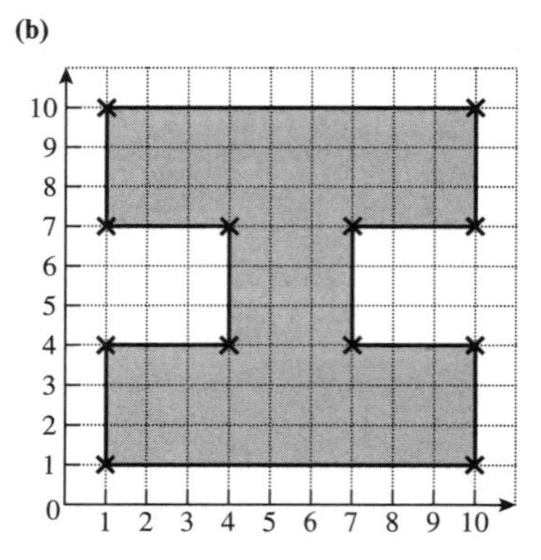

(c)

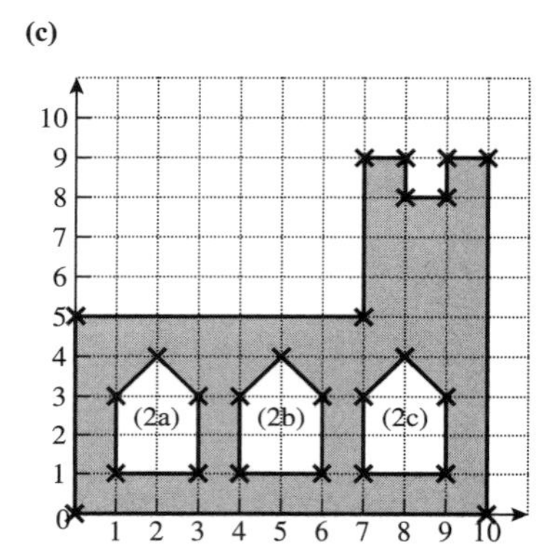

3

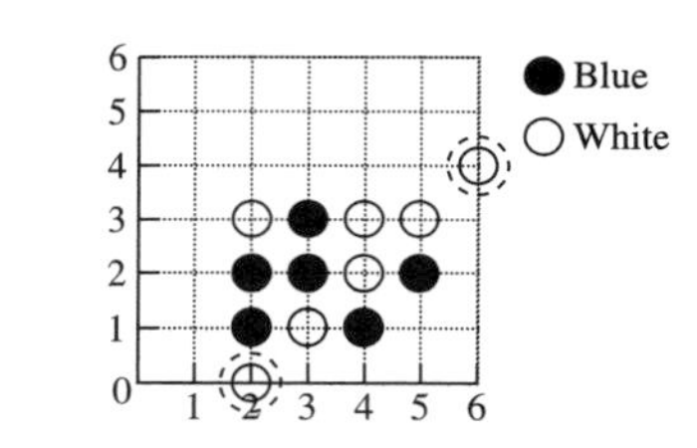

White (6, 4) or (2, 0)

Exercise 12.3 Links: 12D

1 **(a)** £9 **(b)** £6
(c) £7.50 **(d)** £1.50
(e) $4\frac{2}{3}$ or 4.67 metres
(f) 5 metres **(g)** $1\frac{1}{3}$ or 1.3 metres
2 **(a)** £1.00 (100p) **(b)** £2.50 (250p)
(c) £3.50 (350p) **(d)** 25p, £0.25
(e) 8 packs **(f)** 12 packs
(g) £1.75
3 **(a)** 10 hours **(b)** 60 litres
(c) 5 hours
4 **(a)** £5 **(b)** £40
(c) £25 **(d)** 9 tickets
(e) 6 tickets

Exercise 12.4 Links: 12E

1 → (5, 6) → (6, 6)
m2 → (6, 7) → (6, 8) → (6, 9) → (6, 10) m3
m3 → (7, 10) → (8, 10) → (9, 10) → (10, 10) m4
m4 → (10, 9) → (10, 8) → (10, 7) → (10, 6) m5
m5 → (9, 6) → (8, 6) → (8, 5) → (8, 4) → (8, 3) → (8, 2) → (8, 1) m6
m6 → (7, 1) → (6, 1) → (5, 1) → (4, 1) → (3, 1) → (2, 1) → (1, 1) m7

2 m7 → (2, 1) → (3, 1) → (3, 2) → (3, 3) → (3, 4) → (3, 5) → (3, 6) → (2, 6) → (1, 6) → (1, 7) → (1, 8) → (1, 9)

3 **(a)** B = (5, 0) C = (0, 11)
(b) (12, 7) → (12, 6) → (12, 5) → (13, 5) → (14, 5) → (14, 4) → (14, 3) → (14, 2) → (13, 2) → (12, 2) → (11, 2) → (11, 1) → (10, 1) → (9, 1) → (9, 0)
(c) (1, 3) → (1, 4) → (1, 5) → (1, 6) → (1, 7) → (1, 8) → (2, 8) → (3, 8) → (4, 8) → (4, 9) → (4, 10) → (4, 11) → (3, 11) → (2, 11) → (1, 11) → (0, 11)
(d) (5, 0) → (5, 1) → (5, 2) → (4, 2) → (3, 2) → (3, 3) → (3, 4) → (3, 5) → (4, 5) → (5, 5) → (6, 5) → (6, 6) → (6, 7) → (7, 7) → (8, 7) → (9, 7) → (10, 7) → (11, 7) → (12, 7) → (12, 6) → (12, 5) → (13, 5) → (14, 5) → (14, 4) → (14, 3) → (14, 2) → (13, 2) → (12, 2) → (11, 2) → (11, 1) → (10, 1) → (9, 1) → (9, 0)

Unit 13 Angles

Content summary

This unit begins with turns and makes use of this in identifying rotational symmetry. Then degrees are introduced and angles drawn and measured with a protractor. Students estimate angles and use the terms right angle, acute and obtuse.

Book 1R Unit 14 goes from this basis to consider angles on a line (180°), at a point (360°) and in a triangle (180°). Reflex is added. Triangles are constructed by drawing lengths and angles.

NC level

Level 2: Turns.

Level 4: Rotational symmetry. Language of angle.

Level 5: Measure, estimate and draw angles

S4b(KS1) *S3b* S2b S3b S4d

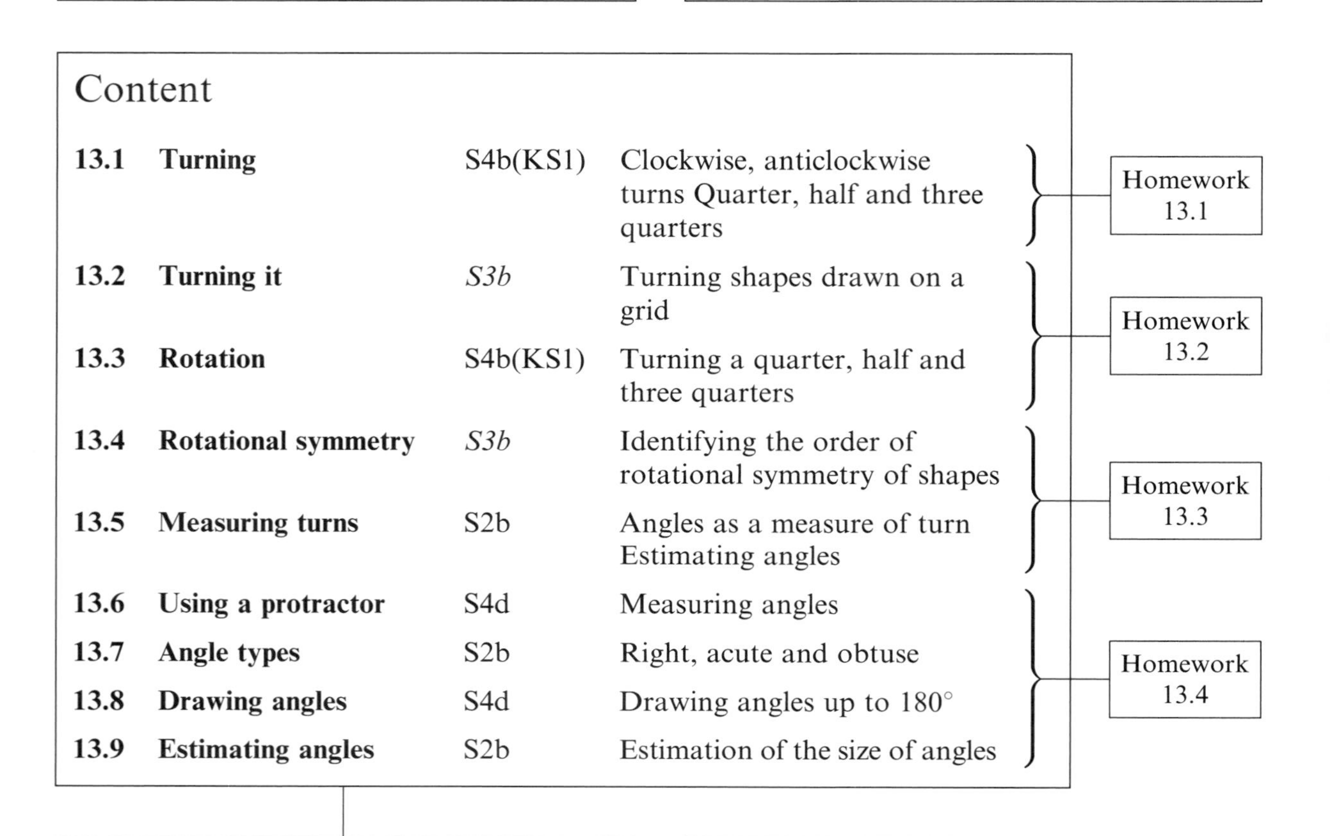

Content

13.1	**Turning**	S4b(KS1)	Clockwise, anticlockwise turns Quarter, half and three quarters	Homework 13.1
13.2	**Turning it**	*S3b*	Turning shapes drawn on a grid	Homework 13.2
13.3	**Rotation**	S4b(KS1)	Turning a quarter, half and three quarters	
13.4	**Rotational symmetry**	*S3b*	Identifying the order of rotational symmetry of shapes	Homework 13.3
13.5	**Measuring turns**	S2b	Angles as a measure of turn Estimating angles	
13.6	**Using a protractor**	S4d	Measuring angles	Homework 13.4
13.7	**Angle types**	S2b	Right, acute and obtuse	
13.8	**Drawing angles**	S4d	Drawing angles up to 180°	
13.9	**Estimating angles**	S2b	Estimation of the size of angles	

Assessment

Assessment 13 covers the key concepts in Unit 13.

Remediation

Remediation sheets 13.1 and 13.2.

Assessment

The assessment is marked out of 30.
Achievement of 20 or more marks indicates a good understanding of the key concepts.
Marking guidance, answers and links to remediation are provided on page 265.

Equipment

	Pupil's Book page
Tracing paper is useful	
Protractors	191ff

ICT links

13.1 – 13.4
Use *Geomat for windows* to draw some simple geometric shapes and:

- rotate them clockwise and anticlockwise through a quarter, half and three quarter turns
- Identify positions of rotational symmetry.

13.6 and 13.7
Use *WinLogo* to draw a variety of different angles.

13.8 and 13.9
Use *The Geometer's Sketchpad* to draw some angles. Estimate the size of the angles and then display their value to check the estimates.

13.9
Use *MicroSmile for Windows Pack 2* to estimate the size of angles and use a knowledge of angles to play snooker.

Remediation

Drawing and measuring angles:
The measurement of angles relies on the concept of turn so start with pupils facing the front of the class, then the side, then the back to reinforce quarter turn, half turn, all the way round, etc.

Before measuring angles always get pupils to make an estimate first. Provide plenty of practice for bigger/smaller than 90°. Pupils can use the angle measurer from Activity sheet 10 to measure angles to the nearest 10 degrees. Once the pupil is capable of using the angle measurer, repeat the exercises using a protractor to get exact answers. Further worksheets can be made to give extra practice if needed.

Questionbank CD

All homeworks and extension questions also appear on the CD.

Pages xvii and xviii of this pack show you how to use the CD to select questions from the Questionbank and further customize them if you wish to.

13 Angles

framework teaching objective	§	lesson starter	f/w ref
Understand and use the language and notation associated with reflections, translations and rotations.	13.1	What units would I use to measure . . . . . . How far a battery operated toy car has travelled? (cm, m) How far a piece of wood in a fast stream has travelled? (m) The second hand of a clock as it *travels* around the clock? (Students may suggest 'cm.' – For the tip of the hand? – Half way down the hand? – One part of the hand doesn't travel at all.) We measure how far the hand has **turned**. What fraction of the clock has it turned through when it starts at 12 and reaches 6? reaches 3? reaches 9? reaches 1?	202–3
Recognise and visualise the transformation and symmetry of a 2-D shape – rotation about a given point, and rotation symmetry.	13.3/ 13.4	Here is a square box with a logo on it. What will it look like if I roll it onto its side? Students volunteer to come to the board and fill in second square with arrow and dot. How many turns before it is upright again? (*4*) What will this box look like? Will it **look** the right way up **before** it has gone through the 4 turns? (*Yes, after turn 2.*)	202–12

framework teaching objective	**§**	**lesson starter**	**f/w ref**
Use a protractor to measure and draw acute and obtuse angles to the nearest degree.	13.6	Ikram has used a protractor to draw a 50° angle. When he measures it again one minute later it measures 44°! Has the angle shrunk? What mistake has Ikram made? (*not aligned the base line of the protractor with the base line of the angle*). Gary uses his protractor to measure the angle on page 192 of the textbook. The textbook says that the angle is 46°. When Gary measures it, it measures 134°! What mistake has Gary made? (*He's used the outer, clockwise scale.*) Another angle measures 50°. **If he makes the same mistake**, what will Gary measure it as?	220–3
Use angle measure; distinguish between and estimate the size of acute, obtuse and reflex angles.	13.7/ 13.9	Which angle is largest? (*H*) 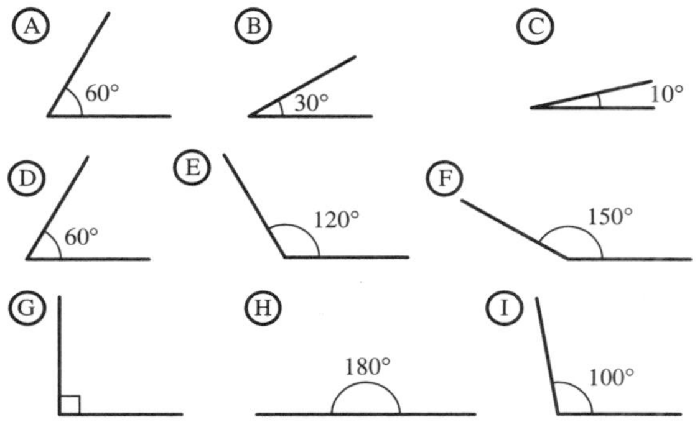 (A) 60° (B) 30° (C) 10° (D) 60° (E) 120° (F) 150° (G) (H) 180° (I) 100° The angles should **not** include measurements. Which two angles are the same? (*A*) and (*D*) Sara says 'D is bigger than angle A.' Is she right? How has she made this mistake? Put the angles in order of size. C, B, A + D, G, I, E, F, H. Draw a bubble around angle drawings C, B, A + D and another around I, E, F, M. How can I sort these angles into 2 groups? (*'size, second group has turned further'*) Students encouraged to relate membership of 'acute' and 'obtuse' groups to the right angle.	232–3

13 Angles

Exercise 13.1 — Links: 13A

1 Which number will the arrow point to after these numbers of $\frac{1}{4}$ turns from the number 12:

(a) 2 **(b)** 8 **(c)** 11

(d) 15 **(e)** 23?

2 Which letter will the arrow point to after:

(a) $\frac{1}{2}$ turn from C

(b) $\frac{1}{4}$ turn anticlockwise from H

(c) $\frac{1}{4}$ turn clockwise from J

(d) $\frac{3}{4}$ turn clockwise from I

(e) $\frac{1}{2}$ turn from L

(f) $\frac{3}{4}$ turn anticlockwise from C?

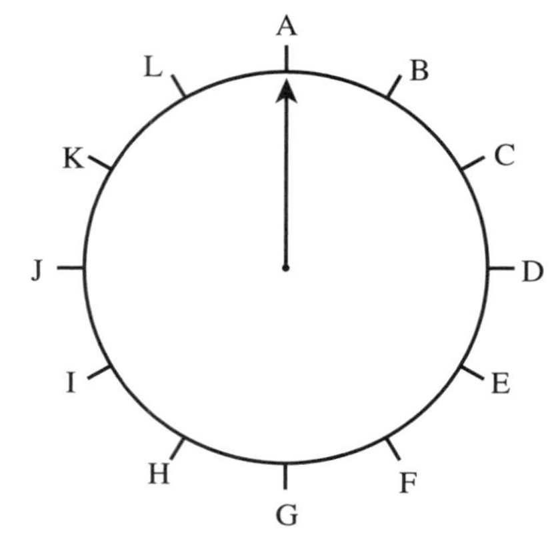

3 Describe the turn needed to move from:

(a) B to H **(b)** K to H **(c)** F to I

(d) A to D **(e)** C to I **(f)** E to B

Exercise 13.2 — Links: 13B, 13C

1 Draw each shape after:

- $\frac{1}{4}$ turn
- $\frac{1}{2}$ turn
- $\frac{3}{4}$ turn

When does it look exactly the same as the original shape?

Hint: trace the shapes first.

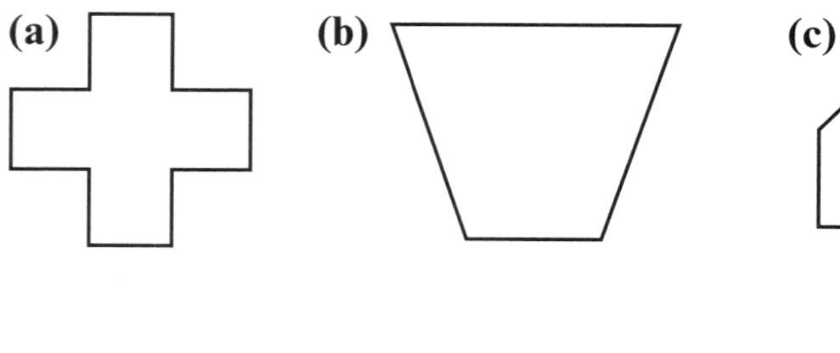

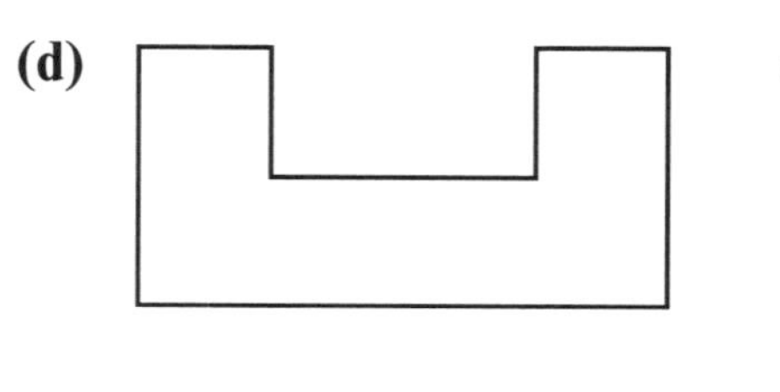

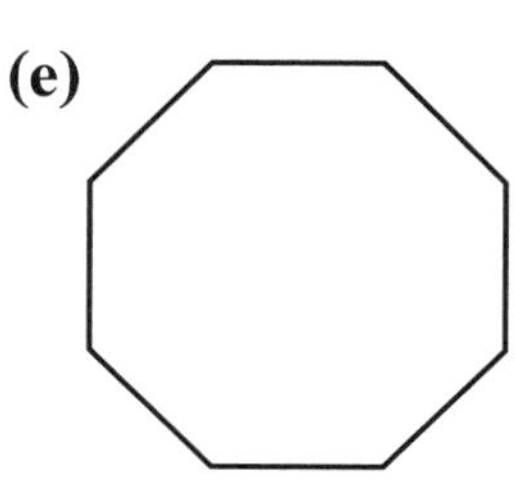

Exercise 13.3 Links: 13D, 13E

1 Which of these shapes have rotational symmetry?

(a) 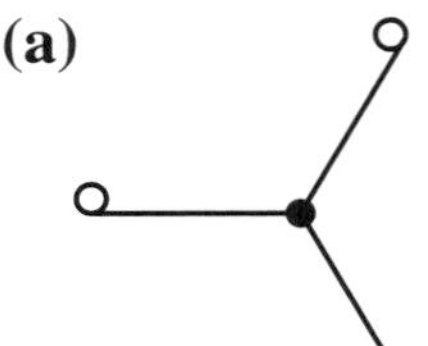

(b) 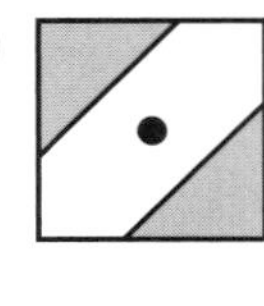

(c) 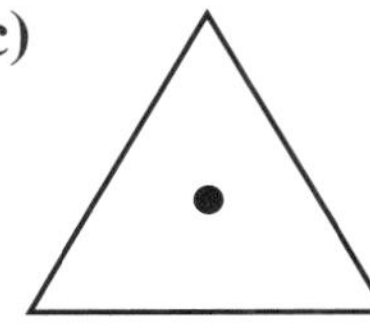

2 Draw the following turns and say how many degrees are in each.

(a) 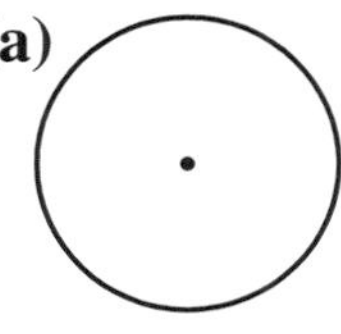
$\frac{1}{4}$ turn

(b) 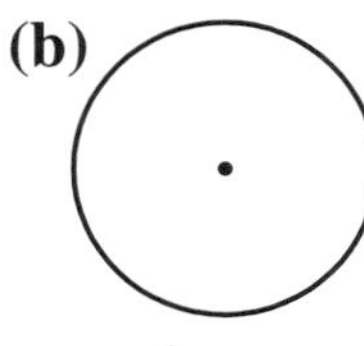
$\frac{3}{4}$ turn

(c) 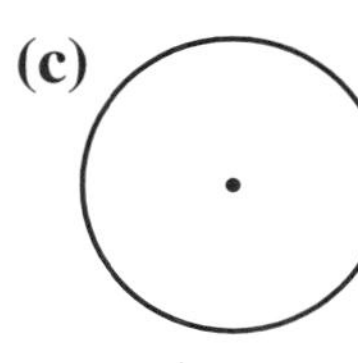
$\frac{1}{2}$ turn

(d) 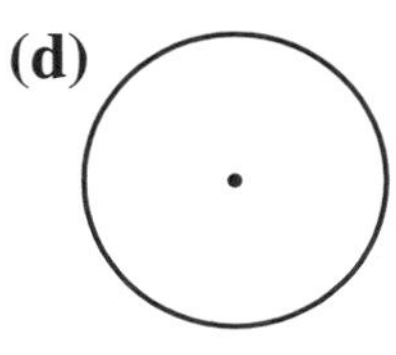
full turn

3 How many degrees are in these turns?
Choose from: 45°, 100°, 135°, 200°, 340°

(a) 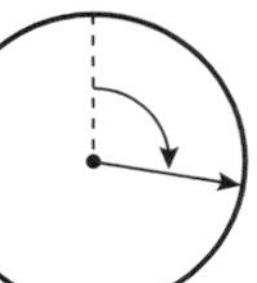

(b)

(c) 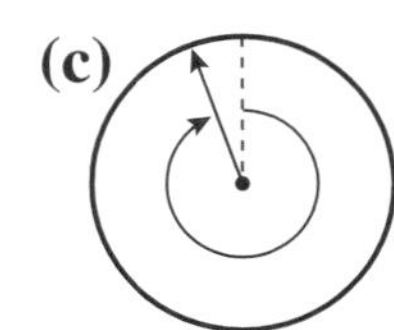

(d)

(e) 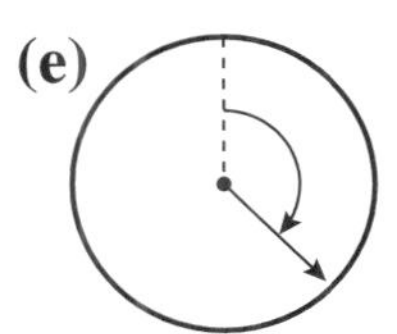

Exercise 13.4 Links: 13F, 13G, 13H, 13I

1 For each angle:
- estimate the size of the angle
- write down the angle type
- accurately measure the angle.

(a) 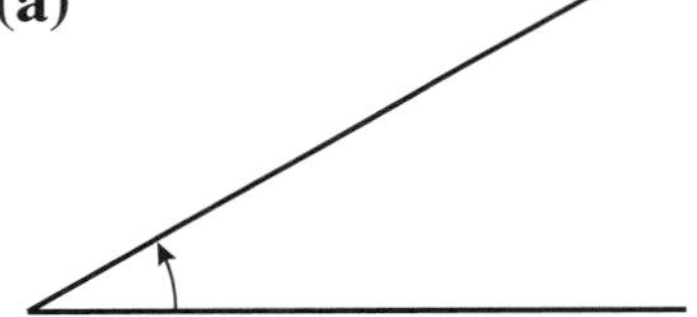

(b) 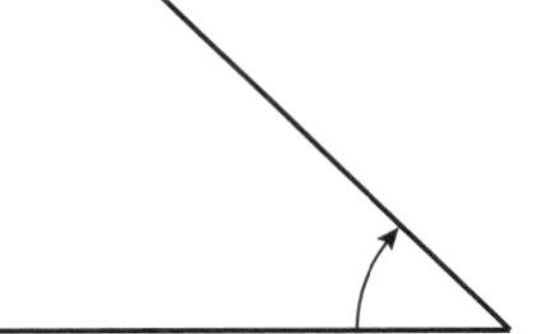

(c) 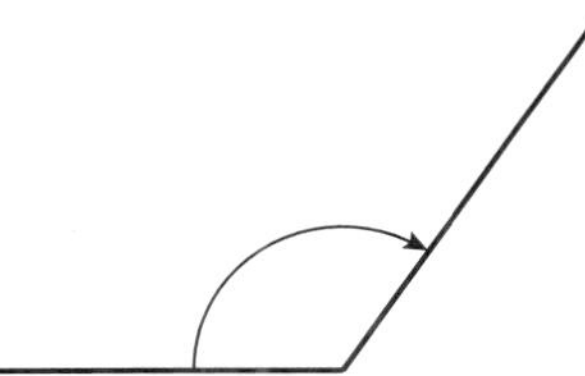

(d) 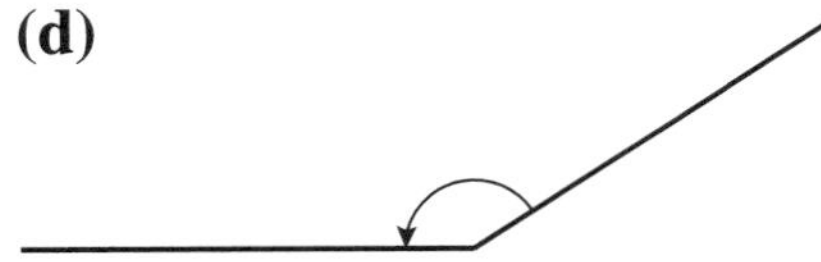

(e) **(f)** 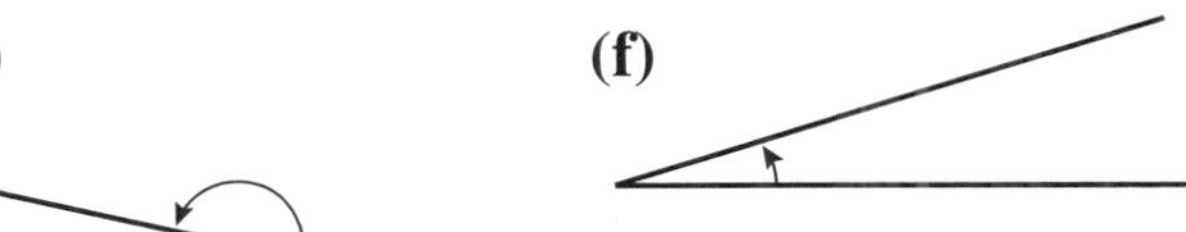

2 Write down the angle type of these angles:
(a) 63° **(b)** 100° **(c)** 172° **(d)** 90° **(e)** 115° **(f)** 5°

3 Draw each of these angles accurately:
(a) 25° **(b)** 170° **(c)** 45° **(d)** 68° **(e)** 133° **(f)** 164°

Name ....

13 Angles

1 In this diagram the arrow is pointing to the letter A.

B

A ←•— C

D

Which letter will the arrow be pointing towards after it makes:

(a) half a turn from A ....

(b) $\frac{1}{4}$ turn clockwise from A ....

(c) $\frac{3}{4}$ turn clockwise from A ....

(d) $\frac{1}{4}$ turn anticlockwise starting from C? .... **(4 marks)**

---

2 This picture of an L shape is in its starting position.

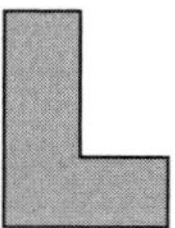

(a) Draw the L shape when it has made $\frac{1}{2}$ a turn.

(1 mark)

(b) The L shape returns to its starting position.
Draw the L shape when it has made $\frac{1}{4}$ turn anticlockwise. **(1 mark)**

(c) The L shape returns to its starting position like this:

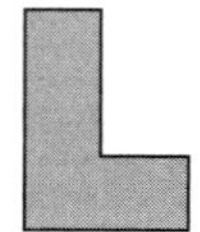

It is **rotated** to finish like this:

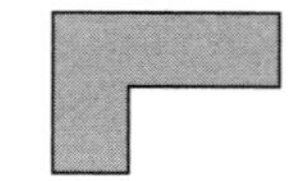

Describe this rotation as fully as you can.

.... **(2 marks)**

---

3 Which of these flags have rotational symmetry?

A B C D E

.... **(2 marks)**

---

4 Write down the number of degrees in each of these turns:

(a) a full turn ....°

(b) a $\frac{1}{4}$ turn ....°

(c) a $\frac{1}{2}$ turn ....°

(d) a $\frac{3}{4}$ turn ....° **(4 marks)**

---

5 **You will need a protractor.**
Measure each of these angles.

(a)

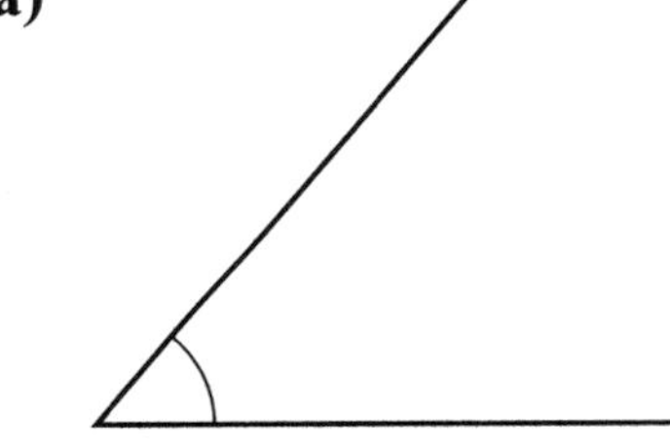

..........°

(b)

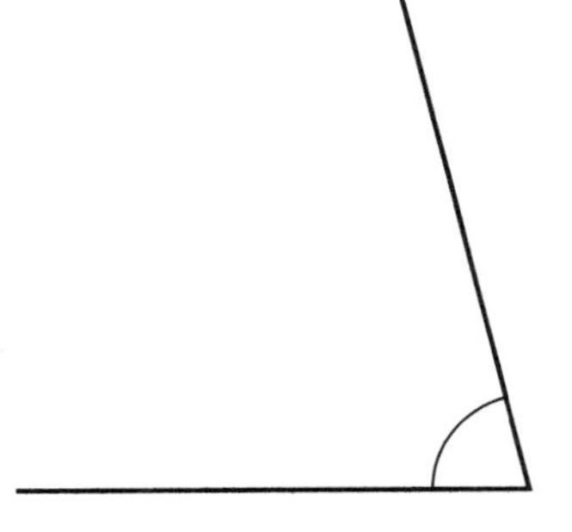

..........°

(c)

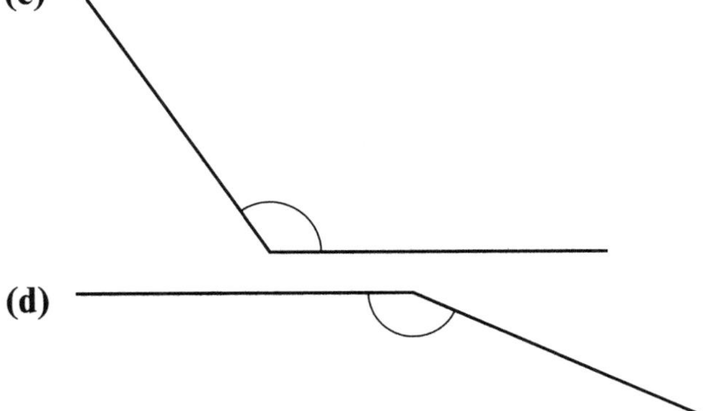

..........°

(d)

..........° **(4 marks)**

---

6 Look at these angles. Each angle is marked with a letter.

A B C D

Write the angles in order of size. ....
Start with the smallest. **(2 marks)**

---

7 Look at the shape below. On the diagram label:

all the **acute** angles inside the shape with the letter **A**.
all the **obtuse** angles inside the shape with the letter **O**.
all the **right** angles inside the shape with the letter **R**.

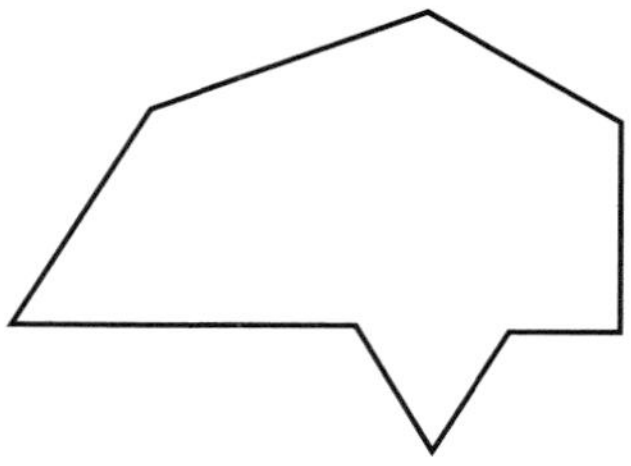

(4 marks)

---

8 Write down all the angles in this list which are **obtuse**:

57° 103° 45° 148° 90° 85° 175°

.... **(1 mark)**

---

9 **You will need a protractor.**

(a) Draw an angle of 70°.

(1 mark)

(b) Draw an angle of 157°.

(1 mark)

(c) Draw a right angle.

(1 mark)

10 You MUST NOT use a protractor.

Estimate the size of this angle.

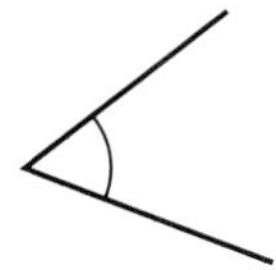

.... ° **(2 marks)**

Unit 13 Angles

Question		Answer	Marking guidance and remediation sheet links	
1	**(a)**	C	A1	less than $\frac{6}{8}$ use remediation sheet 13.1
	(b)	B	A1	
	(c)	D	A1	
	(d)	B	A1	
2	**(a)**	 [shape]	A1	
	(b)	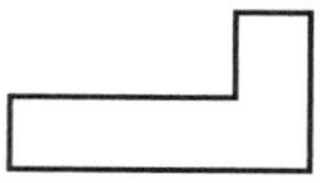 [shape]	A1	
	(c)	$\frac{1}{4}$ turn clockwise	B1 for $\frac{1}{4}$ turn, B1 for clockwise	
3		A, D, E	B2 for all 3, B1 for one correct	
4	**(a)**	360°	A1	
	(b)	90°	A1	
	(c)	180°	A1	
	(d)	270°	A1	
5	**(a)**	50°	A1 ± 2°	less than $\frac{3}{4}$ use remediation sheet 13.2
	(b)	75°	A1 ± 2°	
	(c)	125°	A1 ± 2°	
	(d)	156°	A1 ± 2°	
6		C, D, B, A	B2 for all correct, B1 for 1 wrong or largest first	
7		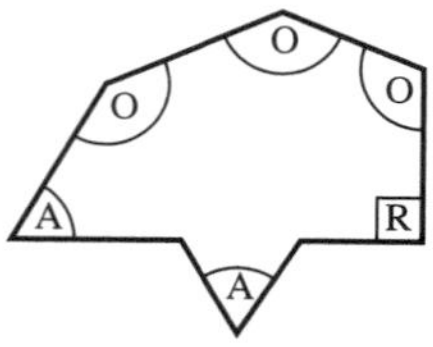 [shape with angles marked O, O, O, A, A, R]	B1 for 1 acute angle B1 for 1 obtuse angle B1 for right angle B1 for both acute and all 3 obtuse angles	

Key to mark scheme
A marks: correct answer
M marks: correct method
B marks: independent work

Page 265 gives a general guidance on use of this assessment scheme with some examples.

Assessment and remediation links

Question		Answer	Marking guidance and remediation sheet links	
8		103°, 148°, 175°	B1 for all 3 correct	
9	**(a)**	70°	B1 ±2°	less than $\frac{3}{3}$ use remediation sheet 13.2
	(b)	157	B1 ±2°	
	(c)	90°	B1 ±2°	
10		60°	B2 ±10° B1 ±15°	

Key to mark scheme
A marks: correct answer
M marks: correct method
B marks: independent work

Page 265 gives a general guidance on use of this assessment scheme with some examples.

13.1 Angles and turns

At 3 o'clock the minute hand on a clock points straight up.
The hand **turns** to:

quarter past 3 ...

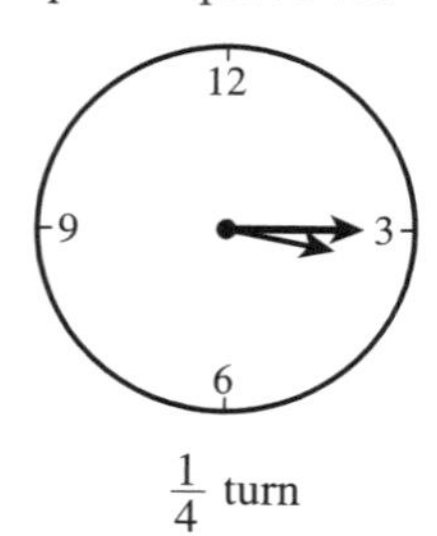

$\frac{1}{4}$ turn

half past 3 ...

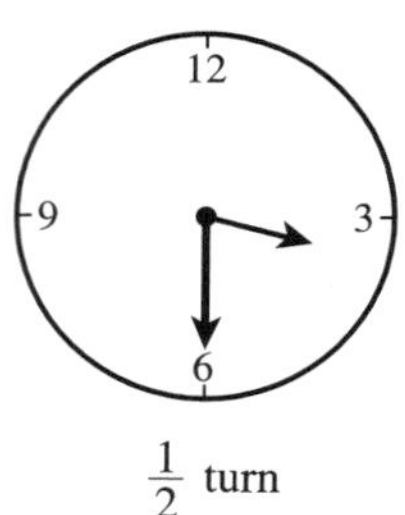

$\frac{1}{2}$ turn

4 o'clock.

full turn

Exercise 1

1 Which of these are: • $\frac{1}{4}$ turns • $\frac{1}{2}$ turns

(a) **(b)** **(c)**

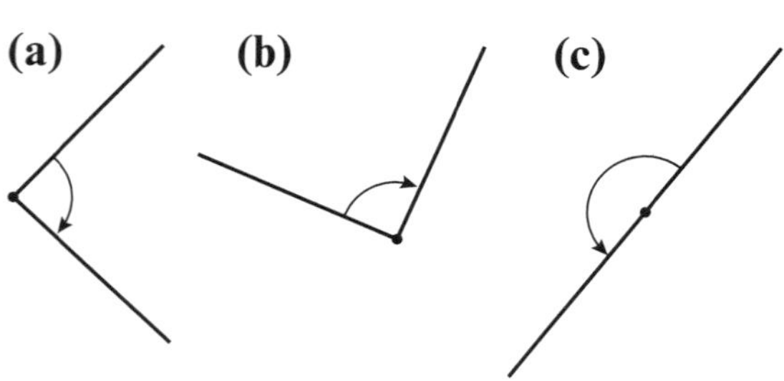

(d)

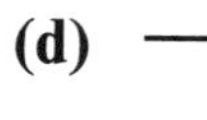

(e) **(f)**

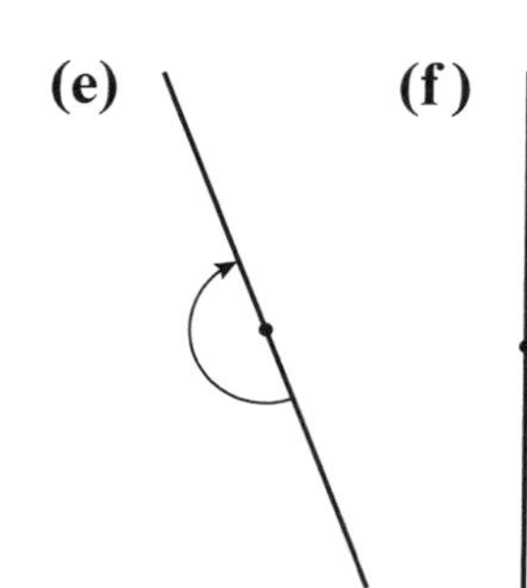

An **angle** is the amount of turn.
Angles are measured in **degrees**.

There are 360 degrees in a full turn.

There are 90 degrees in a quarter turn.

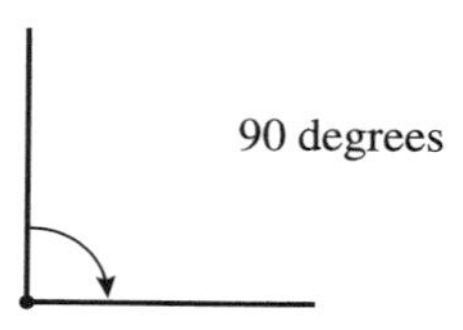

Example 1

Which of these angles are bigger than 90°?

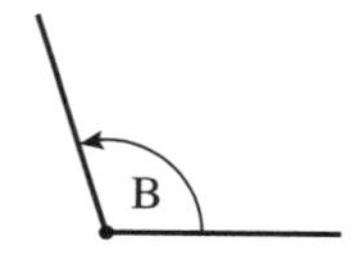

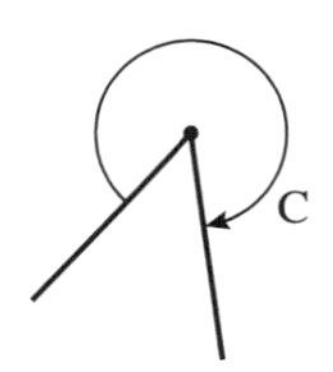

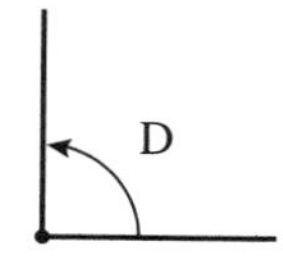

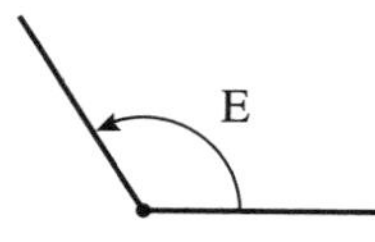

Answer: B, C, E

Exercise 2

Which of these angles are smaller than 90°?

(a)

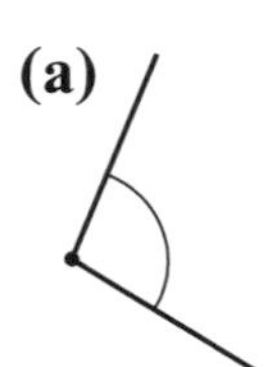

(b)

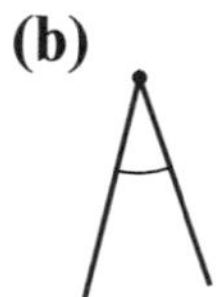

(c)

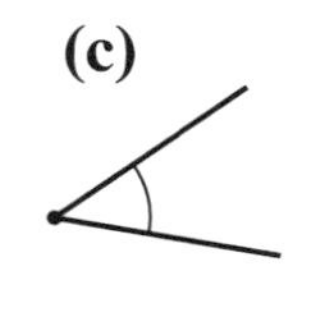

(d)

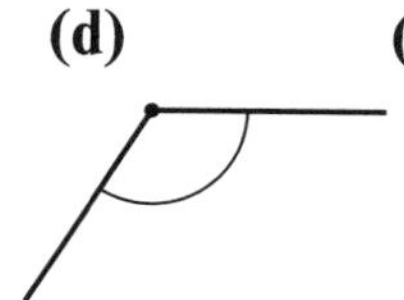

(e)

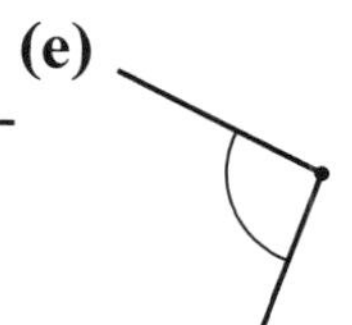

(f)

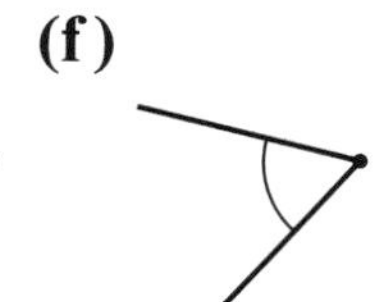

(g)

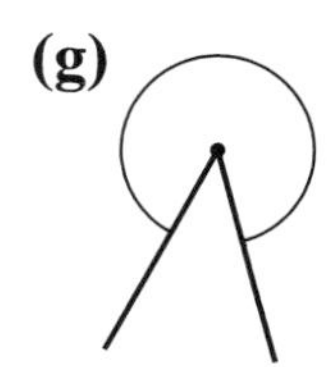

13.2 Measuring angles

Here is a simple angle measurer.
Each section is 10°.

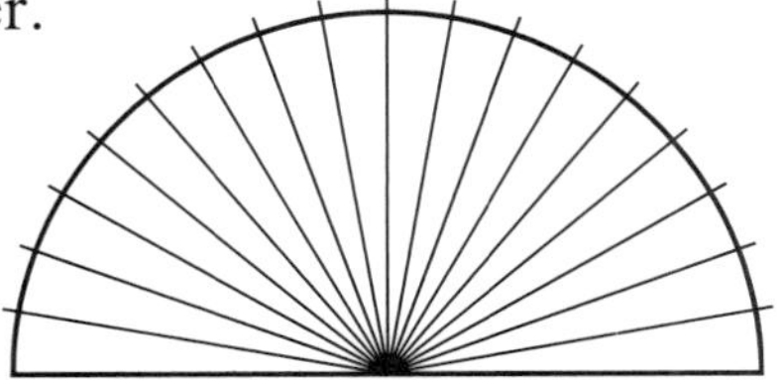

Remember:
10° means 10 degrees

To measure this angle first decide if it is smaller or bigger than 90°.

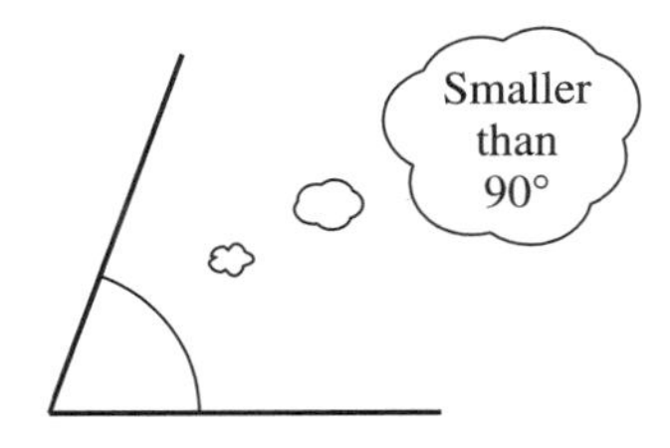

Put the straight edge of the measurer along one of the angle lines, with the middle at the point where the lines meet, like this:

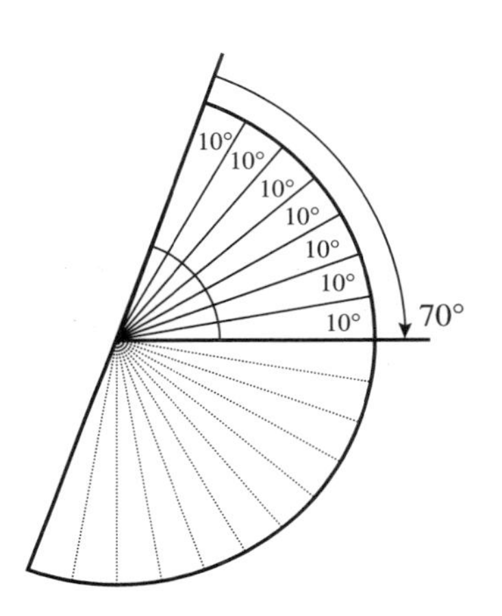

Then count the sections between the two angle lines. (Remember each section is 10°).

This angle measures 70° (which is smaller than 90°)

This angle is bigger than 90°.
Using the measurer, it is 120°.

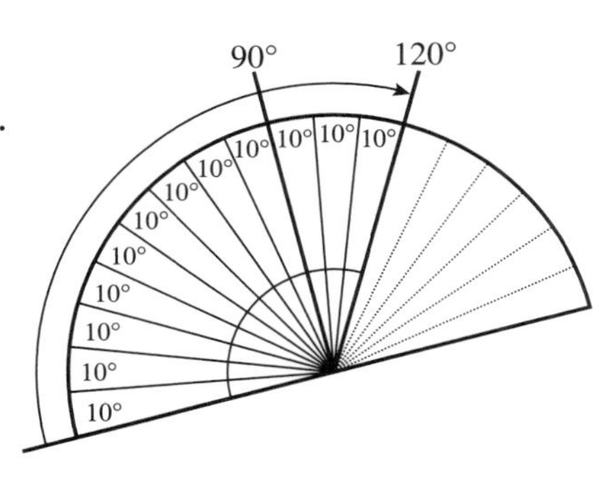

Example 1

Use your angle measurer to measure, then write down the size of these angles:

(a)

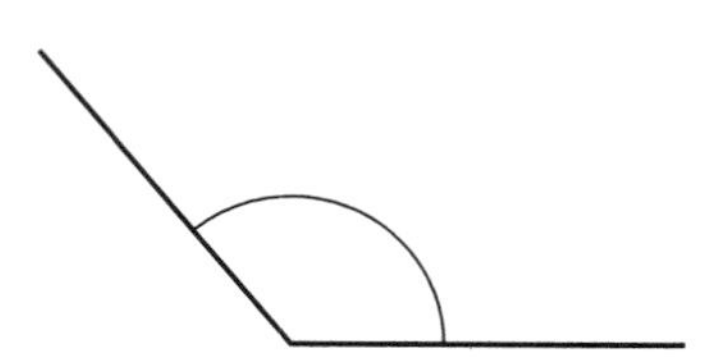

(b)

(a)

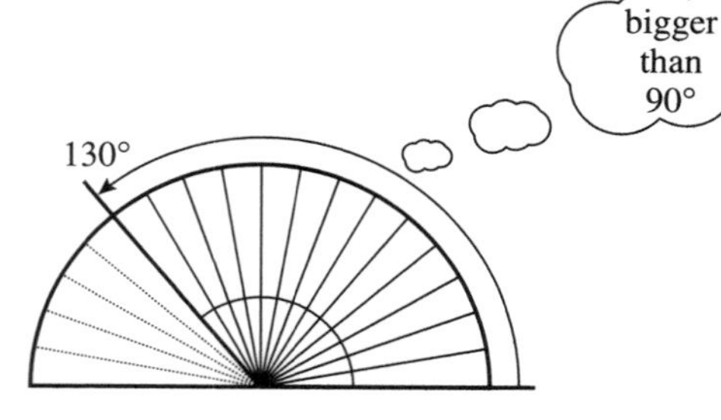

(b)

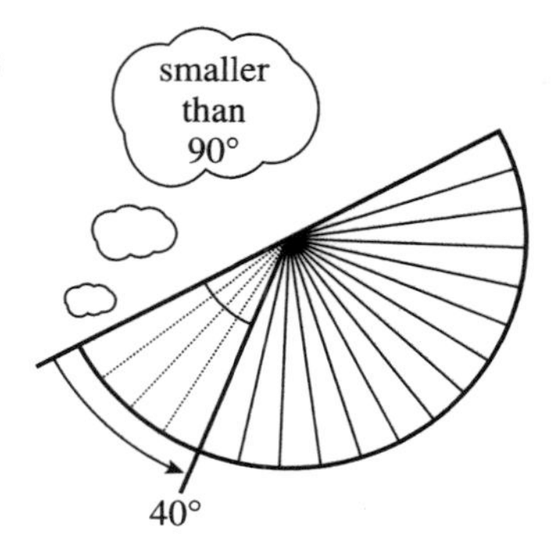

Answer: **(a)** 130° **(b)** 40°

Exercise 1

1 Measure and write down the size of these angles:

(a)

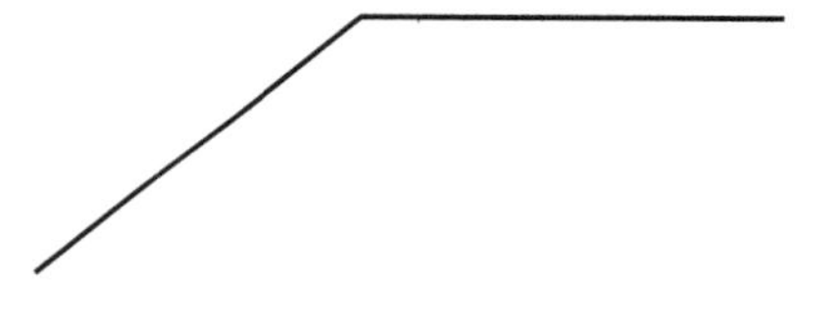

(b)

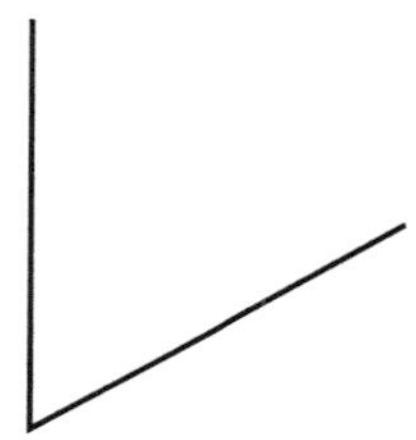

(c)

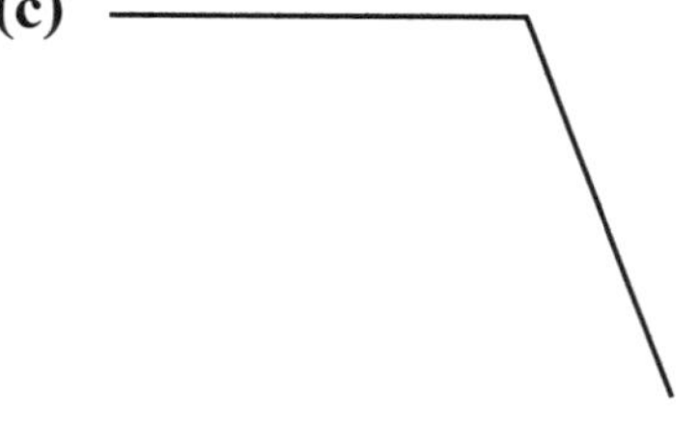

(d)

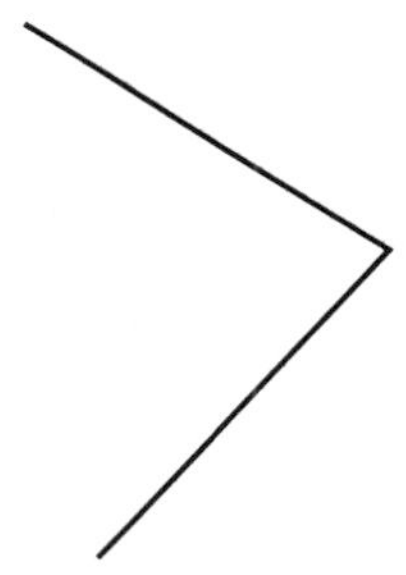

(e)

(f)

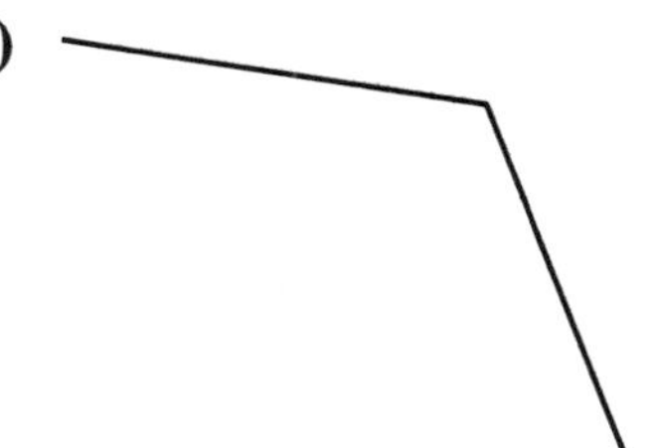

Answers to Pupils' Book

13 Angles

Exercise 13A

1 C	2 H	3 B	4 G	5 D
6 A	7 E	8 H	9 H	10 B

11 $\frac{1}{4}$ turn clockwise
12 $\frac{1}{4}$ turn anticlockwise
13 $\frac{1}{2}$ turn
14 $\frac{1}{4}$ turn anticlockwise
15 $\frac{1}{4}$ turn clockwise
16 $\frac{1}{4}$ turn clockwise
17 $\frac{1}{4}$ turn anticlockwise
18 $\frac{1}{2}$ turn
19 $\frac{1}{4}$ turn clockwise

Exercise 13B

1 (a) 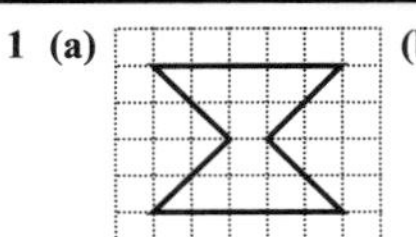 **(b)** 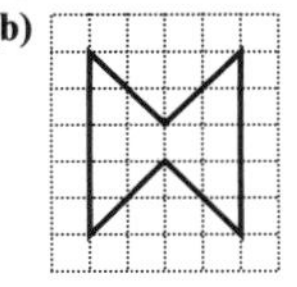

(c) 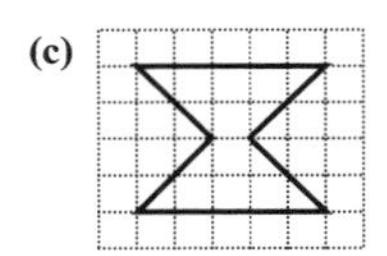

2 (a) 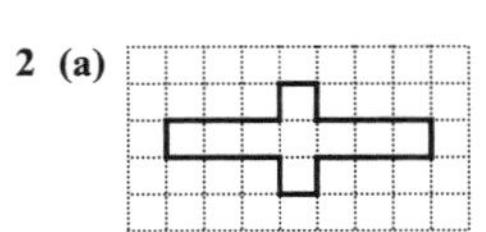

(b) **(c)** 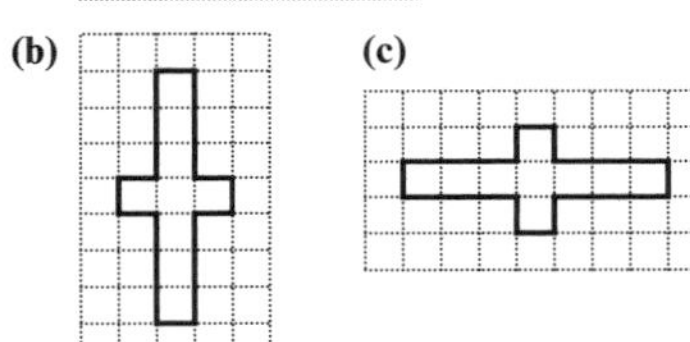

3 (a), (b) and (c) 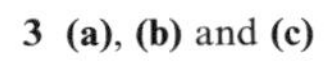 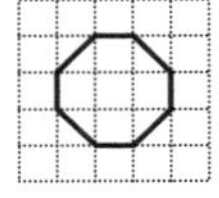

4 (a) 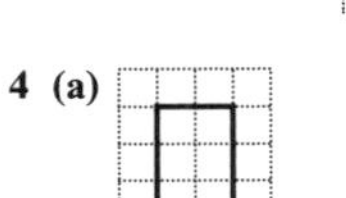 **(b)** 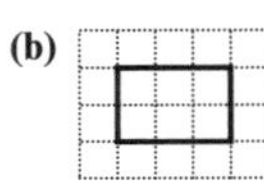

(c) 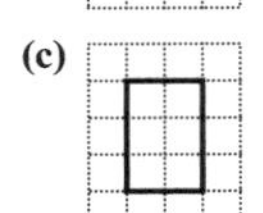

5 (a) 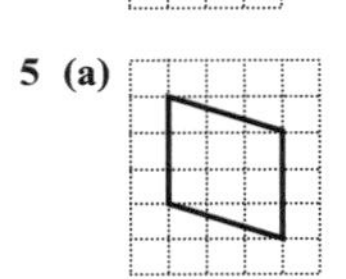 **(b)** 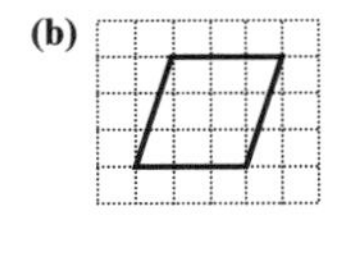

(c) 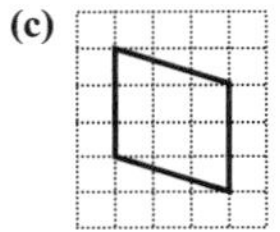

Exercise 13C

1 (a) 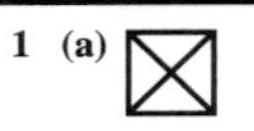 **(b)** 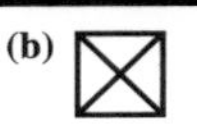 **(c)** 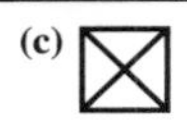

(d) every $\frac{1}{4}$ turn.

2 (a) **(b)** **(c)**

(d) every $\frac{1}{2}$ turn.

3 (a), (b) and (c)  **(d)** every $\frac{1}{4}$ turn.

4 (a) **(b)** **(c)** 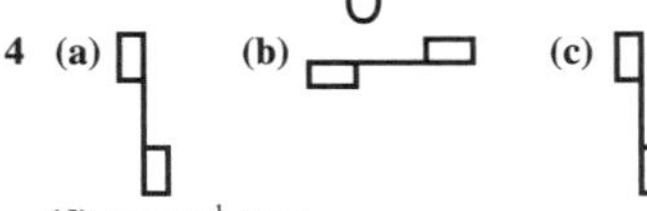

(d) every $\frac{1}{2}$ turn.

5 (a), (b) and (c) 

(d) every $\frac{1}{4}$ turn.

6 (a) **(b)** **(c)** 

(d) every $\frac{1}{2}$ turn.

7 (a) 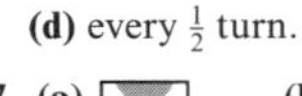 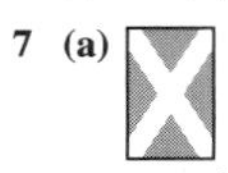 **(b)** 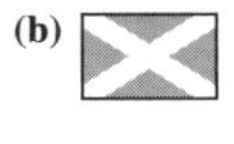 **(c)** 

(d) every $\frac{1}{2}$ turn.

8 (a) 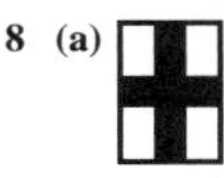 **(b)** 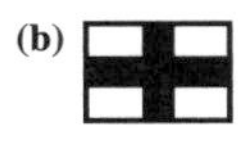 **(c)** 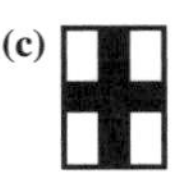

(d) every $\frac{1}{2}$ turn.

Exercise 13D

1 All of them.
2 No rotational symmetry; **(d) (f) (h) (l)**

Exercise 13E

1 **(a)** 90° **(b)** 360° **(c)** 30° **(d)** 270°
(e) 0° **(f)** 60° **(g)** 180° **(h)** 120°
(i) 10° **(j)** 80° **(k)** 45° **(l)** 350°

Exercise 13F

1 37°	**2** 134°	**3** 64°	**4** 43°
5 89°	**6** 45°	**7** 115°	**8** 136°
9 32°	**10** 94°	**11** 80°	**12** 125°
13 97°			

Exercise 13G

1 acute	**2** right
3 obtuse	**4** obtuse
5 acute	**6** obtuse
7 acute	**8** acute
9 acute	**10** obtuse
11 obtuse	**12** acute
13 acute	**14** obtuse
15 acute	**16** obtuse
17 obtuse	**18** acute
19 right	**20** acute
21 **(a)** 180°	**(b)** 90°
(c) 360°	**(d)** 270°

Exercise 13H

Check answers with a protractor.

Exercise 13I

Actual angle sizes:

1 30°	**2** 69°
3 40°	**4** 25°
5 43°	**6** 54°
7 53°	**8** 25°
9 48°	**10** 153°
11 130°	**12** 173°
13 119°	**14** 154°
15 106°	**16** 165°
17 104°	**18** 140°

Answers to Homeworks

13 Angles

Exercise 13.1 Links: 13A

1 **(a)** 6 **(b)** 12
(c) 9 **(d)** 9
(e) 9

2 **(a)** I **(b)** E
(c) A **(d)** F
(e) F **(f)** F

3 **(a)** $\frac{1}{2}$ turn
(b) $\frac{1}{4}$ turn anticlockwise
(c) $\frac{1}{4}$ turn clockwise
(d) $\frac{1}{4}$ turn clockwise
(e) $\frac{1}{2}$ turn
(f) $\frac{1}{4}$ turn anticlockwise

Exercise 13.2 Links: 13B, 13C

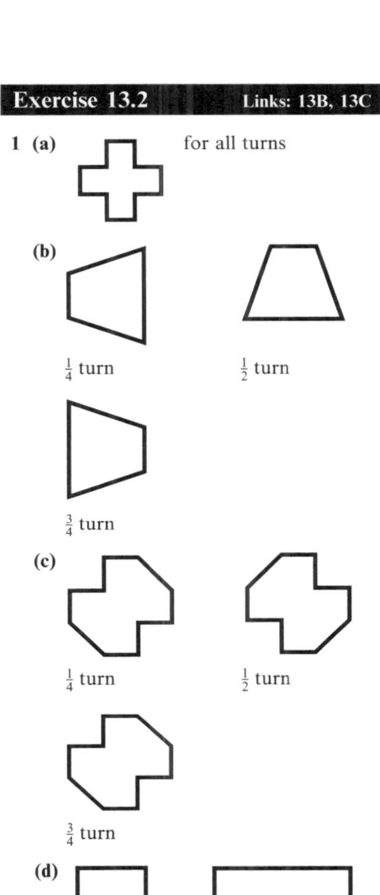

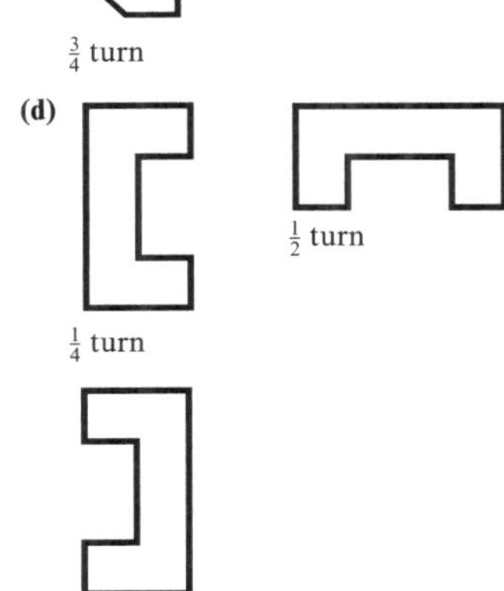

(e) All turns 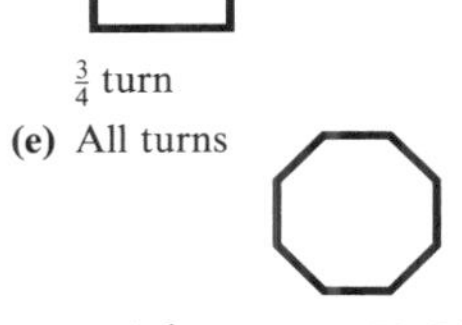

(a) each $\frac{1}{4}$ turn **(b)** full turn
(c) each $\frac{1}{2}$ turn **(d)** full turn
(e) each $\frac{1}{8}$ turn

Exercise 13.3 Links: 13D, 13E

1 (b), (c)

2 (a) $\frac{1}{4}$ turn 90°   (b) $\frac{3}{4}$ turn 270°

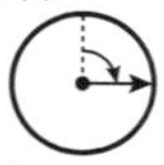

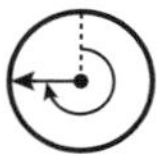

(c) $\frac{1}{2}$ turn 180°   (d) full turn 360°

3 (a) 100°   (b) 45°   (c) 340°
(d) 200°   (e) 135°

Exercise 13.4 Links: 13F, 13G, 13H, 13I

1 (a) acute, 30°
(b) acute, 45°
(c) obtuse, 125°
(d) obtuse, 147°
(e) obtuse, 168°
(f) acute, 17°

2 (a) acute   (b) obtuse   (c) obtuse
(d) right   (e) obtuse   (f) acute

Remediation answers

13.1 Angles and turns

Exercise 1

1 (a) $\frac{1}{4}$ (b) $\frac{1}{4}$ (c) $\frac{1}{2}$
(d) $\frac{1}{4}$ (e) $\frac{1}{2}$ (f) $\frac{1}{2}$

Exercise 2

(b), (c) and (f)

13.2 Measuring angles

Exercise 1

1 (a) 140°   (b) 60°   (c) 110°
(d) 80°   (e) 30°   (f) 120°

Unit 14 Handling data

Content summary

This unit shows how to collect and organize data in tally charts. Bar charts and pictograms are covered as methods for displaying data. The importance of the scale of an axis is introduced.

Book 1R Unit 15 extends the work to dual bar charts and pie charts. It also covers the distinction between discrete and continuous, trends identified from line graphs, the use of scatter diagrams and correlation.

NC level

Level 2: Organizing data. Tally charts.

Level 3: Pictograms and Bar Charts.

H2b *H2c* *S4b*

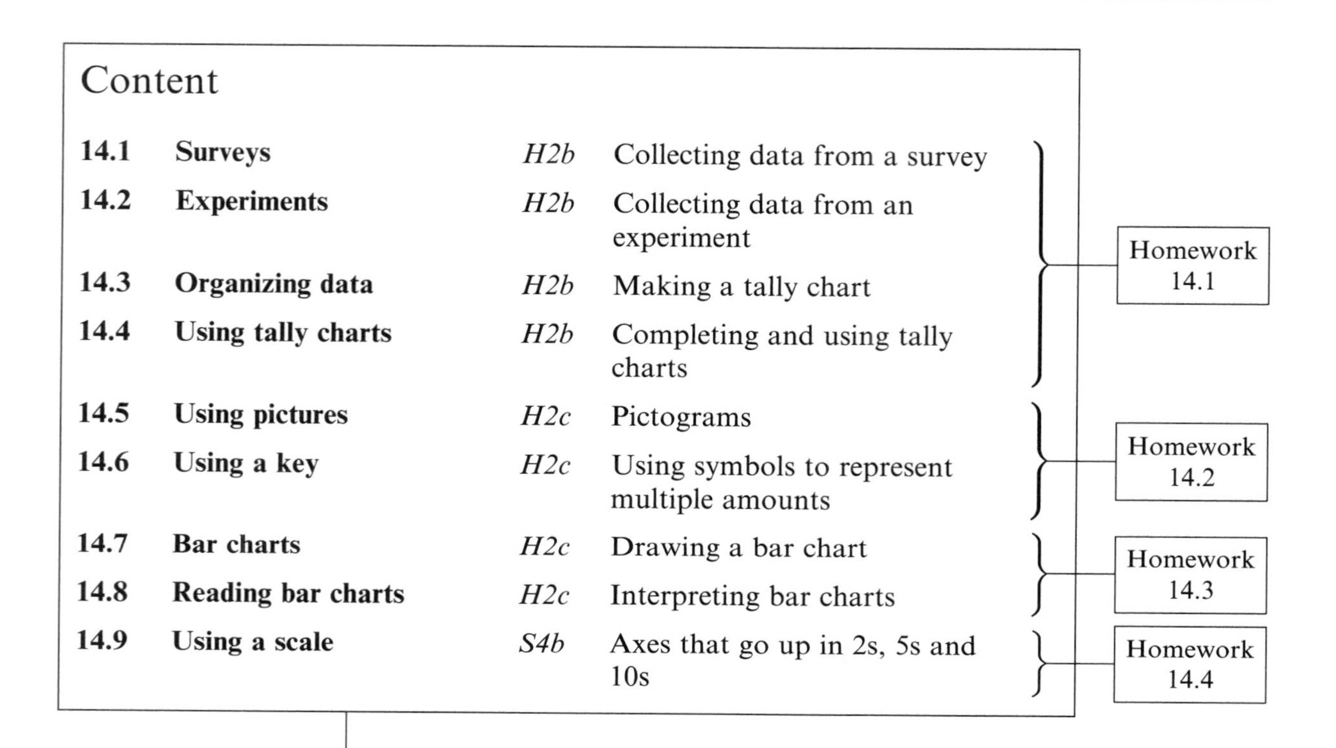

Content

14.1	**Surveys**	*H2b*	Collecting data from a survey	Homework 14.1
14.2	**Experiments**	*H2b*	Collecting data from an experiment	Homework 14.1
14.3	**Organizing data**	*H2b*	Making a tally chart	Homework 14.1
14.4	**Using tally charts**	*H2b*	Completing and using tally charts	Homework 14.1
14.5	**Using pictures**	*H2c*	Pictograms	Homework 14.2
14.6	**Using a key**	*H2c*	Using symbols to represent multiple amounts	Homework 14.2
14.7	**Bar charts**	*H2c*	Drawing a bar chart	Homework 14.3
14.8	**Reading bar charts**	*H2c*	Interpreting bar charts	Homework 14.3
14.9	**Using a scale**	*S4b*	Axes that go up in 2s, 5s and 10s	Homework 14.4

Assessment

Assessment 14 covers the key concepts in Unit 14.

Remediation

Remediation sheets: None.

Assessment

The assessment is marked out of 30. Achievement of 20 or more marks indicates a good understanding of the key concepts.
Marking guidance, answers and links to remediation are provided on page 265.

Equipment

	Pupil's Book page
Dice	200
Coins	200
Squared paper for bar charts	213

ICT links

Use the Internet to obtain a variety of cross-curricular data. Enter the data into a spreadsheet to display it in a variety of forms. Suggested Web sites are listed on page vi. The sites listed provide data on:

- Extreme weather conditions in the UK and USA
- Olympic records in all sports
- Statistics on organ transplants

Use the data to suggest trends.

Remediation

There is no remediation for this unit.

Questionbank CD

All homeworks and extension questions also appear on the CD.

Pages xvii and xviii of this pack show you how to use the CD to select questions from the Questionbank and further customize them if you wish to.

14 Handling data

framework teaching objective	§	lesson starter	f/w ref
Collect small sets of data from surveys and experiments	14.3	I have recorded some data. The data shows the flavour of ice-cream which customers buy at the fairground ice-cream stand. V St Ch Ch R V V St V Ch Ch = chocolate St = strawberry R = raspberry V = vanilla Why haven't I written out the whole word? How many ice-creams have I recorded? 10 Which was the most popular ice-cream? Vanilla Why might it be important to record and study this data? Have I got enough data to spot patterns?	254–5
Plan how to collect and organise small sets of data.	14.3	I have some more data. V St Ch Ch R V V St V Ch V Ch St St R St V V Ch V St St R St St Ch V V St R Ch R R St St Ch V V Ch St R V St Ch Ch Is vanilla still the most popular? Which was the second popular? How can I **organize** this data to help me to spot patterns?	252–5
Construct diagrams to represent data.	14.6	Sometimes to help people to spot patterns, we draw pictures which make it easier to read – and more 'eye-catching.' The pictogram. What symbol can we use for the ice-cream data? The ice-cream cornet. In the survey, 14 people bought strawberry ice-creams. 14 people = Have I drawn enough cornets? What number of people does each cornet represent? (*2*) 11 people bought chocolate. How can I show this on my pictogram? Why did I decide to use one cornet to represent 2 people? *'Save space.' 'Easier to count.' etc.*	262–5

framework teaching objective	§	lesson starter	f/w ref
Construct graphs and diagrams to represent data.	14.7	Over the course of one day, the ice-cream stand sells: 38 Vanilla 12 Raspberry 41 Strawberry 33 Chocolate ice-creams. Can I change my pictogram to show such large pieces of data? If I make one cornet = 4 people. How many would I need for vanilla? How do I show strawberry? How do I show 1 person? For largest pieces of data it is sensible to simplify the symbols. Instead of drawing cornets, I will draw simple blocks. If I connect all the blocks together to make a bar, it is easier to draw? How will I read it if the blocks are connected together to make a bar?	262–5

14 Handling data

Exercise 14.1 **Links: 14A, 14B, 14C, 14D**

1 Drop three different valued coins (e.g. 5p, 2p, 1p) on to a table and note if each is a head or tail.

Draw up a table like the one below and enter the result.

Repeat this experiment 48 times and complete the tally chart.

5p	2p	1p	Tally	Frequency
H	H	H		
H	H	T		
H	T	H		
H	T	T		
T	H	H		
T	H	T		
T	T	H		
T	T	T		

2 This tally chart (frequency table) shows the day of the week pupils in 7A were born.

Day	Tally	Frequency
Sunday	||||	
Monday		2
Tuesday	~~||||~~ |||	
Wednesday	|	
Thursday	|||	
Friday		7
Saturday		5

(a) Copy and complete the frequency table.

(b) How many pupils were born on a Tuesday?

(c) How many more pupils were born on Friday than on Sunday?

(d) How many pupils are there in the class?

Exercise 14.2 Links: 14E, 14F

1 The pictogram shows the number of coins that each pupil had in class 7J.

0 coins	🯅🯅
1 coin	🯅
2 coins	🯅🯅🯅
3 coins	🯅🯅🯅🯅🯅
4 coins	🯅🯅🯅🯅
5 coins	🯅🯅🯅🯅🯅🯅🯅
6 coins	🯅🯅
7 coins	🯅🯅🯅🯅
8 coins	🯅🯅🯅

🯅 represents one pupil

(a) How many pupils were there in the class?

(b) How many pupils had more than three coins?

(c) How many pupils had an odd number of coins?

2 **(a)** Draw a pictogram to show this data.
Use ⁘ to represent 4 books.

Number of books sold	Tally	Frequency
Monday	𝍸 𝍸 ||	12
Tuesday	𝍸 𝍸	10
Wednesday	𝍸 𝍸 𝍸 𝍸	20
Thursday	𝍸 |||	8
Friday	𝍸 𝍸 𝍸 |	16
Saturday	𝍸 𝍸 𝍸 𝍸 ||||	24

(b) On which days were over 16 books sold?

(c) How many books were sold altogether?

3 Pupils in Year 7 were asked 'What is your favourite ice cream'. The pictogram shows the result.

Ice cream	
Strawberry	○○○
Coffee	○◠
Vanilla	○○○○◔
Raspberry	○○◜

○ = 4 pupils

(a) How many pupils chose Coffee?

(b) How many more pupils chose Vanilla than Strawberry?

Exercise 14.3 Links: 14G, 14H

1 Geoffrey recorded the colour of ties people were wearing:

Colour	Number
Black	2
Blue	7
Green	5
Red	8
Patterned	11
Grey	6
Other	4

(a) Draw a bar chart to show this data.

(b) How many people wore a blue or grey tie?

(c) Which was the least popular colour?

2 Gita counted the number of times that each vowel occurred in a sentence of her book.

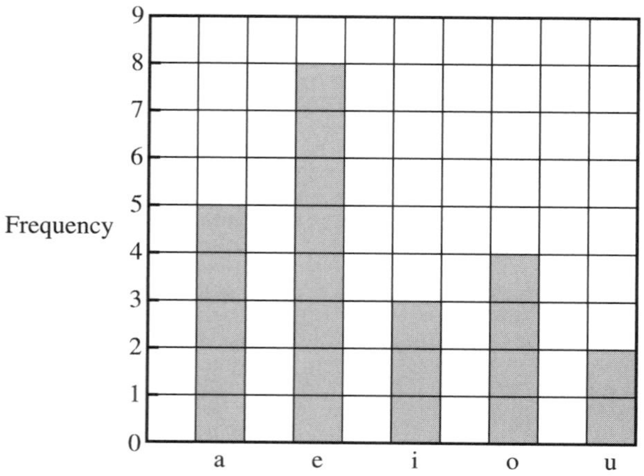

(a) Which vowel occurred four times?

(b) How many more times did 'e' occur than 'u'?

(c) How many vowels were there in the sentence altogether?

3 A shopkeeper noted the first fifty flavours of ice cream he sold. The results are shown in the table.

R	B	R	V	B	V	C	S	B	S
B	R	C	C	R	V	C	V	S	C
V	S	R	V	C	S	V	R	V	R
C	V	C	S	B	C	S	C	C	V
S	V	C	C	S	V	V	R	C	S

Key
C = Chocolate
V = Vanilla
S = Strawberry
R = Raspberry
B = Banana

(a) Draw up a frequency table to represent this data.

(b) Draw a bar chart.

(c) Which was the least popular flavour?

(d) How many people chose Raspberry flavour?

Exercise 14.4 Links: 14G, 14H, 14I

1 The marks out of 20 in a monthly test are shown in the table.

Name/Subject	English	Mathematics	Science	Humanities
Patel	18	12	11	15
Chapman	13	15	10	15
Morgan	15	14	13	16
Simpson	20	16	8	14
Edwards	14	18	11	11
McIntyre	12	15	10	12

(a) Draw a horizontal bar graph to show the Science results.
(b) Draw a vertical bar graph to show the Mathematics results.
(c) Which did you find the easiest to draw? Give your reason.
(d) Which test appears to be the hardest? Give your reason.
(e) How many more marks were scored in English than Mathematics?
(f) Which pupils scored the highest overall total?

2 Sheila noted the colour of cars passing as she waited for a bus.

Colour	White	Red	Green	Yellow	Black	Grey	Blue
Number	12	9	16	1	22	11	16

(a) Using a suitable scale, draw a bar chart to represent this data.
(b) How many cars passed her?

3 Eight pupils raised money for a local charity. The amount they collected is shown in the table.

Name	Peter	Anne	Rachid	Rita	Carole	Hamid	Beth	Henry
Amount	£6	£8.50	£3.25	£7.50	£9.75	£5.25	£8.25	£6.75

(a) Choose a suitable scale and draw a bar chart to represent this data.
(b) How much more did Anne collect than Henry?
(c) List the pupils in order of the amount collected (highest first).
(d) What was the total sum raised?

Name ....

14 Handling data

1 20 Year 7 students were asked what was their favourite food. Here are their choices.

Chips	Ice cream	Cola	Chips
Burger	Burger	Burger	Cola
Cola	Chips	Chips	Cola
Ice cream	Chips	Chips	Ice cream
Chips	Cola	Burger	Ice cream

Complete this tally chart for the data:

Food	Tally	Frequency
Chips		
Burgers		
Cola		
Ice cream		

(8 marks)

---

2 This tally chart shows the favourite flavours of crisps in a Year 7 tutor group.

Flavour	Tally	Frequency
Cheese & onion	~~IIII~~ ~~IIII~~ II	12
Plain	~~IIII~~ III	8
Salt & vinegar	~~IIII~~ II	7
Bacon	II	2

(a) Which was the most popular flavour? ....

(b) Which was the least popular flavour? ....

(c) How many students took part in the survey? .... **(3 marks)**

---

3 This pictogram shows the favourite subjects of some of Sarah's friends:

English	🯅🯅🯅🯅
History	🯅🯅
Science	🯅🯅🯅🯅🯅
Maths	🯅🯅🯅🯅
Art	

Each 🯅 represents one pupil.

(a) 3 people chose Art. Draw this on the pictogram.

(b) How many people chose English as their favourite subject? ....

(c) Which was the most popular subject? ....

(d) Which was the least popular subject? .... **(4 marks)**

---

4 Draw a pictogram to show this data.

Favourite sport	Frequency
Football	20
Cricket	8
Tennis	12
Netball	6
Hockey	10

Football

Cricket

Tennis

Netball

Hockey

Use [S] to stand for 4 people

(5 marks)

5 This bar chart shows how class 7C got to school yesterday.

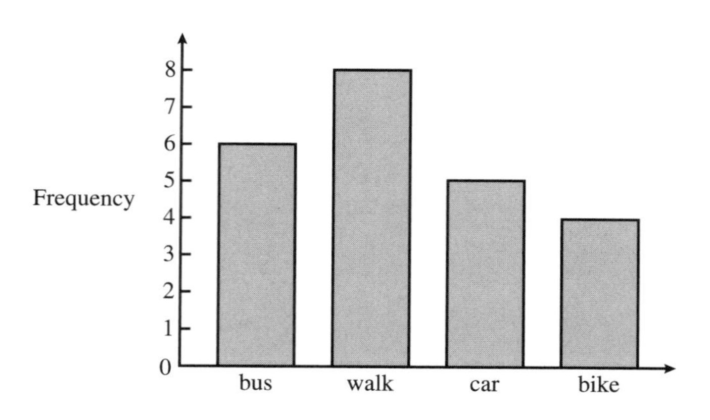

(a) How many came by bus? ....

(b) How many came by bike? ....

(c) What was the most common way of getting to school? ....

(d) How many pupils are in class 7C? .... **(4 marks)**

---

6 The number of letters delivered to a school one week was:

Monday	Tuesday	Wednesday	Thursday	Friday
20	18	16	13	15

Draw a bar chart to represent this data.

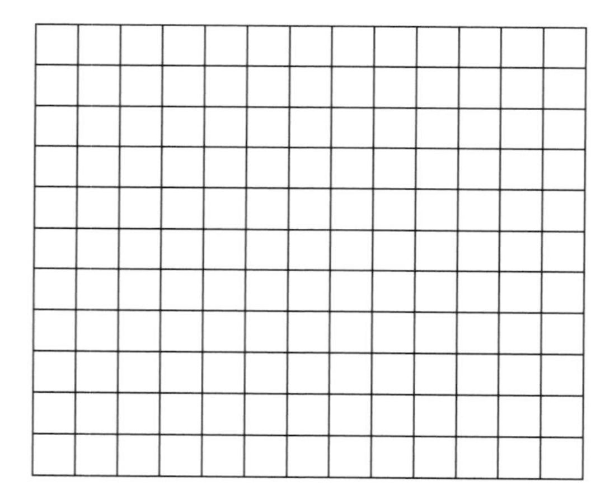

(6 marks)

Unit 14 Handling Data

Question		Answer	Marking guidance and remediation sheet links
1		(table below)	B1 for tallies correct, B1 for 7 B1 for tallies correct, B1 for 4 B1 for tallies correct, B1 for 5 B1 for tallies correct, B1 for 4
2	(a)	cheese and onion	A1
	(b)	bacon	A1
	(c)	29	A1
3	(a)	(three stick figures)	A1
	(b)	4	A1
	(c)	science	A1
	(d)	history	A1
4		Football: S S S S S Cricket: S S Tennis: S S S Netball: S ½S Hockey: S S ½S	B1 for 5 B1 for 2 B1 for 3 B1 for $1\frac{1}{2}$ B1 for $2\frac{1}{2}$
5	(a)	6	A1
	(b)	4	A1
	(c)	walk	A1
	(d)	23 pupils	A1
6		Horizontal axis marked with days of week.	B1
		Vertical axis marked with frequency in 2s or 4s.	B1
		Gap between bars.	B1
			B1 for 1 bar correct or B2 for 3 bars correct or B3 for 5 bars correct

Question 1 answer table:

Food	Tally	Frequency
Chips	~~||||~~ ||	7
Burgers	||||	4
Cola	~~||||~~	5
Ice cream	||||	4

Key to mark scheme
A marks: correct answer
M marks: correct method
B marks: independent work

Page 265 gives a general guidance on use of this assessment scheme with some examples.

Answers to Pupils' Book

14 Handling data

Exercise 14C

3

Fruit	Tally	Frequency
Apple	||	2
Pear	卌 |	6
Strawberry	|||	3
Peach	卌 |	6
Grape	||	2
Orange	|||	3
Banana	|||	3

Exercise 14D

1 (a) Blue (b) Grey
(c) 25
2 (a) Milk (b) Fruit and nut
(c) 41
3 (a) Frequencies are 3, 8, 7, 4, 5 and 2
(b) 1 (c) 29

Exercise 14E

3 (a) 8 (b) 4
(c) Walk (d) 29
4 (a) Clothes (b) Sweets
(c) £17

Exercise 14F

1

Motor racing	☺☺☺☺
Football	☺☺☺☺☺☺☺☺
Rugby	☺☺☺☺☺☺
Cricket	☺
Golf	☺☺
Darts	☺☺☺☺☺☺☺

☺ = 2 people

2

Plain	□□
Cheese and onion	□□□□□
Bacon	□□□
Salt and vinegar	□□□□
Prawn cocktail	□
Tomato sauce	[

□ = 4 people

3 (a) 10 (b) 7
(c) 45
4 (a) 30 (b) 60
(c) Monday, Wednesday and Thursday
(d) 300

Exercise 14H

1 (a) 3 (b) Wednesday
(c) 23
2 (a) (i) 6 (ii) 11 (iii) 8
(b) The Sun (c) 37

Exercise 14I

1

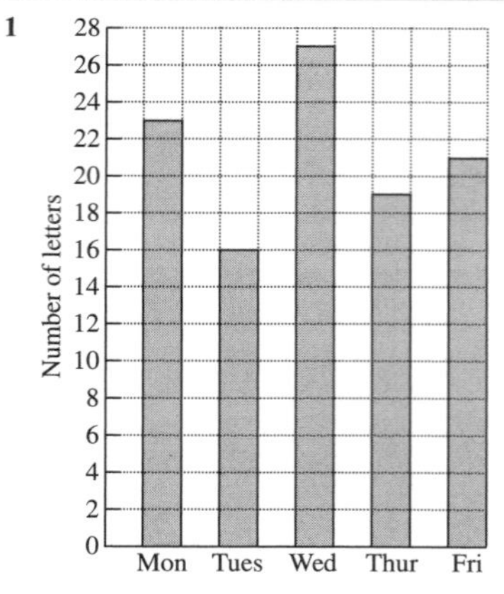

2

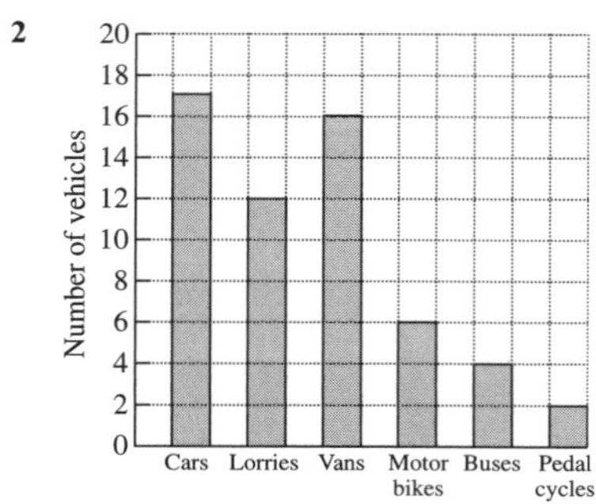

3 (a) E (b) (i) 7 (ii) 6
(c) E, A, I, N, S, T
4 (a) 20 (b) 30 (c) 9 (d) 84

Answers to Homeworks

14 Handling data

Exercise 14.1 Links: 14A, 14B, 14C, 14D

2 (a)

Day	Tally	Frequency
Sunday		4
Monday	||	
Tuesday		8
Wednesday		1
Thursday		3
Friday	卌 ||	
Saturday	卌	

(b) 8 (c) 3 (d) 30

Exercise 14.2 Links: 14E, 14F

1 (a) 31 (b) 20 (c) 17
2 (b) Wednesday, Saturday (c) 90
3 (a) 6 (b) 7

Exercise 14.3 Links: 14G, 14H

1 (a)

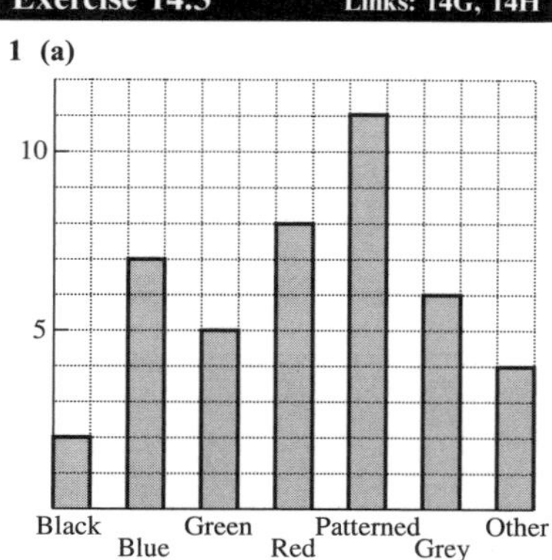

(b) 13 (c) Black
2 (a) Letter 'O' (b) 6
(c) 22
3 (a)

Flavour	Tally	Frequency
Chocolate	卌 卌 ||||	14
Vanilla	卌 卌 |||	13
Strawberry	卌 卌	10
Raspberry	卌 |||	8
Banana	卌	5

(b)

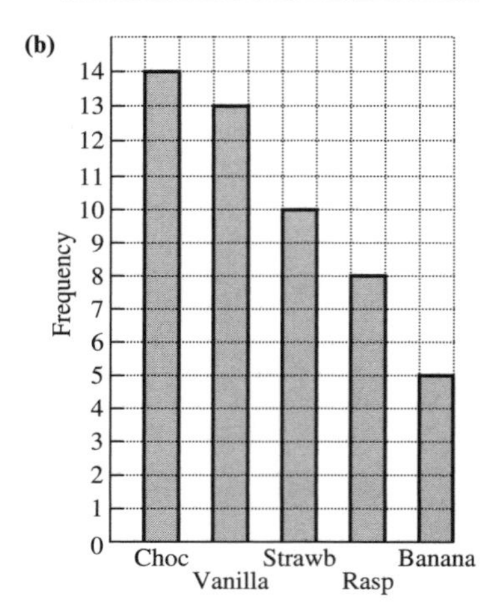

(c) Banana
(d) 8

Exercise 14.4 Links: 14G, 14H, 14I

1 (a)

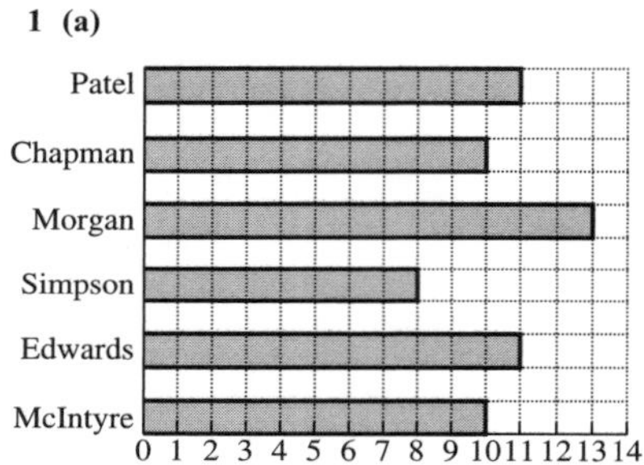

(b)

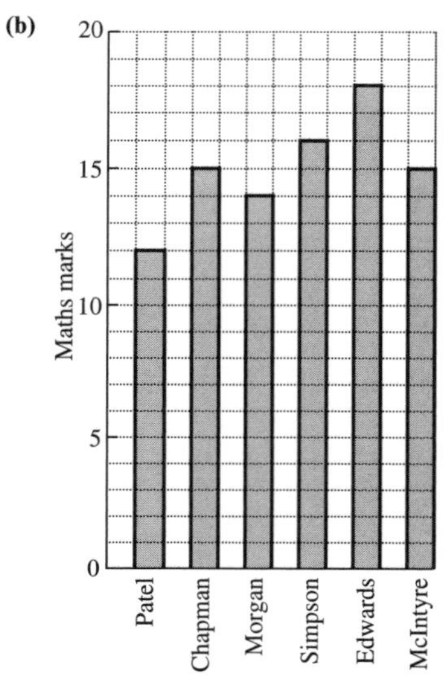

(c) Pupils' own answer.
(d) Science. Lower marks
(e) 2
(f) Morgan and Simpson both 58

2 (a)

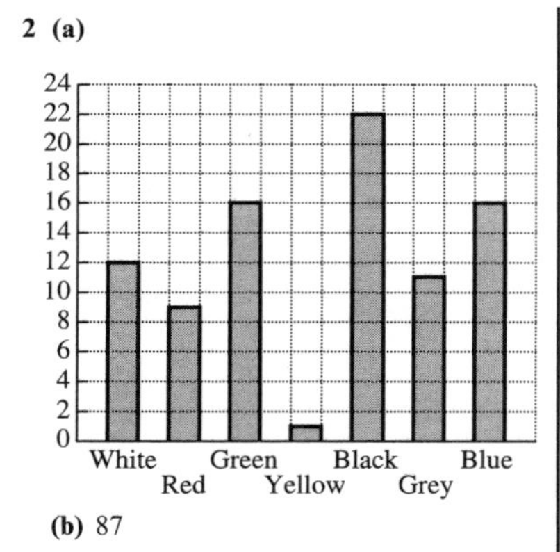

(b) 87

3 (a)

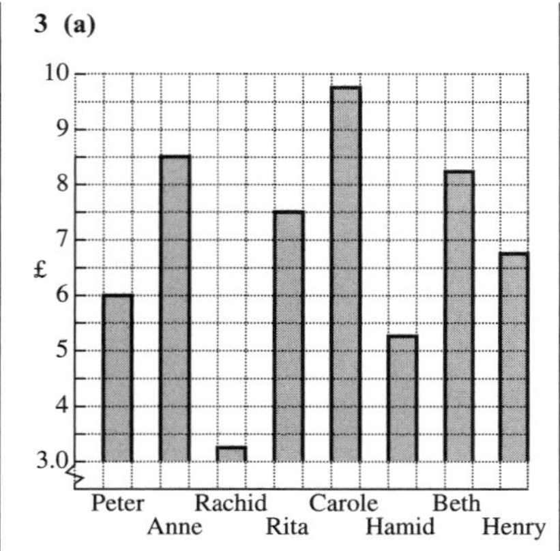

(b) £1.75
(c) Carole, Anne, Beth, Rita, Henry, Peter, Hamid, Rachid
(d) £55.25

1 G

Overview

Unit 15 Percentages

Content summary

This unit establishes what a percentage is and relates this to decimals and fractions.

Book 1R Unit 16 extends the work to include percentages of quantities and percentage increase and decrease.

NC level

Level 4: Although 'recognise and use simpler percentages' is NC Level 4 the work is at the lower end of this level.

NA2e NA3e

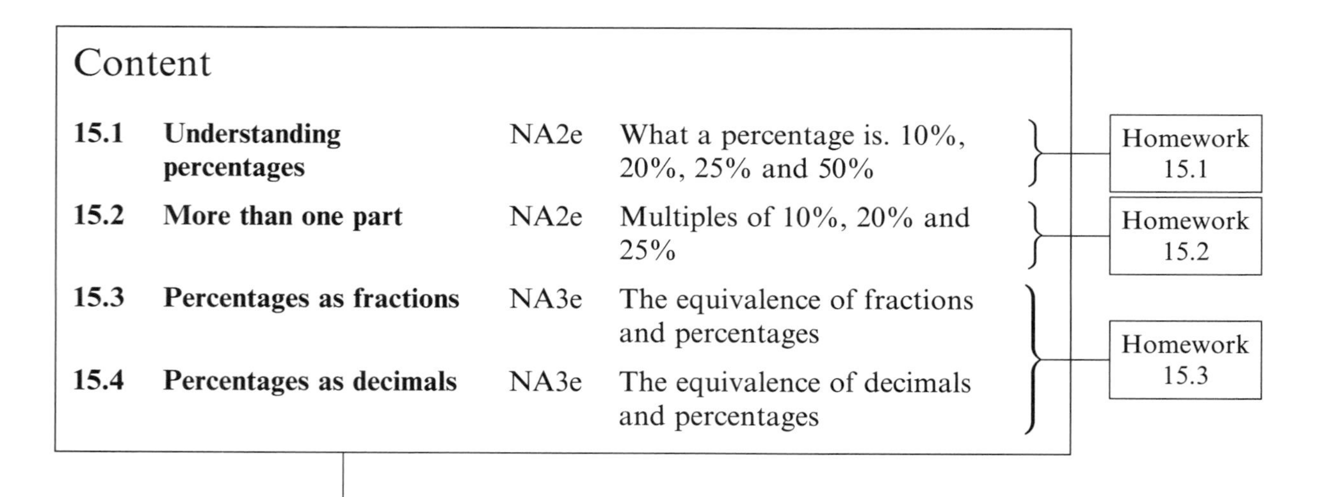

Content

15.1	**Understanding percentages**	NA2e	What a percentage is. 10%, 20%, 25% and 50%	Homework 15.1
15.2	**More than one part**	NA2e	Multiples of 10%, 20% and 25%	Homework 15.2
15.3	**Percentages as fractions**	NA3e	The equivalence of fractions and percentages	Homework 15.3
15.4	**Percentages as decimals**	NA3e	The equivalence of decimals and percentages	Homework 15.3

Assessment

Assessment 15 covers the key concepts in Unit 15.

Remediation

Remediation sheets 15.1 → 15.2.

Assessment

The assessment is marked out of 30.
Achievement of 20 or more marks indicates a good understanding of the key concepts.
Marking guidance, answers and links to remediation are provided on page 265.

ICT links

Use *Numbers You Need: Percentages,* from *BT* to view animations and receive audio instructions on percentages. Answer multiple choice questions on the various topics.

15.3 and 15.4
Use a **spreadsheet** to:
- demonstrate the fraction and decimal equivalent of percentages.
- calculate a percentage of a quantity.
- increase and decrease a value by a percentage.

Equipment

Squared paper is useful

Remediation

Percentages:
The main task is to instill the concept of percentages in the pupil's mind. To provide more practice cut out the cards on activity sheets 12 and 13. The shapes and answers can be stuck back to back for individual practice or given out individually for pupils to work against the clock to pair the shape up with its answer.

Questionbank CD

All homeworks and extension questions also appear on the CD.

Pages xvii and xviii of this pack show you how to use the CD to select questions from the Questionbank and further customize them if you wish to.

15 Percentages

framework teaching objective	§	lesson starter	f/w ref
Understand percentage as the number of parts per 100.	15.1	Town A: 20 people were surveyed. 9 liked the new cherry drink. Town B: 80 people were surveyed. 34 liked the new cherry drink. Town C: 21 people were surveyed. 21 liked Bubber Hubber drink. Town D: 60 people were surveyed. 25 liked Bubber Hubber drink. Which drink is the most popular? Why is it difficult to compare all the data? How could I combine the 4 pieces of data to make just 2 pieces of data that I can compare easily? (Add A + B = $\frac{43}{100}$ like cherry Add C + D = $\frac{46}{100}$ like Bubber Hubber) 'Seven out of every ten people prefer Rolvic water.' Did we simply ask 10 people? What is this as a percentage? 'Seven and a half out of every ten people prefer Ovian water.' Why is this a silly way of representing the people? Why is giving the result as a percentage more sensible?	70–7
Recognise the equivalence of percentages, fractions and decimals.	15.1/ 15.2	The '100%' chocolate bar. 100% If I cut the bar into 2 pieces, what % does each piece become? (50%) What maths? (*÷4 or ÷2 again.*) I cut the 100% bar into 5 pieces. What % is the same as one fifth? (*20%*) If each fifth is 20%, what will $\frac{2}{5}$ be? $\frac{3}{5}$? Which is bigger, $\frac{3}{4}$ or $\frac{4}{5}$? How do percentages help us to compare these amounts easily?	70–7

15 Percentages

Exercise 15.1 — Links: 15A

1 An apple is cut into two equal pieces.
What percentage of the apple is each piece?

2 Write down the percentage of each shape that is shaded.

(a)
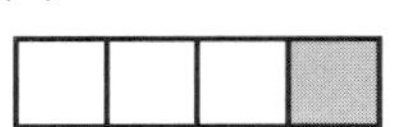

(b)
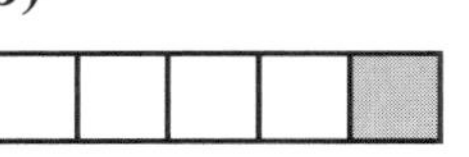

(c)
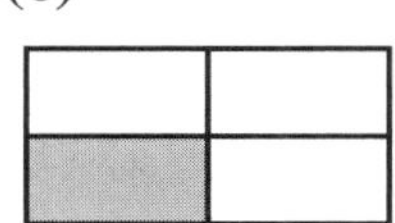

(d)
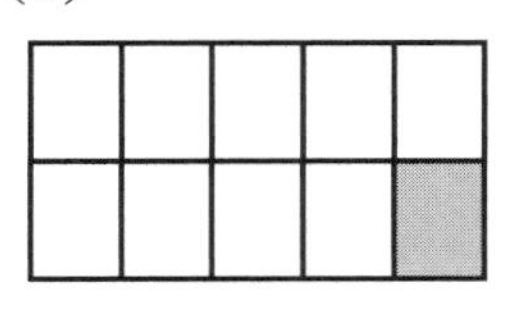

(e)
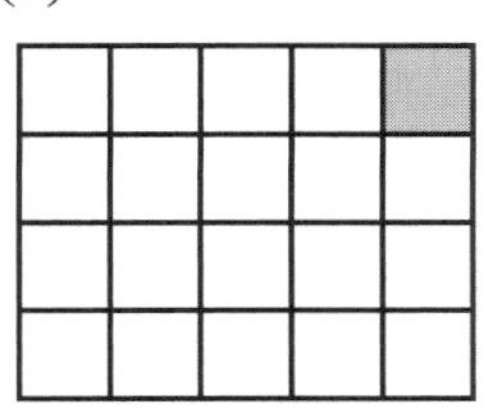

(f)
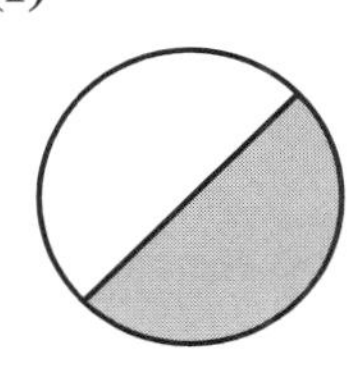

3 Copy each diagram. Shade the given percentage.

(a) 20%

(b) 25%

(c) 10%

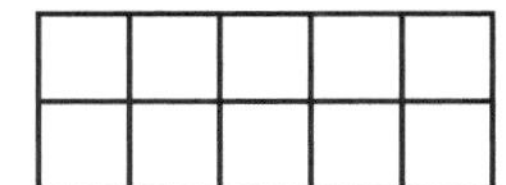

Exercise 15.2 — Links: 15B

1 A cake has been cut into 4 equal pieces.
What percentage is:

(a) one piece **(b)** 2 pieces **(c)** 3 pieces?

2 This jelly block has 20 equal pieces.
What percentage is:

(a) one piece **(b)** 3 pieces
(c) 4 pieces **(d)** 7 pieces?

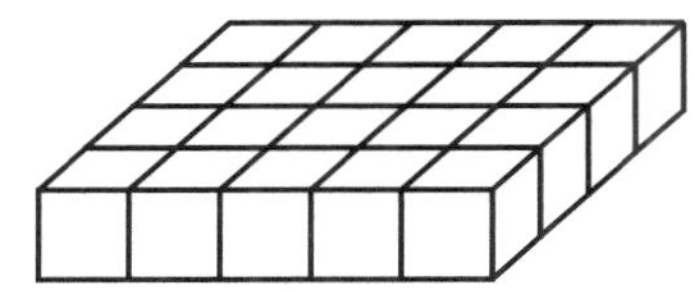

3 For each shape, write down the percentage shaded.

(a)
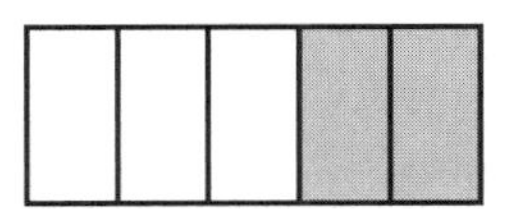

(b)
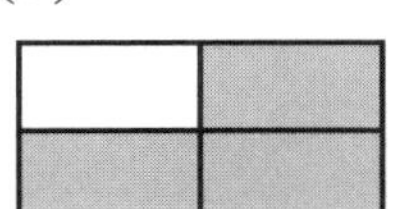

(c)
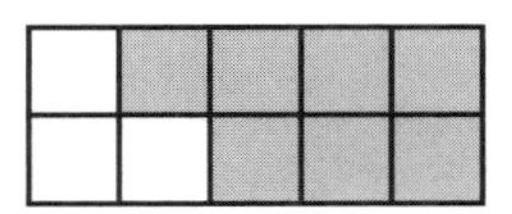

4 Copy each diagram. Shade the given percentage.

(a) 75% **(b)** 80%
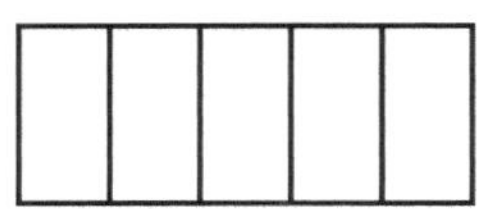

(c) 30%
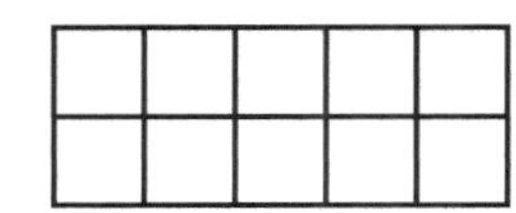

1 G

Homework

Exercise 15.3 Links: 15C, 15D

For each 100 square write down:

(a) the fraction shaded

(b) the percentage shaded.

1

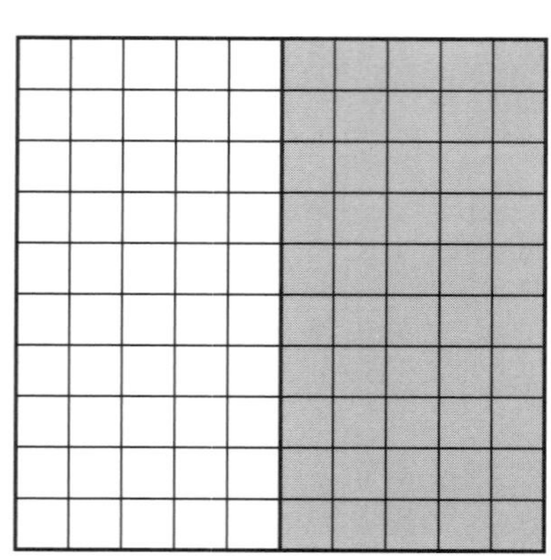

2

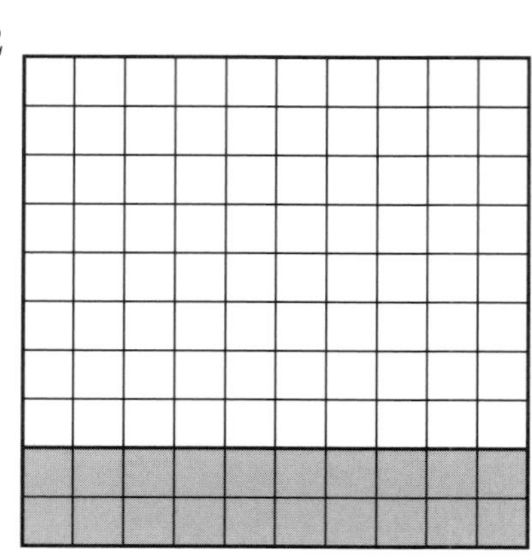

3

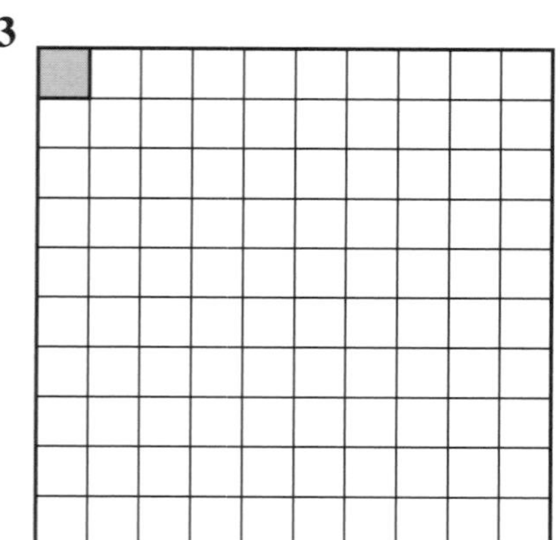

4

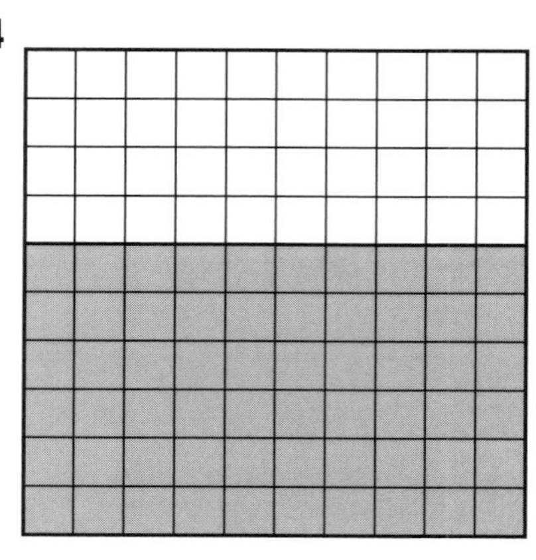

5

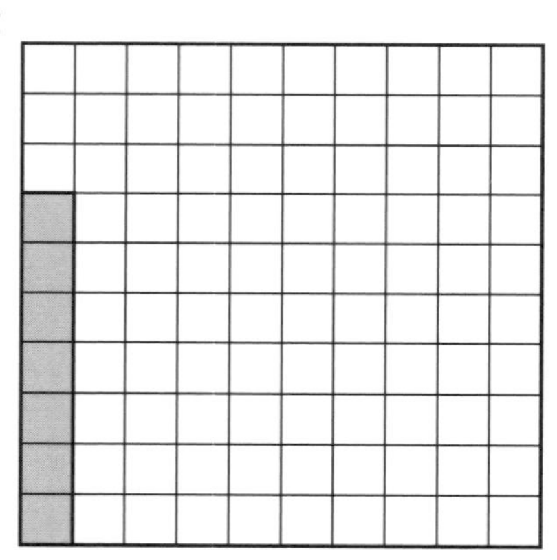

6

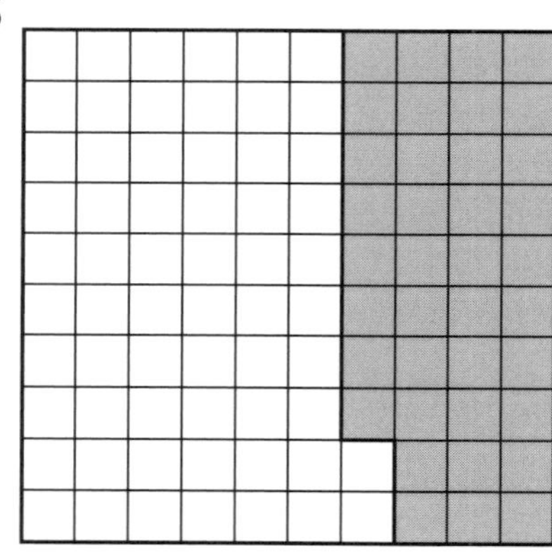

7 Using a hundred square, shade in:

(a) 10% **(b)** 25% **(c)** 40% **(d)** 30% **(e)** 17%

Change these percentages to decimals:

8 21%	**9** 43%	**10** 6%	**11** 58%
12 4%	**13** 16%	**14** 50%	**15** 90%
16 63%	**17** 5%	**18** 2%	**19** 110%
20 130%			

Name ....

15 Percentages

1 This chocolate bar has 10 pieces.

(a) What percentage of the bar is 1 piece? ....%

(b) What percentage of the bar is 4 pieces? ....% **(2 marks)**

---

2 Write down the percentage of each shape that is shaded.

(a)

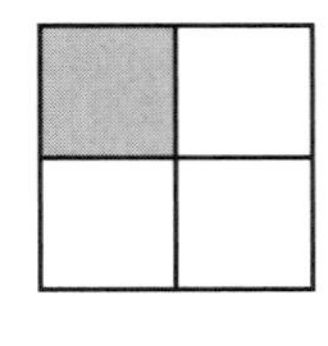

....................%

(b)

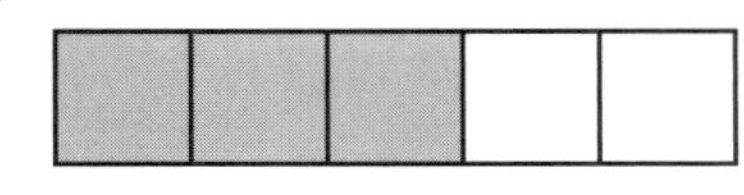

....................% **(2 marks)**

---

3 This pizza has been cut into 10 equal pieces.
What percentage is:

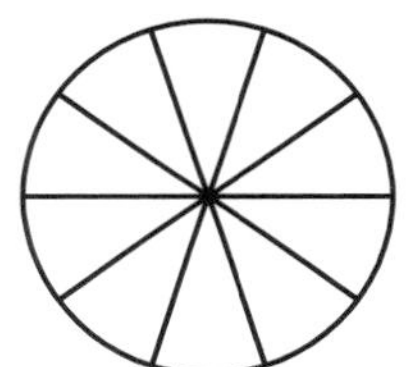

(a) one piece ....

(b) three pieces ....

(c) six pieces? .... **(3 marks)**

---

4 For each shape write down the percentage that is shaded.

(a)

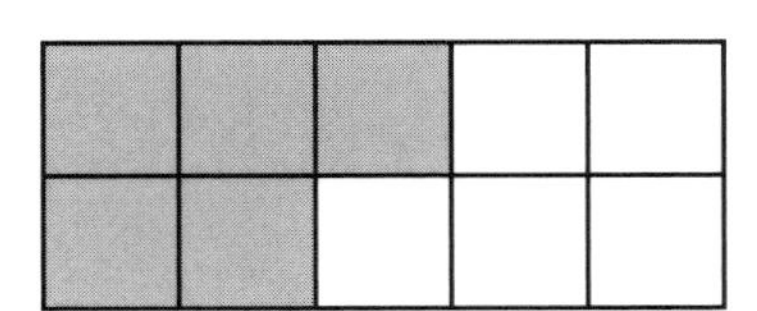

....................%

(b)

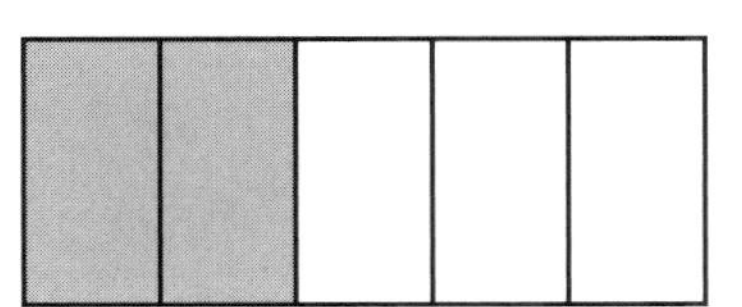

....................%

(c)

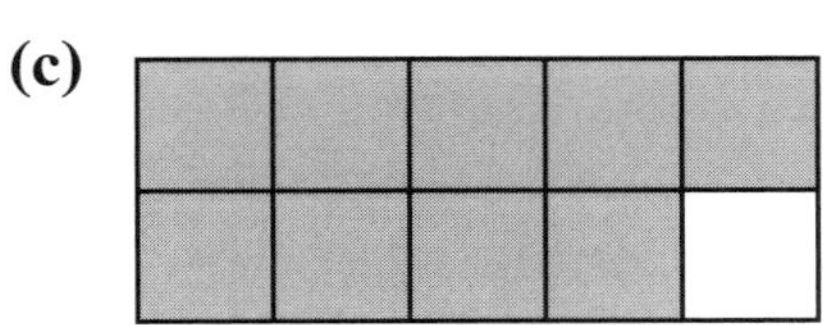

....................%

(d)

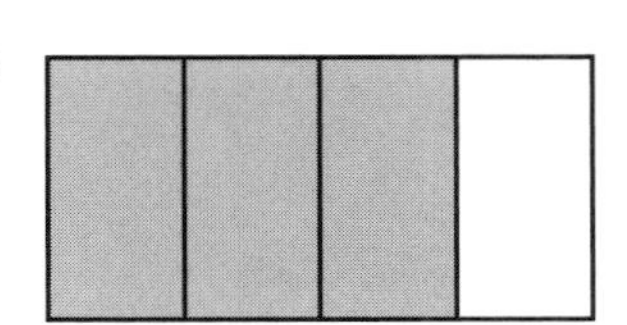

....................% **(4 marks)**

---

5 Shade in the percentage shown for each shape.

(a)

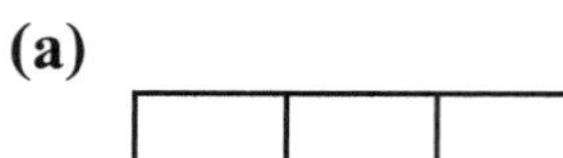

Shade 20%

(b)

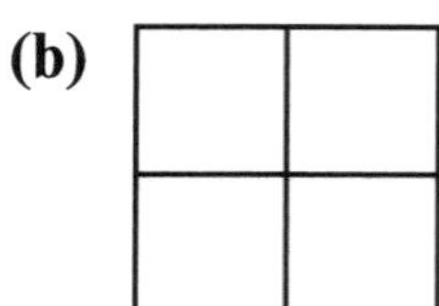

Shade 75%

(2 marks)

---

6 Shade in the percentage given for each shape.

(a)

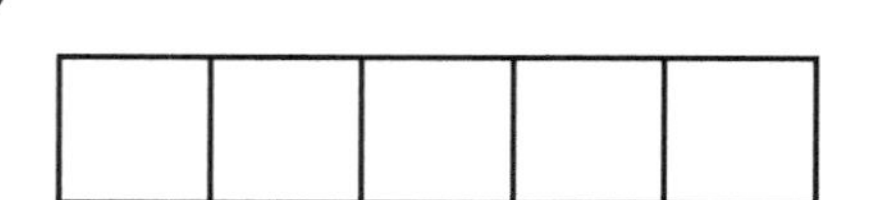

Shade 40%

(b)

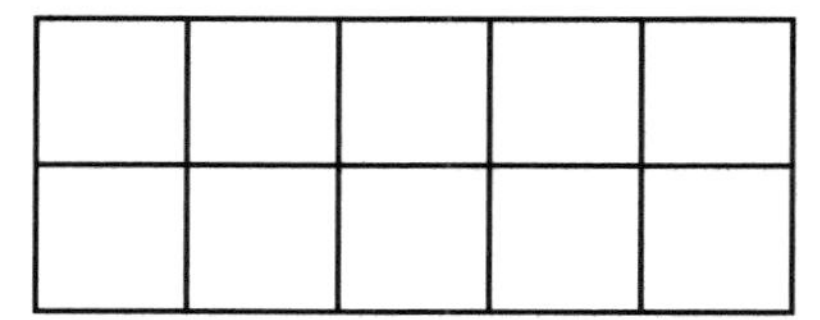

Shade 70%

(2 marks)

---

7 For each 100 square write down:

(a)

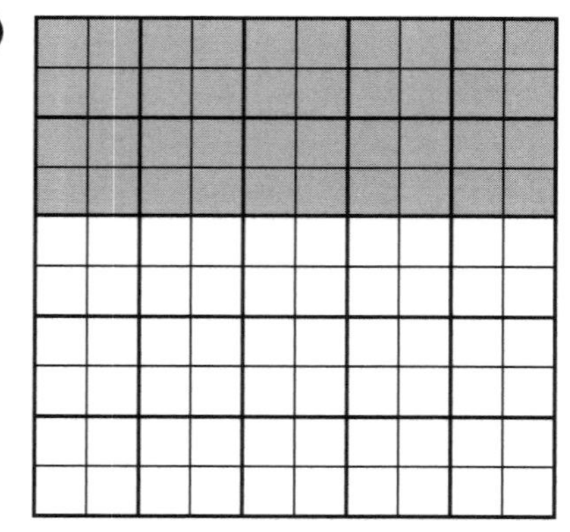

(i) the percentage shaded

....................%

(ii) the fraction shaded

....

(b)

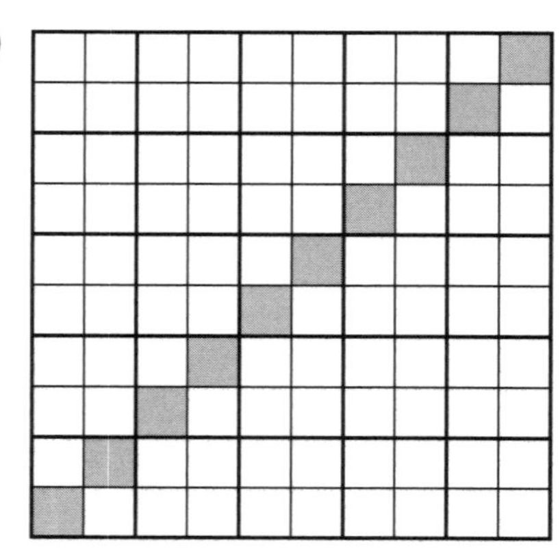

(i) the percentage shaded

....................%

(ii) the fraction shaded

....

(4 marks)

---

8 Change these percentages to decimals.

(a) 25% ....

(b) 57% ....

(c) 86% ....

(d) 15% .... **(4 marks)**

---

9 Change these percentages to decimals.

(a) 5% ....

(b) 10% ....

(c) 50% ....

(d) 140% .... **(4 marks)**

---

10 Write these percentages as fractions.

(a) 25% ....

(b) 40% ....

(c) 65% .... **(3 marks)**

Unit 15 Percentages

Question		Answer	Marking guidance and remediation sheet links	
1	**(a)**	10%	A1	
	(b)	40%	A1	
2	**(a)**	25%	A1	
	(b)	60%	A1	
3	**(a)**	10%	A1	
	(b)	30%	A1	less than $\frac{9}{11}$ use remediation sheet 15.1
	(c)	60%	A1	
4	**(a)**	50%	A1	
	(b)	40%	A1	
	(c)	90%	A1	
	(d)	75%	A1	
5	**(a)**	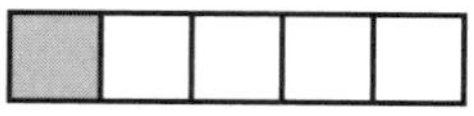	A1 for one square shaded	
	(b)	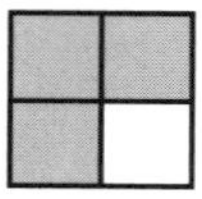	A1 for three squares shaded	
6	**(a)**	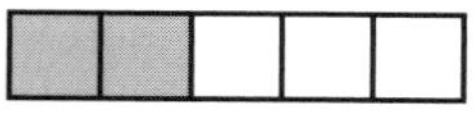	A1 for two squares shaded	
	(b)	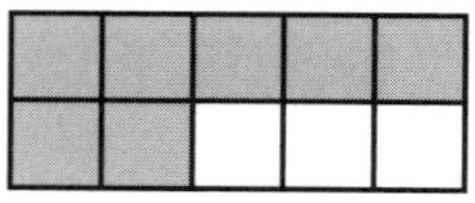	A1 for 7 squares shaded	
7	**(a) (i)**	40%	A1	
	(ii)	$\frac{2}{5}$ accept $\frac{40}{100}$	A1	
	(b) (i)	10%	A1	
	(ii)	$\frac{1}{10}$ accept $\frac{10}{100}$	A1	

Key to mark scheme
A marks: correct answer
M marks: correct method
B marks: independent work

Page 265 gives a general guidance on use of this assessment scheme with some examples.

Assessment and remediation links

Question		Answer	Marking guidance and remediation sheet links	
8	**(a)**	0.25	A1	less than $\frac{6}{8}$ use remediation sheet 15.2
	(b)	0.57	A1	
	(c)	0.86	A1	
	(d)	0.15	A1	
9	**(a)**	0.05	A1	
	(b)	0.1	A1	
	(c)	0.5	A1	
	(d)	1.4	A1	
10	**(a)**	$\frac{1}{4}$	A1	
	(b)	$\frac{2}{5}$ accept $\frac{40}{100}$	A1	
	(c)	$\frac{13}{20}$ accept $\frac{65}{100}$	A1	

Key to mark scheme
A marks: correct answer
M marks: correct method
B marks: independent work

Page 265 gives a general guidance on use of this assessment scheme with some examples.

15.1 Percentages

In a test Peter got 53 out of 100.

His mark is $\frac{53}{100}$.

You write 53%.

You say '53 per cent'.

Exercise 1

1 Write these fractions as percentages:

(a) $\frac{20}{100}$ **(b)** $\frac{35}{100}$ **(c)** $\frac{7}{100}$ **(d)** $\frac{87}{100}$ **(e)** $\frac{50}{100}$

2 Write these percentages as fractions:

(a) 25% **(b)** 20% **(c)** 6% **(d)** 43%

You can count squares to find percentages.

Example 1

What percentage of each shape is shaded?

(a)

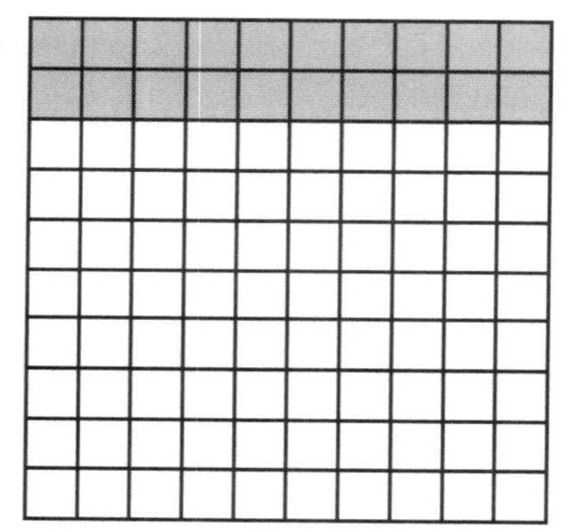

(b)

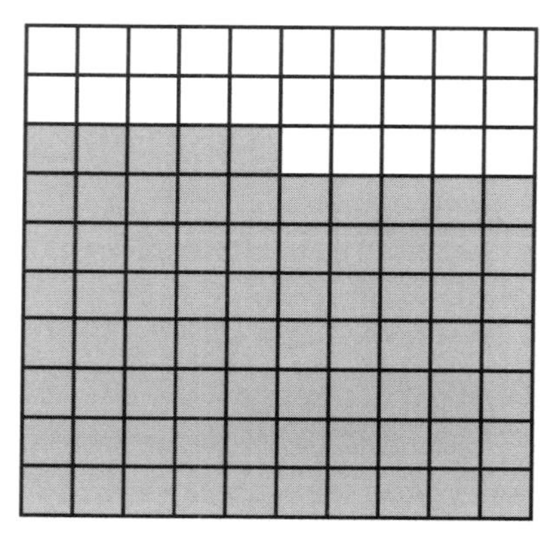

(a) 20 squares out of 100 shaded = 20% **(b)** 75 squares out of 100 shaded = 75%

Exercise 2

1 What percentage of each shape is shaded?

(a)

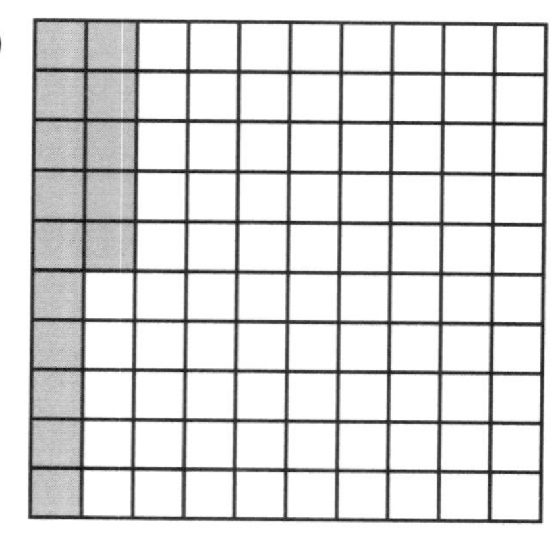

(b)

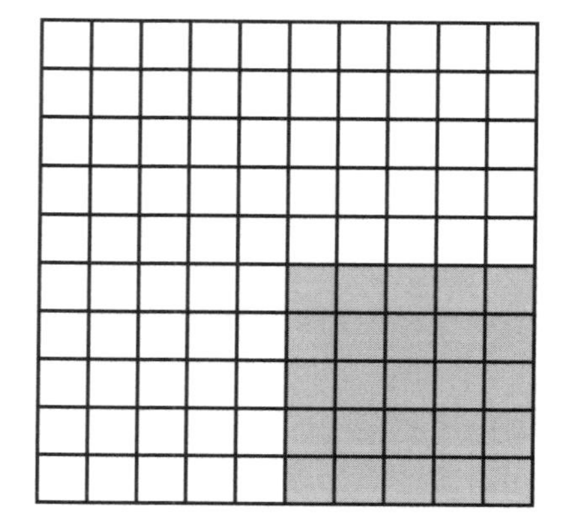

(c)

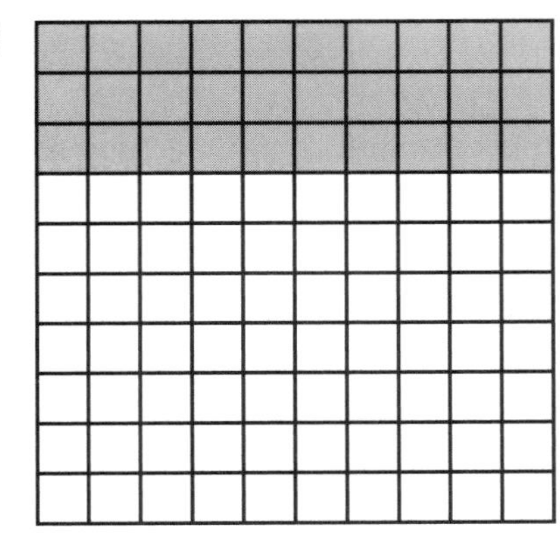

(d)

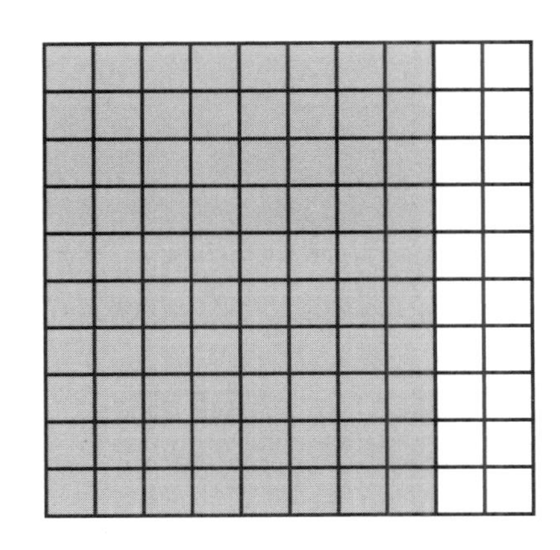

Here are some percentages you should remember.

	100 ÷ 10 = 10		100 ÷ 5 = 20
so	10 lots of 10% = 100%	so	5 lots of 20% = 100%
	100 ÷ 4 = 25		100 ÷ 2 = 50
so	4 lots of 25% = 100%	so	2 lots of 50% = 100%

Example 2

What percentage of this shape is shaded:

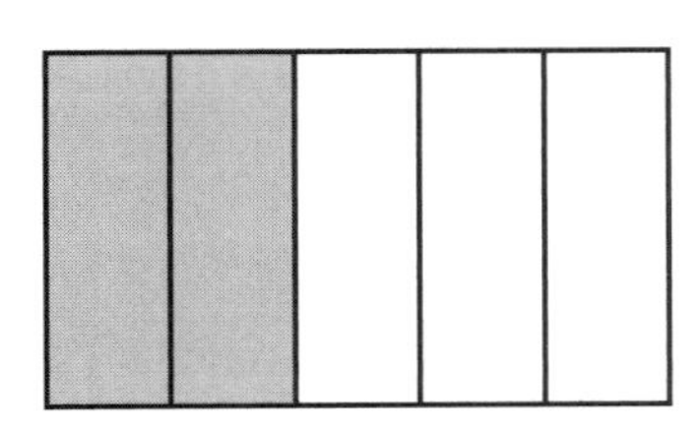

The whole thing is 100%.

There are 5 parts so each part is

100 ÷ 5 = 20%

2 lots of 20% is 40%.

40% of the shape is shaded.

Exercise 3

What percentage of each shape is shaded?

(a)

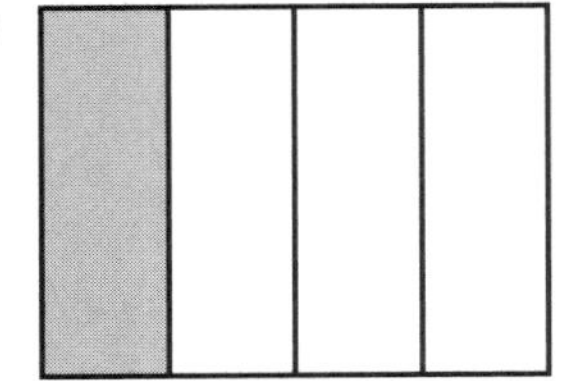

(b)

(c)

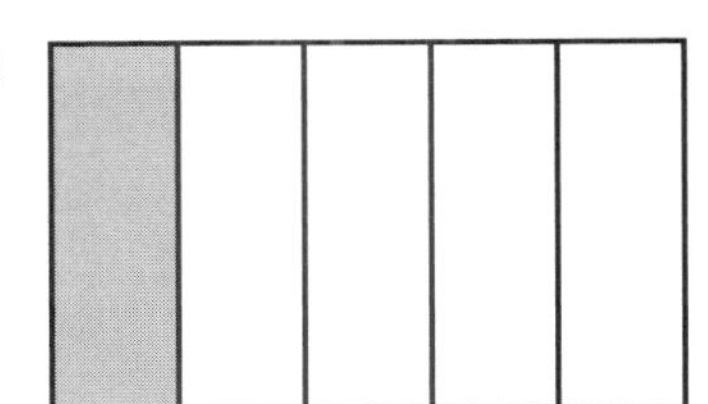

(d)

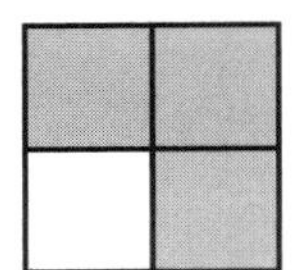

(e)

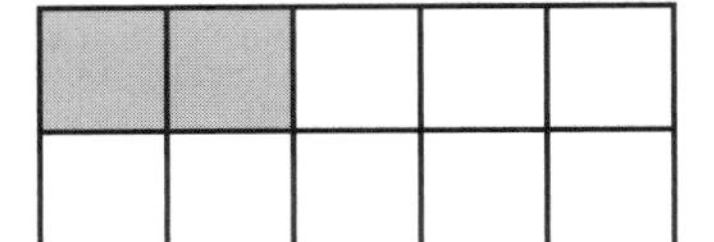

(f)

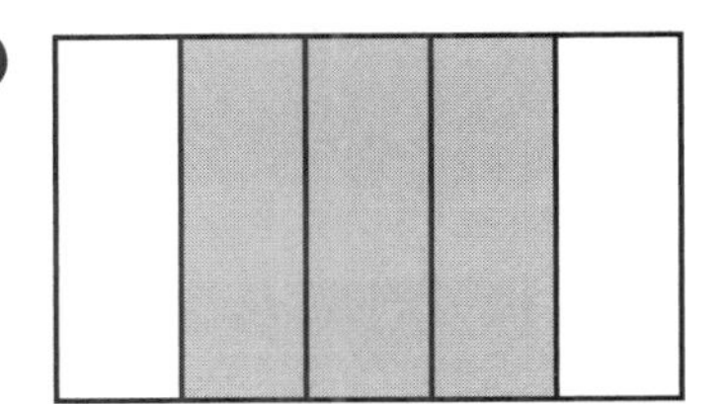

1 G

15.2 Percentages to decimals

45% is the same as $\frac{45}{100}$

You can think of fractions as divisions waiting to be done:

$\frac{45}{100}$ is the same as $45 \div 100$.

Using a calculator:

45	÷	100	=	0.45

Exercise 1

1 Turn these fractions into decimals:

(a) $\frac{28}{100}$ **(b)** $\frac{16}{100}$ **(c)** $\frac{64}{100}$ **(d)** $\frac{80}{100}$

(e) $\frac{2}{100}$ **(f)** $\frac{95}{100}$ **(g)** $\frac{100}{100}$

2 Turn these fractions into decimals:

(a) $\frac{3}{4}$ **(b)** $\frac{1}{2}$ **(c)** $\frac{2}{5}$ **(d)** $\frac{6}{15}$

(e) $\frac{8}{16}$ **(f)** $\frac{64}{80}$ **(g)** $\frac{36}{90}$

R15.2

You can use this number machine to turn percentages straight into decimals.

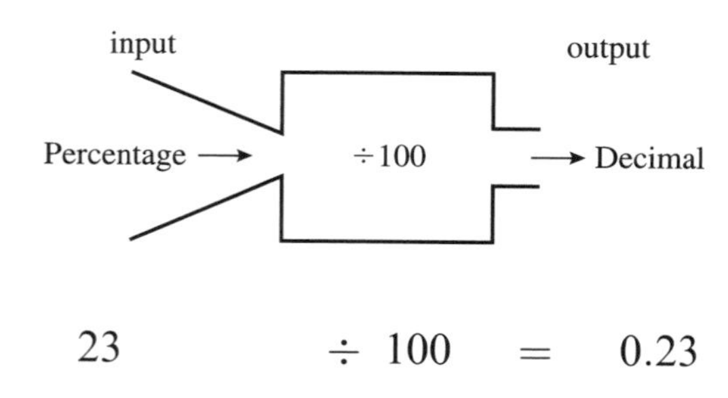

23 $\div$ 100 = 0.23

so 23% is 0.23 as a decimal.

Exercise 2

Complete this table:

Percentage ÷100	Decimal
50%	
75%	
28%	
	0.14
	0.30
20%	0.2
55%	
5%	
81%	
	0.9
	1.00

What number machine turns decimals into percentages?

Answers to Pupils' Book

15 Percentages

Exercise 15A

1 20%
2 25%
3 (a) 50% (b) 25%
(c) 20% (d) 25%
(e) 10% (f) 25%
4 (a) (b)
(c) (d)

Exercise 15B

1 (a) 10% (b) 70% (c) 30%
2 (a) 20% (b) 60% (c) 40% (d) 80%
3 (a) 75% (b) 30% (c) 50% (d) 75%
(e) 90% (f) 80%
4 (a) (b) (c)
(d) (e)

Exercise 15C

1 (a) $\frac{50}{100}$ (b) 50% 2 (a) $\frac{25}{100}$ (b) 25%
3 (a) $\frac{75}{100}$ (b) 75% 4 (a) $\frac{25}{100}$ (b) 25%
5 (a) $\frac{10}{100}$ (b) 10% 6 (a) $\frac{75}{100}$ (b) 75%
7 (a) $\frac{80}{100}$ (b) 80% 8 (a) $\frac{60}{100}$ (b) 60%
9 (a) $\frac{10}{100}$ (b) 10%
10 (a) (b)
(c) (d)
(e)

Exercise 15D

1 0.25 2 0.36
3 0.06 4 0.18
5 0.3 6 0.5
7 0.08 8 0.75
9 0.62 10 0.05
11 0.27 12 0.54
13 0.99 14 0.7
15 0.35 16 0.01
17 0.15 18 0.6
19 1.2 20 1.5

Answers to Homeworks

15 Percentages

Exercise 15.1 Links: 15A

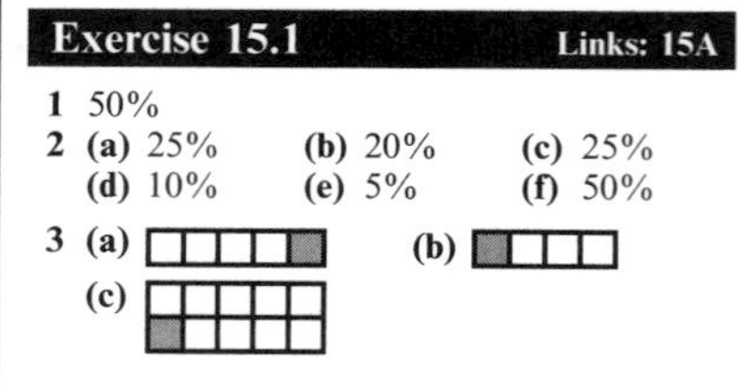

1 50%
2 (a) 25% (b) 20% (c) 25%
(d) 10% (e) 5% (f) 50%
3 (a) (b)
(c)

Exercise 15.2 Links: 15B

1 (a) 25% (b) 50% (c) 75%
2 (a) 5% (b) 15% (c) 20% (d) 35%
3 (a) 40% (b) 75% (c) 70%
4 (a) (b)
(c)

Exercise 15.3 Links: 15C, 15D

1 (a) $\frac{50}{100}$ (b) 50% 2 (a) $\frac{20}{100}$ (b) 20%
3 (a) $\frac{1}{100}$ (b) 1% 4 (a) $\frac{60}{100}$ (b) 60%
5 (a) $\frac{7}{100}$ (b) 7% 6 (a) $\frac{38}{100}$ (b) 38%
7 (a) (b)
(c) (d)
(e)

8 0.21 9 0.43
10 0.06 11 0.58
12 0.04 13 0.16
14 0.5 15 0.9
16 0.63 17 0.05
18 0.02 19 1.1
20 1.3

Remediation answers

15.1 Percentages

Exercise 1

1 (a) 20% (b) 35% (c) 7%
(d) 87% (e) 50%
2 (a) $\frac{25}{100}$ (b) $\frac{20}{100}$
(c) $\frac{6}{100}$ (d) $\frac{43}{100}$

Exercise 2

1 (a) 15% (b) 25% (c) 30% (d) 80%

Exercise 3

1 (a) 25% (b) 50% (c) 20%
(d) 75% (e) 20% (f) 60%

15.2 Percentages to decimals

Exercise 1

1 (a) 0.28 (b) 0.16 (c) 0.64
(d) 0.80 (or 0.8) (e) 0.02
(f) 0.95 (g) 1.00 (or 1)
2 (a) 0.75 (b) 0.5 (c) 0.4
(d) 0.4 (e) 0.5 (f) 0.8
(g) 0.4

Exercise 2

1

Percentage ÷100	Decimal
50%	0.50
75%	0.75
28%	0.28
14%	0.14
30%	0.30
20%	0.2
55%	0.55
5%	0.05
81%	0.81
90%	0.9
100%	1.00

2

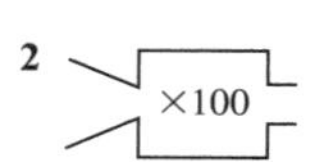

Unit 16 Using and applying mathematics

Content summary

This unit takes students step by step through an investigation.

Book 1R Unit 18 is the same.

NC level

Level 2: The investigation is developed from about Level 2 through a search for a pattern, making a prediction and moving to a generalization which could be about Level 6.

UA1

Content

Investigation guidelines	UA1	Investigating Hop and Step – a game with three rules

Assessment

There is no assessment for Unit 16.

Remediation

Remediation sheets: None.

ICT links

Use *MicroSmile for Windows Pack 6* to develop logical strategies for problem solving.

16 Using and applying mathematics

framework teaching objective	§	lesson starter	f/w ref
Solve word problems and investigate in a range of contexts: number, algebra, shape, space and measures, and handling data.	Chap 16	[7] [12] [19] [31] [50] Ask for a one digit number → 7 Ask for a two digit number → 12 – Where do the next 3 numbers come from? What number goes here to make 8 become 28? (*4*) [8] [ ] [ ] [ ] [28] Not sure? **Have a go.** This method is called 'trial and error.' What number goes in the second square to make 8 become 31? **Predict. Justify your prediction.** 'Must be bigger than 4.' 'Must be 7 because 31 is 3 bigger than 28.' Try your prediction. Find the real number. What do you notice?	2–25
Solve word problems and investigate in a range of contexts: number, algebra, shape, space and measures, and handling data.	Chap 16	[8] [ ] [ ] [ ] [ ] We have seen that 4 makes 8 into 28 and 5 makes 8 into 31. Can I find a **whole number** that will make 8 into 29? – How can you tell? Can 8 be made into: 30? 32? 33? What is the next number after 31 that 8 can 'become'? Can 8 'become' 27? 26? 25? Can you predict which numbers 8 can be made into: 20? 19? 10? 25? We want to spot a pattern separating those numbers that 8 **can** be made into from those 8 **cannot**. How can I recall these results to help me spot a pattern? (*In 2 columns. Order the results.*)	2–25

Answers to Pupils' Book

16 Using and applying mathematics

Exercise 16A

Hop Hop Step
Hop Step Hop
Step Hop Hop

Hop Step Step Step
Step Hop Step Step
Step Step Hop Step
Step Step Step Hop

Step Step Step Step Step

Exercise 16B

1 (a) Hop Step
Step Hop
Step Step Step
(b) 3 ways

2 Hop Hop
Hop Step Step
Step Hop Step
Step Step Hop
Step Step Step Step

Exercise 16C

HHS HSSS SSSSS
HSH SHSS
SHH SSHS
SSSH

Exercise 16D

Number of blue hoops	Number of ways of getting from green to red
0	1
1	2
2	3
3	5
4	8

Exercise 16E

(a) Even
(b) Even
(c) Odd

Exercise 16F

1 3 hoops = 5 ways
4 hoops = 8 ways
So 5 hoops = 5 + 8 = 13 ways.
2 4 hoops = 8 ways
5 hoops = 13 ways
So 6 hoops = 8 + 13 = 21 ways.

Exercise 16G

(a) 55
(b) 89
(c) 144
(d) 1597

Unit 17 Calculators and computers

Content summary

This unit is about extending the use of calculators to include memory, random number generating and the constant operator facility. There is also some computer work in LOGO and with spreadsheets.

NC level

This unit is essentially an enabling unit which allows students to experience some of the possibilities of their calculators and computers.

H4a NA3g NA3o NA3p NA6a S4j

Content

17.1	**Using your memory**	NA3o	Memory on a scientific calculator
17.2	**Square numbers and number chains**	NA3p	Use of square key
17.3	**Ordering whole numbers and decimals using random numbers**	NA3p	Using the random number facility
17.4	**Multiplication tables practice**	NA3g	Using the random number facility to practice tables
17.5	**Recycling machines and number sequences**	NA6a	Generating sequences
17.6	**Symmetry in LOGO**	S4j	Rotation and reflection with LOGO
17.7	**Angles practice in LOGO**	S4j	Angles with LOGO
17.8	**Charts and graphs from data using a spreadsheet**	H4a	Storing data in a spreadsheet for use in statistical displays

Assessment

There is no assessment for Unit 17.

Remediation

Remediation sheets: None.

17 Calculators and computers

framework teaching objective	§	lesson starter	f/w ref
Carry out calculations with more than one step, using brackets and the memory.	17.1	Type the calculation 2 × 10 and press [Min] button. Type the calculation 3 × 4 and press [M+] button. Now press [MR] (*The calculator reads 32*) What has the calculator done with the two calculations? What does the 'M' stand for? R stands for 'recall.' What did this make the calculator do? Use the calculator's memory facility and see if you can predict the answer. (3 × 6) + (2 × 9) + (4 × 5) (*Have the class ready with their mentally calculated answers before pressing* [MR]).	108–9
Carry out calculations with more than one step, using brackets and the memory.	17.2	What do I call it when I multiply a number by itself? (*squaring*) What symbol do I use to show a number that is being squared (6^2 *– the index 2*) Can you find a button on the calculator that shows a symbol being squared? ([x^2]) Why have they used [x]? '*Stands for any number.*' What's 5 squared? (*25*). Experiment with the [x^2] key until you have squared 5 to become 25. Write down the keys you pressed in order. [5] [x^2] [=] (*The* [=] *may have to be pressed on some calculators.*)	108–9

framework teaching objective	**§**	**lesson starter**	**f/w ref**
Enter numbers and interpret the display in different contexts.	Chap 17	Claudia buys two birthday cards – one for £2.30 and one for 90p. Use the calculator to find the total cost. When you typed in 2.30, what happened? (*The calculator removed the 0 at the end.*) How can I get the answer £92.30? Is Claudia **made** of money? What mistake did I make? How can I type in 90p in a way that the calculator will understand? (*0.90 or 0.9*) I have £2.15 and I buy a magazine which cost £1.55. How much money do I have left? Use your calculator. Write down the answer the calculator displays. How much money is this? (*60p*) The display's meaning depends on the kind of problem I am solving. 0.5 means $\frac{1}{2}$ of £1 which equals 50p. What would the display 0.5 mean if I was solving a **time** problem? What is 0.5 of an hour? 0.25 of an hour? 0.1 of an hour?	108–9

Answers to Pupils' Book

17 Calculators and computers

Exercise 17A

1 £9.29, 71p **2** £168.26
3 £2.63 **4** £14.58

Exercise 17B

1 81 **2** 144 **3** 289
4 169 **5** 100

Exercise 17C

1 19 → 82 → 68 → 100 → 1
2 49 → 97 → 130 → 10 → 1
3 82 → 68 → 100 → 1
4 15 → 26 → 40 → 16 → 37 → 58 → 89
145 → 42 → 20 → 4 (→ 16)

Exercise 17J

1 1, 3, 5, 7, 9
2 4, 7, 10, 13, 16
3 3, 6, 12, 24, 48
4 60, 55, 50, 45, 40
5 64, 32, 16, 8, 4

Exercise 17K

1 4, 5, 7, 11, 19
2 2, 7, 22, 67, 202
3 7, 13, 25, 49, 97
4 784, 400, 208, 112, 64
5 ×2 +3
6 ×2 −5

Exercise 17L

1 rotational symmetry order 3

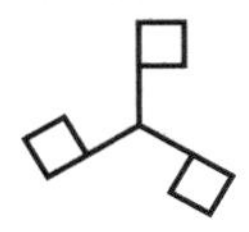

2 rotational symmetry order 2, 2 lines reflective

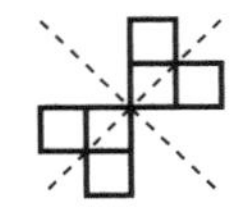

3 rotational symmetry order 8

4 rotational symmetry order 3, 3 lines reflective

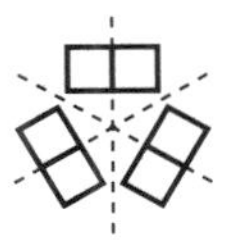

5 rotational symmetry order 4, 4 lines reflective

6 rotational symmetry order 2, 2 lines reflective

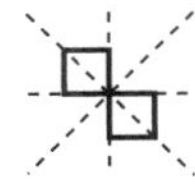

7 1 line reflective symmetry

8 rotational symmetry order 8

National Curriculum Level tests

Guidance on using the level diagnostic tests

The level diagnostic tests are designed with two purposes in mind:

- To indicate the NC level of pupils starting at Year 7, giving an indication of which Impact book to start them on
- To use at any stage during the year to indicate the current NC level of a pupil's work

The tests are all marked out of 50 and are designed to take about 50 minutes to complete. There is guidance at the start of the answers to each test about how to interpret the score to provide an indication of the level that the pupils are working at.

It is recommended that all pupils be given either test C or D first, unless there is good reason to believe that they are under level 3 or above level 4. The results of the KS2 test should provide a good indication of which test it is appropriate to set for which pupil, but note that it may be necessary to set more than one test to be satisfied that the pupil is starting on the correct book.

Notes on marking scheme:
The marking scheme is the same as in the end of chapter assessment tests with A marks for accuracy and M marks for method. There is a summary of how the marking scheme works overleaf.

The tests are aimed at the following levels:

Test:	Level
A	1 2
B	(1) 2 (3)
C	(2) 3 (4)
D	(3) 4 (5)
E	(4) 5 (6)
F	5 6

Note: Tests E and F are in the Impact Maths 1R Pupil Performance Pack

Marking guidance for the assessment tests and National Curriculum level tests

The following abbreviations are used in the marking scheme:

A marks are for correct answers
M marks are for correct method
B marks are for correct answers awarded independently.

Example 1

Find the area of the rectangle:

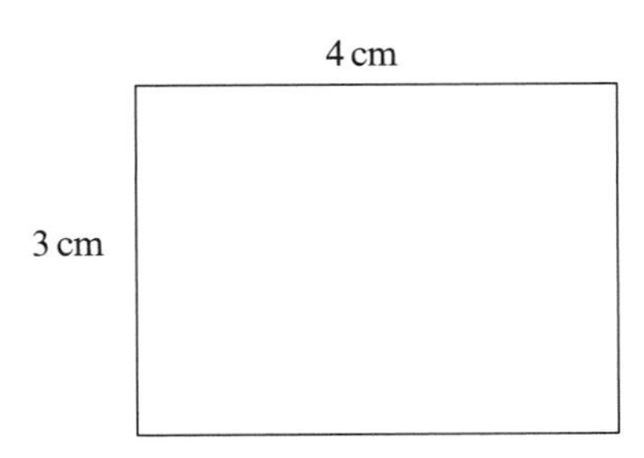

(2 marks)

answer: 3×4 M1
$12\,\text{cm}^2$ A1

The pupil will get one mark if they just put 3×4. The correct answer implies the correct method so 12 will get 2 marks.

Example 2

This is the picture of an L shape in its starting position.

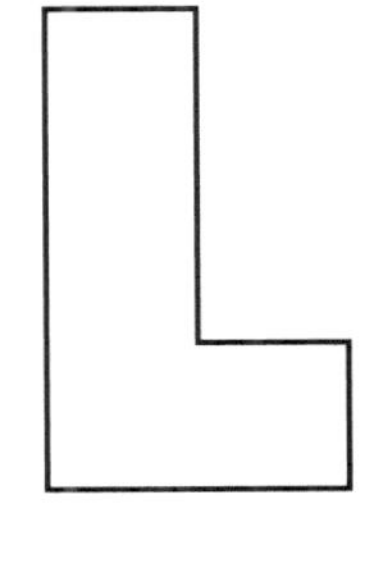

It is rotated to finish like this:

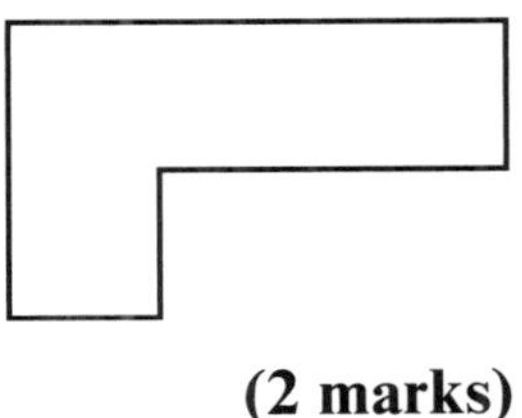

Describe this rotation as fully as you can.

(2 marks)

answer: $\frac{1}{4}$ turn B1
clockwise B1

The pupil will get one mark for each part. Neither answer implies knowledge of the other so the marks are independent.

Test A

1 **(a)** How many cups?

.... cups
(1)

(b) Count the number of cars.

.... cars
(1)

(c) Jenny has 9 sweets.

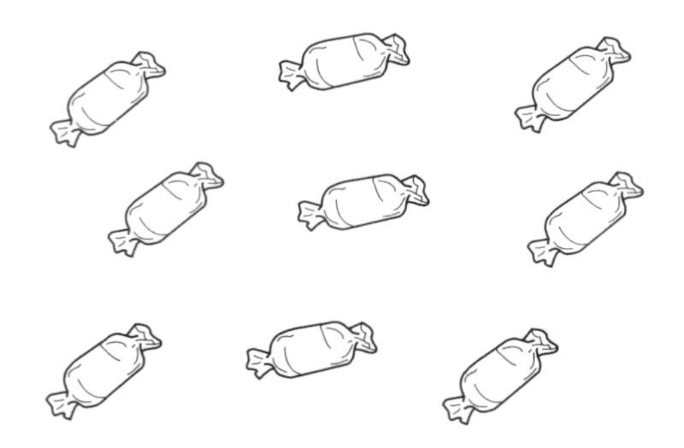

She eats five.
How many will she have left?

.... sweets
(1)

(d) Kevin has 5 marbles.

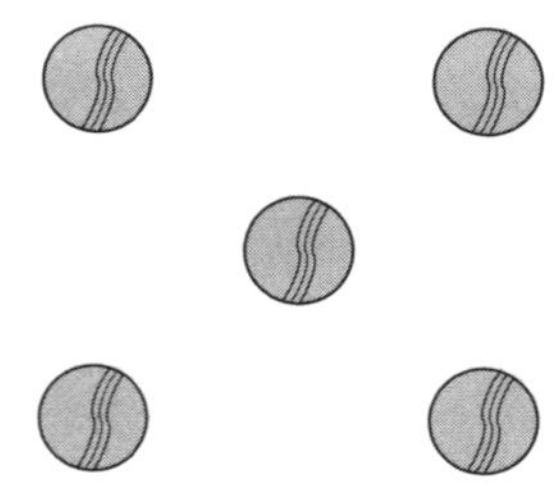

He finds 3 more.
How many marbles does he have then?

.... marbles
(1)

2 Look at this pattern of letters:

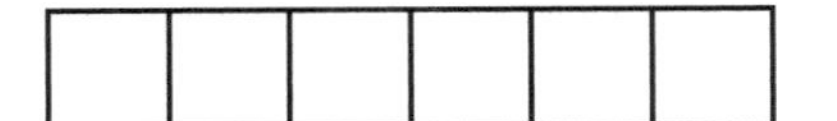

A	C	B	A	C	B	A	C	B

Write in the letters to continue the pattern:

(3)

3 Here are two bowls of fish.

Bowl 1

Bowl 2

Fill in the boxes with numbers

Bowl 1 Bowl 2 = Total

4 fish + ☐ fish = ☐ fish **(2)**

4 Here are 5 cards:

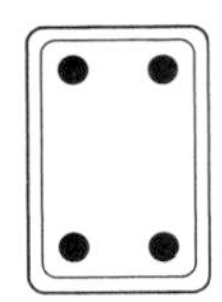

Put them in order of the number of dots.

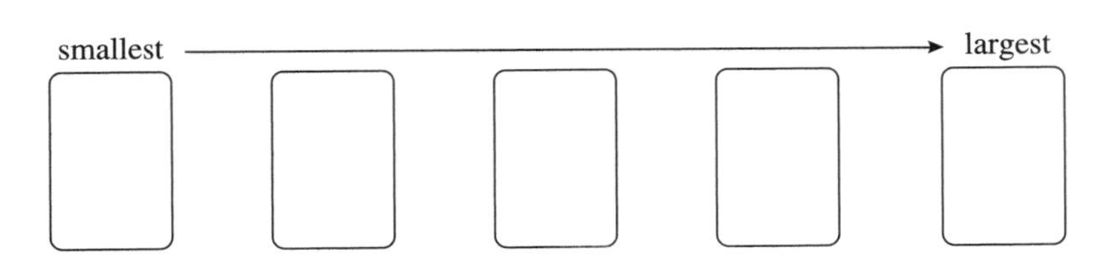

(2)

5 Here are some living things:

Which of these:

(a) live in water?

.... **(1)**

(b) can fly?

.... **(1)**

6 **(a)** How many corners on each shape?
Write your answer in
the shape like this.

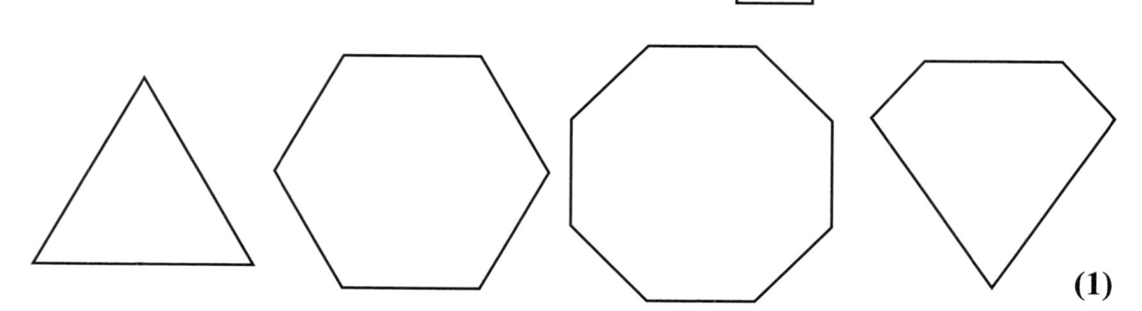

(1)

(b) Write the numbers in size order, smallest to largest:

...................., ..., ...6.........., ..., ... **(1)**

7 Work out the missing number.

(a) $5 + 4 =$ .... **(1)**

(b) $9 - 6 =$ .... **(1)**

(c) $3 +$ .... $= 8$ **(1)**

(d) $10 -$ .... $= 6$ **(1)**

8 **(a)** Shade in $\frac{1}{2}$ of this shape:

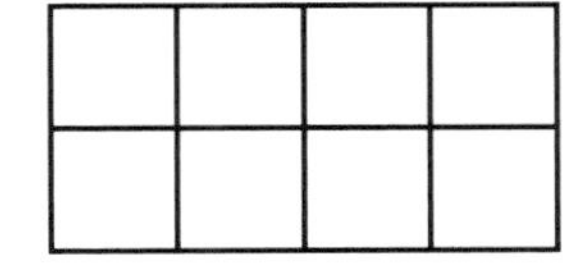

(1)

(b) What fraction of this shape has been shaded?

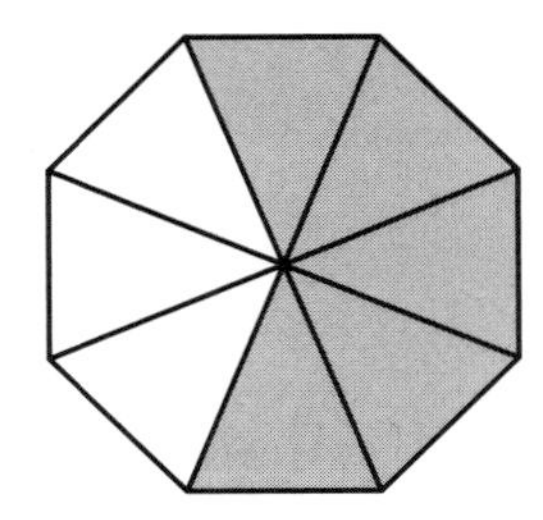

....
(1)

9 The block graph shows the number of Year 7 pupils absent from school last week.

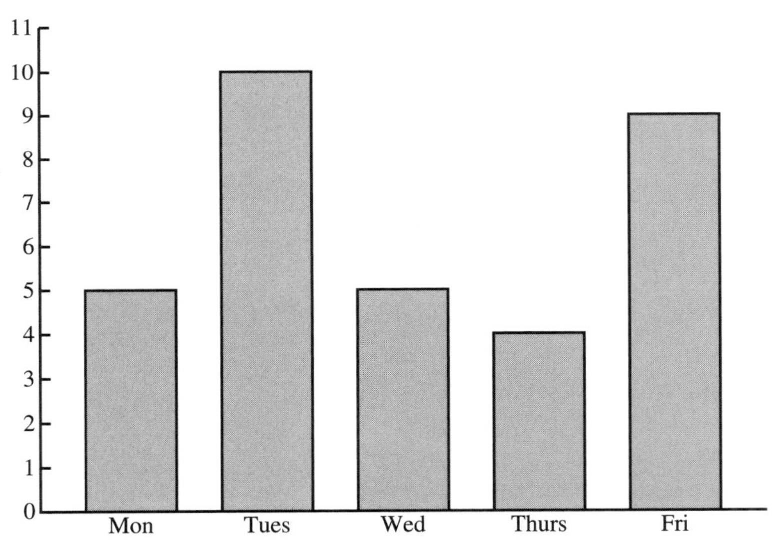

(a) How many pupils were absent on Monday? ....
(1)

(b) On which day were 4 pupils absent? ....
(1)

(c) On which days were an *odd* number of pupils absent? ....
(1)

10 Jane describes a shape.
She says.

- it has 4 sides;
- it has 4 corners;
- all 4 corners are right angles,
- the 4 sides *do not* all have equal lengths,
- each *pair* of opposite sides has equal length.

(a) Draw Jane's shape in the space below.

....
(2)

(b) Write down the *mathematical* name of Jane's shape.

....
(1)

11 Fill in the boxes with +, − or a number to make this true:

10 ☐ 3 = 5 + ☐

(2)

12 Write down the numbers in the cloud that are even.

....
(1)

Test A Levels 1 + 2

1	**(a)**	6 cups	A1
	(b)	7 cars	A1
	(c)	4 sweets	A1
	(d)	8 marbles	A1
2		ACB ACB	A1 for 1st A A1 for 1st ACB A1 for second ACB as well
3		4 fish + 3 fish = 7 fish	A1 for 3 fish A1 for 7 fish
4			A2 if all correct A1 if one card out of order or A1 if in order but largest first.
5	**(a)**	Fish and whale	A1
	(b)	Butterfly, bird and wasp	A1
6	**(a)**	6, 3, 6, 8, 5	A1
	(b)	3, 5, 6, 6, 8	A1 accept reverse order.
7	**(a)**	$5 + 4 = 9$	A1
	(b)	$9 - 6 = 3$	A1
	(c)	$3 + 5 = 8$	A1
	(d)	$10 - 4 = 6$	A1
8	**(a)**		A1 for any 4 squares shaded.
	(b)	$\frac{5}{8}$	A1
9	**(a)**	5	A1
	(b)	Thursday	A1
	(c)	Monday, Wednesday and Friday	A1

10 **(a)**

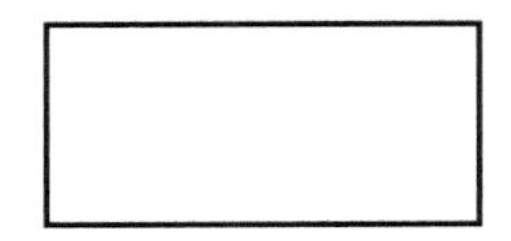

or

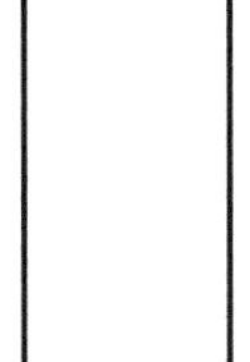

not

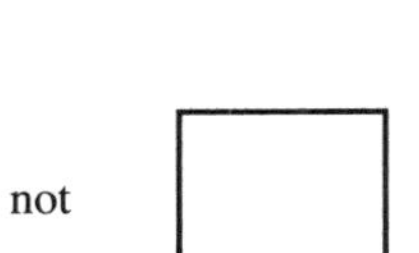

A2
A1 if square drawn

(b) rectangle — A1 follow through from their shape in **(a)**

11	$10 + 3 = 5 + 8$	A2 for + and 8
	or $10 - 3 = 5 + 2$	A2 for − and 2
12	54	A1

Mark scheme – Test A

Teachers may sit with children to ease any language difficulties and show them where to write the answers in this test.

Mark range:	Recommendation:
0 to 15	These pupils are working within level 1. They will need substantial help of an individual nature and will be better advised not to start on the Impact Year 7 materials.
16 to 25	These pupils should be solidly at level 1 and may be at level 2. They will need some help of an individual nature, even working at the level of the Impact remediation materials.
26+	Almost certainly working within level 2. These pupils should be given test B before a final decision is made on which level the pupil should start at.

Test B

1 **(a)** How many cups?

.... cups
(1)

(b) Count the number of plates.

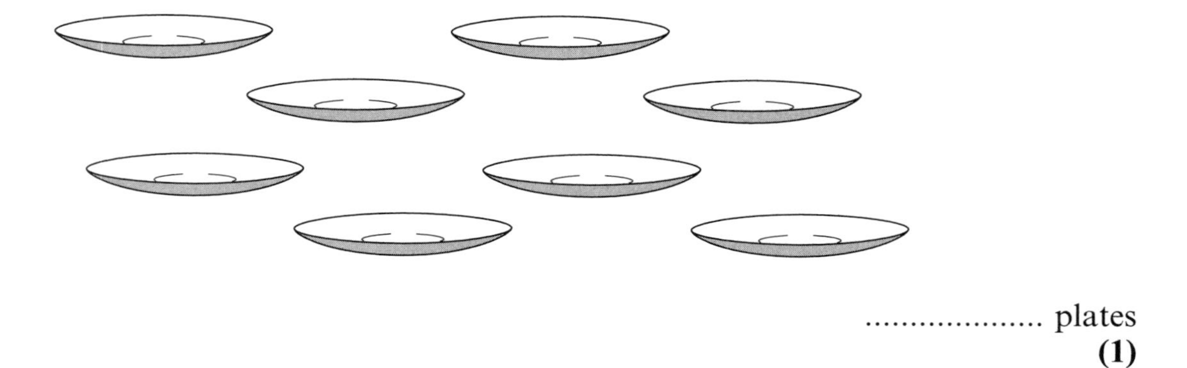

.... plates
(1)

2 Jon has 6 sweets.

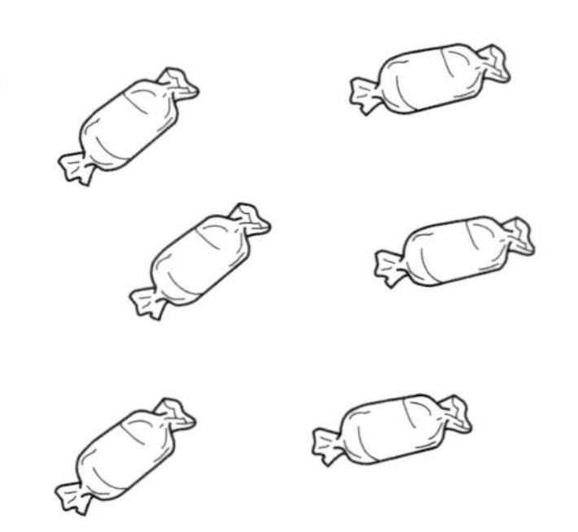

His mother gives him 3 more.

(a) How many sweets does Jon have then? .... sweets
(1)

(b) How many sweets will be left if Jon eats 4 of them? .... sweets
(1)

3

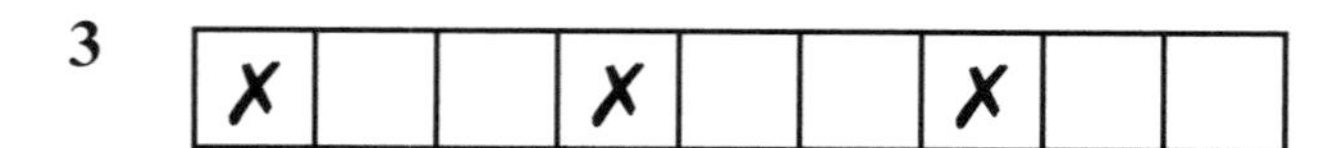

Draw the next four boxes in this pattern.

(2)

4 Put a tick (✓) inside each shape which has any *curved* sides.

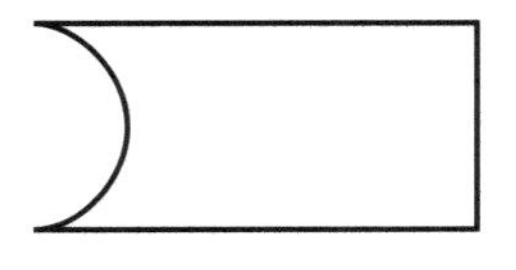 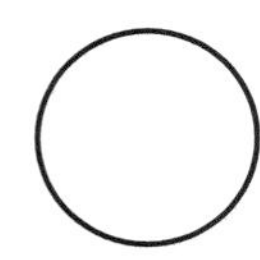  

  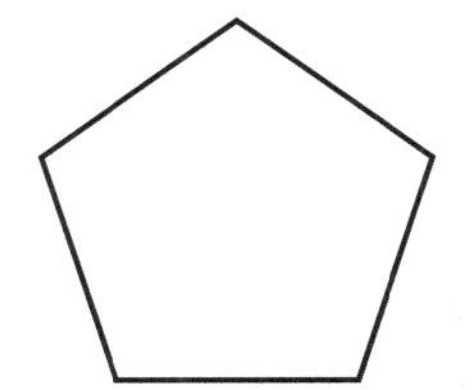 

....
(2)

5 Here are some living things:

(a) Tick each one that can fly. **(1)**

(b) Put a (✗) inside each one that lives in water. **(1)**

6 Work out:

(a) $3 + 7 =$ .... **(1)**

(b) $8 - 3 =$ .... **(1)**

(c) $10 - 4 =$ .... **(1)**

(d) $6 + 2 + 1 =$ .... **(1)**

7 **(a)** Put these numbers in order of size, smallest first.

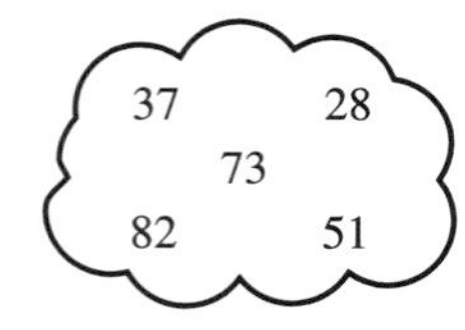

.... **(3)**

(b) 7 4 8 5 3

Use these boxes to make a number which is bigger than 40 and less than 50. .... **(1)**

8 Put + or – in each box to make these true:

(a) 8 ☐ 5 = 3 **(b)** 4 ☐ 9 = 13

(c) 9 ☐ 2 = 4 ☐ 3 **(3)**

9 Shade:

(a) $\frac{1}{2}$ of this shape 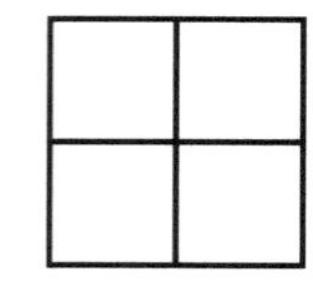 **(b)** $\frac{1}{4}$ of this shape 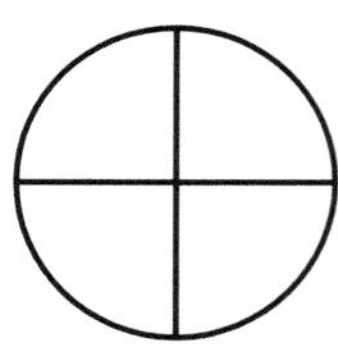

(c) $\frac{3}{4}$ of this shape 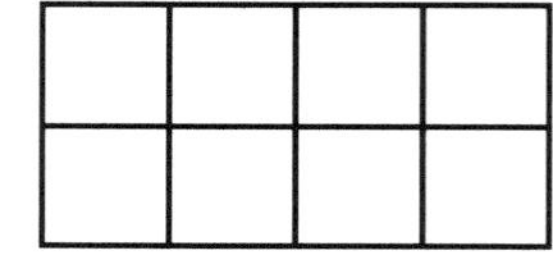 **(3)**

10 Here are some numbers in boxes:

4	10	5
12	9	8
7	20	23

Put a (✓) inside each box which holds an ODD number. **(2)**

11 **(a)** Put a tick (✓) inside each right-angle.

(2)

(b) Draw a shape which has **only one** right angle:

(1)

12 Write the correct name inside each shape. Choose from the list below.

square	circle	pentagon
rectangle	triangle	parallelogram
cube	hexagon	kite

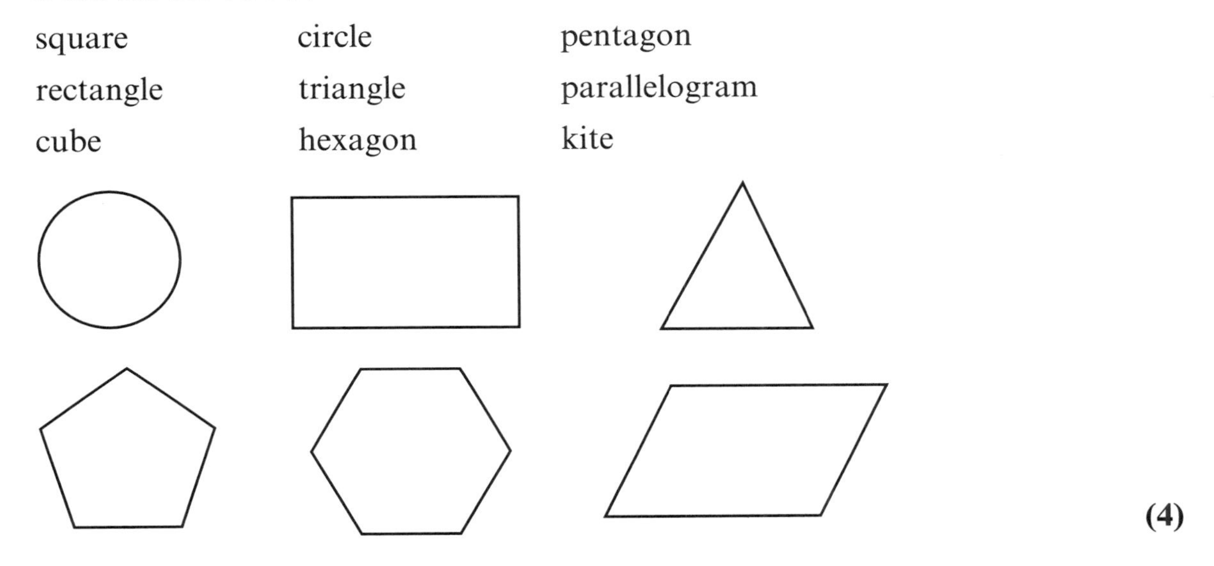

(4)

13 This block graph shows how many children were absent from school last week.

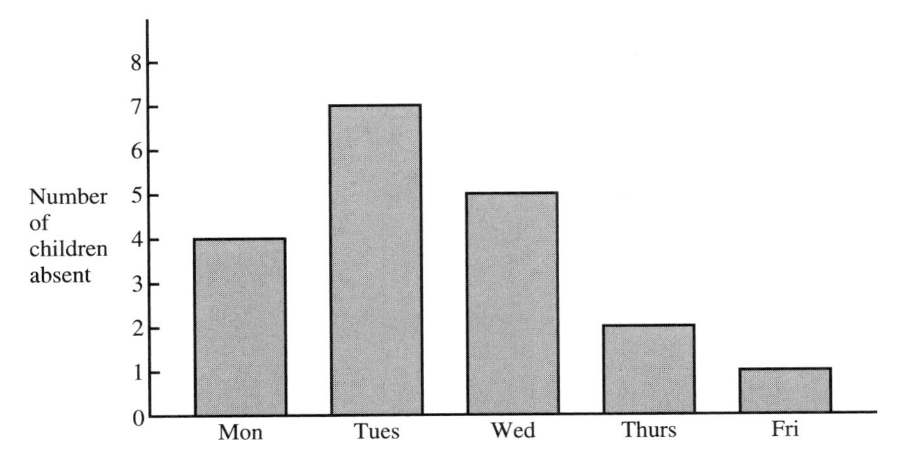

(a) How many children were absent on Tuesday? ....

(1)

(b) On which day were 2 children absent? ....

(1)

14 Here are the names of some children:

DAVID	KATE	ALEYHA
JAMES	NICOLA	EMMA

(a) Which name has exactly 5 letters, *none* of which are the same? .... **(1)**

(b) Which name has exactly 4 letters, two of which are the same? .... **(1)**

15 **(a)** Draw any shape which has exactly 4 corners:

(1)

(b) How many sides does a hexagon have? .... **(1)**

(c) Here is a picture of a cube:

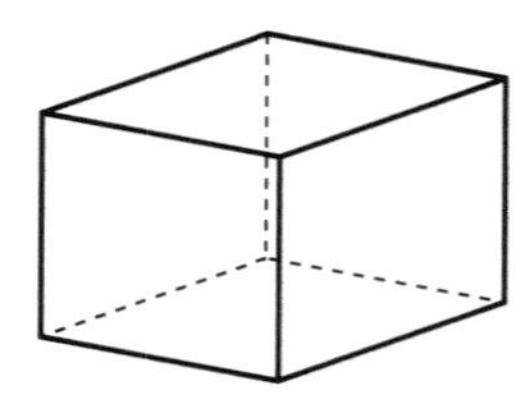

How many corners does it have?

.... **(1)**

16 The pictogram shows how many people went to the swimming pool last week:

Monday
Tuesday
Wednesday
Thursday
Friday
Saturday
Sunday Closed

= 10 people

60 people went to the swimming pool on Saturday.

(a) Complete the pictogram. **(1)**

(b) How many people went to the swimming pool on Thursday? .... **(1)**

17 Work out

(a) $3 \times 5 =$ .... **(1)**

(b) $8 \times 10 =$ .... **(1)**

18 **(a)** A litre of petrol costs 69p.
How much do 10 litres cost?

£ ....
(1)

(b) Mrs Jones shared £20 equally between her 4 children.
How much money did each child get?

£ ....
(1)

19 Put a tick (✓) inside each shape which has one or more lines of symmetry.

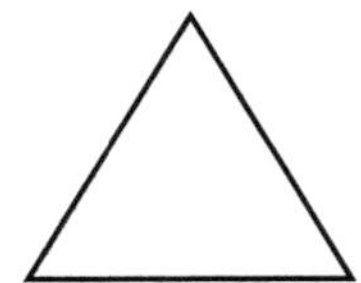
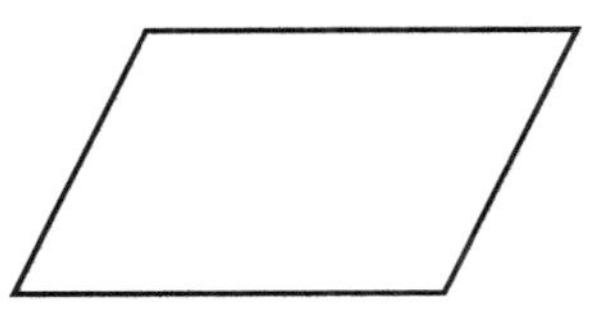

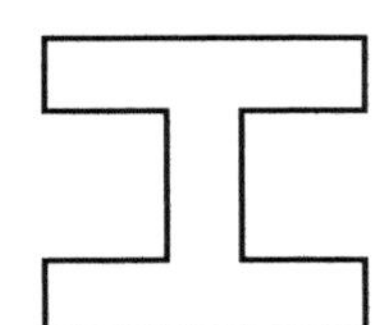
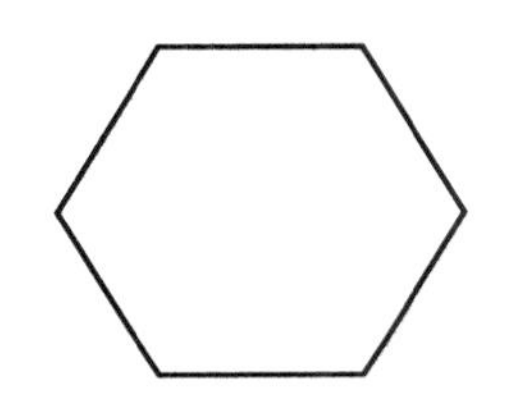

(2)

20 **(a)** Write the number

473

correct to the nearest 100.

....
(1)

(b) What temperature is shown on this thermometer?

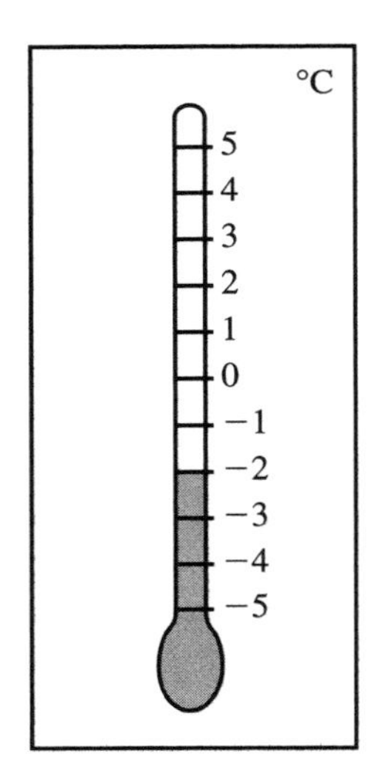

.... °C
(1)

Test B Levels (1) 2 (3)

1 **(a)** 5 cups — A1
(b) 8 plates — A1

2 **(a)** 9 sweets — A1
(b) 5 sweets — A1 follow through for 4 less than answer in (a)

3

✗			✗

A1 for first ✗
A1 for 2 blanks and second ✗

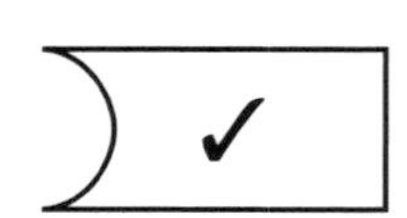

A2 if all correct
A1 if any two correct

5 **(a)** A1 for ticks in bird and butterflies
(b) A1 for crosses in fish and whale

6 **(a)** 10 — A1
(b) 5 — A1
(c) 6 — A1
(d) 9 — A1

7 **(a)** 28, 37, 51, 73, 82 — A3 for all correct
A2 for 1 error or largest first but in order
A1 for 2 errors
(b) 43 or 45 or 47 or 48 or 44 — A1

8 **(a)** $8 - 5 = 3$ — A1
(b) $4 + 9 = 13$ — A1
(c) $9 - 2 = 4 + 3$ — A1

9 **(a)** 2 squares shaded — A1
(b) 1 section shaded — A1
(c) 6 squares shaded — A1

10

4	10	5 ✓
12	9 ✓	8
7 ✓	20	23 ✓

A2 for all 4 odd numbers ticked
A1 for any 2 odd numbers ticked or if extra even ones ticked

11 **(a)**

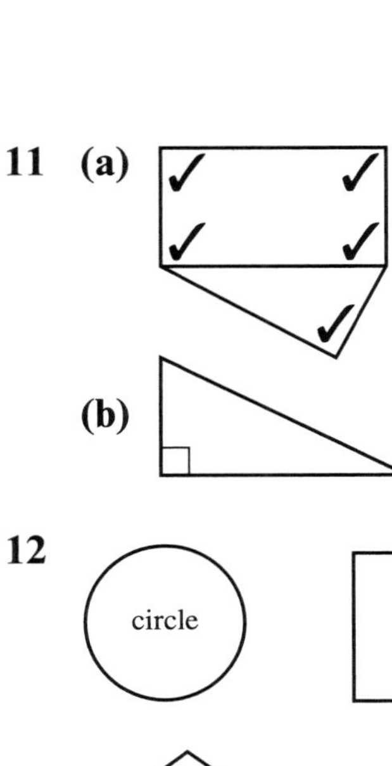

A2 for all correct
A1 if at least 3 correct

(b) A1 for any correct shape with 1 right angle

12

circle

rectangle

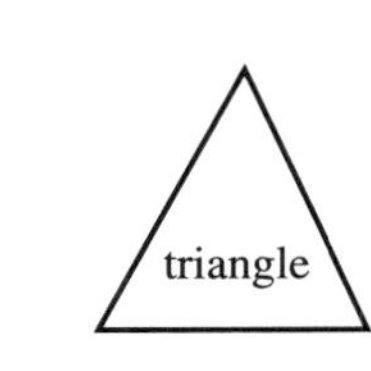

A4 for all 6 correct
A3 for any 5 correct
A2 for 3 or 4 correct
A1 for any 2 correct

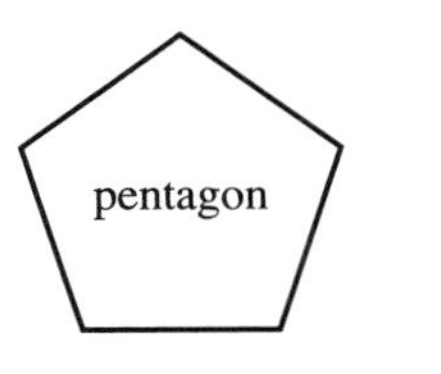

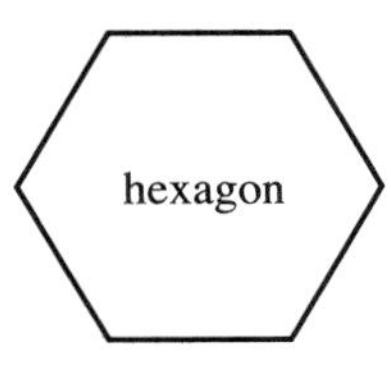

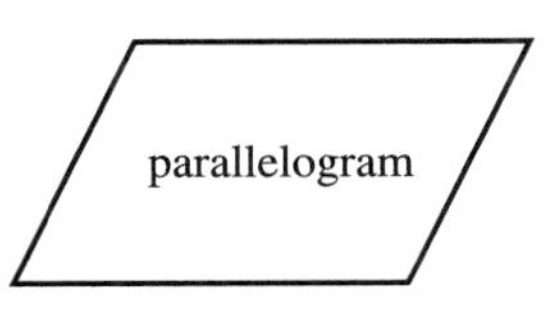

13 **(a)** 7 — A1
(b) Thursday — A1

14 **(a)** James — A1
(b) Emma — A1

15 **(a)** A1 for any 4 sided figure

(b) 6 — A1
(c) 8 — A1

16 **(a)** 웃 웃 웃 웃 웃 웃 — A1 for 6 stickmen
(b) 35 people — A1 for any number from 31 to 39

17 **(a)** 15 — A1
(b) 80 — A1

18 **(a)** £6.90 — A1 do not accept £6.9
(b) £5 each — A1

19

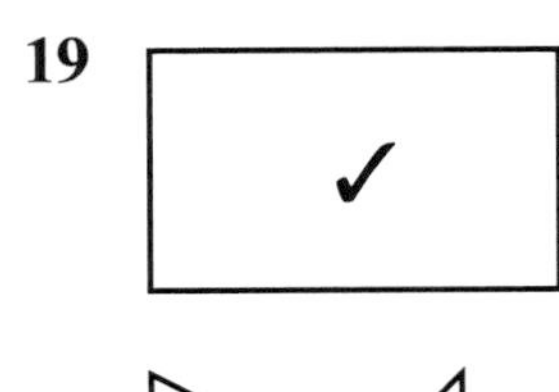

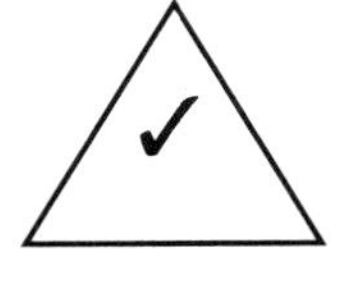

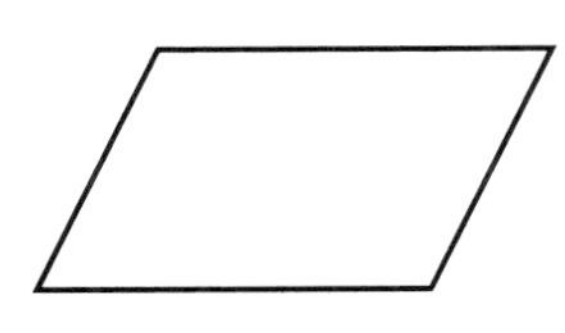

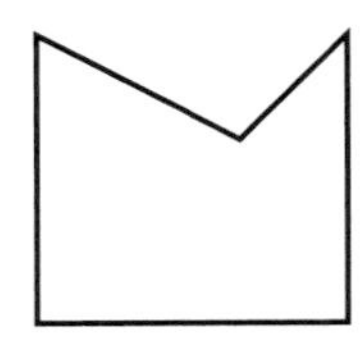

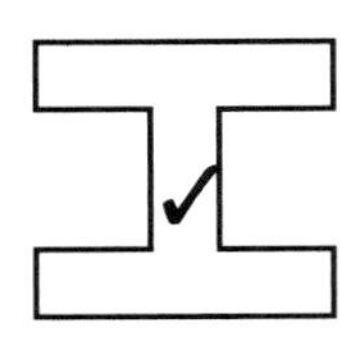

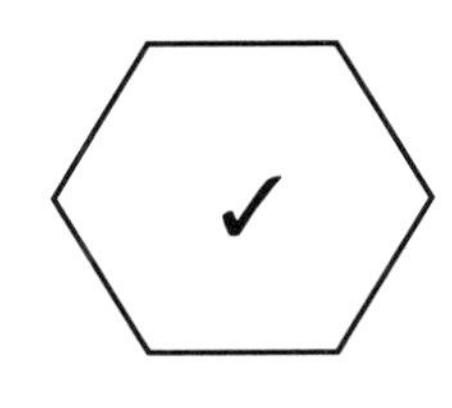

A2 for all 4 correct
A1 for any 2 correct
−1 for each one wrong to a minimum of 0

20 **(a)** 500 — A1
(b) −2°C — A1

Mark scheme – Test B

In this test:

- Teachers can sit with children to ease any language difficulties and show them where to write the answers.
- Children can be given some objects (like multi-link cubes) to represent sweets in question 2.
- Children can be given a cube to help with question 15c but they should *not* be given a hexagon in question 15b.

Mark range:	**Recommendation:**
0 to 15	These children have problems with anything mathematical and will need a great deal of individual attention. They are of virtually reception class level and should be given test A.
16 to 25	These pupils will probably be at about the level of the Impact remediation materials.
26 to 45	The Green book should be accessible to pupils who score within this range.
46+	Pupils should be given test C as they are probably more level 3 than level 2. Should find the Green book more than accessible.

Test C

1 Write these numbers in order, smallest first:

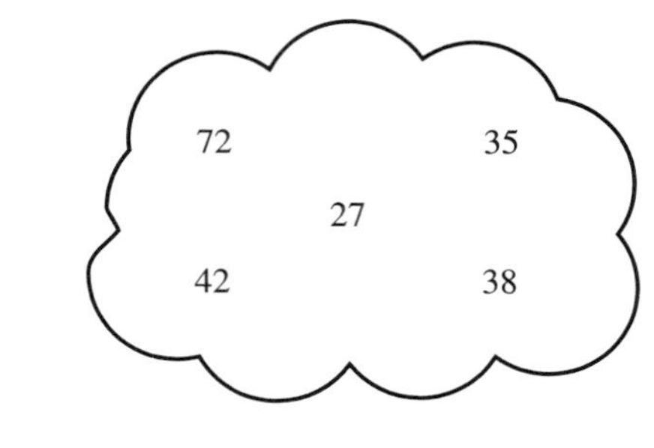

.........., ..., ..., ..., ... **(2)**

2 **(a)** Shade $\frac{1}{2}$ of this shape:

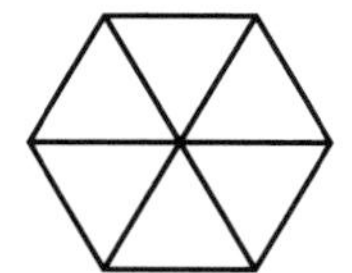

.... **(1)**

(b) What fraction of this shape has been shaded?

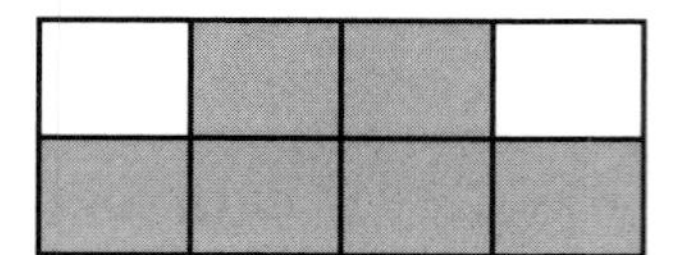

.... **(1)**

3 Put a tick (✓) next to each right-angle:

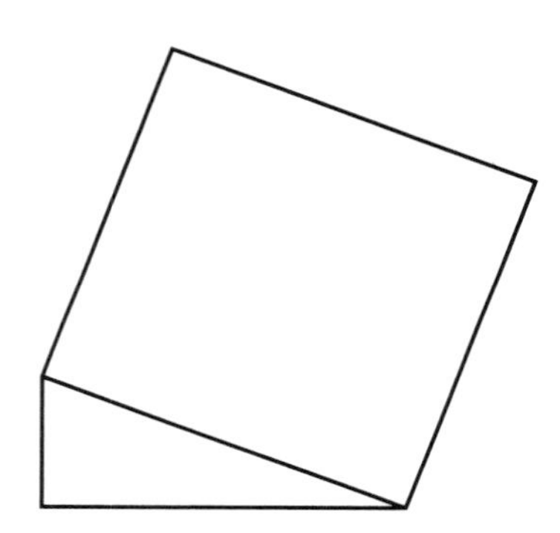

.... **(2)**

4 Write the correct name inside each shape. Choose from the list below.

A 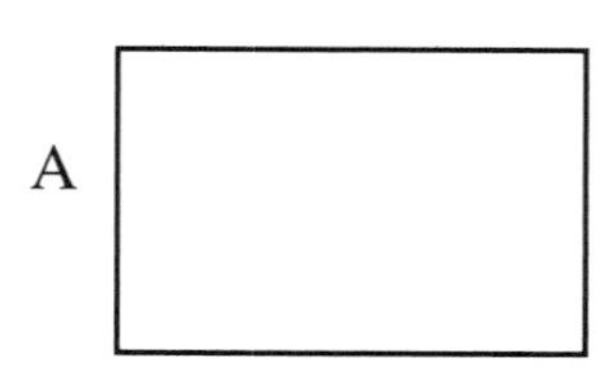

B

C 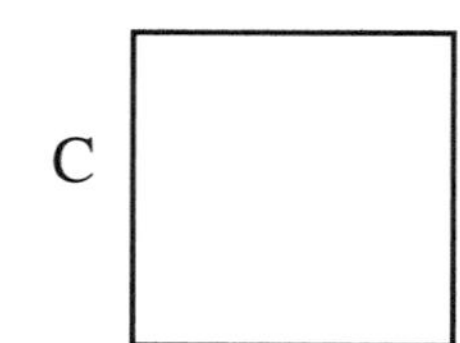

D 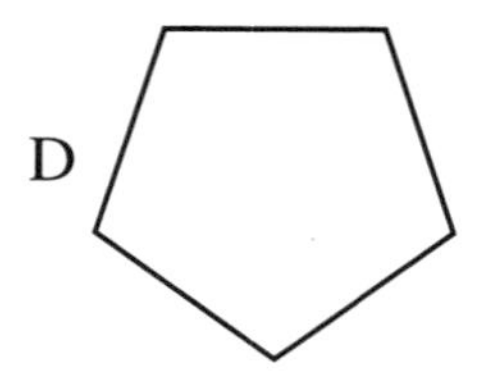

E 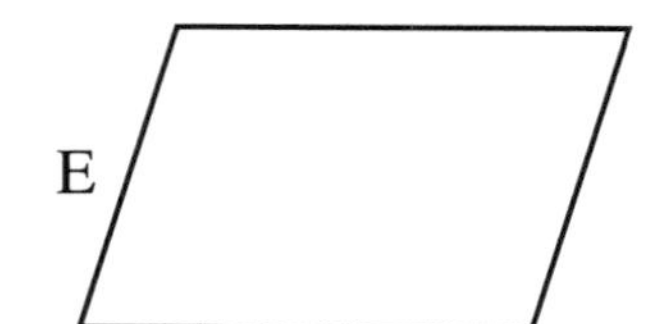

F 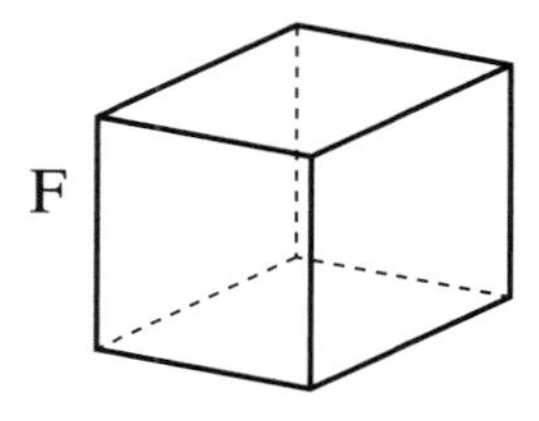

circle
pentagon

cube
rectangle

parallelogram
square **(2)**

5 Jon notes the vehicles that pass his house in one hour:

7 cars   2 buses   3 vans   1 motor cycle

Show this on the block graph below:

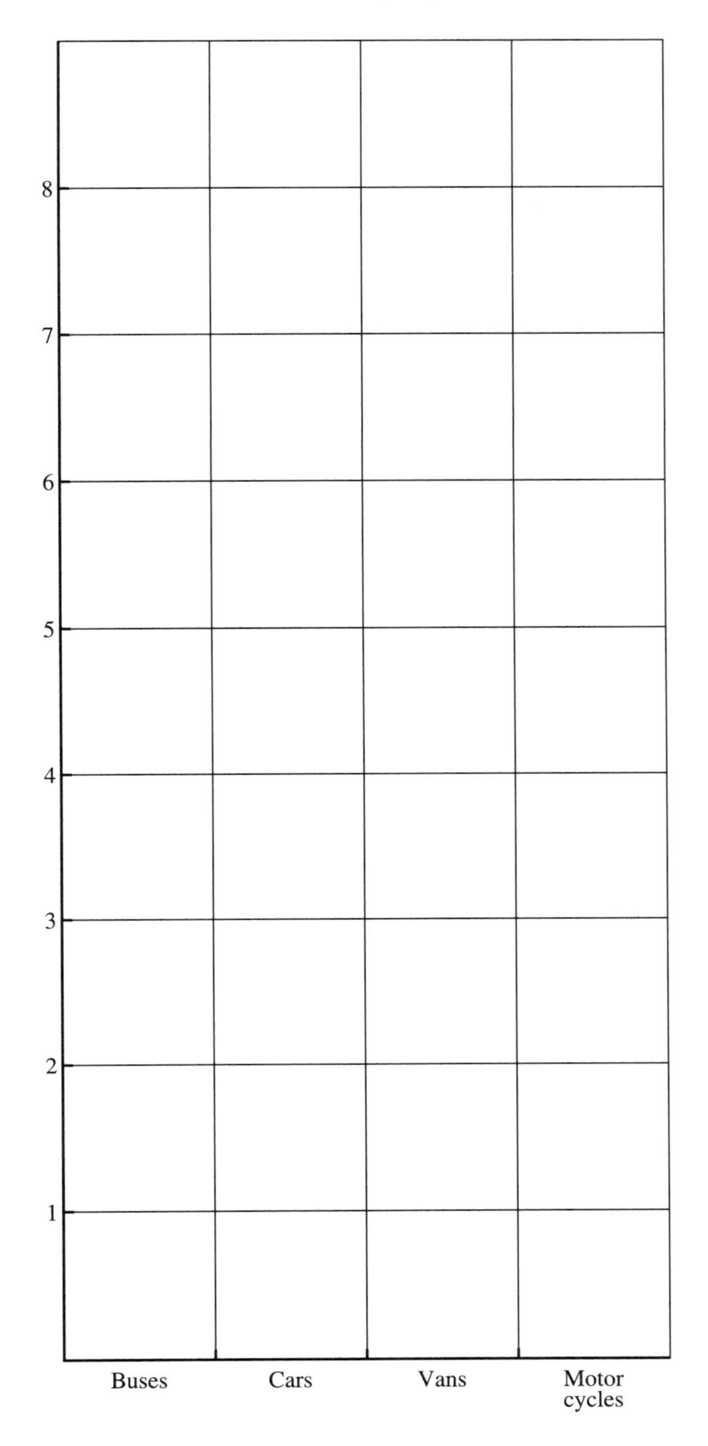

(2)

6 Write the number

3438

(a) to the nearest ten .... **(1)**

(b) to the nearest hundred .... **(1)**

7 **(a)** Petrol cost 67.9 p per litre. Work out the cost of 100 litres of petrol.

.... **(2)**

(b) These thermometers show the temperature in Newcastle and Plymouth.

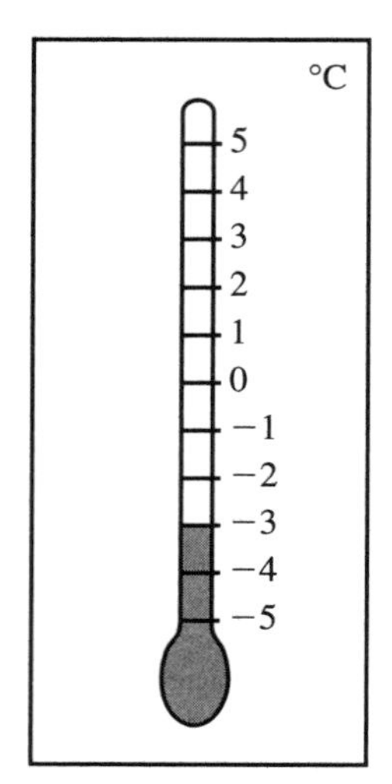

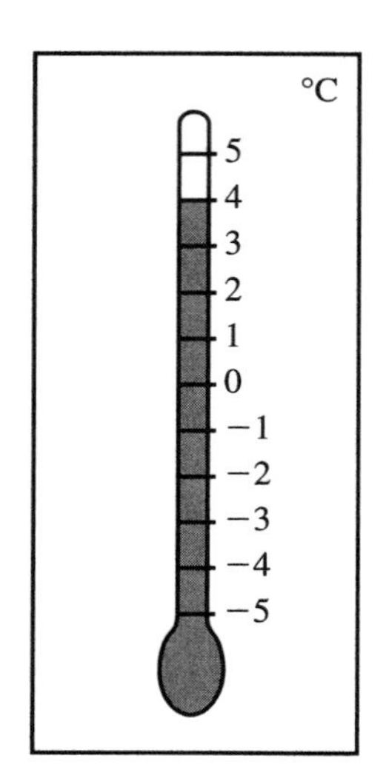

Work out the difference between these two temperatures.

................°C **(2)**

8 Work out:

(a) 4×5

.... **(1)**

(b) the missing number in

$\square \times 12 = 36$

.... **(1)**

(c) $27 + 14$

.... **(1)**

(d) $3 \times 4 + 5$

.... **(1)**

9 A bus left the station at the time shown on this clock.

(a) What time did the clock show?

.... a.m. **(1)**

(b) For how long is the bus away from the bus station if it returns at 9 : 35 a.m?

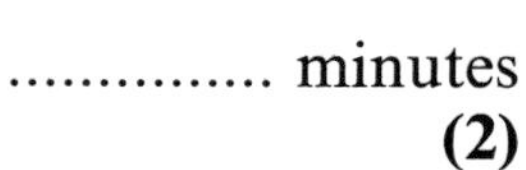

.... minutes **(2)**

10   

Clubs Diamond Hearts Spades

Which of these shapes have:

(a) *No* lines of symmetry ....

(b) *Only one* line of symmetry ....

(c) *Two* lines of symmetry ....

(d) *Three* or more lines of symmetry ....

(3)

Note: If you think that the correct answer to any of the above is none, then write

None

in the answer space.

11 Use these digits to answer this question:

7 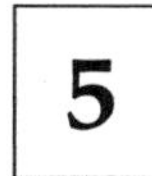 2

(a) Use all three digits to write down a number between 500 and 700

....

(1)

(b) Use all three digits to complete this subtraction

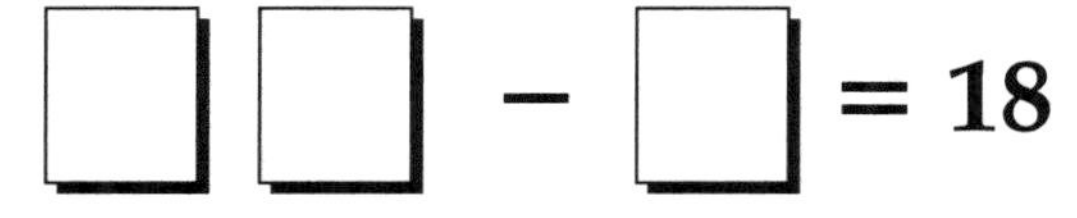

□□ − □ = 18

....

(1)

(c) Use *two* of the digits to make this correct:

$5 \times 5 =$ □□

....

(1)

12 This table and bar chart show the colours of shirts for 20 teams in the league.

Colour	Blue	Green	Red	White	Yellow
Number of teams	6	1	8		

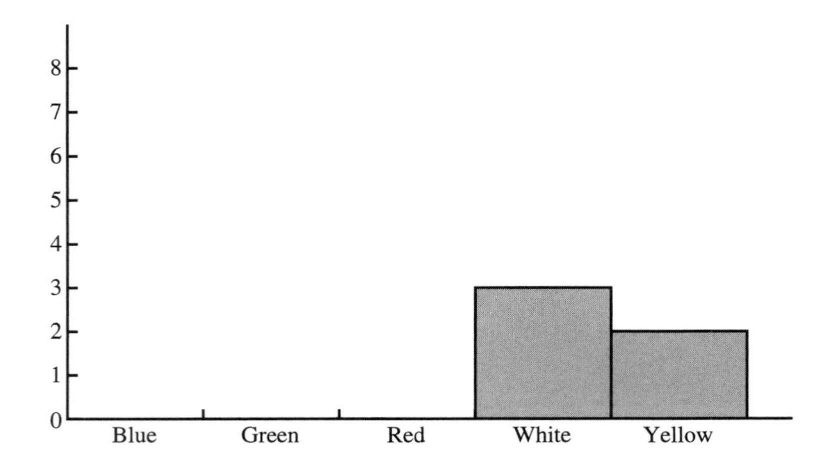

(a) Use the table to complete the bar chart. **(3)**

(b) Use the bar chart to complete the table:

Colour	Blue	Green	Red	White	Yellow
Number of teams					

(2)

13 Work out:

(a) 50 − 13 = ... **(1)**

(b) The total cost of five ice creams at 90 p each. £ .... **(2)**

(c) How much each person will receive when £21.90 is shared equally between:

(i) three people £ ....

(ii) five people £ .... **(3)**

14 Work out

47 + 23 − 18 .... **(1)**

15 This pictogram shows how many people went to the cinema each evening last week:

Sunday
Monday
Tuesday
Wednesday
Thursday
Friday
Saturday

= 10 people

The cinema was full on Friday.

(a) How many people are in the cinema when it is full? .... **(1)**

(b) On which evening were there between 30 and 40 people in the cinema? .... **(1)**

16 Write down the next two numbers in each of these sequences.

(a) 3, 7, 11, 15, 19, ..., ... **(1)**

(b) 4, 5, 7, 10, 14, 19, ..., ... **(1)**

17 Write in the missing number:

(a) $8 \times 7 =$ .... **(1)**

(b) .... $\times 6 = 54$ **(1)**

18 Jenny is a dressmaker.

She charges £9 for each hour she works plus the cost of the materials.

Jenny works for 7 hours on a dress and the cost of the material is £50.

How much will she charge for the dress? £ .... **(2)**

19 This shape is drawn on centimetre squared paper:

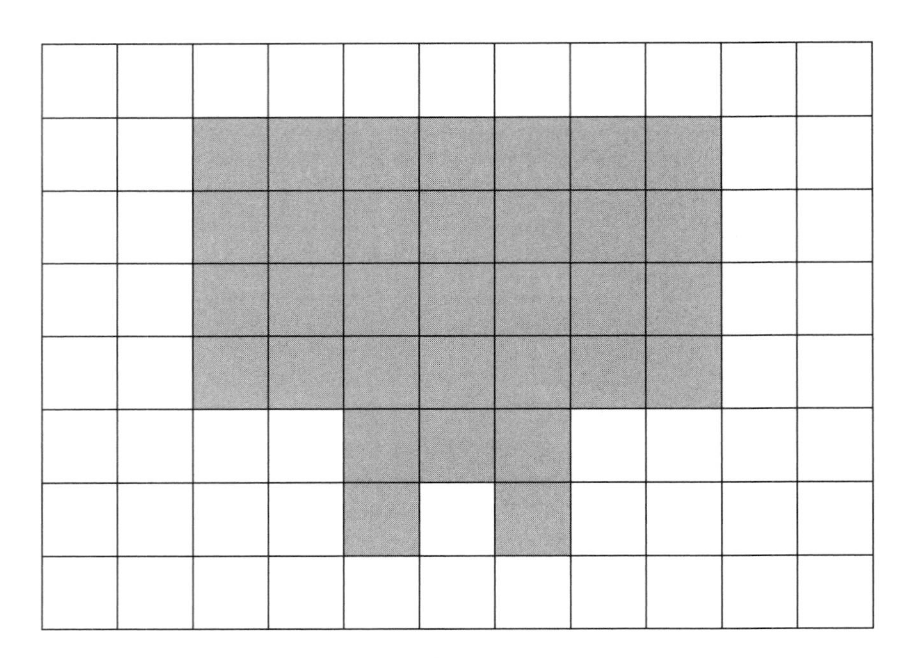

(a) Work out the perimeter of the shape. .... cm **(1)**

(b) Find the area of the shape. .... cm^2 **(1)**

20 Reyhana's marks for nine English homeworks were:

9, 6, 5, 8, 6, 7, 9, 6, 8

(a) Write down the *mode* of these marks. .... **(1)**

(b) Write down the *median* of these marks. .... **(1)**

Test C Levels (2) 3 (4)

1	27, 35, 38, 42, 72	A2 for all correct A1 for 1 error or largest first but order OK
2	**(a)** 3 triangles shaded	A1
	(b) $\frac{6}{8}$ or $\frac{3}{4}$	A1
3	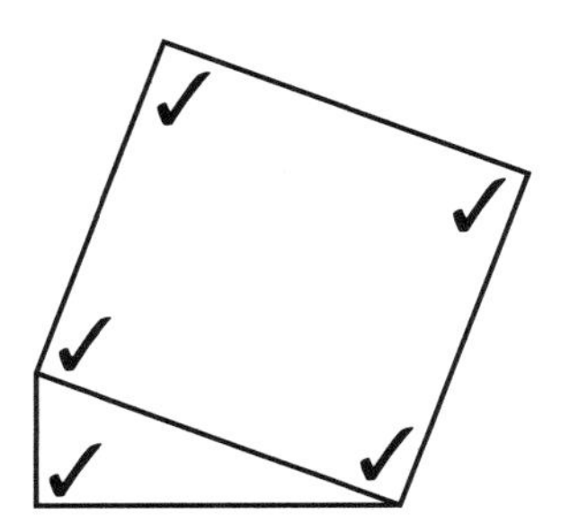	A2 for all 5 ticks correct A1 for 3 or 4 ticks correct
4	A is a rectangle B is a circle C is a square D is a pentagon E is a parallelogram F is a cube	A2 for all 6 correct A1 if 4 correct
5	A2 for all 4 columns correct A1 for 2 columns correct	
6	**(a)** 3440	A1
	(b) 3400	A1
7	**(a)** £67.90	A2 A1 for £67.9 or 67.9×100
	(b) 7°C	A2 for 7 A1 for $3 - (-4)$ or $3 + 4$
8	**(a)** 20	A1
	(b) $3 \times 12 = 36$	A1
	(c) 41	A1
	(d) 17	A1
9	**(a)** Ten to 9 or 8 : 50 a.m.	A1
	(b) 45 minutes	A2 for 45 minutes A1 for 9 : 35–8 : 50
10	**(a)** none	
	(b) club, heart, spade	A1 for all 3 correct
	(c) diamond	A1 for diamond
	(d) none	A1 for none for (a) and (d)
11	**(a)** 527 or 572	A1
	(b) $25 - 7 = 18$	A1
	(c) $5 \times 5 = 25$	A1

12 **(a)** A1 for Blue column at 6
A1 for Green column at 1
A1 for Red column at 8
(b) A1 for White 3
A1 for Yellow 2

13	**(a)** 37	A1
	(b) £4.50	A2 A1 if answer wrong but 90×5 seen
	(c) **(i)** £7.30	A1
	(ii) £4.38	A1 Score an extra A1 if both correct or A1 for £21.90 ÷ 3 or £21.90 ÷ 5
14	52	A1
15	**(a)** 120	A1
	(b) Tuesday	A1
16	**(a)** 23, 27	A1 for both
	(b) 25, 32	A1 for both
17	**(a)** 56	A1
	(b) $9 \times 6 = 54$	A1
18	$7 \times 9 + 50 =$ £113	A2 for £113 A1 if wrong but $7 \times 9 + 50$ seen
19	**(a)** 28 cm	A1
	(b) 33 cm^2	A1
20	**(a)** 6	A1
	(b) 7	A1

Mark scheme – Test C

Mark range:	Recommendation:
0 to 15	These pupils are probably at pre-level 3 and it is recommended that they be given test B before a final decision is made.
16 to 29	These pupils are probably around level 2. Should cope with the Green book, but may need some remediation.
30 to 45	These pupils should be working at level 3 and should cope with Green book.
46+	Above level 3 – should try test D as they may cope with the Red book.

Test D

1 Write in each of the missing numbers.

(a) $10 + 40 +$ .... $= 80$

(b) $8 \times 5 =$ ....

(c) $36 \div$ .... $= 12$

(d) $5 \times$ .... $= 35$ **(4)**

2 Work out:

$10 \times 4 \times 2$ ....

(1)

3 **(a)** Draw the line of symmetry on the triangle

(1)

(b) How many lines of symmetry are there on this equilateral triangle?

....

(1)

(c) Draw any shape which has *exactly* 2 lines of symmetry

(1)

4 Work out 47×4 ....

(1)

5 These are Sally's marks for her last 9 science homeworks:

5 3 8 6 8 8 7 5 7

(a) Write down the *mode* of her marks. ....

(1)

(b) Find the *median* of her marks. ....

(1)

6 The bar chart shows how many of each colour shirt were sold in a shop yesterday:

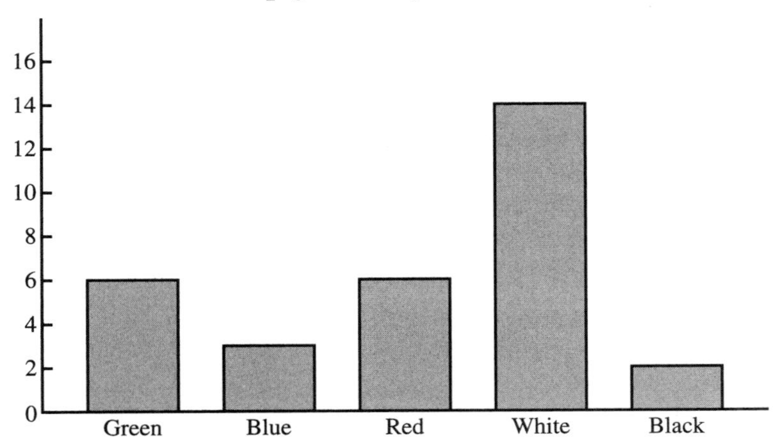

(a) Which colour shirt was most popular yesterday? .... **(1)**

(b) How many blue shirts were sold yesterday? .... **(1)**

7 Work out:

(a) 48×10 .... **(1)**

(b) $48 \div 100$ .... **(1)**

(c) $\frac{220 \times 5}{100}$ .... **(1)**

8

Tick each of the triangles congruent to the one above.

(2)

9 Here are the first four stages in a pattern of dots.

5 dots 8 dots 11 dots 14 dots

(a) Complete the table below for the number of dots in each stage:

Stage	1	2	3	4	5	6
Number of dots	5	8	11	14		

(1)

(b) Find the number of dots in Stage 10. ....

(2)

10

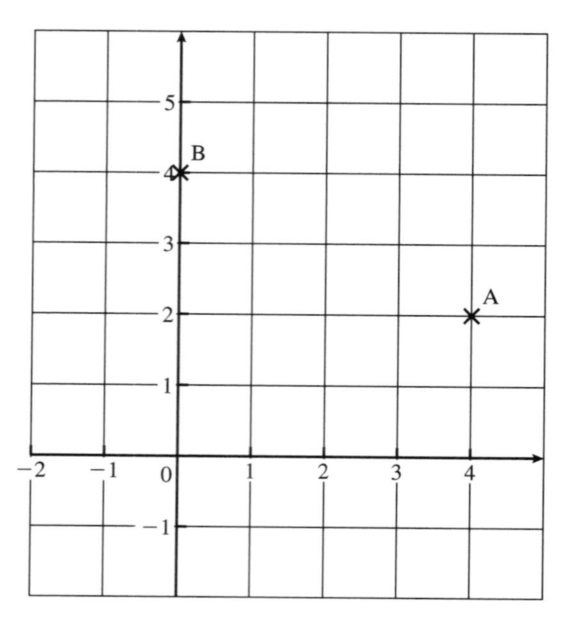

(a) Write down the coordinates of

(i) the point A ....

(ii) the point B. .... **(2)**

(b) Plot and label the point C with coordinates (3, 5). **(1)**

11 Use one of the words

unlikely **evens** **likely** **certain** **impossible**

to describe the chance of each of these happening:

(a) The next baby to be born will be a boy. ....

(b) The next winner of the mens tennis final will be female. ....

(c) The day immediately after Monday will be Tuesday. ....

(d) The number of goals scored in a hockey match will be 12. ....

(4)

12 **(a)** Work out $\frac{1}{3}$ of £12 £ .... **(1)**

(b) Write 70% as a fraction .... **(1)**

(c) Work out 60% of 40 kg .... kg **(2)**

13 **(a)** Reflect the triangle in the mirror line.

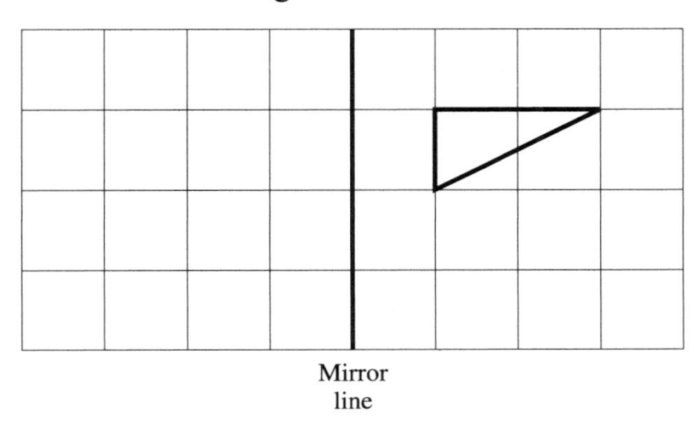

(2)

(b) A special rectangle has exactly 4 lines of symmetry.
What is the correct name for such a special rectangle? .... **(1)**

14 A bag contains 10 coloured beads.
6 are red, **3** are white and **1** is blue.

What is the probability of a randomly selected bead being:

(a) blue .... **(1)**

(b) red .... **(1)**

(c) green .... **(1)**

15 **(a)** Measure the angle marked $x°$.

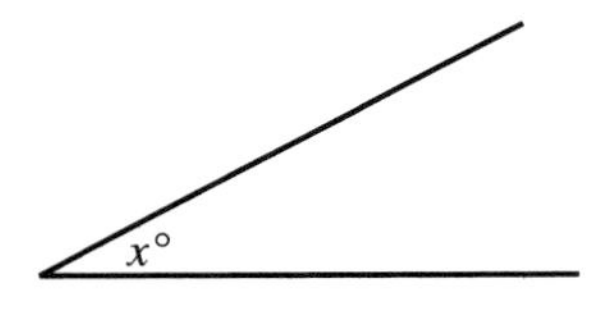

.... **(1)**

(b) Draw an angle of 125°.

______________________________ **(1)**

16 This shape is made out of centimetre square tiles:

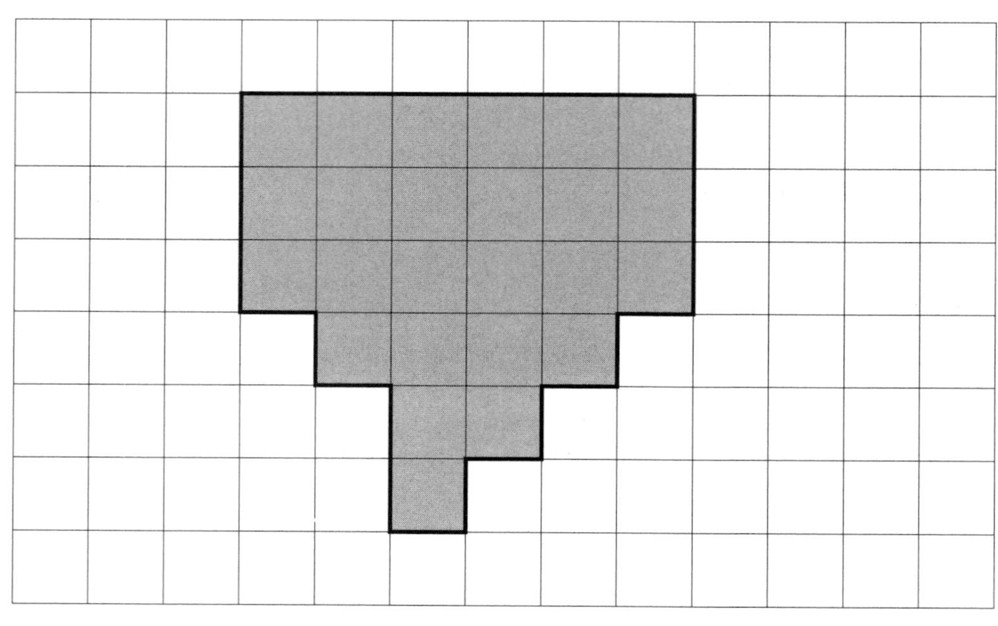

Work out:

(a) the perimeter of the shape .... cm
(1)

(b) the area of the shape. .... cm^2
(1)

All of the tiles are re-arranged to make a square.

(c) Work out the length of a side of the square. .... cm^2
(2)

17 Work out 352 × 23 ....
(3)

18 Work out $\frac{2}{5}$ of £30 £ ....
(2)

Test D Levels (3) 4 (5)

1 **(a)** 30 — A1
(b) 40 — A1
(c) 3 — A1
(d) 7 — A1

2 80 — A1

3 **(a)** — A1

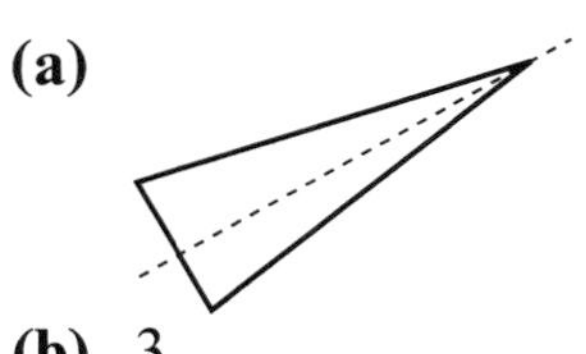

(b) 3 — A1
(c) — A1 for rectangle or shape with 2 and only 2 lines of symmetry

4 188 — A1

5 **(a)** 8 — A1
(b) 7 — A1

6 **(a)** white — A1
(b) 3 — A1

7 **(a)** 480 — A1
(b) 0.48 — A1
(c) 11 — A1

8 A2 for 4 correctly ticked
A1 for 2 correctly ticked

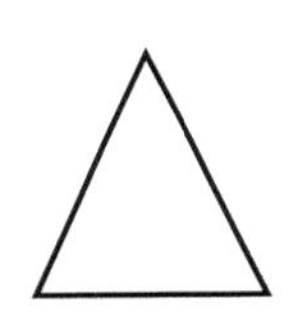
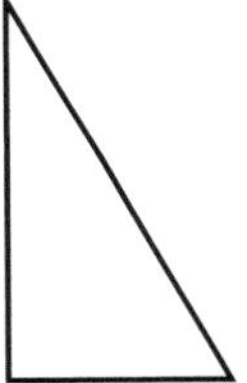

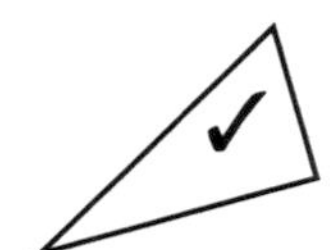

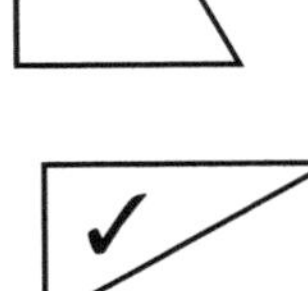

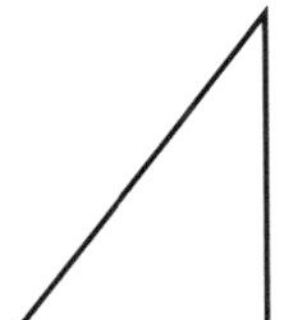
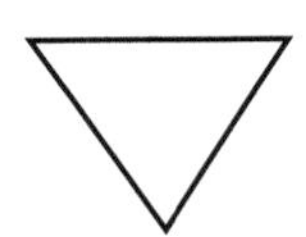
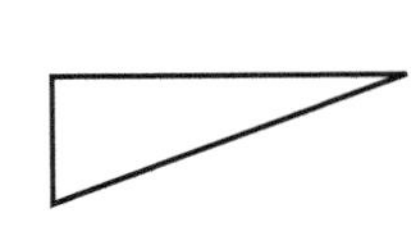
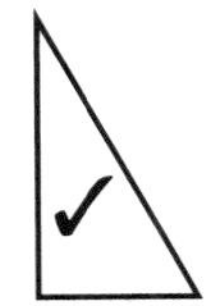

9 **(a)** 5 6
17 20
— A1 for both
(b) 32 — A2 for 32 but
A1 if same method e.g. counting on is shown

Question	Answer	Mark
10 **(a)** **(i)**	(4, 2)	A1
(ii)	(0, 4)	A1
(b)	C plotted correctly	A1
11 **(a)**	evens	A1
(b)	impossible	A1
(c)	certain	A1
(d)	unlikely	A1
12 **(a)**	£4	A1
(b)	$\frac{70}{100}$ or $\frac{7}{10}$	A1
(c)	24 kg	A2 for 24 kg A1 if answer wrong and $\frac{60}{100} \times 40$ seen
13 **(a)**	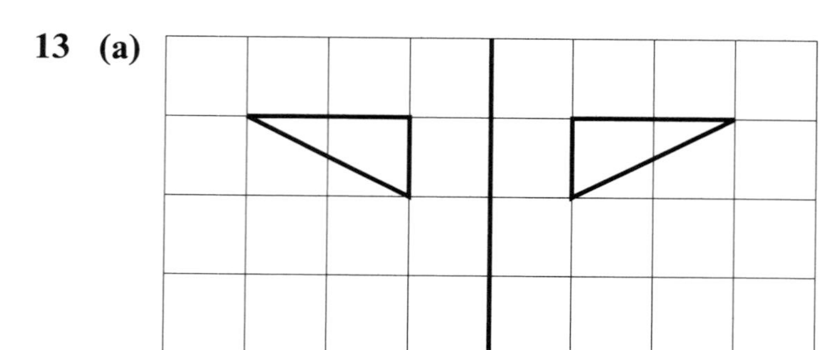	A2 if fully correct A1 if a reflection but position incorrect
(b)	square	A1
14 **(a)**	$\frac{1}{10}$ or 0.1	A1 only accept fractions or decimals
(b)	$\frac{6}{10}$ or 0.6	A1 only accept fractions or decimals
(c)	0	A1 accept nought or zero but not none.
15 **(a)**	28°	A1 $\pm$ 2°
(b)	Measure angle	A1 for 125° $\pm$ 2°
16 **(a)**	24 cm	A1
(b)	25 cm^2	A1
(c)	5 cm	A2 for 5 cm A1 for attempt at $\sqrt{25}$
17	$$\begin{array}{r} 352 \\ \underline{23} \\ 1056 \\ \underline{7040} \\ 8096 \end{array}$$	A1 for 1056 A1 for 704(0) A1 for 8096
18	£12	A2 for £12 A1 for 30 $\div$ 5 or $\frac{1}{5}$ of £30 if £12 wrong

Mark scheme – Test D

Mark range:	Recommendation:
0 to 15	These pupils will be pre-level 4 and should cope with the Green book. It may be worthwhile to give them test C to see whether they are at or below level 3.
16 to 29	Above level 3. Should cope with the Green book.
30 to 45	These pupils will be working at around level 4. It is recommended that they be given test E before a final decision is made.
46+	Almost certainly above level 4. Should cope with Red book.

REED EDUCATIONAL & PROFESSIONAL PUBLISHING LIMITED LICENCE AND WARRANTY

This is a legal agreement between you, the end-user, and Reed Educational & Professional Publishing Ltd (REPP) relating to the enclosed software or database product ('the Product'). By installing the product you agree to these terms. If you do not agree to its terms, return the CD Rom without installing the product and all accompanying materials to the place you purchased them and the purchase price will be refunded to you.

1. Copyright

© Reed Educational & Professional Publishing Limited 1999. A member of the Reed Elsevier plc group of companies. All Rights Reserved.

The Product and all data, software, documentation and other materials contained in it together with the accompanying materials and all intellectual property therein are the property of REPP or its suppliers and are protected by law.

2. Licence

REPP hereby grants you a non-exclusive, non transferable personal licence on the terms in this Agreement to install the Product on up to ten (10) single computers in your school OR to install the Product onto a network provided that the number of users at any one time does not exceed ten (10).

3. You May Not

a. Copy the Product, except to load it into a computer and to make a single backup copy.

b. Distribute copies of the Product or accompanying user manual to any other person except for use within your institution.

c. Modify, adapt, translate, reverse engineer, decompile, disassemble, or create derivative works based on the Product or user manual.

d. Copy, download, save, store in a retrieval system, publish, transmit, to otherwise reproduce, transfer, save store, disseminate or use, in form or by any means, any part of the data contained within the Product.

e. Transfer, resell, or grant any other rights of any kind to any individual copy of the Product, including the user manual, to any other person.

f. Remove any proprietary notices, labels or makes on the Product or user manual.

g. Allow anyone, including employees, to have access to the Product unless it is necessary to do so in order to utilise it for a purpose authorised by this Agreement.

4. Permitted Use
You may copy or print out sections of text or pictures where expressly allowed in the Product and the accompanying materials solely for use within your institution. Apart from this, you may not print off material from the product.

5. Warranty of original discs
REPP warrants that the original CD on which the Product is delivered is free from defects in material and workmanship, assuming normal use, for a period of ninety (90) days from the date of purchase. If a defect occurs during this period, you may return the faulty CD to your dealer, along with a dated proof of purchase and REPP will replace it free of charge. After 90 days you may obtain a replacement by sending your defective CD to your dealer who will charge you a nominal fee for replacement.

6. Please Note
Except for the express warranty regarding the original CD in 5 above, REPP gives no other warranty expressed or implied, by statute or otherwise regarding the CD and accompanying materials or their contents, their fitness for any purpose, their quality, their merchantability or otherwise.

The liability of REPP under 5 above shall be limited to the amount paid by the customer for the Product. In no event shall REPP be liable for special, consequential or other damages for breach of warranty.

You recognise that the Product is to be used only as a reference aid. It is not intended to be a substitute for the exercise of professional judgement by the end-user.

7. Updates, Enhancements and Technical Support
REPP may revise or update the Product, but revisions or updates, as well as technical support for the Product, will be provided to you only if a properly signed registration card has been returned by you and is on file, and if any appropriate payment has been made.

8. Termination
If you should fail to perform in the manner required in this Agreement, REPP may terminate this Agreement or exercise any other rights it may have. Upon termination, you shall immediately return all disks containing the Product as well as the user manual. Alternatively, REPP may require that you destroy all of these materials and so certify, in writing, to REPP. All provisions of this license with regard to the protection of the proprietary rights REPP shall continue in force after such termination.

8. Applicable Law
This agreement shall be governed by the laws of England and Wales and shall be subject to the non-exclusive jurisdiction of the English Courts.

Activity Sheets

Activity sheets 1–13 provide quick and easy resource materials to save you time and let your pupils concentrate on doing work rather than copying into their books.

Activity Sheet 1

(a)

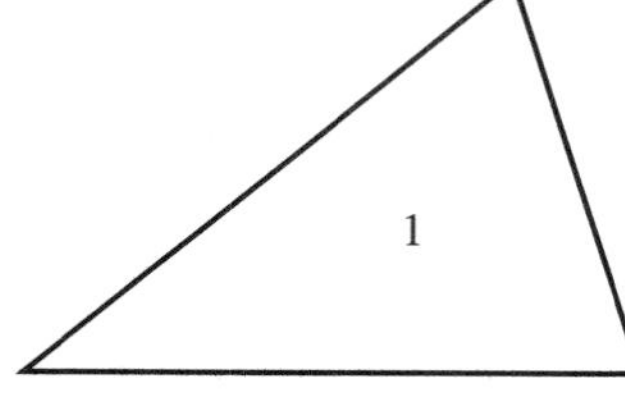

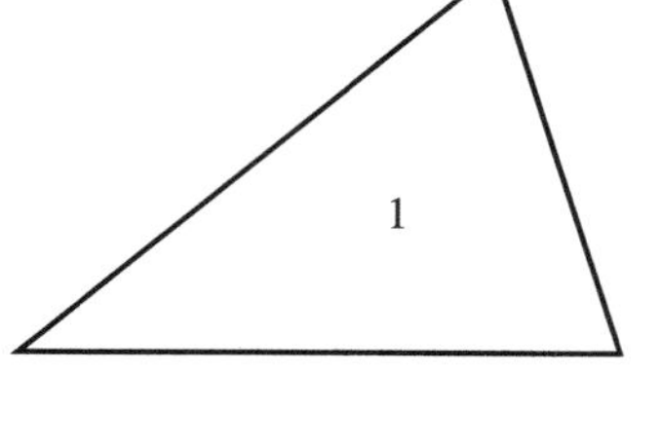

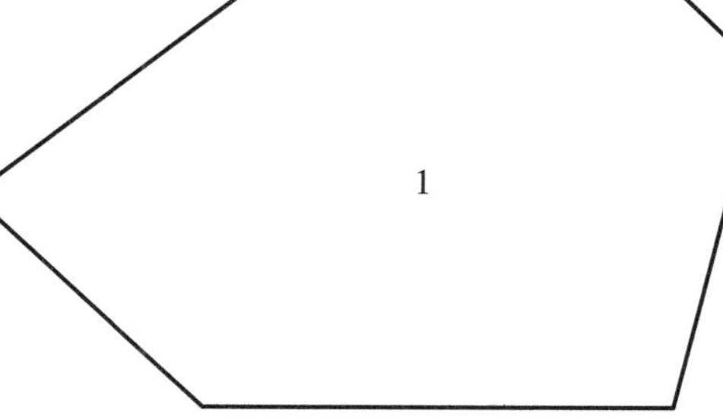

(b)

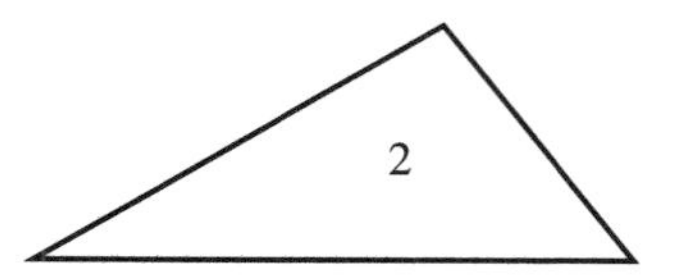

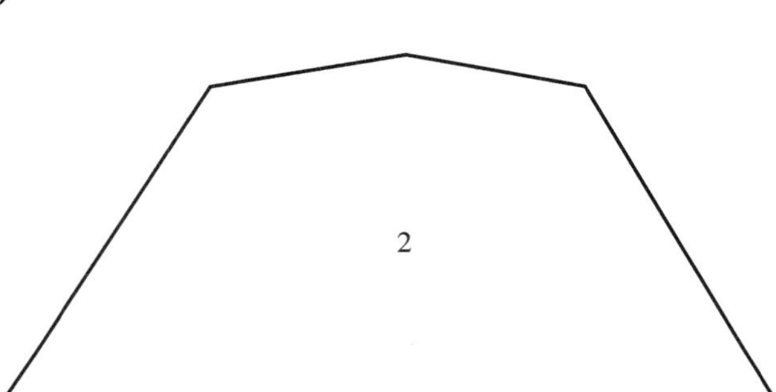

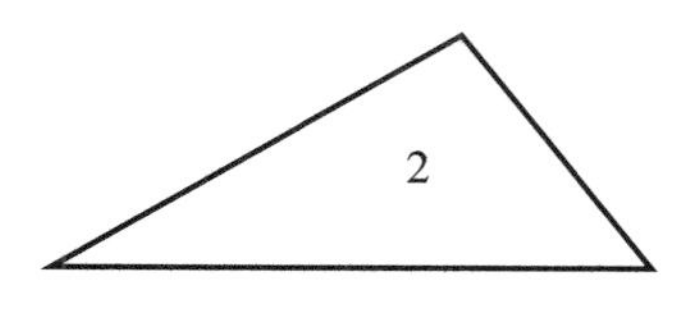

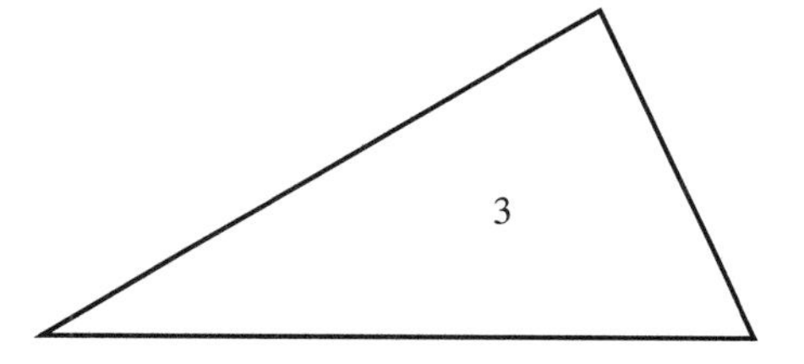

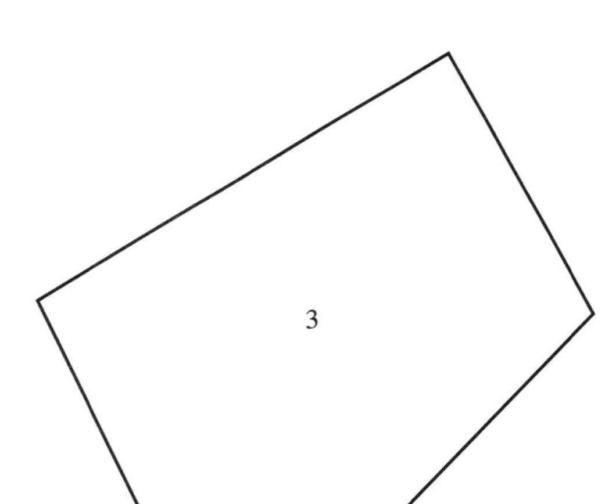

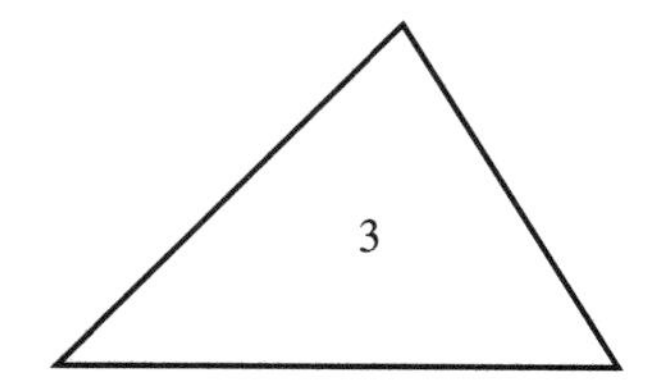

Activity Sheet 2

1

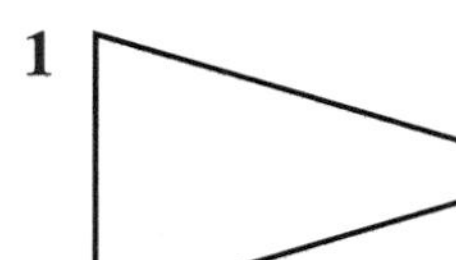

2

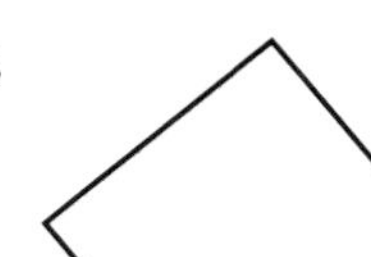

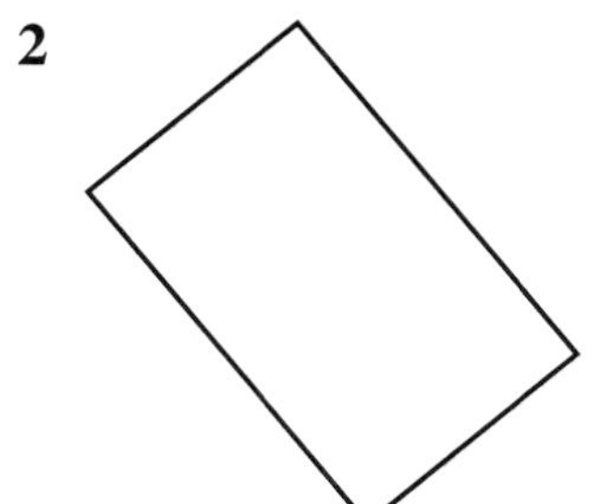

3

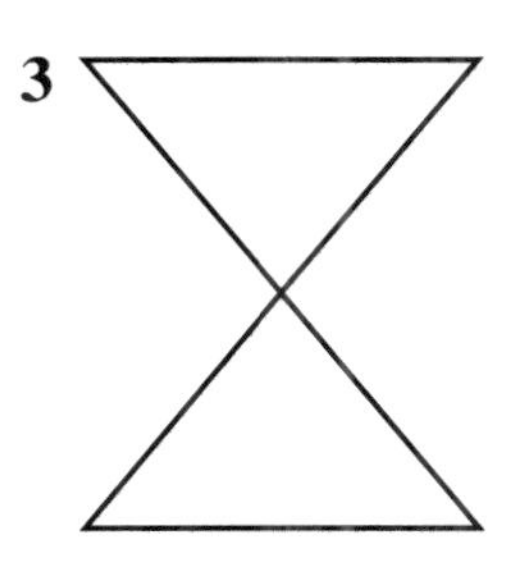

4

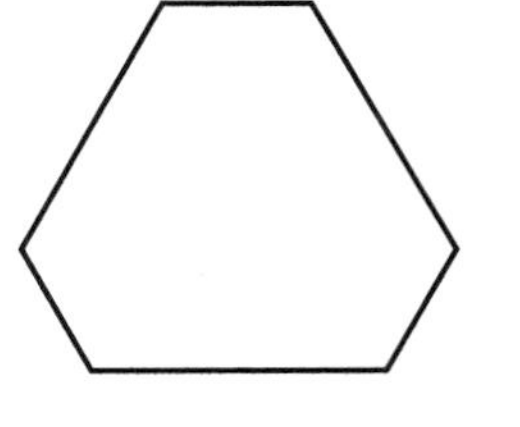

5

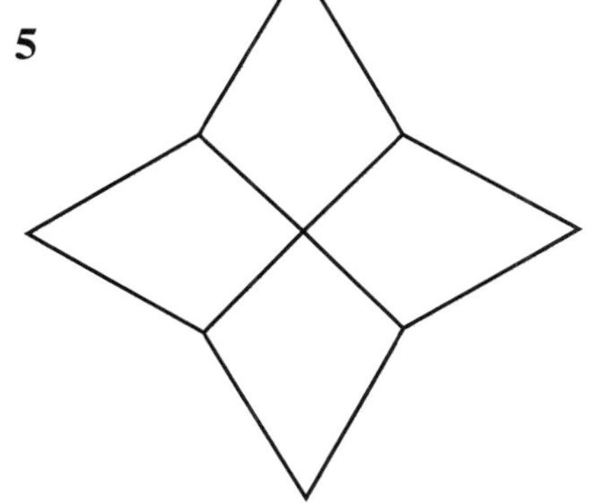

6

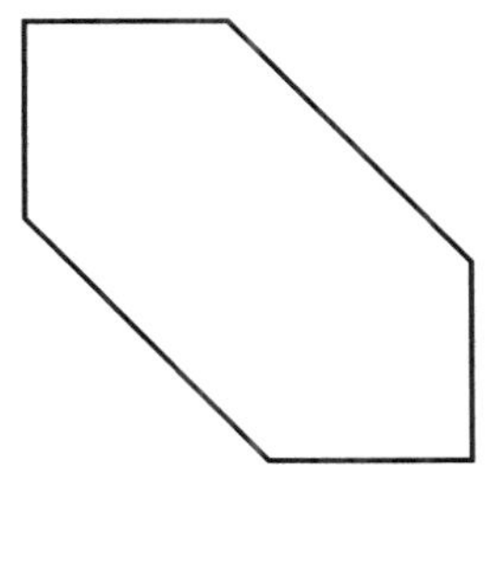

7

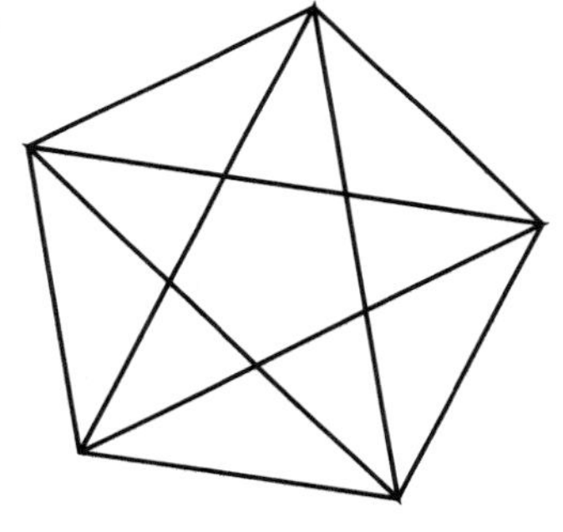

8

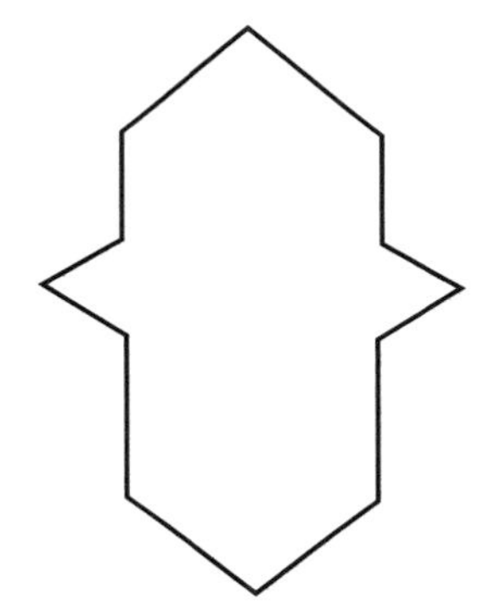

9

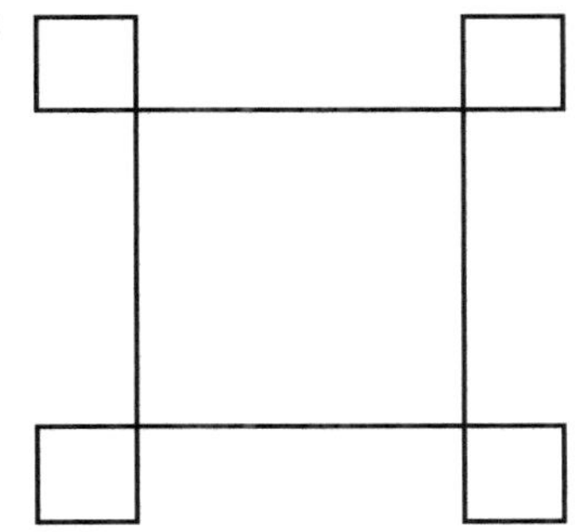

10

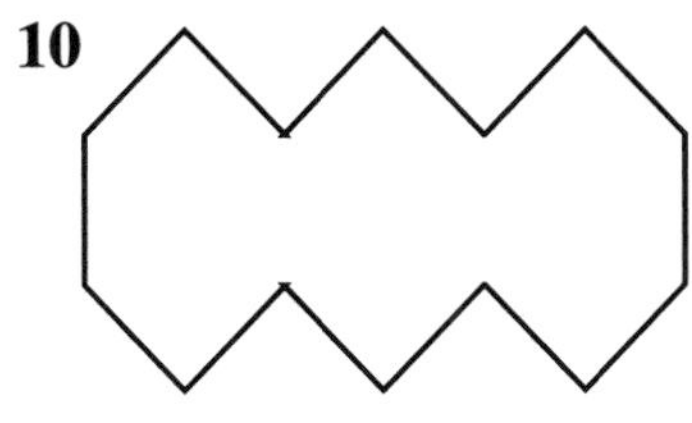

11

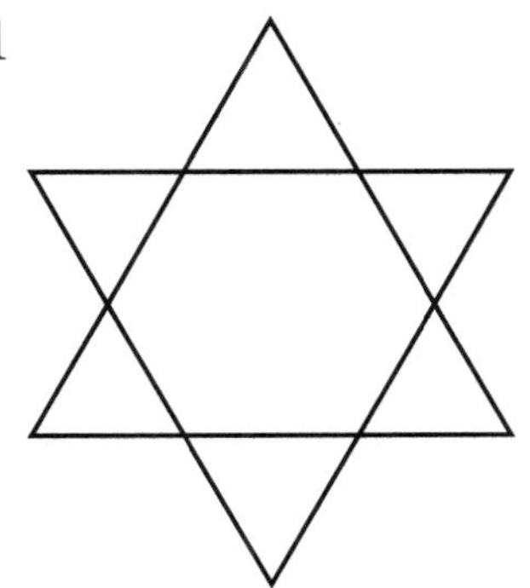

12

Activity Sheet 3

0	1	2	3	4
5	6	7	8	9

0	1	2	3	4
5	6	7	8	9

Activity Sheet 4

1	2	3	4	5	6	7	8	9	10
11	12	13	14	15	16	17	18	19	20
21	22	23	24	25	26	27	28	29	30
31	32	33	34	35	36	37	38	39	40
41	42	43	44	45	46	47	48	49	50
51	52	53	54	55	56	57	58	59	60
61	62	63	64	65	66	67	68	69	70
71	72	73	74	75	76	77	78	79	80
81	82	83	84	85	86	87	88	89	90
91	92	93	94	95	96	97	98	99	100

1	2	3	4	5	6	7	8	9	10
11	12	13	14	15	16	17	18	19	20
21	22	23	24	25	26	27	28	29	30
31	32	33	34	35	36	37	38	39	40
41	42	43	44	45	46	47	48	49	50
51	52	53	54	55	56	57	58	59	60
61	62	63	64	65	66	67	68	69	70
71	72	73	74	75	76	77	78	79	80
81	82	83	84	85	86	87	88	89	90
91	92	93	94	95	96	97	98	99	100

1	2	3	4	5	6	7	8	9	10
11	12	13	14	15	16	17	18	19	20
21	22	23	24	25	26	27	28	29	30
31	32	33	34	35	36	37	38	39	40
41	42	43	44	45	46	47	48	49	50
51	52	53	54	55	56	57	58	59	60
61	62	63	64	65	66	67	68	69	70
71	72	73	74	75	76	77	78	79	80
81	82	83	84	85	86	87	88	89	90
91	92	93	94	95	96	97	98	99	100

1	2	3	4	5	6	7	8	9	10
11	12	13	14	15	16	17	18	19	20
21	22	23	24	25	26	27	28	29	30
31	32	33	34	35	36	37	38	39	40
41	42	43	44	45	46	47	48	49	50
51	52	53	54	55	56	57	58	59	60
61	62	63	64	65	66	67	68	69	70
71	72	73	74	75	76	77	78	79	80
81	82	83	84	85	86	87	88	89	90
91	92	93	94	95	96	97	98	99	100

1	2	3	4	5	6	7	8	9	10
11	12	13	14	15	16	17	18	19	20
21	22	23	24	25	26	27	28	29	30
31	32	33	34	35	36	37	38	39	40
41	42	43	44	45	46	47	48	49	50
51	52	53	54	55	56	57	58	59	60
61	62	63	64	65	66	67	68	69	70
71	72	73	74	75	76	77	78	79	80
81	82	83	84	85	86	87	88	89	90
91	92	93	94	95	96	97	98	99	100

1	2	3	4	5	6	7	8	9	10
11	12	13	14	15	16	17	18	19	20
21	22	23	24	25	26	27	28	29	30
31	32	33	34	35	36	37	38	39	40
41	42	43	44	45	46	47	48	49	50
51	52	53	54	55	56	57	58	59	60
61	62	63	64	65	66	67	68	69	70
71	72	73	74	75	76	77	78	79	80
81	82	83	84	85	86	87	88	89	90
91	92	93	94	95	96	97	98	99	100

Activity Sheet 5

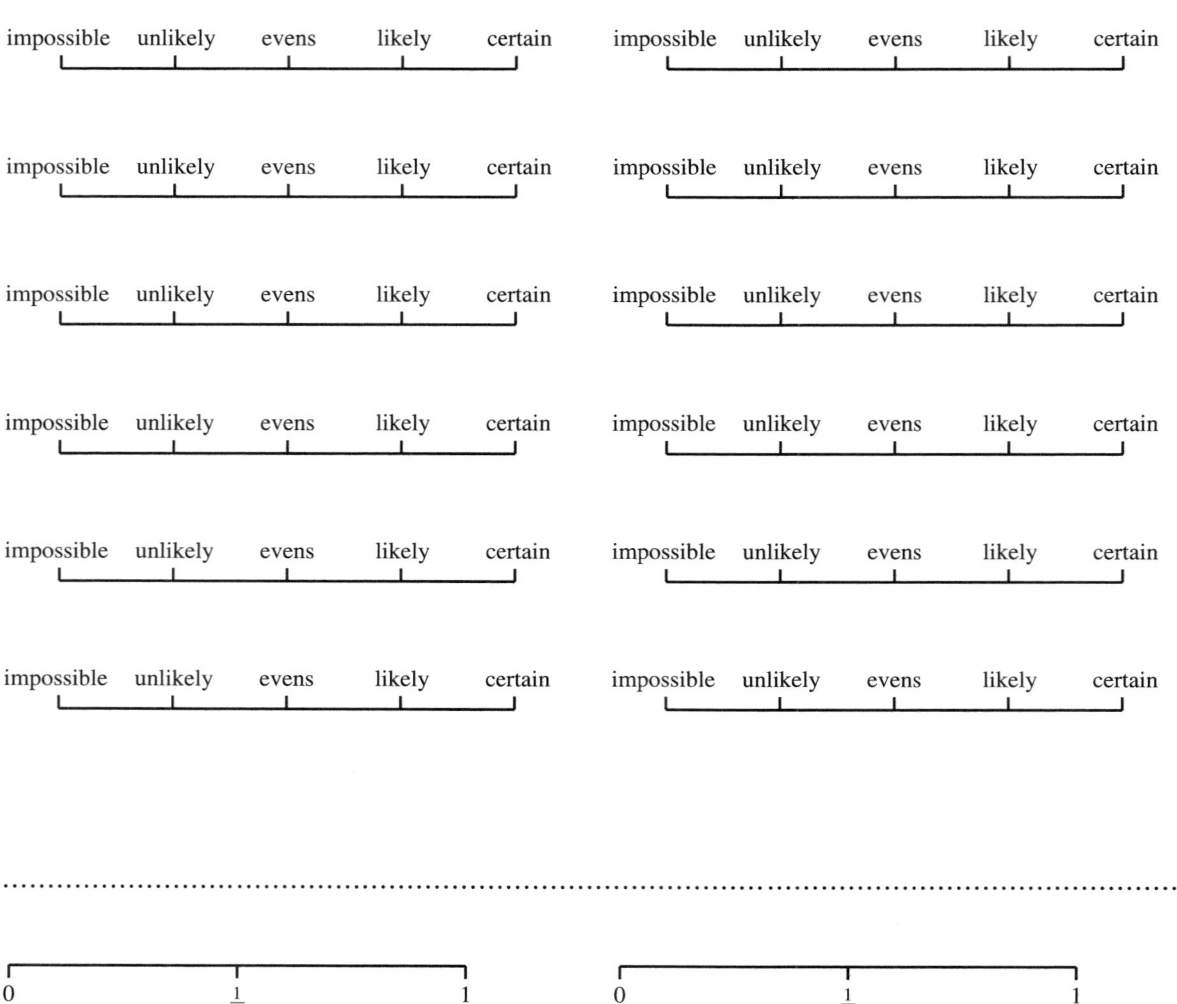

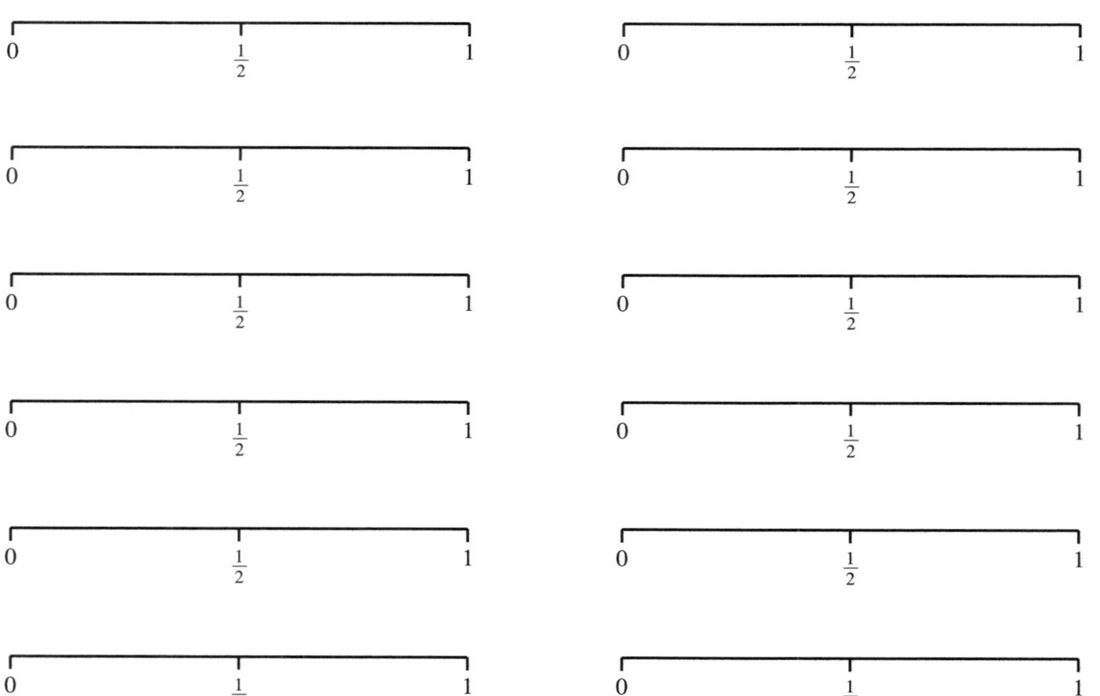

Activity Sheet 6

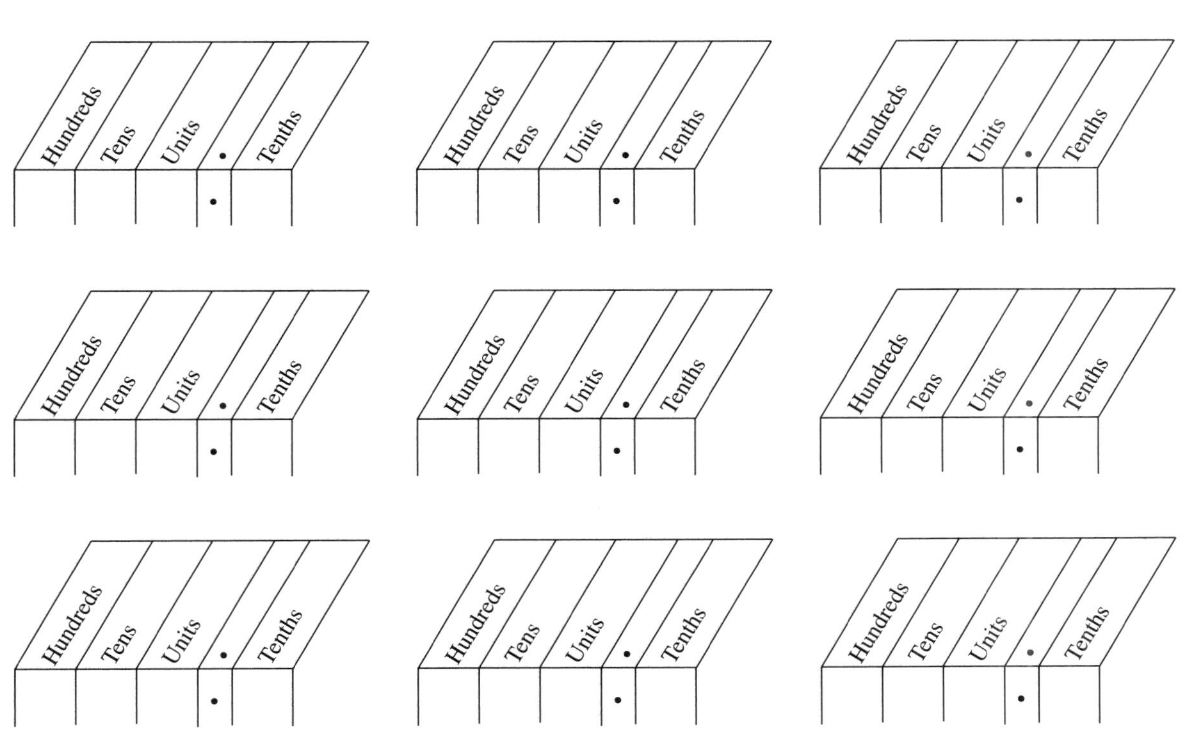

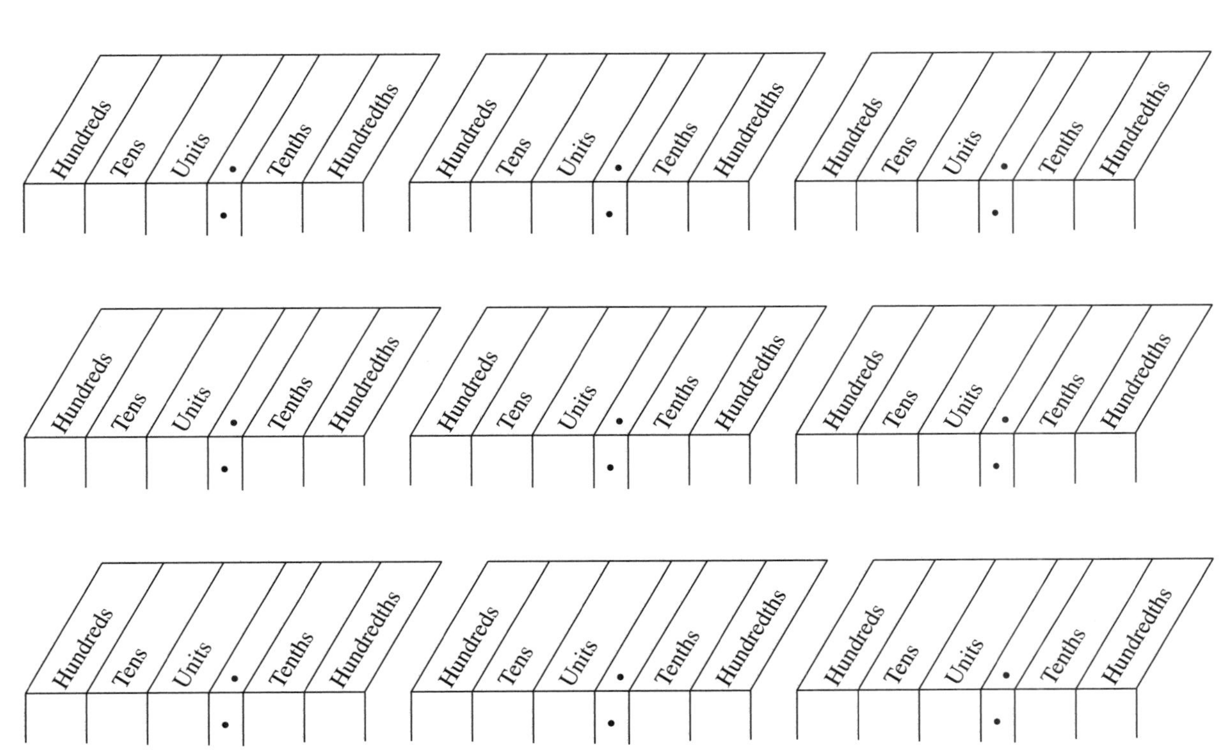

Activity Sheet 7

1	2	3	4	5
6	7	8	9	10

1	2	3	4	5
6	7	8	9	10

Activity Sheet 8

(a)

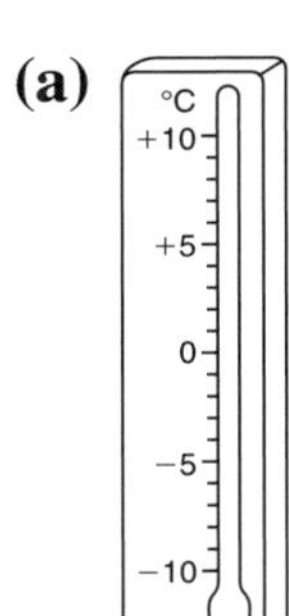

(b) °C +10 +5 0 −5 −10

(c) °C +10 +5 0 −5 −10

(d) °C +10 +5 0 −5 −10

(e) °C +10 +5 0 −5 −10

(f) °C +10 +5 0 −5 −10

(g) °C +10 +5 0 −5 −10

(h) °C +10 +5 0 −5 −10

(i) °C +10 +5 0 −5 −10

(j) °C +10 +5 0 −5 −10

(k) °C +10 +5 0 −5 −10

(l) °C +10 +5 0 −5 −10

(a) °C +10 +5 0 −5 −10

(b) °C +10 +5 0 −5 −10

(c) °C +10 +5 0 −5 −10

(d) °C +10 +5 0 −5 −10

(e) °C +10 +5 0 −5 −10

(f) °C +10 +5 0 −5 −10

(g) °C +10 +5 0 −5 −10

(h) °C +10 +5 0 −5 −10

(i) °C +10 +5 0 −5 −10

(j) °C +10 +5 0 −5 −10

(k) °C +10 +5 0 −5 −10

(l) °C +10 +5 0 −5 −10

Activity Sheet 9

10	10	10	10	10	10	10	10
9	9	9	9	9	9	9	9
8	8	8	8	8	8	8	8
7	7	7	7	7	7	7	7
6	6	6	6	6	6	6	6
5	5	5	5	5	5	5	5
4	4	4	4	4	4	4	4
3	3	3	3	3	3	3	3
2	2	2	2	2	2	2	2
1	1	1	1	1	1	1	1
0	0	0	0	0	0	0	0
−1	−1	−1	−1	−1	−1	−1	−1
−2	−2	−2	−2	−2	−2	−2	−2
−3	−3	−3	−3	−3	−3	−3	−3
−4	−4	−4	−4	−4	−4	−4	−4
−5	−5	−5	−5	−5	−5	−5	−5
−6	−6	−6	−6	−6	−6	−6	−6
−7	−7	−7	−7	−7	−7	−7	−7
−8	−8	−8	−8	−8	−8	−8	−8
−9	−9	−9	−9	−9	−9	−9	−9
−10	−10	−10	−10	−10	−10	−10	−10

10	10	10	10	10	10	10	10
9	9	9	9	9	9	9	9
8	8	8	8	8	8	8	8
7	7	7	7	7	7	7	7
6	6	6	6	6	6	6	6
5	5	5	5	5	5	5	5
4	4	4	4	4	4	4	4
3	3	3	3	3	3	3	3
2	2	2	2	2	2	2	2
1	1	1	1	1	1	1	1
0	0	0	0	0	0	0	0
−1	−1	−1	−1	−1	−1	−1	−1
−2	−2	−2	−2	−2	−2	−2	−2
−3	−3	−3	−3	−3	−3	−3	−3
−4	−4	−4	−4	−4	−4	−4	−4
−5	−5	−5	−5	−5	−5	−5	−5
−6	−6	−6	−6	−6	−6	−6	−6
−7	−7	−7	−7	−7	−7	−7	−7
−8	−8	−8	−8	−8	−8	−8	−8
−9	−9	−9	−9	−9	−9	−9	−9
−10	−10	−10	−10	−10	−10	−10	−10

Activity Sheet 10

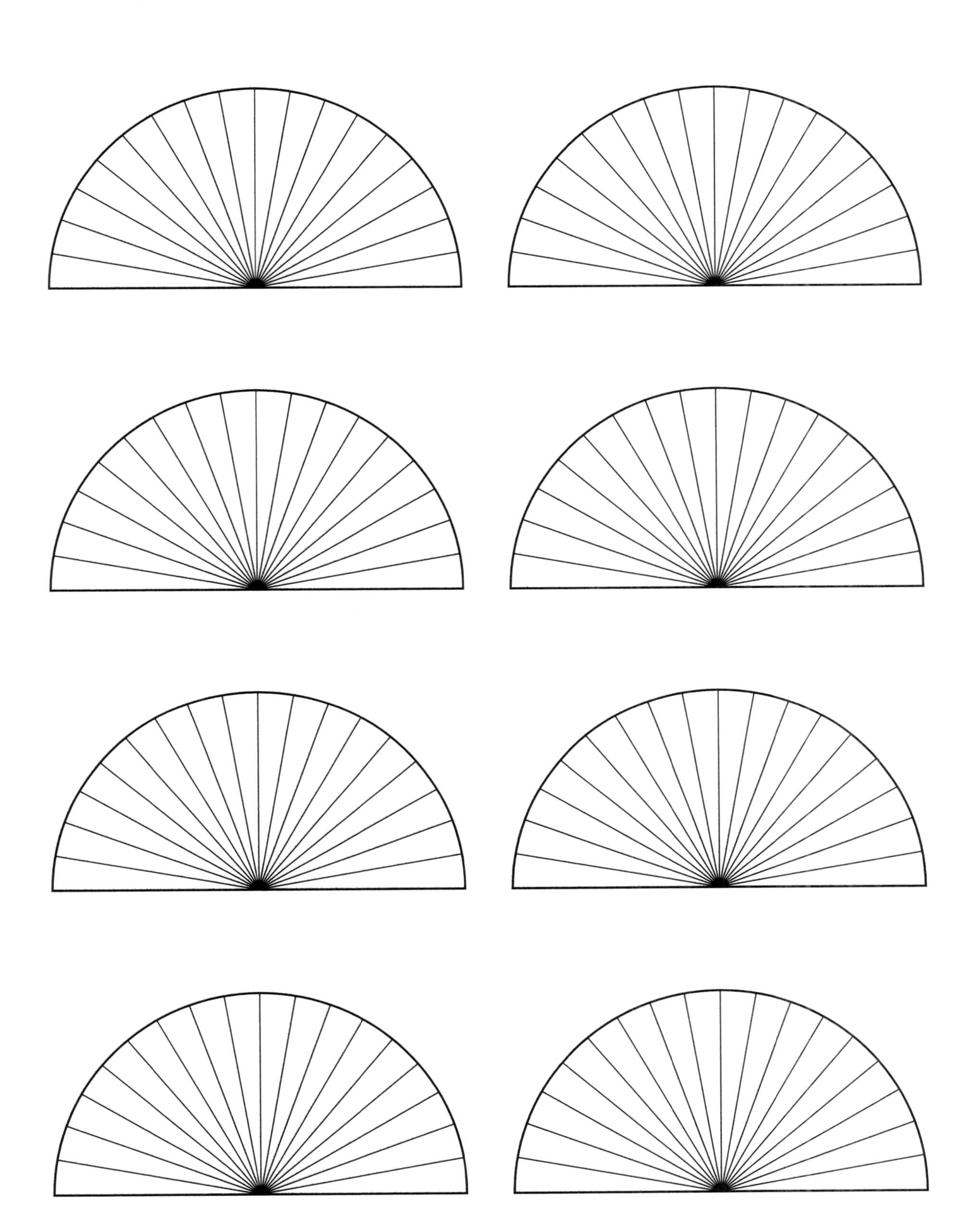

1 G

Activity Sheets

Activity Sheet 11

Fill in all the answers you know in the table.

Write in new answers as you find them out.

x	2	3	4	5	6	7	8	9	10
2			8						
3									
4	8								
5									
6									
7							56		
8						56			
9									
10									

You can learn the missing answers two at a time:

$4 \times 2 = 8 = 2 \times 4$

$8 \times 7 = 56 = 7 \times 8$

Activity Sheet 12

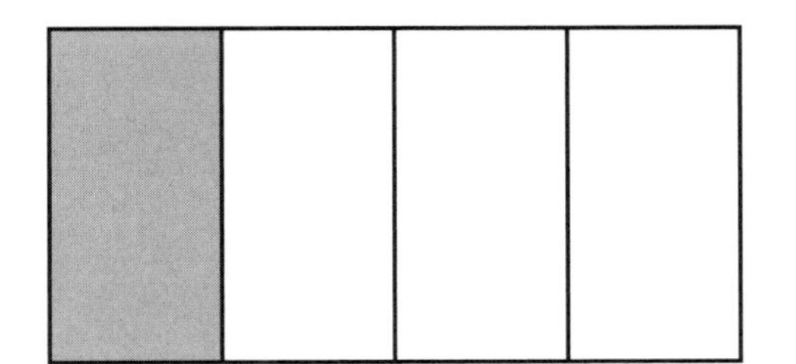

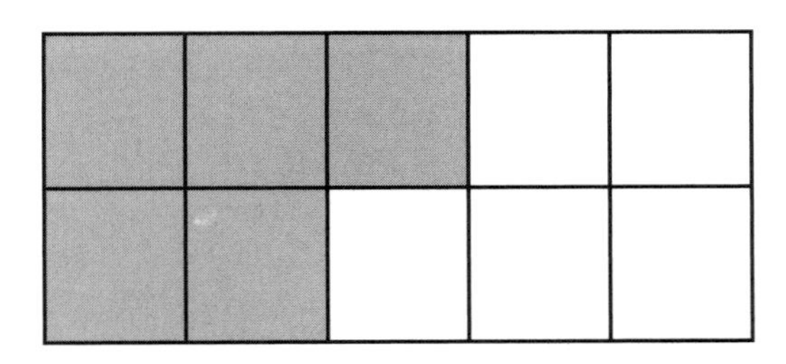

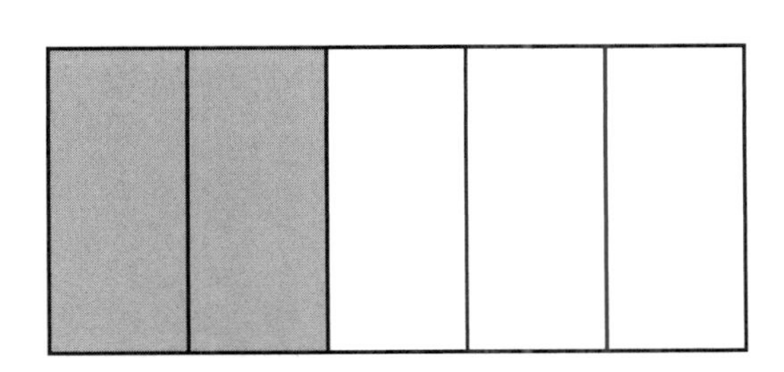

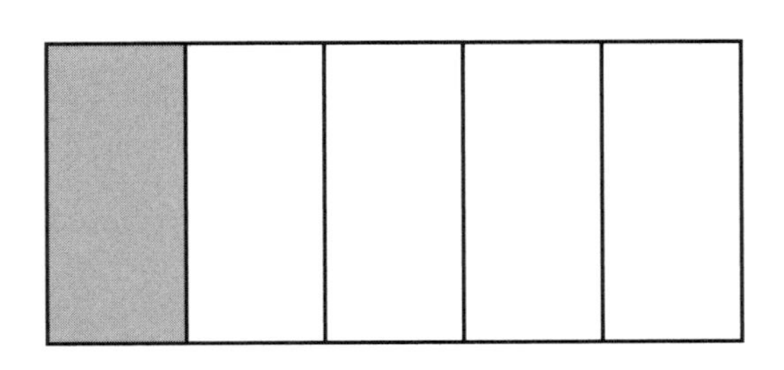

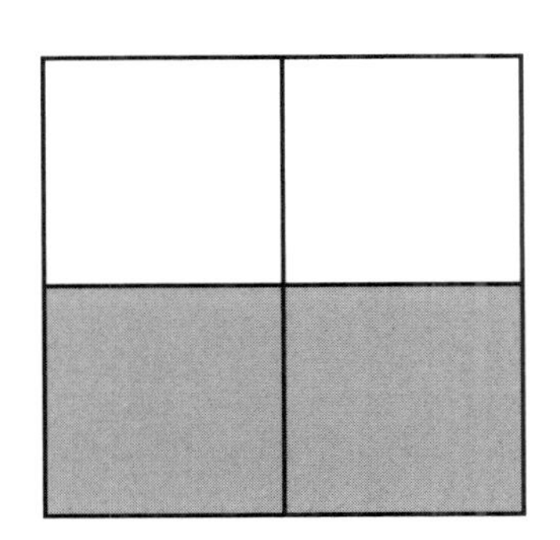

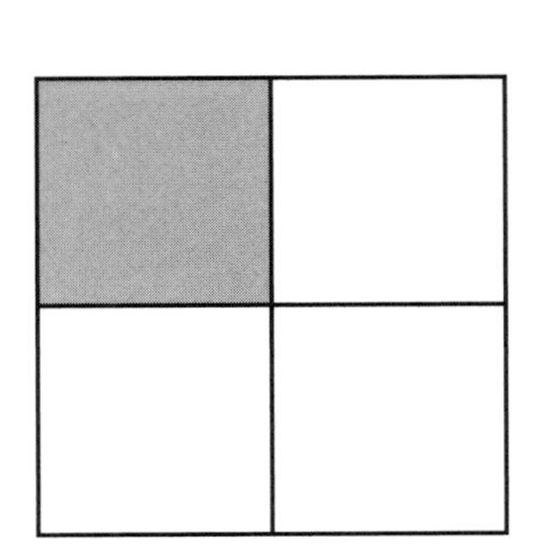

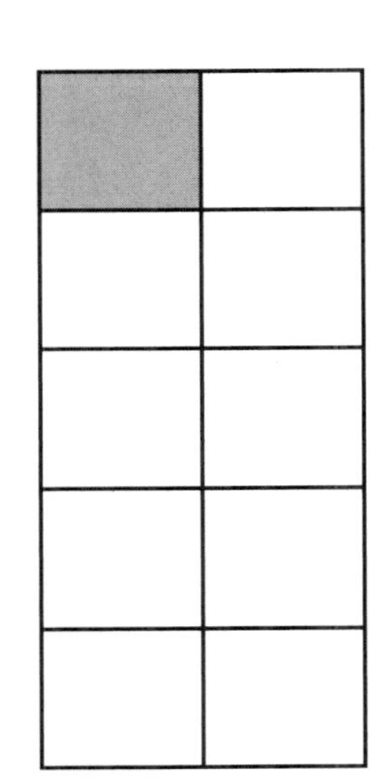

Activity Sheet 13

25%	50%
50%	40%
20%	50%
25%	10%